Mine Drainage

Proceedings of the first International Mine Drainage Symposium
Denver, Colorado, May 1979

Edited by

George O. Argall, Jr.
WORLD MINING and WORLD COAL

C. O. Brawner
Department of Mineral Engineering
University of British Columbia

Copyright © 1979 by MILLER FREEMAN PUBLICATIONS, INC.,
500 Howard Street, San Francisco, California 94105 USA.
Printed in the United States of America.

Library of Congress Catalog Card Number 79-89681
International Standard Book Number 0-87930-122-8

First printing, December 1979
Second printing, July 1982

CONTENTS

SECTION 1
Investigation and Evaluation of
Surface and Subsurface Drainage

SECTION 2
Drainage Control for Surface Mines

SECTION 3
Drainage Control for Underground Mines

SECTION 4
Tailings and Waste Disposal—
Seepage, Contamination, Regulations, and Control

TABLES

ILLUSTRATIONS

* Unnumbered illustrations

* Unnumbered illustrations

FOREWORD

Open pit mines are becoming deeper, new underground mines are developing, and environmental constraints are becoming more restrictive. As a result, the importance of improved understanding and control of mine drainage, dewatering, and the influence of seepage has greatly increased in the past decade.

Considerable advances have been made in mathematical and computer modelling, particularly to compare the influence of variables that affect groundwater flow. Such progress notwithstanding, we must be aware of the trap of over sophistication which may produce misleading results. Experience shows that investigations are usually most successful where they are developed in stages, commencing with models based on elementary principles and advancing to more complex programs. In many instances these complex programs may not be required.

Accurate analysis is dependent upon good quality field data. Recent developments in multi-depth permeability and water-pressure measurement have been very encouraging. This volume documents some of these developments.

A wide range of depressurization and slope drainage procedures is now available to the open pit mining engineer. Most of these are reviewed with numerous excellent case examples presented to illustrate the application of the various techniques. The site-specific nature of any given procedure was an important conclusion of the symposium. The most economical procedure usually involves the installation of horizontal drains.

Important considerations for underground drainage include: prior awareness of potential groundwater zones and problems; selection of the proper dewatering equipment; sufficient overdesign of the system to handle excess volumes of water; and assessment of the influence of mining and dewatering on the regional groundwater regime. Reducing water inflow offers significant economic incentive. Further research in this field is recommended.

There is considerable environmental concern about the movement of underground seepage from tailings dams and waste disposal piles. Extensive study has been directed toward modelling seepage flow. It must be recognized that soil and rock is an excellent natural filter for most contaminants. For example most radionuclides travel only very short distances in groundwater. Greater emphasis must be placed on contaminant movement as compared to seepage movement.

The intent of the symposium was to provide a good combination of theory, design, development, and experience in mine drainage. The authors have contributed effectively to this goal.

C. O. Brawner
Program Chairman and Co-editor
Vancouver, British Columbia, Canada
September 1979

PREFACE

Water, one of the miner's oldest and most persistent problems, was the reason for convening the first International Mine Drainage Symposium. The symposium was held in Denver, Colorado, USA, in May 1979 and was attended by delegates from 19 countries.

Water has always been a removal and disposal problem for both underground and open pit mines. Water compounds problems of physical stability of mine openings. Water inrushes present danger to mine personnel. But water also has blessings for miners. Without water the concentration and beneficiation of ores are, with few exceptions, impossible. Yet this water, too, must be controlled and recycled to prevent pollution.

The symposium was broad based to include technical reports on methods for evaluating, controlling, and draining water from both open pit and underground mine openings. The role of water in the stability of mines and the failure of tailings dams was also described. Transportation and disposal of contaminated water, particularly radioactive water, from mines to the surface and from tailings ponds to natural drainage were also considered.

With the rapid proliferation of governmental environmental laws and regulations, especially in the USA, this last theme of water pollution control and management is of growing importance. The legal aspects of mine water were carefully and accurately summarized by a leading water lawyer who is also a mining engineer. The cases and court decisions cited in his chapter form a comprehensive review of mine water and the law. Another related subject outlined at this symposium was advice on how to cope with mine drainage regulations.

The success of the symposium is due in large part to the hard work and excellent counsel of the advisory committee. Thanks are extended to the members of the committee for their suggestions and guidance. The members were: John Davis, Golder Associates, Toronto, Ontario, Canada; Dan Kealy, U.S. Bureau of Mines, Spokane, Washington; Robert Loofbourow, Multi-Purpose Engineering Group, Minneapolis, Minnesota; Klaus Peretti, Rheinbraun Consulting GmbH, Stuttgenweg, West Germany; Rafael Fernández-Rubio, University of Granada, Granada, Spain; and Roy Williams, Mineral Resources Research Institute, University of Idaho, Moscow, Idaho.

The program chairman, the organizing committee, and the advisory committee are grateful for the advice and assistance of many hydrologists, geologists, mining engineers, lawyers, and public servants. Collectively their contributions were in large part the reason for the success of this symposium.

Several of the speakers provided abstracts with their written papers. In those cases, the abstract is included as the first part of their chapter. Many of the co-authors were not able to attend the symposium even though they contributed to and helped write papers. Every effort was made to obtain a biography for each co-author. If, however, they were not at the symposium and did not provide biographical data, their biographies are not in this book.

The service to the mining industry of the speakers who shared their thoughts and experience at the Mine Drainage Symposium cannot be understated. Without the contribution of the speakers, the symposium and this volume would not have been possible. We again extend sincere thanks for their efforts.

George O. Argall, Jr.
Symposium Chairman and Co-editor
San Francisco, California
September 1979

ABOUT THE AUTHORS

CHAPTER 1
General Report on Mine Drainage

C. O. Brawner has B.Sc. and M.Sc. degrees in civil engineering with specialization in geotechnical engineering. A native of Canada, he spent 10 years with the British Columbia Department of Highways and 15 years as consulting geotechnical engineer with Golder Associates. Since 1978 he has taught rock mechanics at the University of British Columbia, Vancouver. Mr. Brawner was program chairman for the first International Mine Drainage Symposium and co-editor of this book. Further biographical information may be found in "About the Editors" on page 31.

CHAPTER 2
Mine Drainage: The Common Enemy

George Vranesh is an attorney with Vranesh and Raisch, P.C., Boulder, Colorado, USA, a firm that limits its practice to resources law. A native of Minnesota, he has an E. M. degree from the Colorado School of Mines and an LL.B. from the University of Colorado School of Law. Before starting law practice in 1961, he was senior mine engineer with Idarado Mining Co., Ouray, Colorado, and co-owner of Ouray Mining Co., Moab, Utah. He is president of the Boulder County Mining Association and director of the Colorado Mining Association.

CHAPTER 3
Ground Water Design Parameters for Mining and Milling

John C. Halepaska, chief of the Water Resources Division of Woodward-Clyde Consultants, Denver, Colorado, USA, is a native of Victoria, Texas. He graduated with a B.S. in geology from Saint Mary's University, San Antonio, Texas, then earned his M.S. in groundwater hydrology and Ph.D. in geoscience from New Mexico Institute of Mining and Technology in Socorro. Before joining Woodward-Clyde Consultants, he spent five years with the Kansas Geological Survey, as chief of the Groundwater Section.

CHAPTER 4
Hydrogeologic Investigations for Mine Dewatering

Russell G. Slayback, vice president and director of Leggette, Brashears, & Graham, Inc., Westport, Connecticut, USA, has been with the firm since 1960. He received a B.S. in geology from Rensselaer Polytechnic Institute, Troy, New York, in 1959. His experience includes major field investigations in the USA, Canada, Yemen Arab Republic, and Caribbean region. Active in the Association of Professional Geological Scientists, he is past Northeast Section president and is currently on the National Advisory Board.

CHAPTER 5
Groundwater Instrumentation for Mining Projects

Franklin D. Patton, consultant in engineering geology and rock mechanics, is president of Westbay Instruments Ltd., West Vancouver, British Columbia, Canada. Graduating from the University of Alberta, Edmonton, with a B.Sc. in civil engineering in 1957, he earned an M.S. in civil engineering and a Ph.D. in geology from the University of Illinois, then was NATO Postdoctoral Fellow at the National Civil Engineering Laboratory in Lisbon, Portugal. He is currently visiting professor at the University of British Columbia.

CHAPTER 6
Evaluation and Control of Ground-Water Quality in the Rocky Mountain Area

Jim V. Rouse is vice president and general manager of Envirologic Systems, Inc., in Denver, Colorado, USA. Born in Mathis, Texas, he graduated from the Colorado School of Mines in geological engineering in 1961 and received an M.S. in hydrology from Stanford University in 1968. He spent eight years with the U.S. Public Health Service and two years with the Environmental Protection Agency before joining his present firm in 1977.

CHAPTER 7
Effect of Longwall Mining on Ground Permeability and Subsurface Drainage

Barry N. Whittaker has spent 10 years as a professional mining engineer with Great Britain's National Coal Board and 10 years as university lecturer and mining consultant. Born in Castleford, Yorkshire, he holds a B.Sc. in mining engineering and a Ph.D. He is a Fellow of the Institution of Mining Engineers and a chartered engineer. Currently in the department of mining engineering, Nottingham University, he also serves as consulting engineer for several nationalized corporations in Great Britain and for international mining companies.

R. N. Singh is a research fellow in the department of mining engineering at Nottingham University, England. Born in Nainital, India, he holds a B.Sc. degree in mining engineering, an M. Eng., and a Ph.D. A chartered engineer, he has 15 years of operational experience in coal mining and has spent a year as inspector of mines and five years in rock mechanics research. His activities include development of new rock mechanics instrumentation.

Christopher J. Neate has been a research worker at Nottingham University since 1977. Born in London, he holds a B.Sc. in mining engineering. He is currently engaged in mining hydrology studies in the university's department of mining engineering.

CHAPTER 8
Coping with Mine Drainage Regulations

Roy E. Williams is professor of hydrology and director of the Mineral Resources Institute at the University of Idaho, USA. Born in Tennessee, he received his B.S. and M.A. from Indiana University and his Ph.D. from the University of Illinois. From 1972 to 1974 he was on loan to the U.S. Bureau of Mines in Washington, D.C. Currently he is working part time with

Argonne National Laboratory to develop and evaluate practices in disposal of uranium mill waste for the Mill License Branch, U.S. Nuclear Regulatory Commission.

No biographical information was provided for co-author **Joe Baldwin**. Biographical material for co-author **Dale R. Ralston** will be found with Chapter 15.

CHAPTER 9
Dewatering of Mines—A Practical Analysis

Lloyd C. Venburg is principal ground-water geologist for International Engineering Co. Inc., San Francisco, California, USA. A native of Kansas, he majored in geology, receiving a B.S. from the state university in 1950. He was field geologist for the Kansas Highway Commission from 1953 to 1957 and geologist for Stang Hydronics Inc. from 1960 to 1976. He has designed and supervised installations of dewatering and water control systems on major construction and mining projects throughout the world.

CHAPTER 10
Drainage Control and Mine Dewatering at
Faro Open Pit Mine

Randy S. Lopaschuk is geological/geotechnical engineer with Cyprus Anvil Mining Corporation, Faro, Yukon Territory, Canada. Born in Vancouver, British Columbia, he received a BASc. from the University of British Columbia in 1976. Following graduation, he joined Golder, Brawner & Associates in Vancouver as junior engineer, going to his present position with Cyprus Anvil in 1977. He is a director of Faro Branch of CIMM and a member of other professional societies.

CHAPTER 11
Horizontal Drains—Their Use in Open Pit Mine Dewatering

Ben L. Seegmiller, principal, Seegmiller Associates in Salt Lake City, Utah, USA, is primarily interested in solving rock stability problems for mining companies. A native of Utah, he holds B.S., M.S., and Ph.D. degrees from the University of Utah. Before going to his present company in 1974, he was chief rock mechanics engineer for Anaconda. His firm is currently consultant to the People's Republic of China on slope stability and to seven companies involved in coal, uranium, copper, iron, phosphate, and barite mining.

CHAPTER 12
Open Pit Dewatering at Pine Point

Keith J. Durston is mine engineering superintendent for Cominco Ltd., Pine Point, Northwest Territories, Canada. Born in Plymouth, England, he attended the Royal School of Mines, University of London, receiving a B.Sc. in mining engineering and associateship of the Royal School of Mines. Since 1965 he has held positions with Canadian companies involved in mining of copper, nickel, uranium, potash, lead, and zinc, both underground and open pit. **K. U. Weyer** (B.Sc., M.Sc., Ph.D.) is a hydrogeologist at the National Hydrology Research Institute in Calgary, Alberta, Canada, and has been involved in research and consulting related to mining in Europe, Canada, and India since 1965.

CHAPTER 13
The Design of Mine Dewatering Systems in Poland

Jacek S. Libicki is chief geologist for Poltegor, Central Institute for Surface Mining, Wroclaw, Poland. Born in Cracow, he received an M.Sc. in geological exploration from the University of Wroclaw and a Ph.D. in hydrogeology from the University of Mining and Metallurgy in Cracow. In addition to his other duties, he is chief coordinator of Polish-USA cooperation in environmental protection in surface mining and has been director of three international symposiums dealing with the subject.

CHAPTER 14
Case Examples of Open Pit Mine Drainage

David L. Pentz, vice president of Golder Associates, Kirkland, Washington, USA, is a native of London, England. He holds B.Sc. and M.Sc. degrees from Imperial College, London, where he specialized in petroleum technology, soil mechanics, and rock mechanics. He was assistant lecturer at Imperial College, then geotechnical engineer for Atalaya, Palabora, and Bougainville projects before he joined Golder Associates in 1970.

CHAPTER 15
Ground Water Flow Systems in Idaho's
Western Phosphate Field

Dale R. Ralston is associate professor of hydrogeology, College of Mines and Earth Resources, University of Idaho, Moscow, Idaho, USA. Born in Idaho, he received a B.S. in civil engineering at Oregon State University in 1964, an M.S. in hydrology at the University of Arizona in 1967, and a Ph.D. in civil engineering at the University of Idaho. Dr. Ralston has been with the California Department of Water Resources, the U.S. Geological Survey, Idaho Department of Water Resources, and Idaho Bureau of Mines and Geology.

No biographical information was provided for co-authors **Michael R. Cannon** and **Gerry V. Winter.**

CHAPTER 16
Artesian Dewatering Operations at
Morwell Open Cut

C. J. Fraser is geotechnical engineer in the fuel department, State Electricity Commission of Victoria, Melbourne, Australia. A native of Melbourne, he earned a B.E. in civil engineering at the Royal Melbourne Institute of technology and a Dip. Appl. Sci. in geology at Canberra College of Advanced Education. Before taking his present position in 1977, he was with the Snowy Mountains Engineering Corporation from 1969 to 1974, then did research in groundwater hydrology at Canberra College of Advanced Education.

H. A. Pitt, a native of Melbourne, is engineer in the operations planning and coal production department, State Electricity Commission of Victoria. A graduate of the University of

Melbourne with a B.E. in mining, he joined the Electricity Commission in 1975. Currently he is engaged in open cut planning and geotechnical investigations and in operation of the artesian dewatering system. He is a junior member of the Australian I.M.M.

CHAPTER 17
Computation of and Experience on
Lignite Opencast Mine Drainage

Rolf H. Hofedank is geophysicist/senior hydrologist with Otto Gold Consulting Engineers, Cologne, Federal Republic of Germany. Born in Berlin, he received a diploma in geophysics at Frankfurt University. Later he earned a doctor's degree in applied geology at Giessen University, where he specialized in ground and surface water hydrology. In his present position, Dr. Hofedank works on mine drainage, surface and bore hole geophysics, and ground-water modeling. Previously, he has been with construction engineering firms.

CHAPTER 18
Twenty-five Year Experience
in Dewatering at Canadian Mining Complex

Om P. Garg obtained an M.Sc. degree with specialization in rock mechanics from the University of Saskatchewan in Saskatoon, Canada. He joined Iron Ore Company of Canada in 1970 and is currently engineering superintendent at its Knob Lake operations, centered around Schefferville. He has published several papers on topics related to slope design, permafrost, open pit mine planning, applied field physics, and computer applications to mining. He is past chairman of the Knob Lake branch of CIMM and a member of other professional societies.

Gilles Hétu is supervisor of mine dewatering and blasting for Iron Ore Company of Canada at Schefferville, Quebec. He earned a B.Sc. in geology at the University of Montreal, his native city, and has held positions as geologist, development supervisor, and supervisor of mine engineering.

Donald Hindy was born in Newfoundland, Canada, and received a B.Eng. degree from Memorial University at St. John's in that province. Currently mine engineering supervisor for Iron Ore Company of Canada at Schefferville, he has previously held various positions with the company, including engineer and general foreman, operations.

CHAPTER 19
Drainage Used to Control Movements
of a Large Rock Slide in Canada

John Sharp, consultant/principal of Golder Associates in the United Kingdom, received a B.Sc. in civil engineering and a Ph.D. in rock mechanics from Imperial College, London. Born in England, he joined Golder Associates in Canada in 1970 as senior engineer at Vancouver, British Columbia. In 1974 the firm transferred him to its U.K. office, where he specializes in groundwater flow, slope stability, and underground rock engineering.

CHAPTER 20
Dewatering Techniques for
Rheinbraun's Open Pit Lignite Mines

Rudolf W. Voigt, chief geologist for Rheinbraun-Consulting GmbH, Cologne, Federal Republic of Germany, was born in Berlin. Following graduation from Jlena University, he was geophysicist on a seismic field trip and later worked eight years on hydrogeological mapping of the lower Rhine Basin. Receiving his Ph.D. at Aachen Technical University in 1968, he spent two years in the USA in postdoctorate work at the Department of Hydrology and Water Resources, University of Arizona, Tucson. Recently he has been involved on projects in Germany and Turkey.

No biographical information was provided for **Burkhard Boehm** and **Dietmar Schneider**, who co-authored this chapter with Dr. Voight.

CHAPTER 21
Drainage Control at a Central Florida
Open Pit Phosphate Mine

John Harry Paugh, geologist for Swift Agricultural Chemical Corporation, Barstow, Florida, USA, is primarily interested in mining geology, mine engineering, and hydrology. Born in Youngstown, Ohio, he studied geological engineering at the Michigan College of Mining and Technology for two years, then received a B.S. in Geology at Wayne State University, Detroit, in 1964. He joined Agrico Chemical Co., Pierce, Florida, in 1966, leaving in 1974 to take his present position.

CHAPTER 22
Some Technical Aspects of
Open Pit Mine Dewatering

Vladimir Straskraba is senior mining hydrologist with Dames & Moore in Denver, Colorado, USA. He was born in Czechoslovakia where he earned an M.S. in geological engineering. From 1958 to 1968, he was head of the groundwater department of the Geological Survey in Czechoslovakia. Moving to Italy in 1968, he was technical director for Sigma Italiana. He then worked on a hydrology project for D'Appolonia Consulting Engineers until he joined Dames & Moore in 1978.

CHAPTER 23
Drainage of Coal and Lignite Mines

Rafael Fernández-Rubio is professor of hydrogeology at Granada University in Spain. A native of Spain and a Dr. Mining Engineer, he attended the High School of Mining Engineers and the Spanish Institute of Hydrology. He has visited 23 countries as a consulting engineer with UNIDO, UNESCO, and FAO, and has had a good deal of experience on mine dewatering projects. Director of the International Center of Water in Mines, he is author of more than 80 professional papers.

CHAPTER 24
Controlling Mine Water

R. L. Loofbourow, consulting engineer, Minneapolis, Minnesota, USA, specializes in underground construction, limestone mining, metal mining, and water control. He received a B.A. in geology from Stanford University in California and, from 1931 to 1944, he held positions in the USA, the Philippines, Canada, and Mexico. From 1945 to 1953 he was engineer and manager of the Mining Division of Longyear Company in Minneapolis, where he was responsible for shaft and excavation contracts and consulting.

CHAPTER 25
Simple Mine Inflow Evaluation for
Underground Oil Shale Mines

Adrian Brown, associate, Golder Associates Inc., Denver, Colorado, USA, was born in Melbourne, Victoria, Australia. He received a bachelor of civil engineering degree from Monash University, then earned master's degrees in engineering science and business administration at the same university. From 1967 to 1974 he was with Victoria's State Electricity Commission, as stability and groundwater engineer for Latrobe Valley lignite mines. He joined Golder Associates in 1974 as senior engineer in Vancouver, British Columbia, Canada.

CHAPTER 26
Hydrogeology of a Lead-Zinc Mine

Bryson D. Trexler, Jr. is hydrogeologist for Kennecott Copper Corporation's Metal Mines Division in Salt Lake City, Utah, USA. A native of North Carolina, he received a B.S. in geological engineering and an M.S. in geology at the state university. He earned his Ph.D. in geology at the University of Idaho in 1975. Before joining Kennecott, he was assistant professor of geology at East Carolina University, assistant professor of hydrogeology at the University of Toledo in Ohio, and hydrogeologist at the University of Idaho.

CHAPTER 27
Depressurization for Shaft Sinking

William M. Greenslade, partner, Dames & Moore, Phoenix, Arizona, was born in Cleveland, Ohio, USA. He attended the University of Nevada's Mackay School of Mines, where he earned a B.S. in geologic engineering and an M.S. in hydrology. He was with the Desert Research Institute from 1965 to 1967, then joined Dames & Moore. He has been discipline leader for groundwater hydrology and has made mines dewatering studies in the southwestern USA, Mexico, Canada, and Brazil.

CHAPTER 28
Mine Dewatering—A Package Approach

Neil F. Archer, president of Arch Environmental Equipment Company, Paducah, Kentucky, USA, is a native of Iowa. He studied civil engineering at the University of Montana and was general manager of water development for Arch from 1967 to 1972. His special interests include package systems design, applications, mine dewatering and treatment.

CHAPTER 29
High Voltage Submersible Mine Dewatering Pumps for Extremely High Lifts

Otto H. Schiele is a director and member of the board, Research and Development, of Klein, Schanzlin & Becker, Frankenthal, Federal Republic of Germany. Born in Baden-Baden, he attended the University of Karlsruhe and is a Professor Dr.-Ing and a specialist in fluid machinery. He is a nonexecutive member of the boards of three companies and president of the German Association for Research and Development in Mechanical Engineering. No biographical information was provided for co-author **H. Kuntz**.

CHAPTER 30
Hydrogeological Problems and Their Resolutions at the Friedensville Mine

Kenneth R. Cox, manager of the New Jersey Zinc Company's Friedensville mine, Center Valley, Pennsylvania, USA, started his career with St. Joe Lead Co. in Missouri. After completing his military obligation, he joined New Jersey Zinc Company in 1963. He is currently chairman of the Lehigh Valley section of the American Institute of Mining Engineers. He holds a B.S. in mining engineering from the University of Missouri.

CHAPTER 31
The Role of Water in the Failure of Tailings Dams

Edwin S. Smith, chief engineer for International Engineering Company's Geotechnical Division, San Francisco, California, USA, graduated from Queens University, Northern Ireland, in 1951 with a B.S. in civil engineering and later received a master's degree in soil mechanics from Harvard University, USA. After assignments in the United Kingdom and Canada, he joined IECO in British Columbia in 1952. Transferred to San Francisco in 1954, his work on resource planning, engineering, and tailings disposal has taken him to many parts of the world.

David H. Connell, project engineer for International Engineering Company at San Francisco, is responsible for the investigation, analysis, and design of earth dams and tailings structures and disposal systems. He has also been in charge of reconnaissance and feasibility studies and final geotechnical design for water supply dams in the western United States. Receiving his B.S. degree from Iowa State University in 1968, he earned his M.S. from Massachusetts Institute of Technology in 1972.

CHAPTER 32
Acid Mine Drainage Modeling of Surface Mining

Vincent T. Ricca is professor of Civil Engineering at The Ohio State University, Columbus, Ohio, USA. Born in New York, he received a bachelor's degree in civil engineering from City

University, then earned his master's degree and his Ph.D. from Purdue University in Indiana. Before moving to Ohio, he served terms as engineer for the California Department of Water Resources and New York Department of Public Works and was a consultant in hydrologic and hydraulic engineering.

Ronald R. Schultz, project engineer for Burgess & Niple, Ltd., Parkersburg, West Virginia, USA, has particular interest in surface water hydrology and acid mine drainage. Born in Cincinnati, Ohio, he received a B.S. in civil engineering from the state university in 1975 and an M.S. degree in 1977. His M.S. thesis was "Application of the Combined Refuse Pile Strip Mine Model for Acid Mine Drainage."

CHAPTER 33
Seepage Control for Tailings Dams

Earle J. Klohn, president of Klohn Leonoff Consultants Ltd., Richmond, British Columbia, Canada, is a geotechnical engineer with more than 25 years of consulting experience. He has been active in design and construction of earth and rockfill dams and heavy industrial foundations and has worked on projects in many parts of the world. In recent years much of his activity has been related to tailings dam design and construction. He has B.Sc. and M.Sc. degrees in civil engineering from the University of Alberta, Canada.

CHAPTER 34
Control of Seepage from Uranium Mill Tailings Ponds in the Elliot Lake Area

J. B. Davis, principal, Golder Associates Ltd., Toronto, Ontario, Canada, is responsible for all geotechnical investigations undertaken by that office. He holds B.E.Sc. and M.E.Sc. degrees from the University of Western Ontario. Since he joined Golder Associates as soils engineer in 1964, he has been involved in investigations in Ontario and abroad, including stability studies for open pit mines, tailings dams, and conservation dams and embankments. No biographical information was provided for co-authors **R. A. Knapp** and **K. W. Sinclair**.

CHAPTER 35
Groundwater Contamination Problems Resulting from Coal Refuse Disposal

Jeffrey P. Schubert, hydrologist at the Argonne National Laboratory in Argonne, Illinois, USA, is associated with the Land Reclamation Program, conducting hydrogeologic and geochemical research related to surface and underground coal mining and mineral waste disposal. Born in Louisville, Kentucky, he received a B.S. in geology from the University of Illinois in 1972 and an M.S. in hydrogeology from Pennsylvania State University in 1978.

CHAPTER 36
Case Histories of Different Seepage Problems for Nine Tailings Dams

Keith E. Robinson, partner, Dames & Moore, North Vancouver, British Columbia, Canada, is responsible for technical review and quality control coordination for tailings and earth dams. His work has involved more than 50 tailings and 20 earth and rockfill dams as well as open pit slope stability and groundwater seepage studies. A native of Canada, he holds a BASc. in civil engineering from the University of Illinois, USA. No biographical information was provided for co-author **G. C. Toland**.

CHAPTER 37
Excursion Potentials at
Uranium Tailings Disposal Sites

Michael Taylor of Denver, Colorado, USA, is manager of projects for D'Appolonia Consulting Engineers Inc. in the Rocky Mountain region. He received his B.S. and M.S. from Carnegie Institute of Technology. He spent two years on Arctic work with the U.S. Corps of Engineers in Alaska and has over ten years of diversified experience in multidisciplinary geotechnical, structural, hydrologic, and environmental projects. His particular interest is in dam and uranium tailings embankment engineering. No biographical information was provided for co-author **Phillip E. Antommaria**.

ABOUT THE EDITORS

George O. Argall, Jr., an internationally known mining engineer, has been associated with *World Mining, World Coal,* and affiliated publications since 1950. During his 29 years as editor of the Miller Freeman Publications' mining magazines, Argall has visited mining, milling, and smelting operations in 63 countries and has published detailed—often exclusive—reports about remote and unusual developments in these fields.

Born in Denver, Colorado, USA—the son and grandson of mining engineers—Argall was raised in Leadville and received a B.S., Engineer of Mines, degree from the Colorado School of Mines. Following graduation in 1935, he held supervisory positions in gold, silver, tungsten, molybdenum, and uranium mines. Later he was supervising mining engineer with the Reconstruction Finance Corporation.

He joined Miller Freeman Publications as editor of *Mining World* and, when that publication was sold, continued as editor of *World Mining.* For five years (1964 to 1969) he made his editorial headquarters in Brussels, Belgium, and from 1974 through 1977 he was publisher of *World Mining* and *World Coal* in addition to his editorial duties. At the present time he is senior editor of *World Mining* and consulting editor for *World Coal.*

One of Argall's pioneering communications projects is a series of international symposiums covering special themes in the minerals industries. *Mine Drainage* is the most recent proceedings book recording the information exchanged at these international meetings.

George Argall is the author of two books—*Occurrence and Production of Vanadium* and *Industrial Minerals of Colorado*—and the editor of *Minerals Transportation,* Volumes 1 and 2, *Tailing Disposal Today,* Volumes 1 and 2, and the *World Mining Glossary of Mining, Processing, and Geological Terms.* In 1969 his special issue of *World Mining*, "Japan and the World of Mining," won the Associated Business Publications' Jesse H. Neal award for editorial excellence.

Argall is a professional engineer, a member of the Mining and Metallurgical Society of America, the Colorado Mining Association, the Northwest Mining Association, the Nevada Mining Association, and the American Institute of Mining, Metallurgical, and Petroleum Engineers.

C. O. Brawner has been associated with drainage and stability studies on over 300 mining projects around the world. After 15 years as a consultant, Mr. Brawner resigned as president of Golder, Brawner & Associates, Ltd., in 1978 to join the faculty of the University of British Columbia and give instruction in geomechanics. He continues with some private consulting.

A native of Canada and graduate of the University of Manitoba and Nova Scotia Technical College in soil mechanics, foundations, and geology, Mr. Brawner worked with the Province of British Columbia Department of Highways prior to joining Golder Associates in 1963. He is a registered professional engineer.

Among other awards, Mr. Brawner received the 1978 B. T. A. Bell Commemorative Medallion for service to the Canadian mining industry and, recently, the Meritorious Service Award of the Association of Professional Engineers of British Columbia. His advisory activities include work with the Canadian Department of Mines as specialist consultant for development of the "Design Guide of Mine Waste Embankments in Canada." He is a past member of the National Research Council of Canada Associate Committee on Geotechnical Research and served as vice chairman of the Canadian Advisory Committee on Rock Mechanics.

Mr. Brawner is the co-editor of three other books: *Stability in Open Pit Mining, Geotechnical Practice for Stability in Open Pit Mining,* and *Stability in Coal Mining.* He has written over 60 technical papers on soil and rock mechanics engineering.

1

General Report on Mine Drainage

by C. O. Brawner,
Department of Mineral Engineering,
University of British Columbia,
Vancouver, British Columbia, Canada

INTRODUCTION

The requirements for effective control of water in mining are increasing as mines became deeper and larger and as environmental controls became more stringent.

The First International Symposium on Mine Drainage was organized to interrelate theory with practice and to emphasize current procedures being used to solve mine drainage problems. To illustrate this approach numerous case examples are included.

No extensive theoretical treatment has been included in the program since the Conference on Water in Mining in Granada Spain in August 1978 dealt with this aspect in considerable detail.

This program included sessions on investigation and evaluation of surface and subsurface water, drainage control for surface and underground mines and tailings disposal facilities, regulations and typical case examples.

INVESTIGATION AND EVALUATION

Measurements of groundwater conditions may be required on mining projects for the following purposes:
- to develop hydrogeochemical profiles to assist in locating

potential orebodies.
- to determine groundwater levels and groundwater pressure profiles with depth.
- to obtain water samples to assess background water quality levels prior and during exploration, during mining and after mining is complete.
- to establish the three dimensional flow pattern prior to mining.
- to determine the groundwater flow and pressures and their influence on stability in open pit mining.
- to determine deep groundwater flow volumes and pressures and assess this influence on stability in underground mining.
- to assess methods of controlling groundwater flow and stability.
- to monitor ground water seepage and potential contamination from leach dumps, wastes dumps and tailings dams.

The diversity of hydrogeological problems encountered in surface and underground mines is great. If the geology is well understood an evaluation of the hydrogeology may not be difficult. However extensive testing may be required. One of the most difficult conditions to evaluate acquifers or aquitards in most rock is where flow is through fractures, joints, faults, or other openings.

The control of water in mining is a multi team effort. Specialists should typically include the following:
    Climatologist - seasonal and peak precipitation conditions
    Hydrologist - surface water studies
    Hydrogeologist - subsurface water studies
    Mining Engineer - influence of water on mining and mine stability.
    Drainage Engineer - dewatering studies
    Hydraulic Engineer - pump and pipeline design
    Reservoir Engineer - gas effect studies (if present)

The two most important factors to interrelate subsurface ground water studies are the influence of geology: faults, fractures, joints, solution cavities and the method and care of mining. Fracturing induced by the mining has major influence on permeability.

The primary tasks of this group are to determine the probabilities and volume of water inflow, evaluate the influence of the inflow and where necessary develop a preventative or control program.

The standard procedures have been generally to install

a single piezometer in a number of boreholes in the general area of exploration, around the potential mine site. The cost of the piezometers is only a small fraction of cost of the drilling.

On most mining projects the total depth of mining is such that multi-geologic sequences and multi-aquifers exist. It is obvious to define the ground water profile and flow that the water pressure in each aquifer should be known. A single piezometer cannot possibly provide this information.

Patton has described a "Profiler" which can measure permeability at intervals during the drilling operation so that the best location for piezometers can be established.

Patton suggests that the least number of piezometers required for minimum coverage is 2n + m where n is number of aquifers present with appreciable thickness and m is the number of aquitards below the water tables. For adequate coverage he suggests 4 n + 2 m piezometers.

This density of piezometers can be achieved by (a) several piezometers in separate boreholes (b) conventional multiple piezometers installed in one drill hole or (c) multiple piezometers of the enclosed type in a single bore-hole. The latter technique is very recent (the Westbay MP System described by Patton). This technique has the advantage of reasonably rapid response, the calibration can be checked periodically, negative pore pressures can be measured, low cost per piezometer point, large number of possible reading points, reduced scheduling problems and capability to obtain water quality samples. The major disadvantage has been the increasing complication of installing many seals. This has recently been overcome with the development of multiple casing packers.

In numerous instances piezometers are necessary when the rock is not competent. The use of special bio-degradeable muds assist in the advancement of the borehole, allow installation of the piezometer without seriously affecting permeability near the borehole. Water samples should be taken during the early part of any investigation to establish the base line water quality parameters. Rouse emphasizes the importance of obtaining representative samples. To ensure this, samples should not be taken until a constant value of pH and conductivity occurs.

Regional long term climatic conditions have a major

influence on ground water balance. In hot dry climates the
ground water flow may be upward due to the high evaporation
influence. In heavy rainfall areas the net flow is obviously downward.

For deep underground mining Halepaska suggests the analyses make use of the reduction in the mine plan geometry
to "effective radius". He suggests three methods:

Method 1 entails approximation of the mine plan as a
well and uses the constant head Jacob-Lowman equation to
calculate flow rates. This method generally yields a pumpage rate that is too high.

For Method 2, the technique of interfering wells is
utilized, wherein each drift face of the proposed mine plan
is considered to be a well. The cumulative production of
the drift "wells", which typically are mutually interfering,
is an approximation of the expected production from the mine.

For Method 3, the technique of confined-unconfined
theory and the Jacob-Lowman theory are combined to calculate
the required pumpage. The effective radius in this method
is chosen as the radius at which the aquifer of interest
goes from the confined to the unconfined state. Therefore,
the concept focuses on fluid entering the unconfined state
from elastic yield of the confined state.

Permeability changes in caving ground can be of major
importance when the mine is located near or under water
courses or bodies of water. Recent full scale by Whittaker
on two longwall coal projects indicates that appreciable
change in the insitu permeability occurs between the face
and 40 meters behind the face and above the extraction horizon. The increase in the permeability is a function of
the natural rock jointing and bedding and the thickness of
the seam being extracted. Beyond about 40 meters behind
the face the permeability begins to reduce due to reconsoli-
dation.

The increase in permeability during the test program
ranged from about 40 to 80 times the undisturbed permeability.

Venburg describes the practical requirements of geohy-
drological evaluations for mining projects with emphasis on
pre-drainage. Considerable emphasis is placed on obtaining
preliminary data from local sources such as climatological
offices, water resources branches, drilling companies, water

well developers etc.

With minimal additional expense, exploratory boring can be used to show depths of unconsolidated sediments, classification and lithology of bedrock, location and orientation of discontinuities, zones of caving or heavy mud or water loss and artesian water conditions. The use of geophysical logging is strongly recommended. These should include temperature, flow meter and tracer logs.

Chemical and bacterial analyses of water encountered should be tested for background data, well and dewatering equipment selection and environmental consideration.

Detailed consideration must be given to cost assessments for pre-drainage schemes. Vensburg lists items for a typical well de-watering system:

Drilling costs	Surface casing
Mud pit excavation	Well screen
Well casing	Gravel filter
Grouting	Well development
Test pumping	Fuel, oil and grease
Power	

Labor, including supervision
Mobilization and demolization of equipment, including freight
Cost of obtaining a water supply, including supply pump and hose
Pumps and discharge pipe, including installation
Front end loader, crane, welder, tools, light plant, air compressor and transportation
Miscellaneous items including taxes, licenses and permits.

To evaluate mine ground water problems it is usually necessary to determine the following properties or conditions.
(a) Acquifer Coefficients - Transmissivity and Coefficient of Storage
(b) Boundary Conditions
(c) Local water budget or sources of recharge.
Slayback describes several case examples which illustrate practical investigational programs and interpretation of these programs to solve unusual groundwater conditions.

A typical field test program was used for the Dundee Cement Company to determine whether a sand acquifer might provide a conduit for water from the Mississippi River 4,000 feet away from a planned limestone quarry. A test production well and a pattern of observation wells were drilled between the proposed quarry and the River. No significant recharge was indicated by the plots of the test data. This low cost program indicated that recharge from the Mississippi was manageable at low cost.

A major concern at the Pine Point Mine in N.W.T., Canada owned by Cominco was recognition that the dewatering combined a transition from a confined or artesion aquifer to a water table aquifer.   Slayback indicates that in his experience no other single phenomena in hydrogeology has caused more problems in groundwater evaluation. This case results in differences of more than one order of magnitude between the artesian and water-table storage coefficients. This can lead to delay time in pumping between the artesian condition and water table condition which can be devastating. If the delay period were to extend through three log cycles a delay period from 10 to 10,000 days or 27 years could occur. The solution at Pine Point was to promote sufficient pump capacity to drive through the delay barrier early.

In the Athabasca tar sands, conditions have been found to vary greatly. At the Great Canadian Oil Sands project there are no aquifer problems and no ground water control system. On the Syncrude project up to three aquifers were encountered below the feed zone. Aquifer pressures must be dewatered to ensure the water pressure does not cause the mine floor to heave or to pipe where the aquifer sand is directly below the feed. Extensive field tests were performed. The testing & evaluation was complicated by the evolution of dissolved gas, creating a four phase hydrocarbon system. The analysis made use of an oil-reservoir computer model to predict depressurization.

The depressurization program at Syncrude involves over 500 depressurization wells.

At the Alsands project a basal aquifer zone exists which contains clean coarse sand but with no dissolved gas present. As a result more water is likely to be discharged with fewer wells than at Syncrude.

Loofbourrow quotes pumping costs for an efficient design pumping system to range generally from $0.20 to $0.30 per million foot gallons. The key to economy is to reduce the pumping energy. Indirect costs must be considered due to increased production, maintenance and increased transportation costs.

The most effective planning to control water is one

that is instituted during the mine design stage. Special consideration should be given to pre-mine dewatering and in underground mines to mining from the bottom up. This planning should also consider normal methods of seepage reduction, such as the use of clay or slimes grouts or plugging with chemical or bacterial precipitates. In addition the planning should include an ongoing program to drill ahead of the working levels, maintain up to date plots of water data and to have repair equipment and tools immediately available.

Hofedank, Consulting Engineer from West Germany states that no other water problem, aside from those having to do with the drainage of mines, needs such a large number of different sciences for its solution. He outlines the programs recommended to evaluate the influence of groundwater, surface water, precipitation and environmental impact on the mine.

He reviews an open pit coal project where two aquifers separated by a clay seam exist. Leakage appears from the lower aquifer when the upper aquifer is pumped. After several years the rate of leakage reduced. The use of Boulton's concepts of a semi-confined aquifer may explain decreasing leakage taking into account the difference in short and long term dynamics. The author would note that as depressurization of the upper aquifer progresses a substantial increase in effective pressure occurs which could cause consolidation of the drainage layers, reduce permeability and leakage.

Careful planning and meticulous field work are required to successfully assess mine dewatering problems. However, it must be recognized that comprehensive programs do not eliminate the risk of unforseen anomalous conditions. Properly designed groundwater investigations will reduce the probability of encountering unforseen conditions to reasonable limits.

DRAINAGE IN OPEN PIT MINES

Surface and subsurface water creates a wide range of problems on surface mine projects. The most important of these include the following:
Surface water-
(a) Pit slope, haul road and drainage ditch erosion.
(b) Haul road softening, frost heave in winter.
(c) Erosion fan deposition.

(d) Water pressure build-up in tension cracks.
(e) Glaciation in winter.
Subsurface water–
(a) Reduction of soil and rock shear strength.
(b) Pit slope instability which requires flatter slopes.
(c) Increase in blasting costs.
(d) Pit slope and floor bottom heave.
(e) Slope seepage and associated erosion and glaciation.

Procedures to control surface drainage are simple and well understood. Control of subsurface drainage has only recently been recognized on many projects as a serious and potentially costly problem. The case examples in this symposium have been selected to provide a cross section of typical problems as well as control and stabilization procedures. Table 1 provides a summary of these examples.

Where the open pit mine extends below the water table the least expensive method of slope drainage usually involves horizontal drains. Specialized equipment and procedures can install drains up to 300–400 feet long. Greater lengths are usually not required. The drains should be installed at an entry gradient of about 5 per cent. If the drain holes collapse, 1 to 2 inch plastic pipe should be installed. The outer sections of the pipe above the water table should not be perforated. The inner lengths should have the perforations down to allow the water in the pipe.

To reduce set up costs and collection costs, 4 to 6 drains can be angled and from one location.

If the rate of drilling is too fast the drill rod will climb above the water table and the program will be ineffective. If the rate of drilling is slow the drain gradient will drop below horizontal. This is not serious as the drain will operate under pressure. For long term operation the drains must be flushed occasionally. The amount of water which flows from the drains is not a good measure of the effectiveness. Piezometers should always be installed to monitor the drop in the water pressures.

Perimeter and in pit wells have been used on many projects to lower the water table. In situ pumping and permeability tests are a recommended prerequisite to the design of the well and pumping system. One frequent benefit of the well system, provided the water level is lowered below all mining levels, is that less expensive explosive can be used. Numerous projects have reported that blasting costs

TABLE 1 - SUMMARY OF OPEN PIT STABILIZATION BY DRAINAGE

Location	Problem	Solution
Cyprus Anvil Mine Faro, Yukon	Surface inflow from Faro Creek causing erosion in summer and glaciation in winter. Subsurface seepage into the mine causing unstable pit slopes, increased blasting costs, glaciation on slopes, increased haul and maintenance, ice build up in truck boxes and shovel buckets. Overly wet ore required stockpiling for drainage. Excess stockpile time lead to oxidation.	Diverted creek and placed water proof lining along high permeability zones. Six thousand feet of horizontal drains were installed with 1.5 inch O.D. slotted plastic pipe. Average drawdown ranged from 7-14 feet. Daily volumes of water averages about 100,000 gal./day. Collector sump in bedrock constructed with pumps and 6-8 inch polyethylene pipes used to remove water from pit. A steamer is used to thaw frozen pipelines.
Pine Point Mines Pine Point, N.W.T.	Extensive seepage into numerous open pits cause difficult and hazardous mining conditions and high explosives costs. Seepage is from aquifers that continuously recharge from mountains to the south. Sinkholes are frequently encountered in the open pit areas.	Installation of deep wells (400-500 ft.) and pumps around the perimeter of the open pits. Design based on pumping tests and analysis methods of Cooper and Jacob and of Thiem. Well design allows for 10 percent loss due to well collapse and 80 per cent effective pumping rate. Well locations selected away from sinkholes. Wells 14-3/4 inch diameter with no casing or screens at depth. Dewatering costs represent 16 per cent of direct mining costs. Volume is 60 million gallons/day.
Bougainville Copper Mine Papua and New Guinea	Very high rainfall region combined with severe earthquake potential would require expensive flat pit slopes to maintain stability unless the water pressures in the rock slopes could be minimized. The rock contained high fracture frequency with a majority of steeply dipping joints.	Development of drainage adits below the orebody developed an extensive zone of depressurization near the adits. Flows increased when semi impervious zones were intersected, i.e. clay filled faults. Field permeability values ranged from 10^{-2} to 10^{-5} cm/sec.
Twin Buttes Mine Arizona	Two large slide zones developed in the pit over a vertical depth of some 600 feet. The movement was largely influenced by high water pressures in the slope. These pressures varied due to numerous clay filled fault and shears in the slope.	An underground adit 3400 feet long was mined and 25,500 feet of drain-holes was drilled from the edit to increase the effective drain radius. PVC slotted pipe was installed in the drain holes. The water pressure in monitoring piezometers dropped an average of 67 percent. The overall permeability averaged 10^{-6} cm/sec. If a risk factor of 12 percent is acceptable the average slope angle can be increased from 27° to 35°.

TABLE 1 (con't)

Location	Problem	Solution
Jeffrey Mine Canadian Johns Manville Quebec	Granular soils overlying the bedrock provide a major ground water supply to develop water pressures in the pit slopes. This lead to a major slide involving about 20,000,000 tons of rock. The slide intersected the ore skipway and came within 75 feet of the primary crusher building. The instability was aggravated by leakage of water from town service mains and mining at the toe of the slope. Considerable water infiltrated tension cracks.	Horizontal drains were installed from the skipway bridge area. Drain holes were drilled upward from a horizontal adit to intersect the failure zone. The adit was used for previous mining and exploration. Tension cracks were filled in. Horizontal drains were installed into the granular layers in the upper overburden slopes to reduce recharge into the rock. Surface interception and diversion ditches were developed.
Iron Ore Company Quebec	High precipitation, very cold winter climate, variable strength rock with considerable folding and faulting led to numerous slope stability problems. The high water table resulted in a high moisture content of the ore and very wet haulage access with high maintenance of roads and trucks.	Surface drainage was installed around the pit to control surface water. 47 in pit and perimeter wells (15-inch diameter) have been installed to lower the water table. Special precautions are required to protect the pipelines from freezing. Problems still exist with operating delays due to blasting, relocation of pipe lines and inspection of pumps.
Konin and Turow Mines Poland	A shallow water table existed where 40 to 150 meters of overburden required removal to expose the coal measures. Depressurization of the overburden, coal and underlying strata was required to maintain slope stability and prevent pit bottom heave.	The zone proposed for initial mining was dewatered by deep wells and drainage galleries in the coal horizon. As mining progresses wells are installed ahead of mining and from the galleries. These latter wells drain by gravity as pressure relief wells. Horizontal drains are installed from the pit slopes. Dewatering trenches and pumping stations are developed in the pit bottom. Pumping systems are designed for 120 per cent capacity.

TABLE 1 (con't)

Location	Problem	Solution
Rhenish Lignite Mining District West Germany	Water bearing sand zones exist between multi layered coal horizons. The lignite extends to a depth of over 600 meters. Some major faults exist in the deposits which usually act as barriers to ground water flow. The topwall aquifers in the pit area must be completely dewatered and the footwall aquifers sufficiently depressurized to maintain stability and control heave. Continued monitoring of groundwater is essential each year. About 82,000 feet of monitoring holes are drilled. Local depressurization of sand pockets is required ahead of the dredgers to control slope blowouts.	Groundwater budgets to evaluate parameters, yields and boundary conditions are developed. Design diagrams based on Dupuit-Thiem and Sichardt are used for design of gravel packed dewatering wells. One and two dimensional numerical aquifer models have been developed. Because of high transmissivities and largeareal extent of the aquifer, gravity discharge into vertical tube wells is used with high capacity submersible motor pumps to lift the inflow. Well depths extend to 1650 feet. Drilling diameters range from 48 to 71 inches with well screens and inner casings of 12 to 32 inches. Reverse circulation air injection drilling is used. Vacuum dewatering is used to lower the water table ahead of excavators in the slopes in areas of low hydraulic conductivity.
Morwell Open Cut Brown Coal Project. Australia	Two water bearing aquifers are located below a coal seam up to 400 ft. thick. The water pressure below the base of the pit must be reduced to control pit bottom heave and development of zone of tension near the toe of the pit batters. High water pressures in the slopes partially induced by surface watering to minimize fire potential must be reduced to reduce risk of batter movement. Water pressure reduction to improve stability has increased the effective vertical stress in the coal which is slightly compressible. This has resulted in differential settlement of up to 5 feet near the open cut and some settlement up to 10 miles distance.	Wells have been developed into both aquifers to reduce the water pressure to control pit bottom heave and horizontal movement at the toe of the batters. Piezometers have been installed as control installations. Control elevations have been established at each piezometer to assist in determining the required pumping rates. To minimize differential settlement near the open cut, depressurization wells can be located to develop uniform levels of vertical effective stress. The stability of the batters has been maintained by extensive installation of horizontal drains up to 600 ft. long.

TABLE 1 (con't)

Location	Problem	Solution
Swift Agricultural Chemicals Phosphate Mine, Florida	The major problems to maximize phosphate recovery are pit slope stability, ground-water control and influence on spoil volume to matrix recovery. In cohesive soil the existence of water pressure increases the potential for sliding. In cohesionless soil the slopes tend to flow. Surface water in the pit base can cover the base and make spotting of the bucket for efficient matrix recovery impossible.	Drilling and aquifer water pressure testing revealed a deep aquifer in the Avon Park formation (approx. 700 ft. below surface) had a lower piezometric top elevation then the shallow Hawthorne aquifer immediately below the matrix to be excavated. Connector wells joining the surface sediments and Hawthorne to the deeper Avon Park formation have resulted in a vertical flow by gravity reducing the water levels in the upper formations some 42 feet. This has allowed prestripping with scrapers, steeper pit slopes and increased matrix recovery.
Western Phosphate Field, Idaho	Water resources within the phosphate field exist in complex ground water and surface flow systems. The water has the potential to hamper mining operations by pit flooding and pit and waste dump stability. It is desireable to be able to predict in advance of mining the imput of water on the mine program.	Extensive use of stream flow gain - loss monitoring indicated that certain geologic formations support ground water flow systems while others did not. Structural geologic features have a significant effect on the development of ground water and surface water flow systems. Major surface drainages are generally parallel to fold or fault structures. Geologic sections for various combinations of formation dip, smooth or broken ridges, valley or ridge location were developed to allow a prediction of ground water systems at proposed mine sites.

have been reduced by over $500,000 annually following dewatering.

In deep coal mines and strip mines, water pressures below the base of the pit can cause heave of the pit bottom. The installation of pressure relief wells commonly used to control water pressures below dams is very effective. Usually vertical holes can be drilled with available mine equipment. The depth depends on the depth of the aquifer and weight of the rock. In many instances free flowing wells will be adequate. Where considerable depth or large flows are required to depressurize, pumping wells are required.

Drainage adits have been installed at a number of mines. They are expensive. Provided they are located in the most suitable location and agumented with drain holes from the adit they can be very effective. The drain holes should be directed to intersect as many structural discontinuities as practical. The effectiveness of the adit system can be significantly improved by installing twin bulkheads and a vacuum system to put the adit under negative pressure.

Lowering of the water table will induce weathering in the dewatering zone. The influence of this on the mineralogy and mineral processing should be assessed.

The type of dewatering and design and location of the dewatering system is very site specific. The maximum cost effective benefit can only be achieved when the installation is preceeded by a comprehensive field test program.

DRAINAGE IN UNDERGROUND MINES
The costs of dewatering are increasing due to inflation and mine expansion. Improved knowledge and efficiency to reduce the risk of sudden water inflows, to improve stability and to reduce dewatering and mining costs is a goal at many underground operations.

The most important initial program is to determine the general geologic stratigraphy, water pressure profile and permeability. This program should always be an order of magnitude investigation. The primary purpose being to determine the conditions and parameters which will have a significant bearing on the project. Thousands of dollars and much time has been wasted on many projects in the past in attempting to develop extensive data for factors that are relatively unimportant. By recognizing the important factors there is less likelihood of hydrogeologic surprises. Brown emphasizes that since the accuracy of geologic and hydro-logic data is usually low it is inappropriate to use highly sophisticated analytical methods to evaluate conditions and to develop design systems.

Most groundwater problems can be approximated using Darcy's Law, the well equation modified from the Theis equation and the Steady State Leaky Aquifer equation.

Uncertainty of the results relates to inaccuracies of the idealized hydrological model, the analytical evaluations performed by the model and the measurement of parameters for the model.

Once the type and magnitude of the problem is defined the potential solutions to reduce or control the problem can be developed. Most of these programs comprise proce-dures to reduce the inflow of water. The primary reason being to reduce pumping energy which usually will be re-quired throughout the entire year.

To control ground water during shaft sinking it should be recognized that the problem is short term, until the lining is complete.

It is recommended that a drill hole always be drilled at the shaft location. In addition to determining geologic factors important to rock stability, excavation methods and lining requirements, rock permeability and water pressure head profiles can be assessed.

In small inflows, sumping and pumping from within the shaft will normally be adequate. For larger flows procedures to reduce inflow will usually be necessary.

Typical Methods include:
(a) Installation of dewatering wells around the shaft
(b) Grouting of pervious rock zones
(c) Freezing ahead of shaft sinking

Where several aquifers exist it will be expensive to perform separate pumping tests. One procedure to reduce this cost described by Greenslade involves drilling a well to the lowermost aquifer, installing casing and cement the well to the surface. The well is pump tested. Overlying formations are tested by installing a wire line bridge plug below each zone and perforating the casing over the entire aquifer thickness. Following pumping of the perforated zone a second wireline zone is set below the next overlying zone and the perforating pumping sequences repeated for each zone going up the hole.

The effects of water in underground mining are many. They include:
(a)   Large scale rapid inflow can halt production.
(b)   Corrosion of steel ropes and members is increased.
(c)   Timber rot is increased by wetting and drying.
(d)   Machine and labor productivity is reduced.
(e)   Maintenance costs are increased.
(f)   The cohesive strength of many types of rocks is reduced.
(g)   The migration and contamination or rock fines is increased.
(h)   Weak ground is washed out of rock discontinuities.
(i)   More expensive explosives are required.

Water associated factors outside the mine include:
(a)   Moisture in the ore increases the costs of handling, shipping and treatment.
(b)   Dewatering may induce weathering and reduce mineral recovery.
(c)   Drawdown in and around the mine may deplete regional water supplies.
(d)   Dewatering may lead to surface subsidence, or collapse.
(e)   Effluent may reduce the quality of surface water.

Loofborouw suggests two methods should be considered where dewatering of underground mines will reduce overall costs. Mining up from the bottom of the orebody will greatly reduce pumping requirements at sites where rock becomes less pervious with depth. There would also be a postponement in the time and rate of depressurization of the near surface water table. The mined and lower area of the mine can be used as a storage reservoir during major inflow or as a settling & clarification horizon.

In fractured and jointed rock, fine grained clay grouts may be effective in reducing permeability. This fine grout is usually quite effective in sand and sandstone. Pregrouting ahead of shaft sinking has proven to be effective on projects in South Africa.

Areas of promising research include chemical and bacterialogical treatment which develop precipitates and reduce permeability.

Methods to control the flow of water include:
(a)   Divert or intercept surface water.
(b)   Dewater prior to mining.
(c)   Minimize water flow by selective shaft location,
mining from the bottom up or leaching insitu (where practical)
(d)   Develop impervious linings around shafts.
(e)   Reduce the permeability of the rock mass.
(f)   Protect the work area from inflow. Plug alldrillholes.
(g)   Over design the dewatering and pumping system. Maintain an adequate supply of stabilization and control equipment available and operational.

Trexler describes a program to monitor underground inflow at the Bunker Hill Mine near Kellogg, Idaho. The mine
has been in operation since 1885 and has many drill holes,
drifts, stopes, shafts and one major caving area. Inflow
into the mine is controlled by five conditions –
(a)   natural ground water seepage
(b)   geological discontinuities
(c)   diamond drill holes
(d)   underground excavations
(e)   injected potable and sand fill water.
Some of this water flows through pyrite rich zones and results in production of acid discharge with a pH from 3.3
to 4.7.

Flow studies revealed there was a low time lag, generally less than 24 hours between changes in surface creek flows
and discharge volumes. Rhodamine WT dye studies also revealed
a short time lag.

The surface recharge contributes to several problems–
(a)   additional dewatering.
(b)   additional discharge treatment.
(c)   wet mining environment.
(d)   potential water to flush acid producing water.
Programs to reduce the water inflow included:
(a)   relocation of raises and construction of cut-off walls
(b)   installation of pipes & flume to bypass water around
pervious areas.
(c)   Capping and valving drill holes.
(d)   Increasing the slurry density for sand backfill.
This example illustrates the importance of site specific
studies and design.

A dramatic example of a major water problem is described
by Cox for the Friedensville mine. The normal dewatering

program discharged about 26,500 gpm. A sudden major inflow of 35,000 gpm developed in one of the stopes. Immediate steps were instituted to establish maximum pumping plant efficiencies. Fortunately the total dewatering capacity was available so the mine was not flooded.

To control the free flow a series of concrete plugs were developed and finally a 30 inch pipe line was installed to carry the water to a pump station.

This example illustrates the desireability for excess pumping capacity in the event that abnormal water flow is encountered.

The selection of the proper pumping system is one of the most important decisions in underground mine design.

Schiele presents a strong case for the use of water filled submersible pumps for depressurization and mine dewatering.
The advantages given are:
(a)   Water is an excellent conductor of heat.
(b)   Will not fail if leakage develops.
(c)   Will operate at a high ambient temperature.
(d)   Naturally firedamp proof.
(e)   Instant startup characteristics.

To control the ingress of dirt common on mining projects a special system has been developed. The rotor is guided in two radial bearings. The thrust bearing plate is mounted at the lower end of the rotor shaft, and it rotates against a ring of tilting pads which are stationary in the peripheral direction, but which are otherwise free to tilt in all directions.

In underground mines submersible pumps are used in sumps. The trend is toward pumping from one deep location with one pump.

In large pumps operating at high flow rates the double suction design is recommended to balance the hydraulic thrust on the thrust bearing.

Pump sizes up to 1800 KW have been used for several years with heads up to 3300 feet and flow rates in excess of 13200 USGM. In the Rhineland Coal fields 2500 submersible pumps are in use with diameters up to 32 inches and depths to 1700 feet.

For the most efficient design of well dewatering systems Archer recommends the well diameter should not be established until the volume and head of water is reasonably well known.

It is very important to determine the quality of the water to assess if corrosion will be a problem. Special attention to top quality gate and check values is imperative. Flow meters are recommended for all installations so that changes in flow characteristics or pumping problems can be quickly recognized.

SEEPAGE CONTROL FOR WASTE DISPOSAL

Extensive experience is available internationally in the design and construction of earth dams for hydro electric development, commercial and residential water supply and for irrigation purposes. The control of seepage has essentially been for the purpose of maintaining stability. A secondary reason is to reduce storage losses. Seepage control, for these reasons is being incorporated in most of the dams developed for tailings storage. The tailings however usually contain materials introduced in the extraction process which in some instances could lead to some degree of contamination of seepage waters.

When design programs and regulations are developed it should realistically be recognized that it is practically and economically impossible to completely stop all contaminants from being released into the seepage system. A reasonable approach is to require that any contaminants in the seepage water should be controlled by design and location so that regulatory maximum allowable criteria are met with a specified distance from the tailings storage area.

A common assumption made by many people is that the contamination is carried as far as the seepage water flows. It should be recognized that transport of contaminants is a complex function of parameters such as conductivity and dispersivity of the underlying soil and rock strata, hydraulic gradients, ion exchange and buffering capacity of subsurface materials and amounts of precipitation and evaporation. Soil and rock is a better natural filter than usually realized. In general, natural subsoil conditions will tend to remove many heavy metals and radionuclides such as radium and thorium from the tailings seep.

Precipitation will occur primarily as a result of chemical precipitation and sorption processes.* Some heavy trace metals such as selenium, arsenic and molybdenum may form ions which behave similarly to anion contaminants such as sulphates which do not tend to be removed by sorption.

Taylor and Antommaria present an excellent case example where the subsurface seepage courses below a tailings impoundment area were monitored at varying distances. The tailings disposal area had been in operation for about 20 years. The following elements were evaluated:
(a)   Uranium
(b)   Thorium
(c)   Lead - 210
(d)   Radium - 226
(e)   Polanium - 210

The results of the monitoring program revealed that at short distances below the pond the contaminant concentrations were all within permissible limits. At this site it was concluded that isolation barriers would do little to decrease the detrimental effect of tailings disposal other than to reduce the distance of effects away from the pond.

An important factor which influences contaminant movement is soil alkalinity. Isolation barriers or precipitation media should be considered for non-alkaline soil conditions.

Schubert describes a monitoring program to assess groundwater contamination, around a coal refuse pile that had been unreclaimed for over 50 years. The natural soil conditions at the site comprised glacial till with low permeability. Twenty seven wells were installed at the site to monitor the ground water. Thirteen existing residential wells were also monitored near the pile.

Based on the monitoring program the shallow ground water quality had not been significantly affected at distances greater than 200 meters from the refuse pile. Surface water flowing off the pile and onto the adjacent surface tends to infiltrate and recharge the ground water. This could be the source of some of the local contamination.
* "Generic Environmental Impact Statement on Uranium Milling" (draft) U.S. Nuclear Regulatory Commission, NUREG-0511, Office of Nuclear Material Safety and Safeguards. Washington, D.C., April, 1979.

Control of this surface flow would likely have reduced sub-surface contamination. The author concluded that by developing a better understanding of the reactions of contaminants with the soils it should be possible to develop disposal sites with adequate "absorption" capacity to adequately retard contaminant migration.

One of the most effective research programs that can be undertaken in North America would be to measure contaminant movement profiles around waste disposal areas on as many projects at as many locations as possible for as many minerals and industrial wastes as possible.

Considerable time and money has been spent on evaluating seepage flow paths, volumes and areal extent. It is important to recognize that it is the contaminant flow that is the most critical environmental concern. What concern is it if the seepage travels 20 miles but the contaminants are carried along that seepage path only 200-500 feet.

Where there is a likelihood that tailings seepage could contaminate ground water supplies several procedures to reduce this seepage are available.

The use of natural clay liners is the most common procedure and the procedure with which we have the most long term experience. The rate of seepage can be reduced to 10^{-6} to 10^{-8}cm per sec. At these low rates, dilution in the ground water system generally reduces contaminant levels to meet regulatory requirements. In addition base exchange, chemical reaction etc. in the clay reduces contaminant movement.

Recently the use of synthetic liners has become widespread. Provided the problems of seam separation and gas bubble breakage can be overcome liners provide positive seepage control. In very dry areas where the tailings disposal system will dry out the long term disintegration of the liner is not important. However in wetter climates, 15 to 20 inches of annual rainfall or more, the tailings ponds will not completely dry out and disintegration of the membrane could result in a large scale release at a later and unexpected date. In this condition it is suggested it would be better to use a synthetic semi pervious membrane to allow a very slow continued release from day one.

There is some experience to show that peat and glass fiber filters will act as absorption media to reduce contaminant movement. Further research is recommended in this area. If the benefit is significant one or more trenches could be cut across the zone of seepage path and the trench filled with the absorbing media; the slurry trench concept. An alternative procedure would be to drill vertical large diameter holes and fill them with purifying, neutralizing or absorbing materials. In the case of acid water, fill the holes with crushed limestone and for radionuclides, use barium chloride.

In many cases in the past regulatory staff have required contaminant values to meet regulations starting at the toe of the dam. This is not realistic. The area below the disposal area for 1500 to 2000 feet should be considered as part of the decontamination control area. Installation of special programs near the toe of the dam are much easier and less expensive than above or through the dam.

Whatever programs are selected, it is essential that the original background levels of water, soil and rock chemistry be determined before any mining or construction proceeds. There will be instances where background levels will exceed maximum regulatory levels. The mine should not be responsible to reduce these values to legal limits.

Smith has emphasized that most failures of tailings have occurred as a result of inadequate consideration of the influence of surface and subsurface water. The importance of seepage control and methods for this control are summarized effectively by Klohn.

The excellent case examples by Davis and Robinson illustrate a key concern that all investigation design, construction and regulatory programs must be site specific.

2

Mine Drainage: The Common Enemy

by George Vranesh, Attorney at Law,
Vranesh and Raisch, P.C.,
Boulder, Colorado, USA

I. INTRODUCTION

The problems related to mine drainage have been with us from the beginning of mining.

> Until the 18th century water formed the limiting factor in the depth of mines. To the great devotion of this water problem we owe the invention of the steam engine. In 1705 Newcomer--no doubt inspired by Savery's unsuccessful attempt--invented his engine and installed the first one on a colliery at Wolverhampton in Staffordshire.(1)

Mining has enjoyed a preferred status as reflected by the Court's decision in an early Pennsylvania case:

> The plaintiff's grievance is for a mere personal inconvenience, and we are of opinion that mere private personal inconvenience, arising in this way and under such circumstances, must yield to the necessities of a great public industry, which, although in the hands of a private corporation,

subserves a great public interest. To encourage
the development of the great natural resources of
a country, trifling inconveniences to particular
persons must sometimes give way to the necessities
of a great community. Nor do we say that a miner,
in order that his mines may be made available, may
enter upon his neighbor's lands or inflict upon
him any other immediate or direct injury, but we
do say that in the operation of mining in the
ordinary and usual manner, he may, upon his own
lands, lead the water which percolates into his
mine into the streams which form the natural
drainage of the basin in which the coal is situated, although the quantity as well as the quality
of the water in the stream may thereby be
affected.(2)

Not being content with this language the Court quoted part of
the dissenting opinion from the prior case between these same
parties:

The population, wealth, and improvements are
the result of mining and that alone. The plain-
tiffs knew when they purchased their property that
they were in a mining region. They were in a city
born of mining operations and which had become
rich and populous as a result thereof. They knew
that all mountain streams in that section were
affected by mine water, or were liable to be.
Having enjoyed the advantages which coal mining
confers, I see no great hardship nor any violence
to equity in their also accepting the inconveniences necessarily resulting from the business.(3)

There is no doubt that mining has enjoyed a preferred status
in this country. The entire westward expansion was accele-
rated by the search for minerals. Congress encouraged the
westward expansion by allowing people to trespass on government lands, then recognizing the trespass and eventually
passing appropriate legislation encompassing local laws,
rules and regulations. Congress passed the 1866 and the 1872
Mining laws which further encouraged development of unoccupied
lands in the West through mining.

The early statutes were drawn to encourage any industrial
activities, including mining. The laws of the Eastern states
allowed virtually any means of disposal of industrial waste

to encourage such development. The Western states, however, had no specific rules as to waste disposal.

Recently there has been a change in the public's attitude toward the value of industrial growth and this attitude has affected mining. No one today argues that one can indiscriminately dump waste or tailings into the stream system. Nor can one leave the mined land scarred and unproductive. Miners throughout the world are more aware of the beauty of their surroundings. They are in fact outdoorsmen who enjoy all the fruits of an unspoiled countryside.

The shift in emphasis as to the value of mining has been gendered in part by those least effected by mining. Bureaucrats throughout the world are learning to say "no" in more and more ways.

Overregulation may in time inhibit needed mining, which in turn will cause us to come full circle. For now, the pendulum has swung aginst mining, resulting in overregulation of an industry that no doubt needed some regulation.

This paper is written as a general overview of what is required of a mine operator when mine water is discharged.

II. HISTORIC APPROACH

The early authority on drainage of mines was Curtis H. Lindley on Mines.(4) Lindley analyzed the laws of many of the states dealing with mine drainage. Historically, the problem was primarily one of getting rid of the water from the mine workings. The questions that had to be resolved concerned various rights of the affected parties.

In Massachusetts, Kentucky, Tennessee, Georgia and North Carolina(5) mining was considered a public use with a right of condemnation which could be lawfully exercised for mining purposes.

A number of state constitutions contained provisions authorizing the legislature to make rules and regulations as may be necessary for mine drainage.(6) In 1893 Pennsylvania enacted legislation pertaining to mine drainage being supervised by state officials.(7) The rules historically applied to mine drainage problems were few and simple, based upon common sense.(8)

Law of Natural Flow

Some of the earlier reported cases dealing with mine drainage were contests between mine owners who worked different levels of the same structure. This type of case was generally regarded as the basis for determination of the rights, obligations and duties of mine operators. Lord Tenterden(9) said that in conducting mining operations, water is a sort of common enemy against which each man must defend himself. He went on to further state that the defense must be exercised so as not to endanger the lives or property of others.

> The rule defining the rights and liabilities of adjoining mine owners may be stated in this form: For damages resulting from natural causes or from lawful acts done in a proper manner, the law gives no redress; but where one of the two adjoining mine owners conducts water into his neighbor's mine which would not otherwise go there, or causes it to go there at different times and in larger quantities than it would go there naturally, he commits a wrong which the law will redress.(10)

This factual situation is not generally of concern to the miners of today, although the problem has not entirely disappeared.

Flooding by Waters Impounded

Although the owners of an upper mine can discharge natural waters onto a lower mine owner, the Courts have not allowed waters which are foreign to the mine to be so discharged. In Fletcher v. Rylands,(11) the leading case as to flooding resulting from contained water, the Court ruled that the doctrine of absolute liability controlled:

> We think that the rule of law is, that the person who, for his own purposes, brings on his land and collects and keeps there anything likely to do mischief if it escapes, must keep it at his peril; and if he does not do so, is prima facie, answerable for all the damage which is the natural consequence of its escape. . . .

In Colorado, this pronouncement applies to reservoirs constructed for any use and is not limited to mining.(12)

The Courts have attempted to define and solve the recurring problem attributed to drainage of water. The geographic area has had some influence on the Court's attitude. The problems in the Eastern section of the country are different from those of the West. The rainfall, topography and type of mining all contribute to the factual solution.

The law applying to mine drainage was well developed throughout this country, but there was no uniformity. The Civil Law Rule(13) states that a person who interferes with the natural drainage is liable for injury to other landowners. There is, however, a recognition that the lower landowner is required to accept the natural drainage. This rule implies that neither party is allowed to disturb the natural drainage conditions and therefore very limited changes can be made to the natural drainage flow.

Since neither the Common Enemy Rule nor the Civil Law Rule resolved the problem of drainage, a compromise rule was required. The Reasonable Use Rule(14) was such a compromise. Under this rule, both the upper and lower landowners have equal rights to the drainage of waters. The rule speaks of correlative rights of the parties and allows each to reasonably alter the amount of drainage naturally occurring. This is the general rule as applied today to mine drainage, although water quality is not considered under this rule. Yet another body of law must be addressed regarding the discharge of pollutants.

Pollution from Mining

Much of our present day law regarding pollution from mining is drawn from the English rule. The common law rule, simply stated is that no one has the right to defile water.(15) But in "streaming" for tin in Cornwall, England, the rule could not be respected in its original form. The tin bounders, as they were called, conducted placer operations and in the process sent down the streams sand, stone and rubble dislodged in processing their workings. This custom was recognized, based on necessity.(16) The courts reasoned that sand, stone and rubble was not pollution as such, since all the materials were an inherent part of the stream system and in time would settle out with no lasting injury to others.(17)

In 1876, however, England recognized the problem of pollution of streams and enacted protective legislation.(18)

The Act prohibited miners from permitting to flow into streams any poisonous, noxious or polluting solids or liquid matter from any mine, unless the water released was in the same condition as that raised or drained from the mine.

The early cases in the Eastern states wrestled with the two conflicting doctrines and, in time, ruled that pollution per se was bad. In Sanderson v. Penn. Coal Co.(19) the coal company argued that it had a right to pollute the water because it was conducting a lawful business. The Sanderson case on fourth appeal stated:

> Undoubtedly the defendants were engaged in a perfectly lawful business in which large expenditures had been made and with which widespread interests were connected; but however laudable an industry may be, its managers are still subject to the rule that their property cannot be so used as to inflict injury on the property of their neighbors.(20)

The common law rule regulating riparian rights was not recognized in the Western states. A parallel can be drawn between the conditions in Cornwall and the West where necessity of action and lack of immediate concern controlled. The right to mine and the right to divert water stood on equal footing--all as determined by miner's courts. The miner's courts determined that "first in time was first in right". Each person took the water as he found it. The first miner had absolute right to the extent of his needs and only then did the second appropriator obtain specific rights.(21)

In Esmond v. Chew(22) the California court expressed the general attitude of the day:

> Each person mining in the same stream is entitled to use in a proper and reasonable manner both the channel of the stream and the water flowing therein, and where, from the situation of different claims, the working of the same will necessarily result in injury to others, if the injury be the natural and necessary consequence of the exercise of this right, it will be damnum absque injuria, and will furnish no cause of action to the party injured. The reasonableness of the use is a question for the jury, to be determined by them upon the facts and circumstances of each particular case.(23)

The Colorado courts, however, refused to accept this holding and in <u>Suffolk Gold M. & M. Co. v. San Miquel Cons. M. & M. Co.</u>(24) issued an injunction preventing an upstream mining company from discharging tailings into the stream. The lower user was a power company that required clean water to drive its Pelton water-wheel. The Court concluded that the mining company might, with little expense, impound the tailings and return the water to the stream in an acceptable condition. In contrast, the United States Supreme Court, in deciding the same general question in <u>Atchinson v. Peterson</u>,(25) held that the subsequent appropriator must construct his own reservoir, impound the water and flush out clear water as he may require.

The general confusion has not been cleared up except to say that today the dumping of tailings directly into the streams is not acceptable under any circumstances.(26) The balancing of equities where the protection sought is relatively small as compared to the benefit to the public in general gave way to the protection of individual property rights.(27) However, while litigation was going forward, the legislatures of many states were enacting laws, rules and regulations to attempt to clarify this very confusing situation.

III. EARLY LEGISLATION

While the courts were busy interpreting the common law, the State and Territorial legislators were also active. In the West, where mining was the primary industry, the state legislators looked upon mining activities in a more favorable light than is evident today.

Colorado, in its constitution, recognized the need for protection of mining activities. Article XVI, Section 3 states: "that the general assembly may make such regulations from time to time, as may be necessary for the proper and equitable drainage of mines." Water and mining took on equal importance.(28) The way was cleared for mining activities to continue.

Colorado first addressed the general problem of mine drainage in 1870(29) when it enacted legislation for a pro-rata assessment of costs for removing water having a common ingress from subterranean sources. Mining companies and individuals were authorized to incorporate for the purpose of draining mines. In water-short areas such as Colorado the mine owner had the first right to use of the water hoisted from the mine, provided that he exercised appropriate dominion.(30) This is still the law as to nontributary waters.(31)

In 1911, the Colorado legislature, pursuant to the section in the Colorado Constitution(32) authorizing legislation on mine drainage, provided for the formation of Mine Drainage Districts(33). These quasi-governmental districts are authorized to levy taxes and conduct whatever other activities are necessary to drain specific mining districts for the benefit of all that may wish to mine the area. Wyoming has a constitutional provision(34) similar to that of Colorado, but the Wyoming legislature has not enacted general laws pertaining to mine drainage. The Arizona legislature passed a statute providing that adjacent or contiguous mines having a common ingress of subterranean water must dispose of their proportionate share of such water.(35) During much of this same period, the Eastern states, including Pennsylvania,(36) Kentucky,(37) North Carolina(38) and others(39), were enacting laws directly related to mine drainage.

The oldest known coal strip mine was reportedly started in 1815 in Pennsylvania.(40) The early cases from that state were not determinative of guidelines for mine drainage and incidental water pollution from coal mines.(41) The Purity of Waters Act(42) was the first attempt by Pennsylvania to regulate discharge into streams. It regulated discharge of sewage but specifically excluded coal mine drainage.(43) Subsequent legislation also excluded mine drainage,(44) giving credence to the overall importance of coal mining to the area.

Finally in 1937, the Clean Streams Law(45) declared it a public nuisance to discharge pollutants into the streams. The Act specifically excluded acid mine water because there was no known solution for this problem.(46)

> Acid Mine Drainage and Silt.--The provisions of this article shall not apply to acid mine drainage and silt from coal mines until such time as, in the opinion of the Sanitary Water Board, practical means for the removal of polluting properties of such drainage shall become known.

In 1945 the Clean Streams Law was amended to address the problem of pollution from mine drainage.(47) The Act did not prohibit _pollution_ but only proscribed drainage into "clean waters" which were devoted to a public use. The most significant part of the Act was that it required the mine operator to submit a drainage plan to obtain a permit from the Sanitary Water Board. The permit would be granted allowing drainage into a stream not designated or not put to a public use.

In 1965, new amendments to the Pennsylvania Clean Streams Law were enacted(48) finally setting out terms and conditions and specific controls over mine drainage. Section 1 of this Act defined industrial waste to include mine drainage. The present Act provides for greater control, making it a nuisance to discharge waste without a permit. The statute defines "operations"(49) to include any activity that will disturb the _status quo_. The Act defines discharge to include water that continues to flow _after_ mining operations have terminated.(50) The Act provides for civil or criminal penalties as well as injunctive relief against violators.(51) The State has taken an active role in assisting mine operators to achieve full compliance(52) and may undertake unilateral action to reduce pollution from abandoned mines.(53)

The foregoing discussion points out the realities of mine drainage. The early-day miners did pretty much as they pleased. The early-day legislators did very little to correct the problem. This was an indication of the strength and influence of mining. That era has long since come to an end. The present-day legislators are not so influenced by the importance of mining. This is reflected in the types of legislation regulating mine drainage. The pendulum has shifted away from encouraging mining to grave concern for the environment. Somewhere there must be a common ground for balancing the equities of all concerned.

Current activities in Colorado are characteristic of this new approach. In 1978, the Colorado Mined Land Reclamation Board enacted rules and regulations under the Colorado Mined Land Reclamation Act(54) to protect the hydrology and water quality(55) of the area to be mined. The Act provides that disturbances to the prevailing hydrology of affected and surrounding areas during and after mining will be kept to a minimum. A major difficulty is that in some areas it may be impossible to not drain an area, or lower the water table, and still conduct mining operations.

The purpose of this rule obviously was to protect vested water rights. In Colorado, as a matter of law, anything can be done with water so long as vested rights of third parties are not adversely affected.(56) The Colorado legislature recognized this principle of law when it rejected a bill(57) that would allow the State Engineer of Colorado to issue orders as may be necessary to "prevent or remedy injury from present or proposed mining, milling, drilling or other operations to persons owning, or entitled to use water under water rights, including injury from drilling of test or prospective holes. . . ." Nonetheless, the state engineer claims to already have such authority.

The Colorado statute defines a "well" as follows:

"Well" means any excavation that is drilled, cored, bored, washed, driven, dug, jetted, or otherwise constructed, when the intended use of such excavation is for the location, diversion, artificial recharge, or acquisition of ground water, but such term does not include an excavation made for the purpose of obtaining or for prospecting for oil, natural gas, minerals, or products of mining or quarrying, or for inserting media to repressure oil or natural gas bearing formation or for storing petroleum, natural gas, or other products.(58)

The Colorado Ground Water Mangement Act(59) also includes the provisions used in permitting wells in Colorado and defines "well" more broadly:(60)

"Well" means any structure or device used for the purpose or with the effect of obtaining ground water for beneficial use from an aquifer.

Such broad definitions may or may not include mine dewatering operations.

Legal Dilemma

In dewatering mines, the right to mine one's property and the vested water rights of third parties may conflict. Under common law a person may make use of his property provided he does not deprive another of his lawful recognized use. This right applies to the removal of minerals as well.(61)

Water is almost universally encountered in mining operations. The earlier cases regarded this water as independent of the stream system, but the present view in Colorado is that there is a _prima facie_ presumption that all water is tributary to the stream system.(62)

Where there is a direct hydrologic connection, the mine operator may well face a court contest because he will be draining the ground water that others may depend upon for irrigation and domestic uses. This will be especially true in the arid West. The appropriation doctrine, _i.e._, "First in Time is First in Right," will turn full circle to the consternation of the miner, who initially developed this concept.

In the East, where water availability is not a problem, the contest may not materialize. Under riparian law of the Eastern states, reasonable use of the water may still be the test. In 1936, the Alabama court concluded that if the mining operations are conducted in an ordinary and careful way and drain the lands of a surface owner, no liability exists.(63)

The courts have made attempts to distinguish between drainage and water rights matters,(64) but regardless of the legal distinction the net effect is the same. The factual situation in each case, under the laws of the particular state will control, but the trend appears to be that the burden of proof is on the mining company to prove non-injury.(65) The question of injury resulting from drainage of mines is but one aspect of a very complicated set of problems. There may in fact be no real question over whether pumping of mine water deprives another of his vested rights. The larger question is whether such drainage causes any adverse effect on the stream system. The effects of mine drainage discharge are not limited to state boundaries, and, therefore, federal laws must be considered.

IV. FEDERAL LEGISLATION

Initially the federal government viewed mine drainage as a matter of local concern, and the disposal of mine water and tailings was left up to state regulation. Before the turn of the century Congress was more interested in opening up the Western lands to settlement and industry.(66) The first federal attempt to control water pollution was contained in the Rivers and Harbors Appropriations Act of 1899,(67) commonly referred to as the Refuse Act. This Act provides that it is unlawful to discharge refuse into navigable waters or their tributaries. Although the Refuse Act conceivably could have applied to mine drainage or tailings disposal, the Act was not used for that purpose.

In 1948 the Federal Water Pollution Control Act (FWPCA)(68) was passed by Congress. The Act called for studies and investigations of water pollution, but still deferred to state regulation. Increasing concern about the deterioration of the quality of our nation's waters led to the 1965 amendments to FWPCA. These amendments provided for the establishment of water quality standards by the states. A water quality standard is a legal limit on the amount of pollutants in a defined water course. Thus, the focus is on the capacity of the receiving body of water to tolerate harmful subtances. Yet, enforcement of the water quality standards was ineffective because of the difficulty in determining which pollution sources caused the standards to be violated.

The Refuse Act(69) was revived in order to control water pollution because of the difficulties in administering the water quality standards. The emphasis was on prohibiting any discharge of refuse material, which is in effect an effluent limitation. As contrasted with water quality standards, effluent standards describe the legal limit of pollutants that can be released from a specific source. In 1966 the Supreme Court ruled that refuse included almost all discharges that adversely affect water quality.(70) Impliedly this definition included mining activities. Pursuant to authority contained in the Refuse Act, the Corps of Engineers announced that industrial discharges into navigable waters would be subject to a strict permit program.(71) President Nixon acted to preempt this scheme, and by executive order substituted a federal permit program to enforce the Refuse Act.(72)

Congress responded to pressure exerted by interested groups by enacting legislation amending the Federal Water Pollution Control Act. A compromise bill was vetoed by President Nixon, but on October 18, 1972, Congress overrode the veto and the bill became law.(73) The 1972 amendments adopted the effluent limitation approach contained in the Refuse Act. Section 101(74) states that it is a national goal to make the waters "swimmable" by 1983 and to eliminate discharge of pollutants into our rivers and lakes by 1985. To accomplish these goals, effluent standards are to be promulgated. By July 1, 1977, all point sources, other than

publicly owned treatment works, were to apply the best practicable control technology currently available" (BPT).(75)   A
July 1, 1983 deadline was set for application of "best
available technology economically achievable" (BAT).(76)

Section 107 of FWPCA authorizes demonstration projects for
the development of programs to control mine water pollution.(77)   The major provisions of the Act which affect mine
drainage matters are Sections 208, 301, 303 and 402.

Section 301--Point Source Regulation

The Act broadly defines pollutants(78) so that mine discharges are covered by the Act.   A major source of controversy is whether mine operations are point sources, and
therefore subject to the effluent standards of Section
301(b)(1)(A) best practicable technology and Section
301(b)(2)(A) best available technology.   The Act describes
point sources as follows:

> The term "point source" means any discernible,
> confined and discrete conveyance, including but
> not limited to any pipe, ditch, channel, tunnel,
> conduit, well, discrete fissure, container, roll-
> ing stock, concentrated animal feeding operation,
> or vessel or other floating craft, from which
> pollutants are or may be discharged.(79)

Two federal district courts have ruled that mining operations
are not a point source.(80)   If these rulings are upheld,
the primary mechanism for control of mine drainage will be
under Section 208.

Section 208--Areawide Waste Treatment Management

Section 208(81) provides that the governor of each state
identify areas within the state which have substantial water
quality control problems.   The boundaries of each area are to
be designated, and a planning agency, including local officials, is formed.(82)   Essentially this agency is to develop
an area waste treatment management plan for that area.   The
development of the plan is to be financed by federal
grants.(83)

Along with other purposes, the 208 plan is to establish a
program to "regulate the location, modification, and construction of any facilities within such area which may

result in any discharge in such area,"(84) and to include "a process to (i) identify, if appropriate, mine-related sources of pollution including new, current, and abandoned surface and underground mine runoff, and (ii) set forth procedures and methods (including land use requirements) to control to the extent feasible such sources; . . ."(85) Thus, it is clear that the Section 208 planning agency must consider the abatement of mine discharges.

Mining operations will be controlled under Section 208 by the development of "best management practices" (BMP).(86) A BMP prescribes a treatment method which must be economically sound, for the Act states that control be "to the extent feasible".(87) In practice 208 planning activities have not significantly addressed mine drainage problems.(88) Municipal and industrial point source discharges have received the most attention, and the difficulties associated with implementing a program for nonpoint sources such as mine discharges has relegated control of mining operations to a low priority.

Section 303--Water Quality Standards

While the 1972 amendments to the Federal Water Pollution Control Act primarily established effluent standards, the amendments also incorporated the 1965 water quality standards approach in Section 303.(89) Section 303(a) provides that water quality standards previously adopted by the state are to remain in effect, unless the Administrator of EPA determines that such standards are inconsistent with the requirements of the Act prior to enactment of the 1972 amendments. If a state fails to submit water quality standards or the Administrator disapproves such standards, the Administrator is authorized to promulgate regulations setting forth water quality standards for the state.(90)

A state with approved standards is to identify those waters for which the effluent limitations required by Sections 301(b)(1)(A) and 301(b)(1)(B) are not stringent enough to implement the water quality standards applicable to such waters, and establish a priority ranking for these waters.(91) In addition, the state is to establish maximum daily loads of pollutants for the above-identified waters in order to meet the applicable water quality standards. Section 303(c)(92) requires that the state hold public hearings for the purpose of reviewing the water quality standards, and modifying them if necessary. Colorado is currently engaged in this process, and is encountering the difficulties inherent in a system which requires that the individual characteristics of the receiving body of water be taken into account.

Section 303 water quality standards could apply to mine drainage. Given that most mine discharge will likely be seepage, it will be difficult to establish maximum daily loads for such a nonpoint source. It is likely that states will concentrate on point sources emitting municipal and industrial waste and defer consideration of the mine drainage problem under Section 303 until later.

Section 402--National Pollutant Discharge Elimination System

Section 402(93) establishes the National Pollutant Discharge Elimination System (NPDES). Under the NPDES program, a point source which discharges pollutants into navigable waters is required to obtain a discharge permit.

A state which is capable of administering the permit program and which insures the compliance with the requirements of the Act is allowed to issue such permits, except that the Administrator of the EPA is authorized to object to the issuance of a permit under this Section.

As shown above, the most likely mechanism for dealing with mine drainage is the Section 208 areawide waste treatment management plan. It is possible that the states will supplement enforcement by enacting stringent water quality standards which could apply to mine discharges. And if the drainage can be characterized as a point discharge, a 402 permit is required and the effluent limitations of Section 301 must be complied with. Yet it is more likely that coal mine drainage regulation will be accomplished through the Surface Mining Control and Reclamation Act of 1977.(94)

SURFACE MINING CONTROL AND RECLAMATION ACT OF 1977

The Surface Mining Control and Reclamation Act of 1977,(95) signed by President Carter on August 3, 1977, marked the end of a bitter struggle over federal legislation regulating surface coal mining. The Act is the result of numerous congressional hearings and reports, including seven different bills passed by either the House or the Senate and two Presidential vetoes.

The Surface Mining Control and Reclamation Act provides a comprehensive scheme for regulating surface mining. Since the Act contains standards relating to mine drainage, a detailed discussion of those standards and the overall scheme of regulation is warranted.

Findings and Policy of the Act. The Act commences with a set of findings, the general tenor of which is represented by Section 101(d), which states that "the expansion of coal mining to meet the Nation's energy needs makes even more urgent the establishment of appropriate standards to minimize damage to the environment and to productivity of the soil and to protect the health and safety of the public." This finding should be read in conjunction with one purpose of the Act, which is to "assure that the coal supply essential to the Nation's energy requirements, and to its economic and social well-being is provided and strike a balance between protection of the environment and agricultural productivity and the Nation's need for coal as an essential source of energy; . . . (96) Thus, the purpose of the Act is to "strike a balance," between energy development and protection of the environment, and not to guard against any adverse environmental effects at any cost.

Also important is the finding that "because of the diversity in terrain, climate, biologic, chemical, and other physical conditions in areas subject to mining operations, the primary governmental responsibility for developing, authorizing, issuing, and enforcing regulations for surface mining and reclamation operations subject to this Act should rest with the States; . . ."(97) This finding is consistent with Section 102(g), which declares that it is the purpose of the Act to "assist the States in developing and implementing a program to achieve the purposes of this Act; . . .(98) It is apparent that Congress intended that the states accept primary responsibility for implementation and regulation of the provisions of the Act.

Major Provisions of the Act.
A. Creation of the Office of Surface Mining. Section 201(99) establishes the Office of Surface Mining Reclamation and Enforcement, which is to be included in the Department of the Interior. A director for the office shall be appointed by the President. The Secretary of the Interior, through the office, shall administer programs required by the Act for controlling surface coal mining operations, review and approve or disapprove state programs for controlling surface coal mining operations and reclaiming abandoned mined lands, and publish and promulgate such rules and regulations

as may be necessary to carry out the purposes and provisions of the Act.

B. <u>Abandoned Mine Reclamation Fund</u>. Section 401(100) creates an Abandoned Mine Reclamation Fund. The Fund is established to reclaim and restore land and water resources adversely affected by past coal mining by providing that coal mining operations subject to the Act pay to the Secretary a reclamation fee of 35 cents per ton of coal produced by surface coal mining and 15 cents per ton of coal produced by underground mining or 10 per centum of the value of the coal at the mine, as determined by the Secretary, whichever is less.(101) The Act provides that fifty percent of the reclamation fees collected annually in any state be returned to that state if the Secretary has approved the state's abandoned mine reclamation program.(102) Programs established under this fund should substantially reduce the amount of presently unreclaimed land disturbed by surface coal mining, which as of January 1, 1974, totalled 621,887 acres.(103) Since much of the adverse impact of surface coal mining results from acid mine drainage and degradation of water quality, the fund allows much needed expenditures for drainage abatement.

C. <u>Enforcement of the Act</u>.
1. <u>Interim Regulation</u>. In order to gradually implement the provisions of the Act, Sections 501(104) and 502(105) provided for promulgation, by the Secretary, of interim regulations concerning performance standards. The interim regulations applied only to states which had existing regulatory authority controlling surface coal mining operations.(106) Any new surface coal mining operations were required to obtain a permit from the state before commencing the new project.(107) Surface coal mining operations which had been issued permits by the states after February 3, 1978 were to comply with the interim regulations immediately, while existing mines were required to come into compliance with the regulations by May 3, 1978.(108) Section 523(c) provided that states with cooperative agreements with the federal government existing on the date of enactment would continue to regulate federal lands if the cooperative agreements were modified to comply with the interim regulatory procedures outlined in Section 502.(109)

Along with the above provisions concerning states with existing regulatory authority, the Act mandated that the Secretary, within six months of enactment, commence a federal

enforcement program that would remain in effect until the
state program had been approved or a federal program had been
implemented. The enforcement program included warrantless
inspections of the mining site without notice.(110) The
regulations provided that an authorized representative of the
Secretary could order cessation of operations if the inspections reveal conditions showing an imminent change to public
health or causing a significant environmental harm.(111)

2. Permanent State and Federal Programs. The Act
allows a state to assume exclusive jurisdiction over regulation of surface coal mining and reclamation operations on
nonfederal lands by submitting to the Secretary a state program which demonstrates ability to carry out the provisions
of the Act.(112) A state with an approval program may enter
into a cooperative agreement with the Secretary to provide
for state regulation of surface coal mining operations on
federal lands within the state if the Secretary determines
that the state can properly implement the cooperative agreement.(113) Even if the state does act to take responsibility
for regulation of surface coal mining on both federal and
nonfederal lands, the Act requires the Secretary to promulgate and implement a federal program.(114) If the federal
lands are situated in a state with an approved program, the
federal program, at a minimum, must incorporate the requirements of the state program, yet the Secretary retains his
duties and responsibilities to oversee federal coal leases
under the authority of the Federal Mineral Leasing Act. The
requirements of the Act with the federal lands program or an
approved state program must be included by reference in any
federal mineral lease, permit or contract issued by the Secretary involving surface coal mining and reclamation operations. No later than two months after approval of a state
program or implementation of a federal program all operators
must submit an application for a permit to the regulatory
authority.

If a state fails to submit a program or a program submitted is disapproved or not enforced by the state, the Secretary is to implement a federal program.(115) The Secretary
thus has exclusive jurisdiction for the regulation and
control of surface coal mining operations taking place on any
lands within the state. Section 503(a)(116) of the Act provides that states are required to submit permanent program
applications by February 3, 1979. However, under Section
504(a) the Secretary can extend the date for permit applications up to an additional six months, if submission of the

application requires an act of the state legislature. This extension has been granted to all states where coal is currently mined, thus states have until August 3, 1979 to submit programs to the Secretary for approval.(117) The Secretary is then given ten months (6 months for initial review and 4 months for resubmission and reconsideration) to approve or reject the state program. Therefore, by June 3, 1980, a state program must be approved or a federal program implemented.

The regulatory scheme provided by the Act is unwieldly and difficult to administer. The Secretary and the state (if a state program is approved) have concurrent jurisdiction over surface coal mining operations. The retention of federal control and the required monitoring by federal officials can be attributed to the involvement of <u>federal lands</u>. The federal government was not quite so sure that the states would not plunder the lands. Yet, as evidenced by the automatic six-month extension for submission of state programs, federal officials are looking to the states to implement the Act. Given the "diversity in terrain, climate, biologic, chemical, and other physical conditions in areas subject to mining operations," the states are the proper governmental authority to administer such programs. Still it seems that the federal government will take an active role in formulation of reclamation policy, especially when federal lands are involved.

D. <u>Standards and Regulations Relating to Mine Drainage</u>. The Secretary of the Interior recently promulgated permanent regulations concerning the provisions of the Surface Mining Control and Reclamation Act.(118) Special attention will be devoted to a discussion of the sections of the Act and those regulations that deal with mine drainage.

1. <u>Application Requirements</u>. First, an application for a permit pursuant to an approved state or federal program must contain, among other things, the name of the watershed and location of the surface stream or tributary into which surface and pit drainage will be discharged; along with

> a determination of the probable hydrologic consequences of the mining and reclamation operations, both on and off the mine site, with respect to the hydrologic regime, quantity and quality of water in surface and ground water systems including the dissolved and suspended solids under seasonal flow conditions and the collection of sufficient data

for the mine site and surrounding areas so that an assessment can be made by the regulatory authority of the probable cumulative impacts of all anticipated mining in the area upon the hydrology of the area and particularly upon water availability: Provided, however, That this determination shall not be required until such time as hydrologic information on the general area prior to mining is made available from an approporiate Federal or State agency: Provided further, That the permit shall not be approved until such information is available and is incorporated into the application; . . .(119)

The application should also include cross-section maps prepared by a qualified registered engineer or professional geologist which show the location of subsurface water, if encountered, and its quality, the location of spoil, waste or refuse areas; constructed or natural drainways and the location of any discharges to any surface body of water on the area of land to be affected or adjacent thereto. A statement of the result of test borings or core samplings is also required.

The regulations which apply to permit applications require a description of the geology, hydrology, and water quality of all lands within the proposed mine plan area, the adjacent area and the general area.(120) The application must describe the ground water hydrology of the proposed mine plan area and adjacent area, including the depth below the surface, lithogy, thickness, and recharge and discharge capacity of aquifers. The quality and quantity of ground water must also be described.

Regarding surface water information, the application must describe the watershed involved, the location of all surface water bodies, and the flow discharge rates of streams in the area. Water quality data is required, showing the total dissolved solids, total suspended solids, total and dissolved iron, total manganese, all in milligrams per liter. Also required is a showing of the acidity and pH levels. If the proposed mining activities may proximately result in contamination, diminution, or interruption of an underground or surface source of water, alternative sources of water supply that could be developed to replace the existing sources shall be identified.(121)

2. <u>Reclamation Plan Requirements</u>. Each application submitted must also contain a reclamation plan.(122) The reclamation plan must include a statement of the engineering techniques proposed to be used in mining and reclamation, including a plan for the control of surface water drainage and of water accumulation. Section 508(a)(13) declares that the application include a statement of:

> a detailed description of the measures to be taken during the mining and reclamation process to assure the protection of:
>
> (A) the quality of surface and ground water systems, both on- and off-site, from adverse effects of the mining and reclamation process;
>
> (B) the rights of present users to such water; and
>
> (C) the quantity of surface and ground water systems, both on- and off-site, from adverse effects of the mining and reclamation process or to provide alternative sources of water where such protection of quantity cannot be assured;(123)

The regulations require that each application include a general plan for each sedimentation pond, water impoundment, and coal processing waste bank dam, or enbankment within the proposed mine plan area.(124) The general plan will additionally contain the hydrologic impact and the operation and maintenance requirements of the structure.

3. <u>Permit Approval or Denial</u>. Consistent with the above requirements, the Secretary cannot approve a permit application unless the assessment of the probable cumulative impact of all anticipated mining in the area of the hydrologic balance has been made.(125) The Secretary must find that the proposed operation "has been designed to prevent material damage to the hydrologic balance outside the permit area, . . ."(126)

4. <u>Performance Standards--Surface Operations</u>. Section 515(127) puts teeth in the Act. The purpose of reclamation is to restore the land affected to a "condition capable of supporting the uses which it was capable of supporting prior to any mining, or higher or better uses of which there is reasonable likelihood, . . ."(128) The Act provides that

operators backfill, grade and compact in order to provide adequate drainage. All acid-forming and toxic materials are to be covered, and spoil sites are to be stabilized to effectively control erosion and attendant water and air pollution. The section also allows creation of permanent water impoundments if such impoundments are stable and safe and will not result in the diminishment of water quality below the applicable state and federal standards. The performance standards also mandate that the operations:

> minimize the disturbances to the prevailing hydrologic balance at the mine-site and in associated offsite areas and to the quality and quantity of water in surface and ground water systems both during and after surface coal mining operations and during reclamation by--
>
> (A) avoiding acid or other toxic mine drainage by such measures as, but not limited to--
>
> (i) preventing or removing water from contact with toxic producing deposits;
>
> (ii) treating drainage to reduce toxic content which adversely affects downstream water upon being released to water courses;
>
> (iii) casing, sealing, or otherwise managing boreholes, shafts, and wells and keep [keeping] acid or other toxic drainage from entering ground and surface waters; . . .(129)

In addition, the Act requires that mining operations be conducted using the best technology currently available, so as contributions of suspended solids to streamflow or runoff outside the permit area. It is emphasized that these contributions are not to exceed state and federal water quality limits for such pollutants. In order to comply with this standard the regulations provide that all surface drainage from the disturbed area shall pass through a sedimentation pond before leaving the permit area.(130) The regulations also supply a table containing numerical effluent limitations for iron, manganese, and total suspended solids. A further provision regulates pH concentration.(131)

Established in the permanent regulations is the preference of changes in flow of drainage over the use of

treatment facilities. Thus acceptable practices to control
and minimize pollution are: (i) stabilizing disturbed areas
through land shaping, (ii) directing runoff, (iii) regulating
channel velocity of water, (iv) diverting flow from perennial, intermittent and epherimal streams, and (v) selectively
placing and sending acid-forming and toxic-forming materials.(132) It is also important that pits, cuts, mine excavation and backfilling be designed and constructed so as to
prevent discharge of acid or toxic materials into the groundwater system. The operator is also required to restore "the
recharge capacity of the mined area to approximate premining
conditions."(133) The regulations provide for monitoring of
ground water quality and quantity, and the results of the
tests are to be submitted to federal or state inspectors.

One major difficulty with the Act is that it fails to
address or acknowledge state water laws. Most states have an
administrative or judicial authority which decides delicate
issues regarding the "hydrologic balance". Section 717(a)
states that "Nothing in the Act shall be construed as
affecting in any way the right of any person to enforce or
protect, under applicable law his interest in water resources
affected by a surface coal mining operation."(134) Yet,
under state law a mining company might own a decreed water
right entitling it to alter or diminish the hydrologic
balance, the exercise of which would seem to contravene the
provisions of the Act. In fact, Section 717(b) provides
that:

> The operator of a surface coal mine shall replace
> the water supply of an owner of interest in real
> property who obtains all or part of his supply of
> water for domestic, agricultural, industrial, or
> other legitimate use from an underground or sur-
> face source where such supply been affected by
> contamination, diminution, or interruption proxi-
> mately resulting from such surface coal mine
> operation.(135)

The above section clearly ignores the existence of the appropriation doctrine, which, as stated previously, controls
water distribution in the West. Under the "first in time,
first in right" rule, it is easy to see that an owner of an
interest in real property may not have a cause of action for
diminution of an underground or surface water supply, where
either the operator owns superior water rights or the
complainant has no vested water rights.

5. Performance Standards--Underground Mines. The Act
expressly covers the surface effects of underground coal mining operations.(136) A substantial portion of the standards
and regulations applying to the underground mines deals with
the hydrologic balance issue, and therefore the standards are
virtually identical to the provisions concerning the regulation of surface coal mining in this area. A major difference
in the two types of mining is the existence of more tunnels
and shafts in underground mining, and Section 516 requires
that operators "seal all portals, entryways, drifts, shafts,
or other openings between the surface and underground mine
working when no longer needed for the conduct of mining
operations."(137) This section also provides that exploratory
holes (the regulations include wells) which are no longer
necessary for mining be filled or sealed to keep acid or
other toxic drainage from entering ground or surface water.
In addition, the operator is required to "locate openings for
all new drift mines working acid producing or iron producing
coal seams in such a manner as to prevent a gravity discharge
of water from the mine."(138)

6. Alluvial Valley Floors. One of the more contro-
versial provisions of the Act is the protection afforded
alluvial valley floors. Section 515(b)(10) states that the
prevailing hydrologic balance should be maintained by "preserving throughout the mining and reclamation process the
essential hydrologic functions of alluvial valley floors in
the arid and semiarid areas of the country."(139) Alluvial
valley floors are defined as:

> [U]nconsolidated stream-land deposits holding
> streams with water availability sufficient for
> subirrigation or flood irrigation agricultural
> activities but does not include upland areas which
> are generally overlain by a thin veneer of collu-
> vial deposits composed chiefly of debris from
> sheet erosion, deposits formed by unconcentrated
> runoff or slope wash, together with talus, or
> other mass-movement accumulations, and wind blown
> deposits.(140)

The Act provides that a permit will not be granted, if the
operation is located west of the one hundredth meridian west
longitude, and it would "interrupt, discontinue, or preclude
farming on alluvial valley floors that are irrigated or
subirrigated, . . . or materially damage the quantity or
quality of water in the surface or underground water systems

that supply these valley floors."(141) Underdeveloped range
lands and small acreage plots are excluded because of their
negligible impact on the farm's agricultural production.
Additionally, a grandfather clause excludes surface coal
mining operations which in the year preceding enactment had
produced coal in commercial quantities and were located in or
adjacent to alluvial valley floors. Also excluded are operators who had obtained a permit from the state regulatory
authority to mine within the alluvial valley floor.

One problem in administering the alluvial valley floors
provision is the difficulty in determining what is an alluvial valley floor. Factors included are geology, hydrology
and biology, yet the determination is apt to be almost sheer
guesswork. The regulations put the burden on the applicant
to prove that it is not an alluvial valley floor, and an
extensive array of maps and studies concerning surface water,
ground water, vegetation and land characteristics is
required. And there is bound to be some disagreement as to
whether the mining operations necessarily "interrupt, discontinue or preclude" farming in areas defined as an alluvial
valley floor.

The Surface Mining Control and Reclamation Act is a difficult act that applies to a difficult problem. While the
federal government does have a stake in the matter because
the coal is primarily situated on federal lands, the state is
a better mechanism to adapt to the local factors which each
reclamation project faces. The inherent ambiguities and
difficulties in defining phrases like "hydrological balance"
and "alluvial valley floor" will prompt litigation over the
proper application of such terms. The interim regulations
themselves spawned an enormous amount of litigation.[142]
Despite its shortcomings, the Act can be a step in the right
direction if it does "strike a balance" between coal
development and environmental and agricultural protection.

However this Act is enforced, the effects are obvious to
mining operations. Mine drainage problems historically were
of concern only to "wet" mines. Today there is very little
distinction among mines, and the problem of compliance exists
for every coal mine.

V. THE CANADIAN EXPERIENCE

Much like the American system, in which the federal government and the states have concurrent jurisdiction over and

responsibility for mine drainage, the Canadian scheme
involves the cooperation of the provinces and the Dominion.
While Canada does not have a statute similar to the Surface
Mining Control and Reclamation Act of 1977 which extensively
deals with land reclamation and mine drainage, there are
provincial and federal statutes which apply to mine pollution
control and surface reclamation.

Federal Powers

The most significant federal legislation providing for the
management of the water resources of Canada is the Canada
Water Act of 1970.(143) The Act calls for the cooperation of
provincial governments and federal officials to set nation-
wide standards of environmental quality. The Minister of
Energy, Mines and Resources is to undertake water resource
management programs where federal waters are involved, or in
connection with interjurisdictional waters and any international waters where there is a significant national interest.(144) In addition, the Minister may make agreements with
provincial governments to implement programs for any waters
in which water quality management has become a matter of
urgent national concern.(145) The Act mandates that no person
shall deposit waste of any type in these water quality
management areas or federal waters except in quantities and
under conditions prescribed by the officials administering
the Act.(146) An interesting provision is the authorization
to require the payment of effluent discharge fees.(147) The
Act also allows the Governor in Council to make regulations
prescribing quantities or concentrations of substances that
can be deposited in the waters, along with the proper treatment processes to be used.(148)

Another piece of federal legislation enacted in the same
year as the Canada Water Act was the Northern Inland Water
Act.(149) This Act applies to inland water resources in the
Yukon Territory and Northwest Territories. The Northern
Inland Water Act is very similar to the Canada Water Act, for
it provides for the establishment of water quality management
areas and prohibits the discharge of wastes into such waters
without a license from the appropriate board.(150) A note-
worthy provision of the Act is Section 11, which requires an
applicant for a license to provide "information and studies
concerning the use of waters proposed by the applicant as
will enable it (the board) to evaluate any qualitative and
quantitative effects of the proposed use on the water management area in which the applicant proposes to use such

water."(151)   This requirement of information and studies
seems comparable to the environmental impact statement
mandated by NEPA.(152)

The pollution from mine drainage may also be regulated by
the Fisheries Act.(153)   The Act prohibits a person from
depositing "deleterious substances" in any water frequented
by fish.(154)   Violations of the provisions of the Act can
result in fines and/or cessation orders.(155)   The Fisheries
Act can be an important tool for water quality management
because of the heavy fish populations throughout Canadian
waters.

The British North America Act, Canada's Constitution,
provides that the Parliament of Canada can make laws for the
"Peace, Order, and Good Government of Canada."(156)   Conceivably Parliament could pass legislation pertaining to pollution control and mine drainage based on the above authority.
The Supreme Court of Canada has recently ruled that pollution
offenses are a violation of public welfare.(157)   Therefore,
it seems that Parliament has the constitutional power to
regulate mine drainage based on its relationship to the
public welfare and good government of Canada, even though
such a statute has not been enacted.

Provincial Governments

The provinces play a major role in the area of pollution
control and mining regulation.   The British North America Act
granted exclusive jurisdiction to the provincial legislatures
over matters concerning:

    5.   The Management and Sale of the Public Lands
         belonging to the Province and of the Timber
         and Wood thereon. . . .

    10. Local Works and Undertakings . . . .

    13. Property and Civil Rights in the Province.

    16. Generally all Matters of a Merely Local or
         Private Nature in the Province.(158)

In addition, Section 109 provides that the provinces have the
proprietary interest of the Crown in any natural resources.

Thus, because of its ownership of natural resources, such
as water and minerals, and its ability to regulate local

works the provincial legislature has been a significant force in land reclamation and water pollution.

All the provinces have statutes that deal with environmental control or water quality.(159)   Alberta is a good example, and the statutes that would affect a mine drainage controversy are numerous.(160)   Similar to the Canada Water Act, most of the provincial water quality statutes prohibit discharge of harmful substances into the water courses without a license or permit.   Also, the clean environment acts and land reclamation statutes often require that a plan for minimization of land disturbance and subsequent reclamation be approved before commencement of the project.(161)

One peculiarity of Canadian law that affects mine drainage is the English rule of capture regarding groundwater, a rule adopted in several provinces.(162)   The retention of this doctrine is probably due to the fact that in some provinces, such as British Columbia, there are groundwater sources that have yet to be tapped.   According to the rule of capture, a land owner could drain his mine without incurring liability for impairing the hydrological balance of the land around him.   In contrast, Alberta has a statute which prohibits the drilling and pumping of groundwater without a permit.(163) The Act applies to wells and shafts that accumulate groundwater.

Also, it should be noted that Canada recognizes the common law remedies of nuisance, strict liability, trespass and negligence.(164)   While these theories can be applied to mine drainage issues, they are not usually successful because of the high burden of proof and other difficulties.

Conclusion

While the Canadian Parliament has enacted legislation dealing with pollution control, the provincial statutes are the primary mechanisms for environmental regulation.   Because the statutes and governing authorities differ from province to province, an overall assessment of the acts that apply to mine drainage is difficult, if not impossible.   Still it is not hard to conclude that governmental regulation of mining, whether it be the province or Parliament, will continue to increase.

VI. AUSTRALIAN EXPERIENCE(165)

The abatement of water pollution in Australia is similar to the Canadian regulatory framework. While the Australian Constitution grants many specific legislative powers to the Commonwealth, none of these powers expressly provide for environmental control. Therefore, much of the regulation is done by the state. However, in 1974 the Environment Protection (Impact of Proposals) Act(166) was passed, in which the Department of Environment, Housing and Community Development was given the authority to oversee environmental concerns. While the Act does not impose specific obligations on industries such as mining, the Minister for the Environment has the power to request that other Ministers block necessary ministerial approval for a new project if the project does not meet the required environmental standards.(167) Therefore, the Department of the Environment is to insure compliance with the previous more specialized acts relating to the environment.

Comparable to the Canadian system where the provinces control discharges of pollutants into the water courses, in Australia the states have primary responsibility for water pollution. In Western Australia, environmental regulation stems from the State Environmental Protection Act.(168) The general object of the Act is "the prevention and control of environmental pollution and protection and enhancement of the environment." The Act sets up three bodies for administering the Act: (1) Environmental Protection Authority (EPA), (2) Conservation and Environment Council (CEC), and (3) Department of Conservation and Environment (DCE). The EPA is the body that deals with the public and industry, while the CEC is an advisory committee and the DCE is the ministerial administrative section of the EPA.

The State Environmental Protection Act in essence creates an administrative agency to oversee compliance with the various acts protecting the natural environment. For example, in the state of Victoria the Fisheries Act of 1958,(169) the Harbor Boards Act of 1958(170) and the Groundwater Act of 1969(171) all control the discharge of harmful substances into the water system. In addition, acts concerning metropolitan water supplies and irrigation affect the discharge of industrial wastes. Large projects, such as mining operations, often come under an agreement act in which it is becoming accepted practice to include specific environmental safeguards and make provisions for an environmental review and management program (ERMP) within the agreement.

Like many other common law countries, Australia has substituted specific statutory regulations relating to pollution
for the common law remedies of nuisance, negligence and
strict liability. All over the world the modern day miner
faces a complex set of local, state and federal regulations
relating to pollution control.

VII. THE BRITISH EXPERIENCE(172)

The early common law principles that have been relied upon
by the English speaking countries have given way to statutory
laws, rules and regulations. The Town and Country Planning
Act(173) governs all land projects in England and Wales.
This Act applies to all phases of land use, including mining
and mine drainage.

The Act is a one-step procedure wherein all aspects of a
project are reviewed at the local level. The Act has gone
through an evolutionary process. The first Town and Country
Act was enacted in 1932(174) but was no more than what we now
consider as zoning matters. During World War II there was a
recognition for more comprehensive planning resulting in the
Acts of 1944(175) but the Act of 1947(176) provided the general framework for the present planning process. The post-
war Act recognized the need for regional planning. A reduction in the number of local planning authorities was made.
The present Act of 1971(177) governs all mining activities.
The local plan process is open to all types of concerns. The
local authority drafts the appropriate plan and holds hearings.
A final report is prepared by an "Inspector" who heads up the
local agency. This plan is presented to the Secretary of
State for the Environment for approval, change or rejection.
Generally the Secretary approves the Inspector's report and
thereafter the proposed project may commence.

One unique feature of the permitting process is that in
England most of the coal mining is done through the National
Coal Board.(178) Surface coal mining is exempt from the Town
and Country Act, but are regulated under the Opencast Coal
Act of 1958,(179) which has similar provisions. The combination of owner, mining operator and grantor of permission to
operate, all in one entity, makes for interesting speculation
of conflict of interests. However, the safeguards built into
the Acts allowing full public participation seem to overcome
the possible conflicts.

Unlike the American plan under the Environmental Protection Agency, Britian has no set rules as to mine drainage and reclamation. The permit is considered and awarded according to the specific local concerns and problems. Mining is not considered bad by the majority of those involved in the permitting process and as a result, an evenhanded balance of equities is easier to attain.

The permits granted are subject to limited judicial review(180) to determine whether the Secretary's order was within the powers of the Act. Injunctive relief and enforcement of the order is provided for in the Act.(181)

It appears that the British system of permitting mining offers a quicker, more realistic approach. There are problems, not unlike those in America, where the staff making the decisions is not technically competent to undertake the burden of analyzing the effects of mining. But, overall, the method, when compared, is more efficient and certainly less time-consuming than that required in the United States.

VIII. THE GERMAN EXPERIENCE(182)

It may be somewhat unfair to make direct comparisons between European and American mining. There are geographical differences since land values are different. But preservation of water quality is a primary goal regardless of other differences.

Generally, West Germany has attained a higher standard of mine reclamation than has America. Europe has long been concerned with external social costs and results from coal mining(183) and has regulated mining activities accordingly. In Germany, both surface and underground coal operations are closely regulated. Water pollution from mining is but one aspect of a bigger overall concern. Pollution measures are generally controlled on-site, supplemented by treatment plants that may process whole rivers to tertiary treatment standards.(184)

Mining operations in West Germany are subject to ongoing review by the State Mining Office as well as other agencies, such as the State Ministries of Economics and Agriculture and state and local water authorities.(185) Mining projects undergo two distinct stages—the initial permit and annual permit review. There are no set standards to guide the

permit applicants. Instead, the problems are resolved on an
ad hoc basis addressing the specific environmental concerns
of the area. The meetings are closed to the public and no
citizen participation is permitted, but the concerns of the
local citizens are met by the various participating agencies
that are obligated to address specific environmental
concerns.

Since the entire permit and review process is staged with
typical German bureaucratic multiple layer investigations and
agency cross-reference reviews, the procedure would not
favorably lend itself to American mining. Two main considerations, however, are evident. The first is that Germany
realizes the need for coal and mineral development. There is
not a polarization of positions as is evident in this country. The general theme is to allow mining with proper protection of the environment. The second consideration is that
one agency has the ultimate authority to grant or deny the
right to mine, as contrasted in this country where a dozen or
more agencies issue separate permits before mining can
commence. Additionally in this country, each agency wants to
be the last one to issue the permit, thereby causing delays
that go on for years instead of months. The delay has very
little to do with actual concern of the subject matter before
that agency.

The concerns of pollution from mine drainage are of significant importance in Europe as well as in America. Germany
started much earlier in attempting to solve the problem, but
the problem is being properly addressed in both countries.

IX. CONCLUSION

The problems related to mine drainage are changing
throughout the world. Several time periods have evolved.
The first set of laws, rules and regulations were concerned
with the physical discharge of the mine waters. The question
was whether or not a mine operator could release water upon a
lower landowner without recourse. Although this may yet be
an unresolved issue in some parts of the world, that question has been pushed aside to address more pressing issues.

The next phase in the law was a concern and determination
of the amount of pollution a mine operator could cause without incurring legal liability and related obligations. This
issue, too, took a secondary position after the courts determined the extent of such permissive activity.

Subsequently, with new awareness and concern, the issue did not focus upon whether one can discharge water into the stream system. That issue, for the most part, is resolved. Such discharge, if pollution results, cannot be permitted.

The present issue is the quality of water discharged to the stream system. Under today's strict standards there will be increasing demands placed upon the mine operator to discharge mine water only if pollution to the stream system does not happen.

The problem is no longer a local issue but is being or will be enforced to some degree throughout the world, wherever mining takes place. The original concern of miners was the common enemy of unneeded water in the mine. Today the common enemy still exists, but within a much larger area of concern. Lord Tenderden's statement that in conducting mining operations water is a sort of common enemy against which each man must defend himself is as true today as when first made in 1828.

REFERENCES

(1) Agricola, De Re Metallica Libri XVI (Hover, L. and H. trans.)

(2) Penn. Coal Co. v. Sanderson, 113 Pa. 126, 57 Am. Rep. 445, 6 A. 453, 459 (1886).

(3) Sanderson v. Penn. Coal Co., 102 Pa. 370 (1883).

(4) Lindley, Mines and Mineral Lands (3d ed. 1914).

(5) Lindley, Mines § 806, at 1983 (3d ed. 1914).

(6) See Colo. Const. art. XVI, § 3.

(7) Pa. Laws 1893, p. 52, art. 14, § 3.

(8) Lindley, Mines § 806, at 1984 (3d ed. 1914).

(9) See Rex v. Pagham Commrs. of Sewers, 8 Barn. & C. 355, 108 Eng. Reprint, 1075 (1828).

(10) Lord v. Carbon Iron Mfg. Co., 38 N.J. Eq. 452 (1884).

(11) L.R. 1 Ex. 265 (1866).

(12) Colo. Rev. Stat. § 37-87-104 (1973).

(13) See Orleans Navigation Co. v. New Orleans, 2 Mart. 214 (La. 1812).

(14) See Bassett v. Salisbury Mfg. Co., 43 N.H. 569 (1862).

(15) MacSwinney on Mines, p. 396 (1884).

(16) See generally, Carlyn v. Lovering, 1 Hurl. & N. 784, 26 L.J. Ex. 251 (1857). Under the laws of the stannaries, they must not, however, in exercising the right, injure rivers or lands adjoining rivers. If, as a consequence of its exercise, lands become overflowed by a river, they are bound within two days after receiving notice from any person thereby injured to clear the river, and in default are liable to damage and a fine; and for the protection of havens and ports in Cornwall, persons who stream for tin near any waters or rivers flowing into such havens or ports are under a statutory obligation to prevent the dislodged sand, stones, gravel, and rubble from being conveyed into such havens or ports.

(17) In Red River Roller Mills v. Wright, 30 Minn. 249, 15 N.W. 167, 169 (1883), the court considered necessity and economic impact in denying injunctive relief from the sawdust and refuse that spilled into the water from defendant's pulp mill.

(18) The Rivers Pollution Prevention Act, 39 & 40 Vict. c. 75 (1876).

(19) Sanderson v. Penn. Coal Co., 86 Pa. 401, 27 Am. Rep. 711 (1878).

(20) Penn. Coal Co. v. Sanderson, 113 Pa. 126, 6 A. 453 (1886).

(21) See Irvin v. Phillips, 5 Cal. 140, 63 Am. Dec. 113 (1855), where the issue was first decided.

(22) 15 Cal. 137 (1860).

(23) Id. at p. 143.

(24) 9 Colo. App. 407, 48 P. 828 (1897).

(25) 87 U.S. 507 (1874).

(26) Wilmore v. Chain O'Mines, 96 Colo. 319, 44 P.2d 1024 (1934); Slide Mines v. Left Hand Ditch Co., 102 Colo. 69, 77 P.2d 125 (1938).

(27) McCleery v. Highland Boy Gold Mining Co., 140 Fed. 951 (1904).

(28) Colo. Const. art. XVI, § 5, 6 and 7.

(29) 1870 Colo. L. P. § 2, § 1, now codified at Colo. Rev. Stat. §§ 34-50-101 to 106 (1973).

(30) Colo. Rev. Stat. § 34-50-106 (1973).

(31) Riley v. Park Central Land & Water Co., 40 Colo. 129, 90 P. 75 (1907).

(32) Colo. Const. art. XVI, § 3.

(33) Colo. Rev. Stat. §§ 34-51-101 to 124 (1973).

(34) Wyo. Const. art. 9, § 2.

(35) Ariz. Rev. Stat. 1887, §§ 2352-2357; Ariz. Rev. Stat. 1901, §§ 3252, 3257, now codified at Ariz. Rev. Stat. § 27-361 (1976).

(36) Pa. Law 1893, Art. 14, § 3.

(37) Ga. Code 1882, Art. 7, § 742.

(38) N. C. Code 1883, § 3293.

(39) Va., Act of February 29, 1892, p. 759.

(40) See F. Graham, Disaster by Default: Politics and Water Pollution 161 (1966).

(41) See generally, the Sanderson cases: 86 Pa. 401 (1878), 102 Pa. 370 (1883) and 113 Pa. 126 (1886).

(42) Act of April 22, 1905, Pa. P.L. 260 (repealed 1937).

(43) Id. Section 4 of the act so specifies.

(44) Act of June 14, 1923, Pa. P.L. 793, section 1 (repealed 1937).

(45) Act of June 22, 1937, Pa. P.L. 1987, as amended.

(46) Act of June 22, 1937, § 310 Pa. P.L. 1998 (repealed 1965).

(47) Act of May 8, 1945, Pa. P.L. 435.

(48) Act of Aug. 23, 1965, Pa. P.L. 372, now codified at Pa. Stat. Ann. tit. 35, §§ 691 et seq. (1977).

(49) Id. § 691.315(a).

(50) Id.

(51) Id. § 691.601.

(52) Id. § 691.8.

(53) Id. § 691.316.

(54) The Colorado Mined Land Reclamation Act, Colo. Rev. Stat. §§ 34-32-101 et seq. (1973), as amended by 1976 Colo. Sess. Laws, chap. 149, p. 724.

(55) Id. § 34-32-116(h).

(56) Sieber v. Frink, 7 Colo. 148, 2 P. 901 (1884); Fuller v. Swan River Placer Min. Co., 12 Colo. 12, 19 P. 836 (1888); Strickler v. City of Colorado Springs, 16 Colo. 61, 26 P. 313 (1891).

(57) H.B. 1123, 1979 Session.

(58) Colo. Rev. Stat. § 37-91-102 (1973).

(59) Colo. Rev. Stat. §§ 37-90-101 et seq. (1973).

(60) Colo. Rev. Stat. § 37-90-103(21) (1973).

(61) Annot. 56 A.L.R. 303 (1928).

(62) See Herriman Irr. Co. v. Butterfield Mining and Milling Co., 19 Utah 453, 55 P. 537 (1899), where the court took judicial notice that tunnels intercept surface waters, and Safranek v. Town of Limon, 123 Colo. 330, 228 P.2d 975 (1951).

(63) Sloss-Sheffield Steel & Iron Co. v. Wilkes, 231 Ala. 511, 165 So. 764 (1936).

(64) Stubbs v. Ereanbrack, 13 Utah 2d 45, 368 P.2d 461 (1962).

(65) See Commonwealth v. Barnes and Tucker Co., 477 Pa. 115, 371 A.2d 461 (1977). In Colorado the primary burden is upon the person claiming injury, but once this burden is met, the other party must provide a method showing how this injury can be overcome. Only then can he continue his activities. See Farmers Highline Canal and Reservoir Co. v. Golden, 129 Colo. 575, 272 P.2d 629 (1954).

(66) This is evidenced by the 1866 and 1872 mining laws; the early Homestead Acts; Act of July 4, 1866, 14 Stat. 86, 30 U.S.C. § 21 (1976); Act of May 10, 1872, 17 Stat. 91, 30 U.S.C. § 22 (1976); Homestead Act of March 3, 1891, 26 Stat. 1097, 43 U.S.C. § 161 (1976), repealed by Pub. L. No. 94-579 (1976).

(67) 30 Stat. 1151, 33 U.S.C. 401 (1976).

(68) Act of June 30, 1948, Pub. L. No. 80-845; ch. 750, 62 Stat. 1155.

(69) See note 64, supra.

(70) United States v. Standard Oil Co., 384 U.S. 224 (1966).

(71) Corps of Engineers Requirements for Permits for Industrial Discharges into Navigable Waters, U.S. Army Corps of Engineers, News Release, Seattle District, Aug. 4, 1970.

(72) Exec. Order No. 11574, 3 C.F.R. 188 (1970).

(73) Federal Water Pollution Control Act Amendments of 1972; Pub. L. 92-500 (1976). 86 Stat. 816 (1972) codified at 33 U.S.C. §§ 1251 et seq.

(74) 33 U.S.C. § 1251.

(75) 33 U.S.C. § 1311(b)(1)(A) (1976).

(76) 33 U.S.C. § 1311(b)(2)(A) (1976). This deadline was altered by the 1977 amendments to FWPCA, Pub. L. No. 95-217, 33 U.S.C. §§ 1251 et seq. The deadline for compliance for

BAT is not later than three years after the date effluent limitations are established, or not later than July 1, 1984, whichever is later, but in no case later than July 1, 1987. 33 U.S.C. § 1311(b)(2)(F) (1978 Supp.).

(77) 33 U.S.C. § 1257(a) (1976).

(78) 33 U.S.C. § 1362(6) (1976).

(79) 33 U.S.C. § 1362(16) (1976).

(80) United States v. Earth Sciences, Inc. (D.C. Colo. 1977); Sierra Club v. Abston Const. Co., 10 E.R.C. 1416 (N.D. Ala. 1977).

(81) 33 U.S.C. § 1288 (1976).

(82) 33 U.S.C. § 1288(a)(2) (1976).

(83) 33 U.S.C. § 1288(f) (1976).

(84) 33 U.S.C. § 1288(b)(2)(C)(ii) (1976).

(85) 33 U.S.C. § 1288(b)(2)(G) (1976).

(86) 40 C.F.R. § 130.2(q) (1976).

(87) EPA Guidelines, Chapter 6, p. 20.

(88) See Ipsen, Water Quality Management Plans and Their Impact on Mining Operations, 23 Rocky Mtn. Min. L. Inst. 551 (1977).

(89) 33 U.S.C. § 1313 (1976).

(90) 33 U.S.C. § 1313(a)(3) (1976).

(91) 33 U.S.C. § 1313(d) (1976).

(92) 33 U.S.C. § 1313(c) (1976).

(93) 33 U.S.C. § 1342 (1976).

(94) For a complete analysis of Pub. L. 92-500, see Keppler, Mining and the Federal Water Pollution Control Act Amendments of 1972, 20 Rocky Mtn. Min. L. Inst. 501 (1975).

(95) 30 U.S.C. §§1201–1328, Pub. L. No. 95–87, 91 Stat. 445 (1977).

(96) 30 U.S.C. §1202(f).

(97) 30 U.S.C. §1201(f).

(98) 30 U.S.C. §1202(g).

(99) 30 U.S.C. §1211.

(100) 30 U.S.C. §1231.

(101) An exception for lignite coal is made, and such coal shall be charged at a rate of 2 per centum of the value of the coal at the mine, or 10 cents per ton, whichever is less. 30 U.S.C. §1232.

(102) 30 U.S.C. §1232(g)(2).

(103) H.R. Rep. No. 218, 95th Cong., 1st Sess. 76 (1977).

(104) 30 U.S.C. §1251.

(105) 30 U.S.C. §1252.

(106) See 30 U.S.C. §§1252(a), (b), (c).

(107) 30 U.S.C. §1252(a).

(108) 30 U.S.C. §1252.

(109) 30 U.S.C. §1273.

(110) 30 U.S.C. §1252(e)(1).

(111) 30 C.F.R. §722.11 (1977).

(112) 30 U.S.C. §1253(a).

(113) 30 U.S.C. §1273(c).

(114) 30 U.S.C. §1273(a).

(115) 30 U.S.C. §1254.

(116) 30 U.S.C. §1253.

(117) 44 Fed. Reg. 14907 (1979).

(118) See 30 C.F.R. §§ 700-890.

(119) 30 U.S.C. § 1257.

(120) 30 C.F.R. § 779.13.

(121) 30 C.F.R. § 779.17 (1979).

(122) 30 U.S.C. § 1258.

(123) 30 U.S.C. § 1258(a)(13).

(124) 30 C.F.R. § 780.25 (1979).

(125) Hydrologic balance is defined as "the relationship between the quality and quantity of water inflow to, water outflow from, and water storage in a hydrologic unit such as a drainage basin, aquifer, soil zone, lake, or reservoir. It encompasses the dynamic relationship among precipitation, runoff, evaporation, and changes in ground and surface water storage." 30 C.F.R. § 701.5 (1979).

(126) 30 U.S.C. § 1260.

(127) 30 U.S.C. § 1265.

(128) 30 U.S.C. § 1265(b)(2).

(129) 30 U.S.C. § 1265(b)(10).

(130) 30 C.F.R. § 816.42 (1979).

(131) Id.

(132) 30 C.F.R. §§ 816.41-.45 (1979). Stream diversion will be approved only under specific guidelines. The preferred action is to create a 100-foot buffer zone around the stream in which surface mining activities are prohibited. See 30 C.F.R. § 816.57 (1979).

(133) 30 U.S.C. § 1265(b)(10(D).

(134) 30 U.S.C. § 1307(a).

(135) 30 U.S.C. § 1307(b).

(136)   30 U.S.C. § 1266.

(137)   30 U.S.C. § 1266(b)(2).

(138)   30 U.S.C. § 1266(b)(12).

(139)   30 U.S.C. § 1265(b)(10)(F).

(140)   30 C.F.R. § 701.5 (1979).

(141)   30 U.S.C. § 1260(b)(5).

(142)   See In re Surface Mining Regulation Litigation, 456 F.
Supp. (1978).

(143)   Canada Water Act, R.S.C. 1970, c. 5 (1st Supp.).

(144)   Id. S. 9.

(145)   Id.

(146)   Id. at S. 8.

(147)   Id.

(148)   Id. at S. 16.

(149)   Northern Inland Waters Act, R.S.C. 1970, c. 28 (1st Supp.).

(150)   Id. at S. 6.

(151)   Id. at S. 11.

(152)   National Environmental Policy Act of 1969, 42 U.S.C.
84321 et seq. (1970).

(153)   Fisheries Act, R.S.C. 1970, c. F-14, as amended by
R.S.C. 1970, c. 17 (1st Supp.).

(154)   Id. at S. 33.

(155)   Id.

(156)   British North America Act of 1867, 30 and 31 Victoria,
c. 3, S. 91. There are some important amendments to the
B.N.A. Act of 1867, such as the creation of new provinces and
the return of natural resources to the western provinces.

(157)   R. V. Sault Ste. Marie (1978), 3 C.R.(3d) 30.

(158)   British North America Act of 1867, S. 92.

(159)   British Columbia
            Environment and Land Use Act, S.B. c. 1971, c. 17
            Pollution Control Act, S.B. c. 1967, c. 34
        Manitoba
            Clean Environment Act, S.M. 1972, c. 76
        New Brunswick
            Clean Environment Act, R.S.N.B. 1973, c. C-6
        Newfoundland
            Newfoundland and Labrador Water Authority, R.S.N.
                1970, c. 44
            Waters Protection Act, R.S.N. 1970, c. 394
        Nova Scotia
            Water Act, R.S.N.S. 1967, c. 335
        Ontario
            Ontario Water Resources Commission Act, O.R.S.
                1970, c. 332
        Quebec
            Water Board Act, R.S.Q. 1964, c. 183
        Saskatchewan
            Department of Environment Act, S. 8, 1972, c. 31
            Water Resources Management Act, S. 8, 1972, c. 146

In addition to the above environmental acts, all provinces
have statutes regulating mining, some of which deal generally
with mine drainage.

(160)   Clean Water Act, S.A. 1971, c. 17
            Department of Environment Act, S.A. 1971, c. 24
            Groundwater Control Act, R.S.A. 1970, c. 162
            Land Surface Conservation and Reclamation Act, S.A.
                1973, c. 34
            Water Resources Act, R.S.A. 1970, c. 388
            Energy Resources Conservation Act, S.A. 1971, c. 30
            Coal Mines Regulation Act, R.S.A. 1970, c. 52

(161)   See Alberta's Land Surface Conservation and Reclamation Act, S.A. 1973, c. 34.

(162)   Comment: Aquaculture: Problems of Implementation
Under Existing Law, 10 Il.B.C.L. Rev. 301 (1975-76).

(163)   Groundwater Control Act, R.S.A. 1970, c. 162.

(164) See Suzuki v. The Ionian Leader [1950] 3 D.L.R. 790
(Ex. Ct.).

(165) For a more complete picture of pollution control in
Australia, see Lanter, The Legislative Control of Air and
Water Pollution in Australia (1970).

(166) Environment Protection Act of 1974, as amended by the
Environment Protection Act of 1975, No. 36.

(167) This is accomplished by denying ministerial approval
of an export license or withholding reserve bank approval for
foreign loans.

(168) State Environmental Protection Act of 1971.

(169) Fisheries Act of 1958, § 48.

(170) Harbour Boards Act of 1958, § 63(1).

(171) Groundwater Act of 1969, §§ 2, 47, 77 (1969).

(172) For a more detailed analysis of British Land Use
Planning, see Dempsey & Fields: Mineral Development in the
United Kingdom, 14 Land and Water L.R. 75 (1979).

(173) Town and Country Planning Act of 1971.

(174) Town and Planning Act of 1932, 22 & 23 Geo. V, c. 48.

(175) Town and County Act of 1944, 7 & 8 Geo. V, c. 47.

(176) Town and Country Act of 1947, 10 & 11 Geo. V, c. 51.

(177) Town and Country Planning Act of 1971, 19 & 20 Eliz.
11, c. 78.

(178) The Coal Act of 1938, 1 & 2 Geo. VI, c. 52: Title to
all coal is vested in the government's Coal Committee.

(179) Opencast Coal Act of 1958, 6 & 7 Eliz. 2, c. 69.

(180) Town and Country Planning Act of 1971, c. 78, § 245.

(181) Town and Country Planning Act of 1971, c. 78, § 87.

(182) For a more detailed analysis of the German experience, see Plater, Coal Law From the Old World, 64 Ky. L.J. 473 (1976).

(183) The Prussian Mining Law of 1865, as amended still serves as a model for mining permits today. See ALLEGEMEINES BERGGESETZ, 24 June 1865.

(184) See generally, E. Knop and H. W. Koenig, The Solution of Difficult Water Engineering Problems by Water Associations (1970).

(185) See generally, Knop and Koenig, Water Supply Associations in the Rhine-Ruhr Industrial Region, in SUR RUHRGEBIET PLANE, PROGRAMME, PROJEKTE 29 (1973).

3

Ground Water Design Parameters for Mining and Milling

by John C. Halepaska,
Chief, Water Resources Division,
Woodward-Clyde Consultants,
Denver, Colorado, USA

INTRODUCTION

The history of mining has been shaped to a large degree through engineering innovation and a variety of economic incentives. Involved in both engineering and economics of mining are a large spectrum of parameters. The evaluation and control of ground water through engineering is one such parameter.

GENERAL

The purpose of this paper is to present alternative mathematical methods that enable prediction of mine dewatering pumpage rates. Those predictions may serve as a basis for both environmental impact assessments and the development of mine design plans and cost estimates.

In development of a mining prospect, ground water is frequently encountered in a variety of geologic conditions, and may be in either a confined or unconfined state. The state of ground water is directly proportional to water level change per unit volume of water introduced or removed from the ground water system of interest.

The spatial change of water level associated with the introduction or removal of water is proportional to the geometry of the system of interest and the hydrologic conductivity and thus is subject to mathematical analysis.

The physical geometry of the mineral of interest relative to the water bearing section or sections is important in the design and operation of ground water control systems.

Ground water level change associated with the locations and timing of pumpage is controlled by the aquifer characteristics. These include hydraulic conductivity, thickness and areal extent of the aquifer, and the storage coefficient. Hydraulic conductivity is defined as the flow of water per unit time per unit area under a gradient of 1-foot per foot. Thickness refers to the vertical dimension of the system or systems of interest. The storage coefficient is defined as the volume of water that a vertical column of aquifer of unit cross-sectional area releases from storage as an average head within the column declines a unit distance.

Therefore, the process is one of determining the aquifer coefficients, development of conceptual mine design, and engineering the associated ground water control systems. The location relative to the mineral interval of interest is important to design of a mine. In order to illustrate some of the above concepts, examples will be used.

EXAMPLES

Example 1 shown on Figure 1 is a typical uranium deposit surrounded by aquifers both above and below. The mineral interval also can be an aquifer of some importance. Typically, deposits of this kind may be mined in three ways: in-situ leaching; open pit mining or underground mining. In order for the engineer to select an approach to development of a mine, he must understand the aquifer system in the vicinity of the mineralized interval. However, independent of how the system is to be developed, explicit information concerning the hydrology is still needed.

Analysis

Initially geologic research and mapping, followed by a drilling and testing program would be needed to develop information on the ground water system. This program

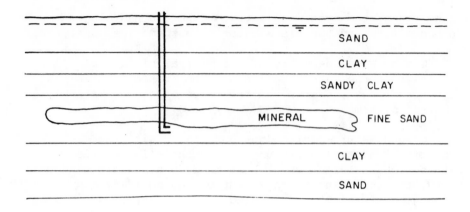

Typical Mineral Deposit.
Figure 1

would result in geologic information as shown on Figure 1,
along with the associated aquifer characteristics of each
part of the system.   Pumping tests require withdrawal of
water from intervals of interest with concurrent measurement of the change in water level in the aquifers of
interest.   These data are then utilized to compute pertinent aquifer properties and coefficients.   One of a variety
of published techniques (1, 2) are used, but the most
common method is by C.V. Theis and can be stated as
follows:

Equation 1

$$s = \frac{Q}{4\pi T} \; W(u)$$

where

     s - drawdown
     Q = pumping rate per unit time
     W(u) - Exponential integral
$$u = \frac{r^2 s}{4Tt}$$
     r = distance from pumping well to the point of
        observation
     s = storage coefficient
     t = time

After the aquifer coefficients from the testing and analysis program are computed, two important types of conditions should be considered: first, a constant pumping condition, which creates a continuously varying drawdown; and second, a constant drawdown condition, which creates a continuously varied rate of pumpage. These two conditions and their method of analysis are well known. The first condition is implicit in Equation 1 above. The second condition is illustrated in a paper written by C.E. Jacob and L.S. Lohman (3). Jacob and Lohman's solution can be stated as follows:

Equation 2

$$Q = 2\pi TSwG(a)$$

where

Q = discharge as a function of time
T = transmissivity
Sw = drawdown at the well
$$G(a) = \frac{4a}{\pi} \int_0^\infty Be^{-ab^2} \{(r/w)+\tan^{-1}[Yo(x)/Jo(x)]\}$$
$a = Tt/sr^2_w$

The use of the above equations can be illustrated by referring to Figure 1. The coefficients of the aquifers shown would be developed through pumping tests and analysis of data using Equation 1. The second equation shown above, would be used to determine the time dependent pumpage rate to maintain the dewatered state.

Even if the horizontal extent of the mineral interval is unknown, the total pumpage required to allow open pit mining per unit pit bottom radius still may be estimated. For example, if pumping tests have yielded a transmissivity of 5000 GPD per foot and a specific yield of .15, the results shown on Figure 2 for various effective radii would be applicable. Constant drawdown for this example problem is 155 feet. Calculation of rates for other constant heads with the same aquifer coefficients can be calculated directly from the figure, as rate is directly proportional to the constant head condition.

Example 2, for underground mining is also shown on Figure 1; however, the vertical scale has been increased by a factor of 10 and clearly there is an immediate need to understand the ground water system for proper dewatering design.

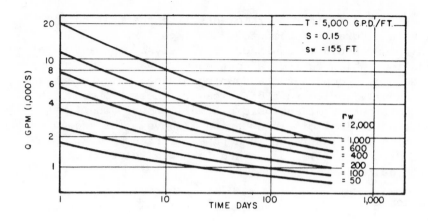

Open Pit Groundwater Flow Rates Based On Pit Bottom Radius.
Figure 2

In deep underground mining, ground water data needs are essentially the same as those required in Example 1. A major problem from the analysis standpoint is a reduction of the mine plan geometry to effective radius. A variety of methods can be used, a few of which are discussed below.

Method 1 entails approximation of the mine plan as a well and using the constant head Jacob-Lowman equation to calculate flow rates. This method generally yields a pump-age rate that is too high.

For Method 2, the technique of interfering wells is utilized, wherein each drift face of the proposed mine plan is considered to be a well. The cumulative production of the drift "wells", which typically are mutually interfering, is an approximation of the expected production from the mine.

For Method 3, the technique of confined-unconfined theory and the Jacob-Lowman theory are combined to calculate the required pumpage. The effective radius in this method is chosen as the radius at which the aquifer of interest goes from the confined to the unconfined state. Therefore, the concept focuses on fluid entering the unconfined state from elastic yield of the confined state.

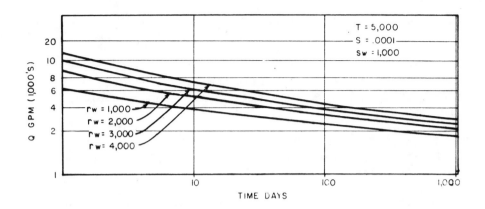

Groundwater Flow Rates Based On Radius To Transition
Confined-Unconfined Flow.
Figure 3

A discussion of the confined-unconfined problem can be
found in Ehlig and Halepaska (4).

Method 3 has been used for analyzing Example 2 where
aquifer transmissivity was 5000 GPD per foot, the storage
coefficient was .0001 and the head change was 1000 feet.
The results, shown on Figure 3, are for four different
effective radii.

CONCLUSIONS

Development of an underground mineral generally
requires design of ground water control systems. This
process entails development of ground water characteristics, development of a conceptual mining plan and prudent
application of the theory. Generally, many different
mining plans will be developed over the design period and
each will have its own dewatering design parameters.

REFERENCES

1. Theis, C.V., The relation between the lowering of the piezometric surface and the rate and discharge of a well using ground water storage, Tans. Amer. Geophys. Union, V.16, pp519-524, 1935.

2. Jacob, C.E., Flow of ground water, In Proceedings of the Fourth Hydraulics Conference, Edited by Hunter Rouse, 1950, John Wiley.

3. Jacob, C.E., and S.W. Lohman, Nonsteady flow to a well of constant drawdown in an extensive aquifer, Tans, AGU Vol.33, No. 4, Aug. 1952.

4. C. Ehlig and Halepaska, J.C., A numerical study of confined-unconfined aquifers including delayed yield and leakage, Water Resources Research, Vol.12, No. 6, December 1976.

4

Hydrogeologic Investigations for Mine Dewatering

by R. G. Slayback, Vice President and Director,
Leggette, Brashears & Graham, Inc.,
Westport, Connecticut, USA

ABSTRACT

Mine drainage involves a wide variety of ground-water problems but evaluation techniques usually focus on common goals. The determination of reliable aquifer coefficients-- the transmissivity or the hydraulic conductivity and the coefficient of storage--together with knowledge of the aquifer geometry and the nature of boundary conditions, as determined by field exploration and testing methods, forms the basis for effective planning of mine dewatering systems. The recent advances in aquifer modeling on digital computers have increased the hydrogeologist's ability to provide reliable quantitative evaluations in the complex geologic settings generally involved in ore-body environments.

Case examples of common aquifer and boundary conditions, including a cement-limestone quarry in Missouri, a complex of lead-zinc open pit mines in the Northwest Territories of Canada, and the Athabasca Tar-Sand mining area of northern Alberta, are cited to demonstrate the diversity of mine ground-water problems and the commonality of approaches to their solution. Early integration of dewatering programs with the exploration, geotechnical, mine planning and operational efforts can have significant economic benefit.

INTRODUCTION

Mine drainage, in the ground water sense, refers to the dewatering or depressurization of water-bearing formations—aquifers—that may occur over, under or within the material being mined or quarried. Such drainage is done for a variety of reasons that start and usually end with economics, but include absolute mining feasibility, operational efficiency, slope stability, and safety.

The hydrogeologic evaluation of ground-water problems may not be difficult if the geology is clearly understood. Many situations, however, require extensive testing and even then, some cases become evaluations of flooding probability rather than reliable projections of ground-water control. Solid rock aquifers or aquitards, in which water movement is through fractures, joints, faults or solution openings, tend to be the most difficult to evaluate. Unfortunately, it is a fact that the investigations of many mining prospects concentrate so intently on the ore that the potential for mine drainage problems is neglected until late in the planning or even into early development stages.

Few areas of hydrogeology offer the diversity of problems encountered in both surface and underground mines. The very nature of many ore bodies, being anomalous concentrations of the desired mineral, often brings out unique hydrogeologic behavior that must be understood to achieve the required ground-water control. Greenslade, Brittain and Baski (1) recently referred to underground mine dewatering as "The Anatomy of Anomalous Conditions"—a beautiful title that says much about the interface of art and science in mine dewatering. Mines and quarries occur in developed and remote areas, both of which may be regarded as hostile environments for differing reasons. The rapid proliferation of environmental and safety laws has had an impact on mine drainage practices. Extremes of climate are another element of variable but often critical impact on mine dewatering systems.

Nevertheless, the evaluations of mine ground-water problems almost always have in common the determination of certain properties of the water-bearing formation or formations and their hydrogeologic environment. In brief outline, these include:

1. Aquifer Coefficients. Transmissivity (T) is a

measure of the ability of the entire thickness of a unit of
aquifer to transmit water from place to place in response
to a unit gradient. It is the algebraic product of the
coefficient of permeability (or more recently, hydraulic
conductivity) and aquifer thickness. The Coefficient of
Storage (S) represents the amount of water released from
(or added to) storage in the pore space of a unit volume
of rock in response to a unit of head change. Reliable
values for these coefficients permit mathematical projections by standard equations of aquifer behavior in response
to pumping. Particularly important in many mining situations
is the degree of uniformity of these properties--vertically
and horizontally within the area influenced by mine pumpage.

   2. Boundary Conditions. Boundary conditions include
sources of recharge, such as surface water bodies or leakage through other formations, or barrier boundaries such as
impervious valley walls, which represent no-flow or lesser
flow conditions in part of the affected area. A pervasive
but commonly exaggerated concern in mining situations is
recharge conditions that are improperly understood or are
perceived as changing dramatically as the result of excavation.

   3. Local Water Budget. The local water budget of an
aquifer or aquifer system refers to the long-term allocation
of the available inflow water--from precipitation, regional
flow or recharge sources--to components of natural or artificial discharge. The goal of a water budget is generally
to determine the perennial or seasonal replenishment that
a mine drainage system will have to handle after a requisite
amount of local aquifer storage is depleted. In many instances, the water budget analysis is critical to the long-term
water supply available to the ore upgrading plant.

The necessary data are obtained by literature search,
integration of available mine exploration data and, most
importantly, by field testing of the aquifer. Aquifer coefficients can be estimated from laboratory tests and boundary conditions can be approximated if sufficient geologic
detail is known, but the most reliable data for projecting
aquifer performance are obtained by controlled pumping
tests. The planning, execution and evaluation of such tests,
and the determination of the adequacy of the resultant data
are among the principal contributions of the hydrogeologist.

By a few case-history examples, this paper will attempt to demonstrate the diversity of mine dewatering problems and the commonality of the analytical approaches to their solution.

DUNDEE CEMENT COMPANY, MISSOURI

The situation of a mine or quarry in close proximity to a large surface-water body recurs frequently, with many interesting variations. The potential hazard of a nearby source of virtually unlimited recharge is apparent to even the untrained observer. Nevertheless, many mines operate successfully with small separating distances from a lake or river, at working levels substantially below the surface water elevation. Loofbourow (2) said it well: "Loss of life, property and production from flooding is grim, yet scores of mines have worked safely for generations under ground-water reservoirs, lakes and even the sea." Examples from the author's experience include limestone quarries in northern Michigan working within two thousand feet of Lake Huron, Lee Creek Mine on the edge of the Pamlico River estuary in North Carolina and underground lead-zinc mines of the Pend Oreille district in Washingron where a hydroelectric reservoir impounded 50 feet of water directly over the mine workings.

These mines succeed from the mine drainage standpoint because the local geology provides a combination of aquifer coefficients and boundary conditions that limits the passage of the surface water to the working area. After the fact of successful operation, the retrospective analysis of why the flood was held out is easy. Without the benefit of after-vision, the hydrogeologist must evaluate the information available, which commonly is a fragmental by-product of ore-zone exploration, and devise a testing program.

Dundee Cement Company was erecting a premium-quality cement plant in Clarksville, Missouri when an artesian sand and gravel aquifer was discovered that might have provided a conduit for Mississippi River water to enter the limestone quarry adjacent to the plant. The situation is illustrated by figure 1A, in which the cement plant and the limestone quarry can be seen in the valley of Calumet Creek and by figure 1B, an idealized section across the valley. The planned quarry location was 4000 feet from the Mississippi River edge.

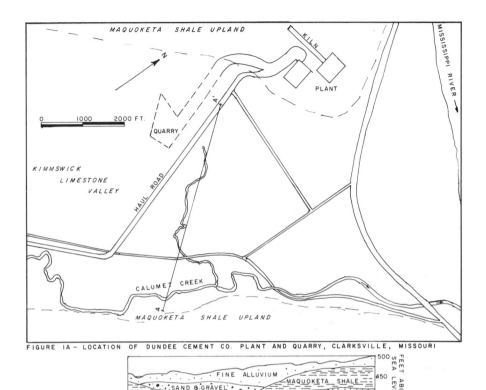

FIGURE IA – LOCATION OF DUNDEE CEMENT CO. PLANT AND QUARRY, CLARKSVILLE, MISSOURI

FIGURE IB – GEOLOGIC SECTION A-A'

When geophysical exploration and a number of drill holes indicated the presence of an alluvial sand and gravel aquifer directly above the Kimmswick Limestone, there was concern that a large-scale dewatering operation or perhaps even an impervious cut-off wall might have to be considered. The sand and gravel, where encountered, ranged from 9 to 36 feet thick, overlying the limestone encountered at depths of 58 to 94 feet.

A test production well and a pattern of observation wells, as shown by figure 2, was drilled between the planned quarry and the Mississippi River. The wells showed that the aquifer was of variable thickness, ranging from 7 to 30 feet, with a generally lens shape thinning toward the valley sides, conforming to the earlier exploration. However, the well completion data indicated that the aquifer was less permeable than the earlier work had suggested. The test production well and the observation well were completed with well screens and developed until clear water was produced.

The test production well was pumped at 125 gpm for two

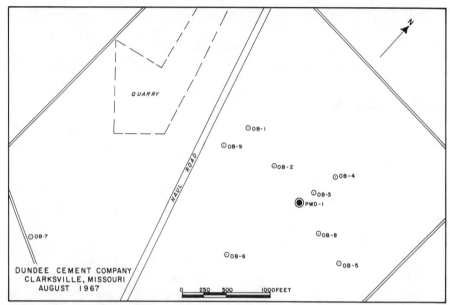

FIGURE 2 — AQUIFER TEST PATTERN

days and then, when the pumping level reached the well screen,
the rate was reduced to 100 gpm for 2 more days. Typical
semi-logarithmic drawdown graphs for observation wells are
shown by figure 3. It is clear from these plots that no
significant river recharge was encountered and that barrier
boundaries, as indicated by the gradual down-turning of the
drawdown graphs, were the dominant influence on the pumping tests. Analysis of the early drawdown data by the
Theis log-log method (3) gave transmissivity values of 5000
to 17,000 gallons per day per foot, and averaging about 8000.
Coefficients of storage were in the range of 0.00006 to
0.00008.

The drawdown-distance data, shown on semi-logarithmic
coordinates by figure 4 indicated the impact of the barrier
boundaries and the apparent large area of significant drawdown influence.

These results were confirmed by a second pumping test in
the immediate vicinity of the planned quarry, with three
test production wells intended as part of the permanent
dewatering system.

The aquifer transmissivity, width and flow gradient
demonstrated that the underflow down the Calumet Creek
valley was on the order of 150,000 gallons per day. It was

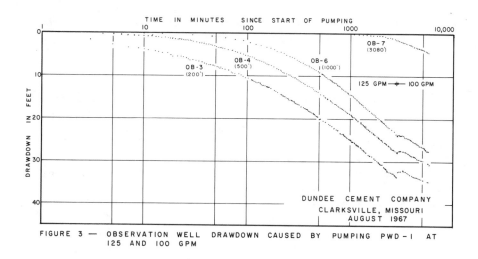

FIGURE 3 — OBSERVATION WELL DRAWDOWN CAUSED BY PUMPING PWD – I AT 125 AND 100 GPM

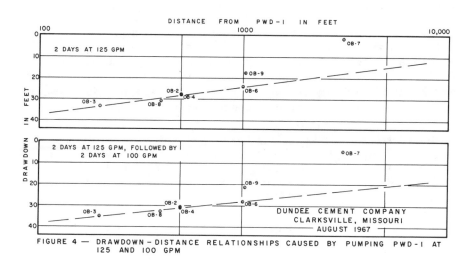

FIGURE 4 — DRAWDOWN – DISTANCE RELATIONSHIPS CAUSED BY PUMPING PWD – I AT 125 AND 100 GPM

further concluded that, at flood stage of the Mississippi River, the aquifer could transmit no more than about 500,000 gallons per day back to the quarry site, provided there was a clean interface with the aquifer. This relatively small scale field investigation quickly demonstrated that all of the ground-water problems, including that of recharge from the Mississippi River were manageable at very low cost.

This simple example of a highly favorable outcome is not necessarily typical, of course. There are many cases where large-scale recharge from a surface-water source is an accepted cost of mining or quarrying.

PINE POINT MINES, NWT, CANADA

Pine Point Mines, a subsidiary of Cominco Ltd, operates open-pit mines in an elongate chain of isolated lead-zinc ore bodies along a Devonian dolomite reef in Canada's Northwest Territories. The location, to the south of Great Slave Lake, is indicated on figure 5 and the general array of ore bodies is shown by figure 6. The ore deposits and their geology have been extensively reported by Campbell (4) and Skall (5), among others.

Shortly after initial operations mined off some of the dry ore bodies, Pine Point Mines proceeded in 1968 into what has become one of the largest mine dewatering projects in North America. Total pumpage has been above 40 million gallons per day for years and reached 66 million gallons per day in 1978. The testing programs, the gradual development of the dewatering systems and the practical problems of dewatering in a frigid environment have been reported previously by Calver and Farnsworth (6), by Brashears and Slayback (7) and by Vogwill (8), and will be further addressed by K. J. Durston at this symposium.

The primary objective in discussing the dewatering operations at Pine Point is to describe the success this mine has had in handling the transition of a confined or artesian aquifer, in which pumping reduces the pore pressure, to a water-table aquifer, in which gravity drainage of the water in pore storage takes place. The change occurs when pumpage causes the piezometric level to fall below the base of the confining bed and into the strata being pumped. In the author's experience, no other single phenomenon in hydrogeology has caused more problems in the proper evaluation of mine dewatering requirements, or for that matter, in groundwater supply analyses.

The transition involves what hydrogeologists refer to as "delayed yield from storage." The general theory was described by Boulton (9) (10), useful type curves were provided by Prickett (11) and the direct description of artesian to water-table conversion was covered by Moench and Prickett (12). The early application to Pine Point Mines was described by Vogwill (8). Rather than go into a detailed description of the theory, this paper will trace

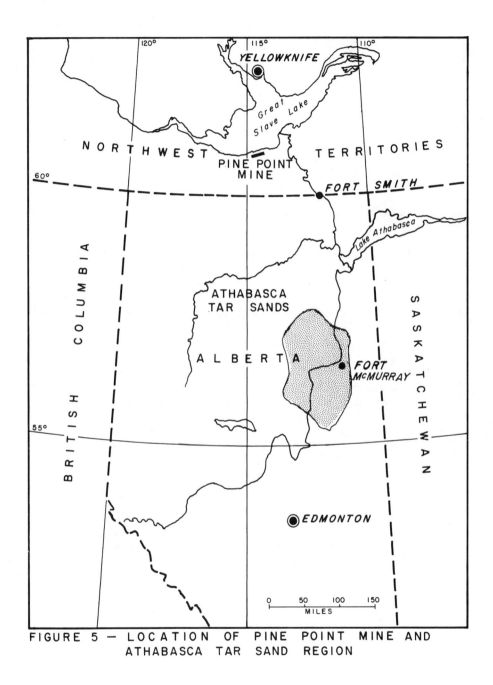

FIGURE 5 — LOCATION OF PINE POINT MINE AND
ATHABASCA TAR SAND REGION

the Pine Point experience and illustrate the interpreta-
tional problems with a hypothetical drawdown graph.

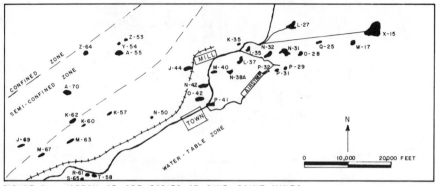

FIGURE 6 — ARRAY OF ORE BODIES AT PINE POINT MINES

The first ore bodies dewatered at Pine Point were in areas with no confining bed and the aquifer response was water-table drainage from the beginning. Figure 7 illustrates a typical family of observation well semi-logarithmic drawdown curves in response to pumping a single well at 1140 US gallons per minute. The curves are typified by an early slow rate of drawdown and the drawdown data gradually fall into a straight-line trend. For this test, the average transmissivity, by log-log and semi-log analysis, was 54,000 gallons per day per foot and the average coefficient of storage was 0.015, or as expressed in water-table terminology, the specific yield was 1.5 percent. These coefficients formed a satisfactory basis for pit dewatering design. The range of aquifer transmissivity at Pine Point is from 35,000 to 90,000 gallons per day per foot. Among the water-table pits, the specific yield ranges from 1.5 to 5 percent (8).

The first ore pit to involve an artesian to water table conversion was designated K-57. When tested, the aquifer coefficients were T =41,000 gallons per day per foot and S = 0.001 (8). Note that the storage coefficient was more than a full order of magnitude smaller than the smallest of the water-table cases. The water levels during the K-57 test were not drawn down below the bottom of the confining bed, but in order to mine to full depth, the required drawdown was to levels substantially below the confining bed. As a result of this situation and some operational problems, dewatering of this pit was about 20 feet less than anticipated after one year of pumping (8) and additional pumping capacity was required to meet the mining schedule.

Disregarding the operational problems, what occurred hydrogeologically can be illustrated by figure 8, the

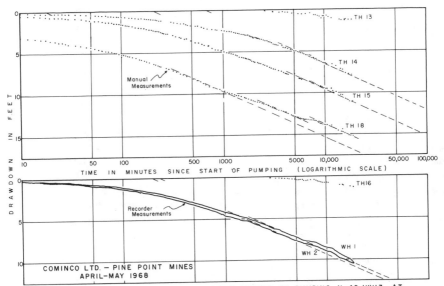

FIGURE 7 — OBSERVATION WELL DRAWDOWN CAUSED BY PUMPING N-42/WH3 AT 1140 USGPM

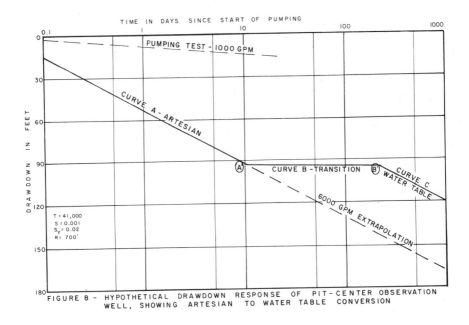

FIGURE 8 – HYPOTHETICAL DRAWDOWN RESPONSE OF PIT–CENTER OBSERVATION WELL, SHOWING ARTESIAN TO WATER TABLE CONVERSION

hypothetical semi-logarithmic drawdown response of an observation well in the central pit area. The upper curve represents the drawdown observed during the pumping test of a single well and Curve A, the extrapolated response to the

pumping of the complete group of pit-rim dewatering wells
operating at a combined yield several times the tested
pumping rate. At Point A' the actual drawdown response
deviates from the extrapolation used for design, which
extrapolation worked well for the water-table pits.

Point A' is not clearly defined, but occurs sometime as
water levels are drawn below the confining bed. Its actual
position at any given observation well is related to the
aquifer coefficients, the location and yield of individual
pumping wells and the geometry of the aquifer-confining bed
interface. Nevertheless, it represents the point at which
the extrapolated artesian drawdown trend, controlled by the
pumping rate, transmissivity and the small amounts of water
released from artesian storage per unit of head change, is
interrrupted by the transition to water-table gravity drainage of water filling the pore spaces.

Curve B represents the transitional period when parts of
the aquifer affected by the cone of depression are changing
to gravity drainage response. In the practical sense, it
is a time when continued withdrawal of water at a given pumping rate produces very little additional drawdown. This
transitional phase is followed at Point B' by Curve C, in
which for a thick water-table aquifer, the logarithmic rate
of drawdown is equal to that of Curve A.

The critical point, of course, is the delay entailed with
Curve B. For the Pine Point case, where the difference
between the artesian and water-table storage coefficients is
generally somewhat more than one order of magnitude, the
approximate delay is a little more than one log cycle of
time, which can be insignificant or devastating depending on
the circumstances. For the situation shown, if Point A' is
reached in 10 days at a given rate of pumping, Point B'
where the extrapolated rate of drawdown will resume, will
be after about 200 days. Similarly, depending on when
Point A' occurs, any drawdown target time would be deferred
by about one log cycle of time—1 day to 10 days, 100 days
to 1000, 1 year to 10 years, and so forth. Although it has
not occurred at Pine Point, it is possible that an artesian
aquifer with a storage coefficient of 0.0001 would change
over to a water table aquifer with a specific yield of 0.1,
a transition involving an effective delay period of 3 log
cycles of time—from 10 days to 10,000 or 27 years, for
example.

A solution to the problem, as Pine Point Mine personnel

have determined, is to estimate the ultimate water-table specific yield and provide sufficient pumping capacity to drive through the delay barrier early. Fortunately, at Pine Point the water table specific yield of the rock--its effective porosity--is known within a fairly narrow range: 1.5 to 5 percent. Where it has been feasible, the mine has conducted multiple-well pumping tests to pass through the confining bed and observe the water-table behavior of the aquifer. However, for deep pits in the artesian zone, where the confining bed is substantially below the static water level, such tests are impractical and the average specific yield of the rock provides a reasonable basis for initial dewatering design. Such design must, of course, be modified by the results obtained by yield and drawdown monitoring.

In proceeding beyond the Pine Point example, return to figure 8 to consider the implications of a pumping test that is concluded during the Curve B phase. In the absence of hydrogeologic understanding and especially when Curve A is poorly developed, many such tests have been misinterpreted as indicating an exceptionally high aquifer transmissivity or a recharge boundary. Either of these erroneous interpretations lead to projections of a requirement for an excessive number of dewatering wells and an unrealistically large total sustained pumpage. Although such interpretation will not result in the underdesign that is the bane of mine planners and operators, such projections may have a significant detrimental effect on mining feasibility evaluations.

ATHABASCA TAR SANDS, ALBERTA

The Athabasca tar sand deposits in the vicinity of Fort McMurray, Alberta, located on figure 5, contain vast petroleum reserves at least partly within reach of surface mining methods. Two large open-pit mines are in operation, a third is planned and presently in the licensing process, and several more have been investigated for future development. The tar sand ore is found in the Cretacious McMurray Formation, which unconformably overlies Devonian limestone and shale bedrock (13). The McMurray Formation is comprised of a complex transgressive sequence of salt marsh, fluvial, estuarine and marine deposits of sand, silt and clay (14).

The sands of the main ore zone are impregnated with bitumen--heavy asphaltic petroleum--at grades commonly in excess of 10 percent by weight. Overburden of highly variable thickness includes the Cretaceous Clearwater Formation clays and sands, Pleistocene tills and stratified drift, and recent deposits including stream alluvium and large areas of muskeg.

The two operating mines and the third proposed by the Alsands Project Group are examples of the extreme diversity of ground-water conditions in the Athabasca tar sand area. Great Canadian Oil Sands Ltd. (G.C.O.S.) has operated an open-pit mine by bucket-wheel excavators since 1967 on the west bank of the Athabasca River, about 25 miles north of Fort McMurray. To date, G.C.O.S. is understood to have had no aquifer problems of significance and operates no formal ground-water control system.

On a property directly abutting the G.C.O.S. lease, Syncrude Canada Ltd. has found very different aquifer conditions. A dragline test pit dug in 1973-1974 encountered significant inflows of water, gas and sand issuing upward from an aquifer in the basal McMurray Formation below the ore body. A dewatering system of 42 wells, having a combined peak yield of almost 350 US gallons per minute, was installed to depressurize these basal water sands beneath the test pit. After about 15 months of pumping, drawdown of as much as 5 feet was discerned 1¼ miles from the test pit. Various back-analyses indicated that aquifer transmissivity was on the order of 750 to 1500 gallons per day per foot, and gave local storage coefficients of about 0.00003. However, variable well productivity, inconsistent results at distance, and the presence of significant amounts of dissolved gas gave indications of the heterogeneous aquifer conditions.

For the commercial mine, which went into dragline-excavation operation in the summer of 1977, Syncrude concluded that depressurization of the basal water sands would be necessary, to enhance stability of the mine high walls and to limit the handling problems inherent in wet tar sand. A testing program, involving two patterns of production and observation wells, was carried out in 1974. A typical test pattern array is shown by figure 9. Step drawdown tests and constant-rate pumping tests were carried out to determine aquifer coefficients, boundary conditions and well performance characteristics. Observation well data gave T values ranging from 225 to 3000 gallons per day per foot and S values in the range of 0.0001 to 0.00001.

These tests formed a basis for basic well design and spacing for a system of five rows of pumping wells along the

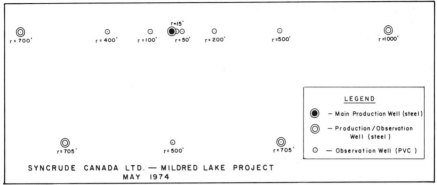

FIGURE 9 — MULTIPLE PRODUCTION WELL AQUIFER TEST PATTERN

14,000-foot long opening cut of the mine. The wells were
initially drilled at 200 and 400 feet spacings at an average density of 20 wells per 1000 lineal feet of opening cut.
Subsequently, a variety of additional test methods was
applied to augment the knowledge of aquifer characteristics,
including falling head tests, slug tests, specific capacity
tests, laboratory permeameter tests and controlled operational
tests. These data indicate a range of field coefficient of
permeability from about 0.2 to 300 gallons per day per square
foot (14), but values in the range of 10 to 100 gallons per
day per square foot were common for the water sands.

Initial storage coefficients were in the range of 0.0001
to 0.00001. However, as depressurization progressed, the
evolution of dissolved gas, mainly methane and carbon diox-
ide, within the aquifer pores, caused substantial changes
in the aquifer and well performance. To the hydrogeologist,
this appeared to be a reduction in transmissivity and accompanying decrease in well production, and a substantial
increase in the coefficient of storage. The reservoir engineers recognized the two-phase behavior as analogous to
solution-gas or depletion drive. The transmissivity effect
was caused by the rapid decrease in relative permeability
to water as the relative permeability to gas increased,
and the storage effect was related to highly expansive gas
behavior in the pore space. Syncrude has made effective
use of an oil-reservoir computer model to predict depressurization progress (14).

Syncrude has drilled about 500 depressurization wells to
date and more will follow. Many of the wells already have
been removed to make room for mining activities, some never
produced significant amounts of water and many have had to
be redeveloped to overcome clogging of the well screens

with bitumen. At any given time, 75 to 150 wells may be operating at an average rate of about 5 gallons per minute. In areas underlain by clearly-recognizable water sands, depressurization of as much as 170 feet has been achieved, but in transitional areas underlain by silty sands, tarry water sands or silts, much less drawdown has occurred. No perennial recharge has been observable but leakage of water stored in the basal clay layers has been demonstrated. Continued drilling has shown that large areas of the mine site have little or no basal water sand, but large areas underlain by productive water sands also remain to be mined.

To the northeast of G.C.O.S. and Syncrude, on the east side of the Athabasca River, is the planned Alsands Project Group mine. Drilling exploration, pumping tests, and a 1974-1975 test pit by Shell Canada Ltd. have revealed a basal-zone aquifer substantially different from that at Syncrude. The water sands are generally coarser, cleaner and thicker, and dissolved gas has not been a hydrogeologic factor. Individual wells are known to yield as much as 175 gallons per minute.

An aquifer test in 1972 indicated an average transmissivity of 7000 gallons per day per foot. For an average aquifer thickness of 35 feet, the average field coefficient of permeability was 200 gallons per day per square foot, at a water temperature of 41 degrees Fahrenheit. The storage coefficient averaged 0.0002. Observation well data indicated that barrier boundaries caused the distant depressurization effect to be greater than the aquifer coefficients would indicate, as illustrated by figure 10. The Shell test pit was successfully depressurized by 7 wells, whose combined pumpage was generally less than one million gallons per day, and demonstrated that the Alsands mine is likely to discharge more water than at Syncrude but with far fewer wells.

Elsewhere in the Athabasca area, further hydrogeologic diversity is apparent. One ore body is known to be overlain by more than 100 feet of Pleistocene outwash sands that have yielded as much as 350 gallons per minute to a test well, and have a transmissivity of about 45,000 gallons per day per foot. Unconfirmed reports indicate that glacial outwash aquifers on other leases have yielded as much as 700 gallons per minute on pumping tests. It requires little imagination to suggest that some tar sand leases may have the ore zone sandwiched between a shallow

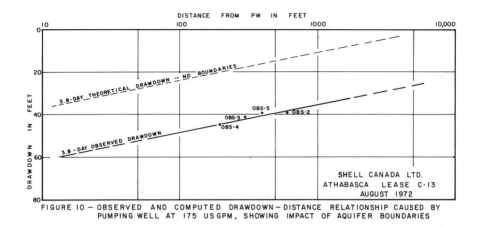

FIGURE 10 — OBSERVED AND COMPUTED DRAWDOWN — DISTANCE RELATIONSHIP CAUSED BY PUMPING WELL AT 175 USGPM, SHOWING IMPACT OF AQUIFER BOUNDARIES

outwash aquifer and deep basal-McMurray Formation water sands--a challenging mine drainage problem.

SUMMARY

These diverse case examples all involved the common thread of field investigations to determine reliable aquifer coefficients, establish aquifer boundary conditions and evaluate aquifer water budgets or sources of recharge. Careful planning and meticulous field work are requisites for any mine dewatering project but even a very large and costly hydrogeologic investigation does not eliminate the risk of unforeseen or anomalous conditions. As with many other aspects of mine development planning, the goal of mine dewatering investigations should be to reduce the probability of drainage risks to acceptable levels.

REFERENCES

1. Greenslade, William M., Brittain, Richard, and Baski Hank, "Dewatering for Underground Mining-'The Anatomy of Anomalous Conditions'", Mining Congress Journal, November 1975.

2. Loofbourow, R. L., "Ground Water and Ground-Water Control", SME Mining Engineering Handbook, Chapter 26, 1973.

3. Theis, C. V., "The Relation Between the Lowering of the Piezometric Surface and the Rate and Duration of Discharge of a Well Using Ground-Water Storage", American Geophysical Union Transactions, v. 16, pt. 2, 1935.

4. Campbell, Neil, "The Lead-Zinc Deposits of Pine Point, CIM Bulletin, v. 59, nos. 647, 652, 1966.

5. Skall, H., The Paleoenvironment of the Pine Point Lead-Zinc District", Economic Geology, V. 70, 1975.

6. Calver, B. and Farnsworth, D.M.J., "Open-Pit Dewatering at Pine Point Mines," CIM Bulletin, v. 62, no 692; CIM Transactions, v 72, 1969.

7. Brashears, M. L. and Slayback, R. G., "Pumping Test Methods Applied to Dewatering Investigations at Pine Point Mines, NWT, Canada", SME-AIME Annual Meeting, New York, March 1971. Preprint No 71-AG-90.

8. Vogwill, R.I.J., "Some Practical Aspects of Open-Pit Dewatering at Pine Point:, CIM Bulletin, April 1976.

9. Boulton, N. S., "Analysis of Data from Non-equilibrium Pumping Tests Allowing for Delayed Yield from Storage", Proc. Institution of Civil Engineers, v. 26, no 6693, 1963.

10. Boulton, N. S., "Discussions of the Analysis of Data from Non-equilibrium Pumping Tests Allowing for Delayed Yield from Storage", Proc., Institution of Civl Engineers v. 28, August 1964.

11. Prickett, T. A., "Type-curve Solution to Aquifer Tests Under Water Table Conditions", Ground Water, March-April, 1965.

12. Moench, A. F. and Prickett, T. A. "Radial Flow in an Infinite Aquifer Undergoing Conversion from Artesian to Water Table Conditions", Water Resources Research, v. 8, no 2, April 1972

13. Carrigy, M. A. and Kramers, J. W., "Guide to the Athabasca Oil Sand Area", Alberta Research Council, Info Series 65, 1965.

14. Coward, J., Illum, S., and Shah, R., "Computer Simulation of the Basal Aquifer at the Syncrude Mine", Conference of Canadian Chapter - International Association of Hydrology, Edmonton, Alberta, October 1978 (publication pending).

5

Groundwater Instrumentation for Mining Projects

by Franklin D. Patton,
Consulting Engineering Geologist and
President of Westbay Instruments Ltd.,
West Vancouver, British Columbia, Canada

Groundwater measurements enter into many phases of the mining industry. Recently, Westbay Instruments has developed new equipment for groundwater monitoring and sampling. This paper presents a brief summary of some of these developments, particularly as they affect the quality of technical data collected and the cost and scheduling of groundwater instrumentation programs.

TYPES OF GROUNDWATER MEASUREMENTS

There are only a few types of groundwater measurements that are commonly required in mining operations. These are the elevation of the groundwater table, water pressure and water quality. Some groundwater parameters are derived from these measurements, particularly permeability and related aquifer characteristics. The collection of groundwater data sounds as though it should be a rather straightforward procedure. One would expect that the best quality and the most cost effective methods would now be well established. However, recent developments promise significant improvements in the quality and cost of groundwater measurements.

The groundwater table should be quite simple to determine. Yet in practice it can be difficult to establish the groundwater table even if it remains stationary with time.

Many devices are available to measure groundwater pressures (1, 2, 3, 4). Groundwater pressures need to be recorded at several locations in order to establish the three-dimensional character of the groundwater flow system. However, in practice, it can be difficult to install and verify the readings from just one water pressure recording device (5). It is even more difficult as more measurement devices are installed in a single hole.

The determination of the permeability of soil and rock to groundwater is relatively straightforward in theory. It can be found by pumping from wells and making time-drawdown measurements in surrounding observation holes (6, 7, 8) or by making slug or response tests in the observation wells themselves (9, 10, 11). The test results permit permeability and other aquifer characteristics to be calculated. These calculated values can be quite dependent upon the duration of the tests, and the number and the quality of the observation points.

Obtaining samples from drill holes for water quality determinations would appear to be quite simple. It is not. Water sampling requires careful attention to drilling procedures, the removal of drilling induced waters prior to sampling, the isolation or sealing of the casing between sampling points, and the use of pressurized containers to maintain the sample in its natural state. When any of these procedures are omitted or unduly relaxed, the sampling results are suspect.

There is an increasing need for multiple purpose groundwater instruments that can be used to measure water levels and water pressures and also allow good quality water samples to be obtained. Adjacent to mining operations there can be a need to measure deformation as well as water pressure distribution in the same drill hole. There are also economic and technical reasons for high-density, multiple purpose instruments to be placed in a single drill hole.

DIFFERENT ROLES FOR GROUNDWATER INSTRUMENTATION IN MINING

The many different roles of groundwater measurements in the mineral industry have not always been fully recognized. Groundwater instrumentation can enter into mineral exploration, mine design, environmental impact assessment, mine production, in-situ and waste dump leaching, and tailings monitoring.

Mineral Exploration

Groundwater geochemistry when combined with a knowledge of hydrogeologic flow systems holds promise of being a powerful tool for mineral exploration. The requirements are only that: 1) an orebody has a perceptible effect on the surrounding groundwater, 2) a representative sample of the groundwater can be taken, and 3) a chemical analysis of the water sample can detect the trace of the orebody. Trace elements can be measured to parts per million and parts per billion making it possible to recognize minor anomalies caused by flow past orebodies. As groundwater flows through the rocks in a region, a large volume of the surrounding bedrock will be sampled. By intercepting the groundwater and carefully analyzing it for its dissolved and gaseous constituents, anomalies can be recognized. With hydrogeochemical sampling of drill holes, an anomaly can be tested so as to determine a vector pointing to its source. Herein lies the greatest potential power in the use of groundwater measurements as an exploration tool.

The possible effect on an orebody by a typical groundwater flow system is illustrated in Figure 1.

To determine this numerous pressure measurement points and sampling points must be placed in small-diameter drill holes. It is important that the measuring or sampling points be properly sealed from each other and that the sampling areas be decontaminated (of the fluids introduced by drilling) prior to sampling.

Mine Design and Environmental Assessment

For the design phase of the mine development, basic data on the properties of the materials and fluids present must be gathered and their probable impact on the mining operation

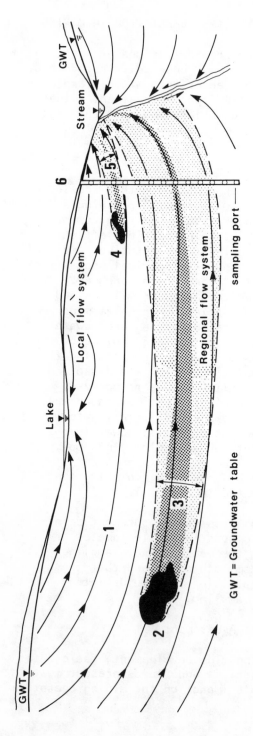

GWT = Groundwater table

sampling port ——

LEGEND

1 Groundwater flow lines showing flow paths penetrating and "sampling" the entire region (flow is driven by differences in fluid potential).

2 Location of hypothetical source of anomaly (orebody).

3 Zone of groundwater affected by orebody (2).

4 Location of another hypothetical orebody.

5 Zone of groundwater affected by orebody (4).

6 Exploratory drill hole with sampling and pressure measuring ports.

Figure 1. Groundwater measurements in mineral exploration.

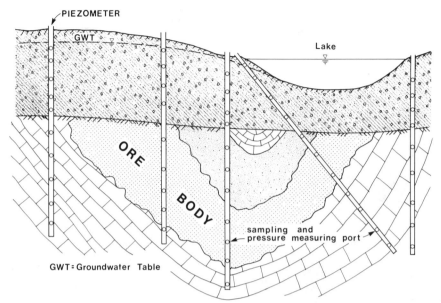

Figure 2. Groundwater measurements in mine design
and environmental assessment.

and the local and regional environment assessed. Water
levels, water pressures, permeabilities and water quality
must be determined. In some cases the dewatering problems
can be the most significant aspect of the mine design since
dewatering costs can affect economic feasibility.

For an environmental assessment, water quality sampling
and pressure measurements are required to estimate local
and regional groundwater flow systems and the character of
the waters that they contain. In some mineralized areas
the mineral content of the natural groundwater discharges is
greatly in excess of that permitted by environmental
authorities. It is important to establish such natural
conditions in advance of mining.

Figure 2 illustrates one situation that could face a
mine designer. In this case saturated and highly permeable
sediments overlie the potential mine. Small differences in
the permeability which can lead to large differences in the
water pressure distribution can become apparent when the
groundwater system is stressed such as during dewatering.
It is therefore important to place an adequate number of
pressure measuring points, often more than might be thought
necessary, so that the effects of dewatering can be observed.

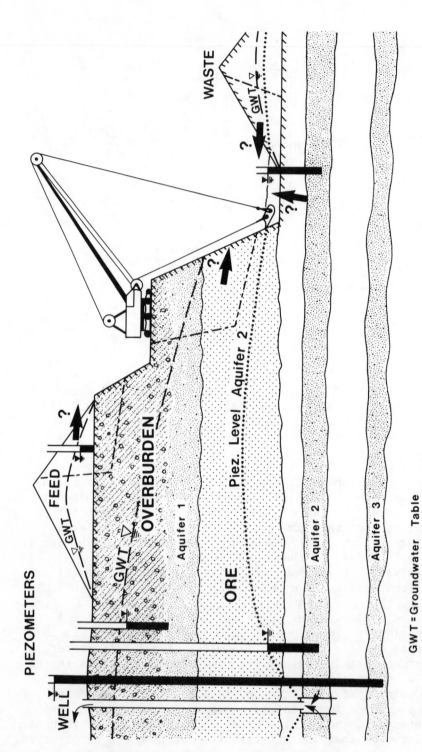

PIEZOMETERS

WELL

FEED

WASTE

GWT

GWT

GWT

GWT

GWT

?

?

?

?

?

OVERBURDEN

Aquifer 1

ORE

Piez. Level Aquifer 2

Aquifer 2

Aquifer 3

GWT = Groundwater Table

Figure 3.   Groundwater measurements in mine production.

Mine Production, Tailings and Waste Dump Monitoring

In some mines groundwater monitoring is required only as a precautionary measure. However, in other cases dewatering and depressurization are required for the safe and economic operation of the mine. Two mines in the latter category are the Lee Creek Phosphate Mine of Texasgulf Inc. in North Carolina and the Syncrude Oil Sand Mine in northern Alberta.

Figure 3 illustrates the variety of problems that can occur in production when two or three aquifers are present. In such cases groundwater conditions can have a controlling effect on production. Allowance must be made for their control and measurement prior to production and their monitoring during production. It may be necessary to take measurements near the actual production area. In order not to interfere with production, it becomes important to place as many monitoring points as possible in a single drill hole and combine monitoring operations that currently require separate drill holes. For example, if both deformation and pressure measurements can be made in the same drill hole, there can be appreciable savings in time and money.

In-Situ and Waste Dump Leaching

Where mineral production is obtained from subsurface or surface leaching operations it is important to be able to monitor and thereby follow the production process within the leaching area.

Most leaching operations involve fluids that are undesirable in the natural environment, and close control of the region surrounding the production area is likely to be a requirement. This environmental monitoring also can be helpful in recognizing and thereby limiting undue losses of the valuable leachate.

Figure 4 illustrates two types of leaching operations where detailed groundwater monitoring of the surrounding groundwater environment can be undertaken. In certain situations it may also be useful to monitor the leaching operation. The sampling aspect of groundwater monitoring is particularly important. Detailed water pressure measurements may also be necessary to understand and predict the flow directions in the saturated zones in the production area and in the groundwater in the surrounding rock.

a) Underground Leaching and Solution Mining

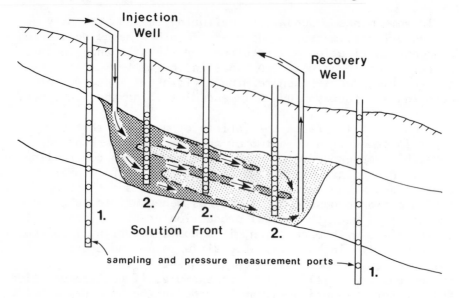

b) Surface Leaching

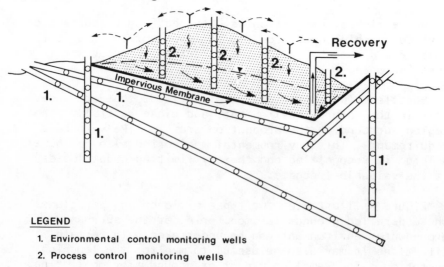

LEGEND

1. Environmental control monitoring wells
2. Process control monitoring wells

Figure 4.   Groundwater measurements in leaching operations.

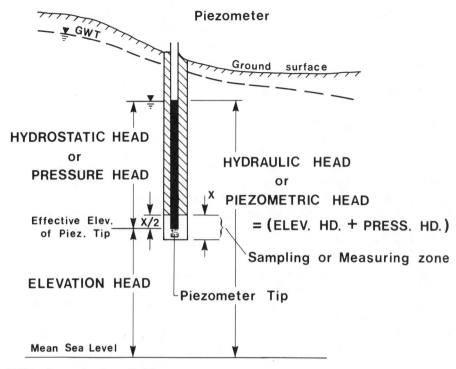

Figure 5. Definition of terms.

DEFINITION OF TERMS

Figure 5 provides a graphic illustration of a number of the terms used in this paper. Piezometers are water pressure measuring devices which are commonly placed in drill holes. True piezometers are sealed along their length except for an open section at their tip in a measurement or sampling zone. The effective elevation of the piezometer is the center of the open sampling or measurement zone. In soils and fine-grained friable rocks, the tips commonly consist of a filter and the space surrounding the tip and the walls of the drill hole is filled with a selected graded sand. In stable rocks the filters and sand are unlikely to be needed.

Piezometers placed in drill holes are commonly constructed with impervious casing or tubing so that the water cannot flow into or be influenced by water in another zone encountered in a different portion of the same drill hole. Water pressure measurements made in open, unlined and unsealed drill holes should be designated as "open hole" measurements. Such drill holes usually provide unsatisfactory pressure measurements and water quality samples.

Figure 5 shows that the piezometer records the mean hydrostatic pressure or pressure head that is present at the tip or sampling zone of the piezometer. The total hydraulic head or piezometric head is calculated from the recorded pressure head and a knowledge of the effective elevation of the piezometer tip. When referring to an individual piezometer it is usually convenient to work with pressure heads. However, in comparing the measurements from different piezometers it is usually necessary to work with piezometric heads related to a common reference plane (sea level) to determine flow directions and related factors.

On Figure 5 the elevation of the piezometric head measured in the piezometer is not equal to the elevation of the sur-rounding groundwater table (GWT). In nature they are equal only when there is no flow (a hydrostatic condition) or when the flow is entirely horizontal. Because hydrostatic conditions are seldom achieved in nature and because the flow usually has a small vertical component, the level to which water will rise in a well constructed piezometer will seldom be equal to the level of the groundwater table. For this reason a reading from a single piezometer is seldom sufficient to define the distribution of water pressures in an aquifer.

In this paper the term "port" is used to describe a point in a piezometer where a groundwater sample may be taken and where groundwater pressures may be measured.

ESTIMATION OF PIEZOMETER REQUIREMENTS

Figures 6 and 7 show how diagrams of depth versus pressure head can be used to estimate the number of piezo-meter ports required to establish the pressure distribution and flow conditions in two different situations: a single aquifer (shown in Figure 6) and two aquifers (shown in Figure 7). The single aquifer in Figure 6 is shown under-lain by a single aquitard--a unit that restricts the flow of water, whereas the two aquifers in Figure 7 are shown sandwiched between three aquitards. These situations are relatively common in mining operations and it is not un-usual to encounter three or more aquifers in a single mine.

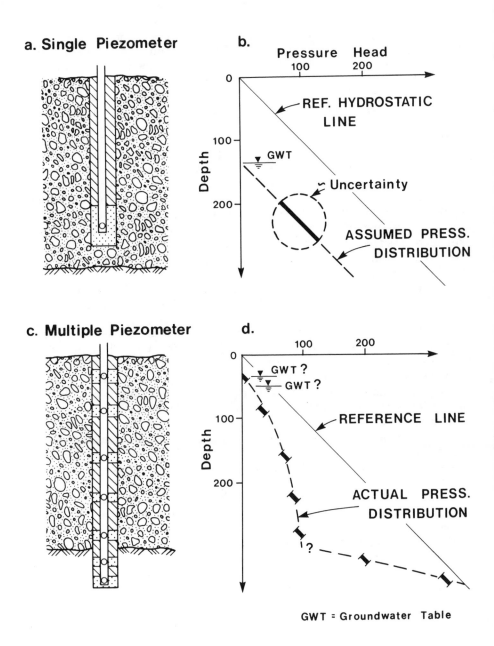

a. Single Piezometer

b.

Pressure Head

ASSUMED PRESS. DISTRIBUTION

REF. HYDROSTATIC LINE

GWT

Uncertainty

Depth

c. Multiple Piezometer

d.

GWT ?
GWT ?

REFERENCE LINE

ACTUAL PRESS. DISTRIBUTION

Depth

GWT = Groundwater Table

Figure 6.   Piezometer requirements,
single aquifer.

The geology and general groundwater situation is shown on the lefthand side of each of the figures and the corresponding depth versus pressure head diagram is shown on the righthand side. On each figure a comparison can be made between the groundwater data obtained with a single piezometer in each aquifer and with multiple piezometers.

The depth versus pressure head diagrams are a convenient method of plotting and interpreting the piezometer measurements in a single drill hole. If possible, both depth and pressure should be plotted in the same units and to the same scale. On these plots it is helpful to show a reference "hydrostatic line" which indicates the slope of a hydrostatic pressure distribution. This line would represent the pressure distribution in an open body of water. When the plot of pressure head versus depth is inclined more steeply than the hydrostatic line, a downward flow condition is indicated. When the pressure distribution is flatter than the hydrostatic line, an upward flow condition is indicated.

The heavy bar on Figure 6b shows the water pressure data obtained from a single piezometer in Figure 6a. The midpoint of the bar is the pressure recorded in the piezometer at a depth which is assumed to be the midpoint of the measurement zone. The heavy bar is inclined parallel to the reference hydrostatic line over the length of the measurement zone shown on Figure 6a. Without further water pressure data one would have to assume that the pressure distribution in the remainder of the aquifer is hydrostatic. Hence, the groundwater table would be estimated to be at a depth of about 135 units as shown on Figure 6b. Increasing the length of the measurement zone can introduce appreciable uncertainty in the depth-pressure relationship. An initial estimate of this uncertainty can be given by a circle with a diameter equal to the length of the bar shown in Figure 6b. The actual measurements can greatly exceed the uncertainty circle, but a circle can provide a reasonable first estimate of the possible errors present.

The identical aquifer is shown in Figure 6c, but with more piezometer ports installed. The corresponding distribution of pressure head with depth is shown on Figure 6d. At first glance it may be difficult to believe that the measurements on Figures 6b and 6d could be made in the same aquifer. For example, the real groundwater table in Figure 6d would appear to be 100 units above that obtained in Figure 6b. Furthermore, in Figure 6d the pressure distribution in the aquifer is steeper than the reference

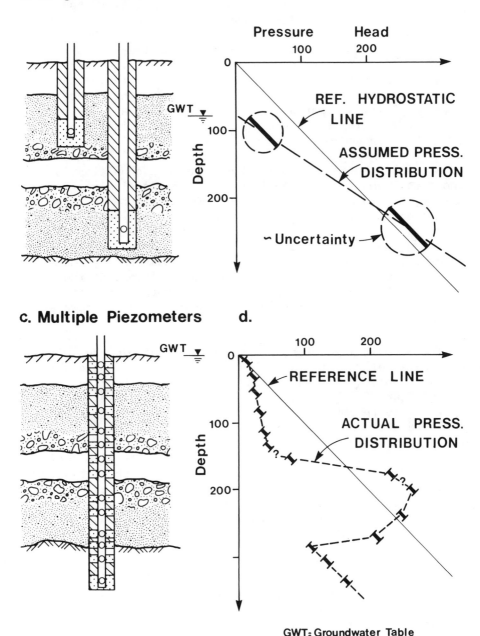

a. Single Piezometers

b.

Pressure   Head
100   200

0

GWT

REF. HYDROSTATIC LINE

Depth

100

ASSUMED PRESS. DISTRIBUTION

200

~ Uncertainty

c. Multiple Piezometers

d.

GWT

100   200

0

REFERENCE LINE

Depth

100

ACTUAL PRESS. DISTRIBUTION

200

?

?

GWT= Groundwater Table

Figure 7.   Piezometer requirements, two aquifers.

hydrostatic line. Figure 6d shows that the pressure distribution in the bedrock below the aquifer is flatter than the
reference line. Thus, the groundwater is flowing downwards
in the aquifer and upwards in the bedrock toward the bedrock
contact. The question marks indicate that there is uncertainty about the water pressure at the bedrock contact and
about the precise position of the groundwater table. Even
more piezometers would be required to remove these uncertainties. It is apparent from this example that measurements from a single piezometer can be highly misleading,
even when the geology is very simple.

A similar but more complex hydrogeologic condition is
shown on Figure 7. The positions of the two single piezometers, one in each aquifer, are shown on Figure 7a. The
corresponding results of the measurements from these piezometers are shown on Figure 7b. As before, the measurements
are shown by the heavy bars. The length of each bar is
determined by the depth interval in the measurement zones.
The slope of each bar is made equal to the slope of the
reference hydrostatic line. The equivalent uncertainty
circles are shown together with an interpreted groundwater
table.

The identical aquifers are shown in Figure 7c, but with
more piezometer ports installed. The corresponding distribution of pressure head versus depth is shown on Figure 7d.
As in Figure 6, the results obtained with more piezometers
show little resemblance to those given in Figure 7b. The
pressure distribution in Figure 7d indicates that the upper
aquifer is draining downwards·and that a second drain occurs
at the top of the bedrock contact. The results also indicate that the top of the lower aquifer is a high pressure
region where flowing artesian conditions are present and
water is being fed both upward through the aquitard between
the aquifers and downward toward the bedrock contact. The
pressure distribution is hydrostatic in the bedrock. Also,
the groundwater table is near the ground surface rather
than 80 units below the surface as indicated in Figure 7b.

Figure 8 shows the pressure distribution versus depth
for a drill hole made in mountainous terrain in central
British Columbia. The pressure distribution given in
Figure 8 was collected with the Westbay Profiler, an
instrument which measures bottomhole pressures and allows
permeability values to be obtained during intervals in the
drilling operation. The Profiler is used inside HQ and

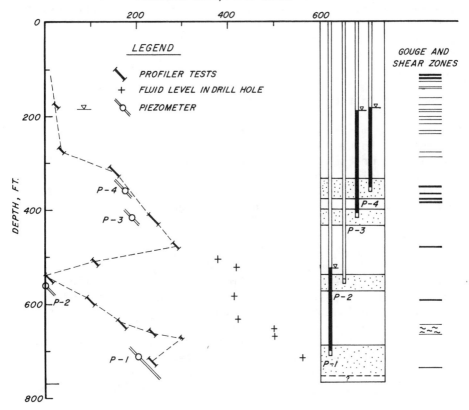

Figure 8.　Field record, pressure head versus depth
using Westbay's Profiler.

NQ-size wireline rods and has been operated to depths of
300 meters.　Figure 8 also shows the results obtained from
the few piezometers installed in this drill hole.　Profiler
measurements were made to establish the best locations for
the permanent piezometers.　It can be seen that without
knowledge of the pressure distribution obtained from the
numerous Profiler water pressure measurements, it would be
easy to interpret incorrectly the results from a few
piezometers.

It is necessary to have at least two data points in each
aquifer when the pressure distribution is represented
by a straight line.　Another data point is required to confirm the straight-line pressure interpretation and a further

data point is required if the monitoring system is to have the minimum amount of built-in redundancy. Thus, two data points per aquifer are the absolute minimum to investigate the pressure distribution and four data points per aquifer are the minimum needed to recognize non-linear pressure distributions and have a single redundant data point. For an evaluation of an aquifer there should be at least one data point in the adjacent unit. Hence, for one aquifer the absolute minimum number of piezometer data points is three. The minimum number does not permit unusual situations to be checked and significant exceptions could easily go unrecognized. For an adequate monitoring system five data points are required, four in the aquifer and one in the layer below. The adequate number has some redundancy and enables one to detect unusual situations.

Assuming that the pressure distribution in the aquitards separating the aquifers will not be particularly significant, a minimum of one and preferably two data points in each aquitard would be required. Thus, for the two aquifers shown in Figure 7 the minimum number of data points would be seven (two in each aquifer and one in each of the overlying, intervening and underlying aquitards), whereas adequate coverage would require fourteen data points (four in each aquifer and two in each aquitard). If the settlement of compressible layers is of concern, then additional piezometers would be required in any compressible aquitards.

TYPES OF PIEZOMETER INSTALLATIONS

The available types of piezometer will generally fall within one of the categories shown on Figure 9. These categories are: a) open piezometers, b) closed piezometers, and c) valved (or combined open/closed) piezometers. This classification has been adapted from those suggested by Schmidt and Dunnicliff (3), Cording et al (2) and Dunnicliff (12). The main modification is the addition of the valved category which was not available at the time these earlier classifications were made.

Open Piezometers

The open piezometers shown in Figure 9a are those in which the air-water interface is contained within the piezometer casing or tubing and the position of the interface is recorded for a particular measurement zone. The open piezometers shown are essentially the same and only differ

a. OPEN PIEZOMETERS

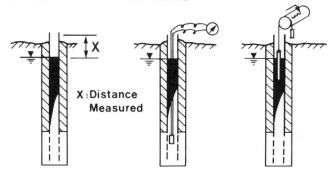

X : Distance
Measured

b. 'CLOSED' PIEZOMETERS

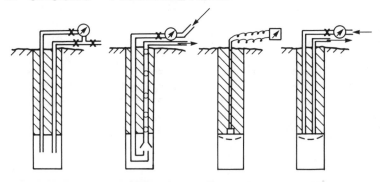

i. Formation Fluid Types   ii. Diaphragm Types

c. VALVED PIEZOMETERS

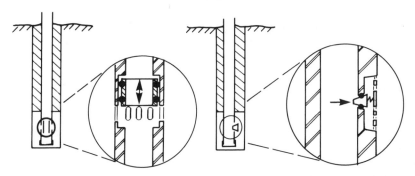

i. Sliding Valve Type   ii. One-way Check Valve Type

Figure 9. Types of piezometers.

in the method used to record the elevation of the interface.

These methods can include tape measurements, sonic measurements, floats attached to rotating drum recorders and almost any of the systems used to measure water pressure in the other types of piezometers (for example, pneumatic or strain-gauge pressure transducers, etc.). The principal advantages of the open piezometers are their simplicity, the ease with which they can be checked by response testing, and the relative ease with which water samples can be obtained. Open piezometers can be constructed so as to permit the "development" of the formation surrounding the tip following installation. This development is often required to remove the effects of natural and added drilling muds and to decontaminate (i.e., remove traces of the drilling fluids) prior to water quality sampling. The principal disadvantages of the open system piezometers are their slow response times in low permeability soil and rock formations and the technical difficulties that can result when one attempts to place several in the same drill hole. Another disadvantage can be that the open piezometers cannot be used to measure negative pore-water pressures. Open piezometers generally cannot handle flowing artesian conditions effectively, particularly in freezing weather.

Closed Piezometers

Closed piezometers are of two main types: those that use the actual pore fluid of the soil or rock to make the measurements and those that sense the fluid pressure through diaphragms. These are referred to on Figure 9 as "formation fluid types" and "diaphragm types," respectively.

The formation fluid type of piezometer is similar in several respects to the open piezometer. Tubes are introduced into the piezometer casing or drill hole which is then sealed and the tubes are led away to a recording station. Here the water pressure is recorded or air is introduced and allowed to bubble out of the end of the tube and the pressures are recorded. Response tests are generally quite difficult to make for calibration of the performance of the piezometers. Water samples sometimes can be obtained from the formation fluid type of piezometer. The response time for this type of piezometer is usually much faster than for open piezometers. An added advantage is that the lines can often be led out horizontally thereby reducing any interference with mining operations. The main disadvantage is that long lines from the tip are susceptible to damage. Damaged or leaking lines can be difficult to detect and repair and can result in incorrect data being recorded.

The diaphragm type of closed piezometer has many variations, but generally the sensing mechanism uses the displacement of a diaphragm to indirectly indicate the water pressure. In certain diaphragm piezometers the diaphragm acts as a butterfly valve. In some the movement or displacement of the diaphragm is sensed. In others the stress in the flexing diaphragm is interpreted by strain measurements. Movement of the diaphragm or the stresses introduced by the movement can be sensed pneumatically, hydraulically or by electrical and electronic means.

The principal advantages of diaphragm piezometers are: 1) their shorter response time in comparison with open piezometers, 2) their ease in adapting to automatic recording devices, 3) the ability of some types to avoid the presence of water either at the top of the piezometer casing or in the measurement lines (important in freezing weather), and 4) their ability to have their measurement lines led away horizontally from the piezometer tip if required. The principal disadvantage is that one is usually unable to check the calibration of these instruments once installed. (In some cases calibration can be achieved with extra lines). Other disadvantages include: the inability to collect water samples, the susceptibility of the electrical systems in the subsurface environment to short circuiting, and the susceptibility of the pneumatic and hydraulic systems to leakage resulting in erroneous results. Furthermore, to attain levels of accuracy comparable with those obtained in open piezometers, relatively expensive electronic apparatus is required. Most electrical systems are susceptible to transient electrical currents as the leads can act as long antennae. Lightning has also damaged permanent electrical/electronic systems. The pneumatic systems become rather slow below depths of 80 meters and readings are often unacceptably slow below 200 meters.

Valved Piezometers

Valved piezometers are a relatively new development of Westbay Instruments Ltd. whereby a valve which can be opened and closed is placed on the side of the piezometer casing. In the two types shown in Figure 9, the valve can be a sliding valve which can remain open or closed or it can be a one-way check valve which remains closed due to external water pressures until it is opened from the inside as shown by the arrow.

The sliding valve type of piezometer can be operated as an open piezometer or as a closed piezometer. In the latter case an inflatable packer would be installed on either side of the valve to seal off a portion of the inside of the piezometer casing.

The valved piezometer with a one-way check valve requires a special probe which can find the valve at the correct depth and orientation, seal the valve from the water inside the piezometer casing, open the valve, and finally sense the exterior water pressure or take a water sample. The probe can contain an electronic, pneumatic or hydraulic pressure transducer which can be read at the surface.

The valved piezometers tend to combine the best attributes of the open piezometers and the closed piezometers and eliminate some of the disadvantages of each. For example, they can be as responsive as all but a few of the closed piezometers yet can readily undergo response testing to check the calibration of the transducers, the operation of the valve, and its connection to the formation outside. Also, when using electrical transducers for pressure measurements no electrical or pneumatic lines are left in the casing between readings unless continuous measurements are required. In the latter case the transducers can still be removed for calibration or repair. This allows one to take advantage of the accuracy and convenience of electrical pressure transducers without leaving such devices in the drill hole with the attendant problems discussed by Casagrande (1). Valved piezometers may readily be used to measure pressures below atmospheric pressure.

A significant advantage of valved piezometers is that large numbers of them can be placed in a single drill hole. With other types of piezometers there are both practical and economic limits to the number that can be placed in a drill hole. For the other piezometers the practical limits are generally reached for all but the most skilled field technicians at about three piezometers per drill hole. The need for multiple piezometer installations becomes apparent when groundwater instrumentation considerations are examined in detail.

GROUNDWATER INSTRUMENTATION CONSIDERATIONS

Cost of Drill Holes

The cost of drill holes is usually a significant factor in groundwater instrumentation budgets. Drill hole costs can run from a few dollars to over $100 per foot with good quality cored drill holes generally running from $20 per foot and up. Costs are influenced by many variables including the size and depth of the drill hole, accessibility, the total footage drilled, etc. Drilling costs typically amount to from 40 to 90 percent of a groundwater instrumentation budget. Thus, reducing the number of drill holes per installed piezometer can appreciably lower the groundwater instrumentation costs.

Scheduling

On many jobs the number of drill holes that can be used for instrumentation is not limited by cost so much as by scheduling. In all phases of mining--exploration, environmental assessment, design, production and monitoring--the drilling operation is commonly on the critical path or can easily interfere with critical path operations. Thus, the fewer the drill holes, the fewer the scheduling problems.

Surface Protection

If the groundwater instrumentation is to survive and permit monitoring over a period of time, it is generally necessary to protect the top of the drill hole. In freezing weather this could mean the construction of an insulated shack. Near mine operations reinforced structures may be required or the area may have to be isolated from operations. Sometimes protection consists of burying the piezometer casing. All of these methods can be costly in terms of labor and capital costs or in terms of reduced operational efficiency. There is an obvious advantage in reducing the number of field protection facilities.

Potential Damage to Formations to be Monitored or Sampled

Unless each drill hole is carefully drilled and sealed after the piezometer casing is installed, it is quite easy to adversely influence the groundwater measurements or samples with the very program that is supposed to obtain these data. The potential for damage can be high in environmental monitoring of hazardous underground fluids. Leakage from one formation to another through the drill hole or casing can be a principal means of spreading a contaminated fluid. Groundwater quality monitoring systems can adversely affect the problem they are supposed to be helping to solve. The potential for formation damage increases directly with the number of holes drilled. Thus, from the viewpoint of formation damage, the more piezometers placed in one drill hole, and therefore the fewer the drill holes, the better.

Three-Dimensional Sampling Requirements

Groundwater sampling and pressure measurements occur in a three-dimensional framework. This requires a spacial distribution of sampling and measurement points. Thus, one must usually consider portraying the groundwater data on plans showing their areal distribution as well as on several hydrogeologic sections made more or less at right angles to each other. To do this, the groundwater data must be available at a considerable number of locations and at numerous depths. Deep groundwater sampling may require that pressurized samples are taken to ensure that no gases have escaped from the sample between the sampling point and the laboratory. The mathematics of the situation can quickly show that great economy in drill holes and data monitoring points can be obtained if numerous measurements can be made in single drill holes. A large number of sampling points can be particularly important in environmental monitoring situations where the actual location of a leakage path is not known in advance of sampling and analyses.

Redundancy Requirements

As previously noted, no good groundwater instrumentation system would be complete without a consideration of redundancy requirements. Installations which achieve over 90 percent functional operation of the completed groundwater monitoring systems are quite rare, particularly when the depths of the drill holes extend below several hundred feet. After the system has been installed, various environmental factors operate the reduce the efficiency of the system and attrition occurs. Human error can also result in losses to the groundwater monitoring system. A fully redundant system might have two data points installed for each one required. The amount of redundancy required is dependent upon the needs of the project, but should commonly range from 10 to 20 percent of the installed system.

Verification Requirements

A good quality groundwater instrumentation system should have a method for verifying the accuracy of the measurements. For pressure and permeability measurements this means that response testing of the entire measurement system must be possible. This would include testing of the transducer, leads, and readout as well as testing of the degree of connection of the interior of the piezometer tip to the water in the geologic formations outside. In water quality sampling 'verification' means that one can demonstrate that the drilling fluids have been removed and that repeated samples can be taken to check the results of anomalous laboratory analyses.

Redundant data from adjacent piezometer ports can help to verify results. Hence, verification can also mean having sufficient piezometer ports so that it can be shown that an adequate number of measurements have been made. Again, it is apparent that multiple measurements in the same location can help solve the verification requirement but only if each measurement itself can be independently checked.

Documentation of the Geology and Hydrology

The groundwater measurements, in most cases, must be closely tied to the geologic conditions encountered in the drill holes. This usually means that the geology of the instrumentation drill holes must be well documented by drill core, geophysical wireline logging or both. This type of documentation can be almost a necessity to enable the seals along the piezometer casing to be placed in the most advantageous locations. When deciding upon the location of piezometer ports and seals, it is particularly helpful if the distribution of the piezometric pressures and the distribution of permeability in the drill hole is known as soon as the drilling is completed and before the permanent piezometer casing is placed in the drill hole. This can be done by single or double-packer injection tests made at intervals during or following drilling and presented as in Figure 8.

When one accepts the necessity for documentation of the geology and hydrology of the instrumentation drill holes, it becomes apparent that a significant advantage can result from increasing the number of piezometers in a single drill hole and thereby reducing the number of the more costly cored and logged drill holes.

Sealing Requirements

Groundwater measurements and sampling can suffer greatly if the seals are not properly made above each piezometer tip and/or between each piezometer port. Seals can be difficult to place in caving hole conditions and where flows can develop between different parts of a drill hole. Seals are made by using bentonite, settable grouts, or solid or inflatable packers. Inflatable packers can be expanded with air, water, or grout mixtures. When flowing conditions are encountered, inflatable packers are usually the minimum treatment required. In the typical drill hole the water pressure distribution is seldom hydrostatic; thus, there is almost always the possibility of flows occurring within the drill hole which are unknown to the surface crew. Hence, inflatable packers can provide appreciable assurance that the piezometer tips or ports are properly sealed.

Where water sampling is undertaken, it can be important that chemically active sealing materials such as bentonite and cement grout do not contact the sampling waters since they could have a significant and irreversible effect on the quality of the sampled waters. Unlike the other items noted in this section of the paper, sealing can become more difficult when the number of piezometers or piezometer ports installed in a single drill hole is increased because this also increases the number of seals required. With all but the valved piezometers, the complexity of each seal increases directly with the number of piezometers placed in a single drill hole.

In conclusion, it is apparent that with all these groundwater instrumentation considerations, except sealing, there is a significant advantage in placing an increased number of piezometers in single drill holes (i.e., multiple piezometer installations). In the matter of sealing the problem is made appreciably more difficult for multiple installations of all types of piezometers discussed except for the valved piezometers. Therefore, it is worthwhile examining multiple piezometer installations in more detail.

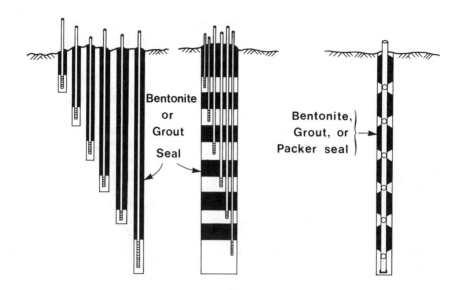

<u>a.</u> Nest of single
standpipe piezometers

<u>b.</u> Single drillhole
with conventional
multiple piezometer
completion

<u>c.</u> Single drillhole
with multiple
valved piezometer
(Westbay's
MP System)

Figure 10. Comparison of multiple piezometer
installations.

MULTIPLE PIEZOMETER INSTALLATIONS

The technical need for multiple piezometer installations
has been discussed but practical considerations, costs,
and scheduling have not received sufficient attention.

Practical Considerations

Figure 10 shows a comparison of three types of multiple
piezometers: a) a nest of several standpipe piezometers
placed in individual drill holes, b) conventional multiple
piezometers installed in one drill hole, and c) a single
drill hole with multiple piezometers of the valved type
(the new Westbay MP System).

A visual comparison of the relative complexity of the
three systems suggests some of the advantages of the valved

type of piezometers for multiple completions. The nest of single position standpipe piezometers can be installed but it is usually time-consuming and costly, even if the successive drill holes did not influence the measurements made in those piezometers placed first. The installation of the conventional multiple piezometer shown in Figure 10b would be a technical challenge even to an experienced field crew. In such types of installations the chances of losing the drill hole and some of the piezometers increases directly with the number of completions attempted. Also, as the number of piezometers increases, it becomes more difficult to place an adequate seal between the maze of tubes, casings or wires within the drill hole. The sealing problems tend to increase geometrically with the number of piezometers attempted. Figures 10a and 10b also illustrate the severe problems that can result when one is confronted with a multitude of similar appearing pipes or wires at the ground surface. If the individual casings or leads are not permanently and correctly labelled, then the best of measurements cannot overcome the error introduced by reading the wrong piezometer tip.

With the valved multiple piezometer installations, such as illustrated in Figure 10c, there is almost no practical limit to the number of piezometer ports that can be installed in a single drill hole. This is achieved because no wires or tubes are required to join each port to the surface. Currently, piezometer ports can be installed as close as 1 foot apart, although it is most convenient to install them at spacings of 5 feet. The plastic casing has been installed to depths of 1000 feet and should be suitable in drill holes extending 2000 to 4000 feet in good quality rock. With valved piezometers 20 piezometer ports can be placed in a 100-foot drill hole or 200 piezometer ports can be placed in a 1000-foot drill hole. Drill holes may be vertical, inclined or horizontal.

Cost and Scheduling Considerations

It is worth reviewing briefly the cost and scheduling considerations which should be taken into account in comparing alternative groundwater instrumentation systems. Estimates of costs and schedules are summarized on Table I. This table compares the three types of multiple piezometer installations shown on Figure 10.

For each of the three types of multiple piezometer installation reviewed, three different numbers of piezometer

Table 1. Comparative summary of costs and scheduling for multiple piezometer installations.

	One Piezometer per drill hole	Three Piezometers per drill hole	Multiple Valved Piezometers per drill hole (Westbay)

	Units	Units	Units
3 Piezometer Installation			
Drill hole costs	2	1	1*
Installation labor	3	1.5-2.0	1
Installation equipment	0.3	0.2	1
Material costs	0.5	0.3	1
Overhead costs	3	2	1
Drill hole protection costs	3	1	1
Schedule Time	3	2	1
10 Piezometer Installation			
Drill hole costs	5.5	3.3	1
Installation labor	8	5	1.1
Installation equipment	0.8	0.5	1.1
Material costs	2	1	1.5
Overhead costs	8	5	1.1
Drill hole protection costs	10	3.3	1
Schedule Time	8	5	1.1
20 Piezometer Installation			
Drill hole costs	10.5	7	1
Installation labor	15	10	1.2
Installation equipment	3	1	1.2
Material costs	4	2	3
Overhead costs	15	10	1.2
Drill hole protection costs	20	7	1
Schedule Time	15	10	1.2

* Includes no allowance for using smaller diameter drill holes.

nests are considered: a) a three piezometer installation, b) a ten piezometer installation, and c) a twenty piezometer installation.

The costs included are for the drill hole, installation labor, installation equipment, materials, overhead and drill hole protection. The schedule time required for each installation is also indicated.

Drill hole costs include all on-site drilling operations as a function of total footage of the drill hole. Installation labor costs are considered to be directly related to the schedule time. Installation equipment costs attempt to account for the cost of rented installation equipment such as grout or water pumps and piezometer readout and sampling equipment. These costs can vary considerably with project requirements. Material costs are the costs of materials placed in the drill hole--usually casing, couplings, piezometer tips, filter sand and sealing materials. Overhead costs are assumed to be directly related to schedule time. Drill hole protection costs will vary directly with the number of drill holes. These latter costs can vary from fifty dollars per drill hole to several thousand dollars or more for winter protection or for reinforced structures in a critical operation area. The schedule time is the total elapsed time from start to finish of the field installation and assumes an increase in efficiency for placing larger numbers of piezometers in single drill holes and a decrease in efficiency for a larger number of conventional piezometers in a single drill hole. On Table I the costs and times are given in terms of units rather than actual dollars or days.

The principal reason for preparing Table I is to show that the material costs tend to be a smaller fraction of the total costs than is commonly assumed. This is true for a small number of piezometers per drill hole, and material costs become an even smaller fraction of total costs as the number of piezometers per drill hole increases.

Perhaps the most significant item on Table I is the comparison of schedule times. Installation of a single piezometer in three separate drill holes is estimated to take three times as long as the installation of three piezometers in one drill hole. Thus, if the valved piezometer installation took one day, then installation of a nest of piezometers would take three days. However, in a real project these figures can be one month and three months, respectively. When large numbers of piezometers are installed, the schedule times can differ by factors of six to ten, or one month versus six to ten months for the cases noted. Thus, the total cost of the installation and the scheduling favor the valved type of multiple piezometer installation.

CONCLUSIONS

The scope of groundwater instrumentation in mining projects is currently expanding rapidly for both mineral exploration and the assessment of water quality for environmental monitoring.

A review of moderately simple single and multiple aquifer situations suggests that the least number of piezometers required for minimum coverage of water pressure distributions is 2n + 1m. For adequate coverage the number is 4n + 2m, where n is the number of aquifers present of appreciable thickness and m is the number of aquitards (confining beds) present below the groundwater table. Thus, when two aquifers and three confining beds are present, fourteen piezometers would be considered adequate coverage. Such geologic field conditions are not unusual but few current piezometer installations have this density. Where water quality monitoring is undertaken, much higher densities may be required for adequate coverage. Where settlement or consolidation of soft sediments is of interest, then additional piezometers should be placed in the compressible aquitard layers.

There are numerous reasons, both technical and practical, for favoring multiple piezometer installations. These include costs, scheduling, surface protection, formation damage, three-dimensional sampling, redundancy, verification, and documentation requirements. All of these favor multiple installations. Only sealing requirements are potentially more difficult with multiple installations. However, the sealing of multiple installations of valved piezometers is essentially no more difficult than sealing a single piezometer tip.

Different types of single position piezometers have been examined. These include open, closed and combined open/ closed or valved types of piezometers. Each has its advantages and disadvantages. However, in multiple instal- lations in the same drill hole, the valved type of piezometer

is clearly superior, particularly as the number of piezometers per drill hole increases. In the past the cost and
scheduling requirements for conventional groundwater systems
strongly discouraged the use of dense multiple piezometer
installations even when they were required for technical
purposes. However, there are no particularly large increases
in costs or the scheduling time required for the valved type
of multiple piezometer. It is now possible to install
groundwater monitoring systems with the piezometer density
that is technically required.

Valved piezometers also permit the installation of a
high density of water quality sampling points and can be
combined in such a way that each sampling point can be
decontaminated prior to sampling by using sliding valves
called "Pumping Ports." Valved piezometers have undergone
field trials for the past year and have been installed in
small-diameter drill holes to depths of 1000 feet with as
many as twelve piezometer ports. Much deeper depths and
much higher sampling densities are possible.

REFERENCES

1. Casagrande, A., 1949, Soil mechanics in the design and
construction of the Logan Airport, Jour. Boston Soc. of
Civil Engineers, Vol. 36, No. 2. Reprinted in Contributions
to Soil Mechanics 1949-1953, pp. 176-205, Boston Soc. of
Civil Engineers, Boston, 1953.

2. Cording, E.J. et al, 1975, Methods for Geotechnical
Observations and Instrumentation in Tunneling, Vols. 1 & 2,
Nat. Science Foundation Research Grant GI-33644X, UILU-ENG
75-2022. Nat. Technical Inf. Service, Springfield, Va.
22161, 566 p.

3. Schmidt, B. and C.J. Dunnicliff et al, 1974, Construction
Monitoring of Soft Ground Rapid Transit Tunnels, Vols. I &
II: A Definition of Needs and Potential Developments, U.S.
Dept. of Transportation, Report No. UMTA-MA-06-0025-74-13,
Rail Program Branch of Urban Mass Transp. Admin., Office
Inf. Service, Springrield, Va. 22161, Report PB 241 536 and
PB 241 537.

4. Hanna, T.H., 1973, Foundation Instumentation, especially Chapter 3 on Pore Water Pressure Measurement, pp. 69-121, Trans Tech. Publications, 21330 Center Ridge Road, Cleveland, Ohio 44116, 372 p.

5. Patton, F.D. and J.D. McFarlane, 1978, Geotechnical Monitoring of Groundwater Conditions, Paper presented at A.S.C.E. Conf., Chicago, October 16-20, 1978, 18 p. plus figures.

6. McCall, J.L. and C.L. McAnear, 1971, Instrumentation of Earth and Rock-Fill Dams, Groundwater and Pore Pressure Observations, Engineers Manual EM 1110-2-1908, Part 1, Dept. of the Army, Corps of Engineers, Washington, D.C. 20314.

7. U.S. Bureau of Reclamation, 1974, Earth Manual, 2nd Ed., Engineering and Research Center, P.O. Box 25007, Denver Federal Center, Denver, Co. 80225, 810 p.

8. Terzaghi, K.T. and R.B. Peck, 1967, Soil Mechanics in Engineering Practice, 2nd Ed., John Wiley and Sons, New York, especially pp. 660-673.

9. Cooper, H.H., Jr., J.D. Bredehoft and S.S. Papadopulos, 1967, Response of a finite diameter well to an instantaneous charge of water, Water Resources Research, Vol. 3, pp. 263-269.

10. Papadopulos, S., J.D. Bredehoft and H.H. Cooper, 1973, On the analysis of 'slug test' data, Water Resources Research, Vol. 9, pp. 1087-1089.

11. Meneley, W.A., 1978, Piezometric/Permeability Profiler, Execution and Interpretation of Field Tests. Consultant Report available from Westbay Instruments Ltd., #1B, 265-25th Street, West Vancouver, B.C., Canada, V7V 4H9, 24 p.

12. Dunnicliff, C.J., 1979, Measurement of Pore Pressure, Notes from Short Course on Field Instrumentation of Soil and Rock, Extension Division, University of Missouri-Rolla.

6

Evaluation and Control of Ground-Water Quality in the Rocky Mountain Area

by Jim V. Rouse,
Vice President and General Manager,
Envirologic Systems, Inc.,
Denver, Colorado, USA

INTRODUCTION

In these days of increasing environmental and regulatory control, the evaluation of natural and affected ground-water quality and the control of the generation, movement, and discharge of pollutants is assuming ever-increasing importance in the development and operation of mineral resource recovery projects. Such evaluation and control is especially critical in areas of diverse geology and mineralization such as the Rocky Mountain mining districts. In the following discussion, specific techniques of ground-water quality evaluation are described, with examples of results of previous evaluations, and a broad outline of ground-water quality control measures is presented.

GROUND WATER QUALITY EVALUATION

The purposes of ground-water quality evaluations are as varied as the geologic conditions. Unfortunately, some evaluations are conducted merely to comply with regulatory requirements, and are not designed to meet actual operational needs. It is true that many regulatory requirements are imposed by existing regulations such as the New Mexico Environmental Improvement Division ground water protection regulations. Additional stringent requirements will be imposed by the Environmental Protection Agency's regulations, including those recently proposed under the authority of the Resource Conservation and Recovery Act for solid waste disposal sites (Federal Register, February 6, 1978) and for hazardous waste disposal sites (Federal Register, December 18, 1978), and under the Underground Injection Control Program of the Safe Drinking Water Act (Federal Register, April 20, 1979) which defines sand backfill operations as underground injection of waste.

There is a need to recognize and document naturally-occurring ground water pollution in areas of mineralization, to forestall imposition of requirements for remedial measures to improve on nature. Such evaluations to document natural conditions should be conducted under custody procedures to assure the admittance of the data into possible future hearings or litigation.

Finally, there is a growing recognition that proper ground-water quality evaluations can be a valuable operational tool, especially in mining techniques such as in-situ and heap leaching.

Since there is a clear, demonstrable, and expanding need for ground-water quality evaluation programs, it is important to factor the program into overall project development plans. Many times, significant time and cost savings could be realized by combining environmental drilling requirements with ongoing exploration drilling requirements. All too often, exploration drilling is completed, followed by separate drilling for environmental assessment. The solution is to involve the environmental personnel early in the exploration program. Much valuable environmental data can be collected at little additional cost during the deposit delineation phase, and exploratory holes converted to use as monitoring facilities.

Additional costs savings can be achieved by most efficient spatial layout of the monitoring network. The Scientific Method should be applied to the extent of the development of a hypothesis of effects to be monitored, followed by the development of a monitoring program designed to most efficiently monitor such effects. For example, a waste storage pond would be expected to impose a mound of contaminated ground water on the regional ground-water body, with waste movement radially out from the pond and most rapid movement in the down-gradient direction. Three or four radial lines of monitor wells would provide much more information on the effect of the source on the ground-water resource than the normal system of a single concentric ring of wells. In an evaluation of waste movement from an Idaho tailings pond, the radial movement concept was merged with a need to document the effect of discrete subsurface gravel channels, by varying the distance from the pond to the observation wells in a "picket fence" of wells around the pond. The density of monitor wells was varied in accord with observed ground-water discharge (Rouse, March 1977).

There is an increasing appreciation of the three-dimensional nature of ground-water flow. Study of a ground-water flow net will demonstrate that significant differences in head can occur, even in isotrophic media, in the recharge and discharge portions of a ground-water flow regime. Often, mines serve as ground-water discharge points, while tailings ponds, often located in discharge points, serve as local sources of ground-water recharge. Therefore a ground-water monitoring program should provide data on the three-dimensional ground-water pressure and quality gradients. This can be achieved by multiple completion wells such as described by Pickens, et.al. (September-October 1978) or by nested ground-water monitoring wells. An evaluation of local conditions will be required to establish the most cost-effective method. Drilling techniques should be selected to minimize contamination and provide the most representative data.

Once the ground-water evaluation network is designed and installed, care must be exercised to assure that the samples are collected, preserved, and analyzed to provide data representative of the formation fluid and documenting the parameters of concern. Analytical costs for ground-water monitoring can be rather substantial, frequently in the range of $200 to $500 per sample. It is not economically justifiable to cut corners in the collection of the sample. This is especially true in view of the fines and possible jail sentences which can be imposed for the presentation of false data to the regulatory agencies.

All too often, ground-water samples are collected by lowering a bailer into the standing water in an observation well. When considered in view of variables such as sulfate reduction, sulfide oxidation, denitrification, surface inflow, bacterial contamination, casing reaction, and the velocity of ground-water movement, it is obvious that a bailer sample represents little but the bottle of water sent to the analytical laboratory.

The next refinement is to pump or bail some finite quantity of water before collection of the sample. The normal rule of thumb is to pump a ground-water monitor well to produce a volume of water equivalent to two or three times the bore volume; however, like all rules of thumb, this is only a first approximation. Work by Envirologics in southeastern Utah and work by Gallagher in the South Texas in-situ leach operations indicates that a much better way is to pump the monitor well until a constant value of pH and conductivity is attained. A sample of the water at this time should represent formation fluid. One well in southeast Utah that required pumpage of approximately 17,000 gallons of water before yielding a constant value of pH and conductivity.

Equipment required for adequate ground-water sample collection varies with site conditions. At the northern Idaho site previously described, ground-water was within potential suction lift of the surface, so samples were withdrawn by use of a gasoline powered centrifugal pump, by inserting a plastic intake line in the wells. Portable equipment developed for blast hole dewatering can be used for pumping of samples out of monitoring wells. The EPA research laboratory in Ada, Oklahoma has developed a design for a truck or trailer-mounted rig that includes a generator, a powered hose reel, and a submersible pump on the lower end of the hose reel, Envirologics has recently purchased such a unit for sample collection and the conduct of pump tests, and are pleased with the design concept.

Once the sample is withdrawn from the well, the problems are only beginning. As stated, the analytical support can be quite expensive. Poor sample collection and preservation renders the results even less than useless because it can give a false sense of security or a false sense of a problem that isn't there. The sampling is for trace quantities of material; for example in uranium mining, one of the parameters of greatest concern is radium-226 which is recorded in pCi/l, a unit representing 1×10^{-12} grams per liter of radium, or almost down to individual atoms of radium. Therefore sample contamination can be critical.

Most monitor wells are not developed as water wells, with the result that the produced water contains suspended sediment. Acidification of such a sample for heavy metals preservation will leach metals and radionuclides out of the solids giving an erroneous reading. Immediate field filtration prior to acidification is required for valid samples. Experience has shown that addition of the unpreserved filtered water to the sample bottle will result in an ion exchange taking place within the bottle wall, resulting in loss of much of the material. It is recommended that the preservative be added to the bottle first, followed by the filtered sample, thereby avoiding some of the ion exchange problem.

Unfortunately development of many resource recovery projects will involve various hearings and, all too often, litigation. For this reason, it is recommended all the sampling be done under custody procedures so that the data will be hearing and/or court admissible. This requires development of a record of the collection, transportation, and analysis of the sample. Envirologics has adopted an EPA custody procedure, so that they would have a hard time objecting to the custody procedure used.

GROUND-WATER QUALITY CONTROL

After a properly designed and operated ground-water evaluation program is active, thought can be applied to use of ground-water quality control measures to prevent quality degradation or to restore the quality of waters.

Ground-water quality control measures can be classified under the broad headings of recharge control, discharge control, and treatment; the latter of which should be avoided whenever possible.

The idea behind recharge control is to prevent the leaching and movement of contaminants by segregation of contaminants and transportation water. This can take the form of construction of an impervious channel for streams crossing subsidence areas or fracture zones, to prevent infiltration leaching soluble minerals from old workings. It can take the form of surface grading and sealing of the upper surface of inactive tailings ponds or waste dumps, to prevent infiltration of precipitation into the dump and subsequent transport of sulfide oxidation products. It frequently takes the form of vegetative transpiration, where growth of vegetation on tailings ponds or waste dumps is used for erosion prevention and also enchances the evapotranspiration of infiltrated water.

During a study of pollution problems in the Grants Mineral Belt of New Mexico (EPA Region VI, September 1975) it was observed that mine water entering the mines through long holes was at concentrations of less than 10 pCi/l, but that, after flowing along the haulage drifts and contacting oxidized ore, the water in the mine sumps was at concentrations of up to 250 pCi/l before discharge. Since it is much easier to treat from 10 pCi/l to 3 pCi/l than from 250 pCi/l to 3 pCi/l, the concept of recharge prevention could be applied by the installation of pipe transport systems to eliminate leaching, or at least by "housekeeping" measures to minimize contact between mine water and ore solids.

Discharge control measures are designed to prevent the movement of contaminated waters into surface or ground water. Such measures can take the form of pond and pit liners. In the case of mine drainage, it can take the form of plugs in mine portals or drifts. This has been widely used in eastern coal mines, but must be used with caution in western hard-rock mines, where excessive water heads could result in danger of seal failures. Discharge control in western mines frequently takes the form of grouting of water-filled fractures. The suggestion has been made that opportunities exist for freezing of inactive workings in certain Rocky Mountain mining districts.

In the case of tailings ponds, discharge control measures may take the form of the provision of an absorption media such as peat or clay, to absorb and hold pollutants contained in seepage through the pond bottom. For example, natural peat deposits left at the bottom of a tailings pond have a substantial capacity to sorb metals and radionuclides from seepage. Similarly, the addition of a clay liner at the bottom of a tailings pond will not only reduce water loss through seepage, but will also improve the quality of the water which does seep, as a result of ion exchange between the clay and the seepage.

In general, treatment systems should be avoided wherever possible, since dependence on treatment can result in a perpetual cost, with significant water quality impacts upon cessation. The only recommended use of treatment is cases such as mill discharge where the water quality problem will cease once the project is completed. In the case of acid mine drainage in the San

Juan Mountains, Ross (September 1973) examined the possibility of producing a salable smelter feed by sequential treatment of acid mine drainage by neutralization and sulfide precipitation.

As shown, ground-water evaluation and control measures need not be expensive. In these days of increasingly stringent environmental controls, the success of a mineral recovery project may well depend on the innovative application of ground-water evaluation and control measures. Failure to apply such innovative approaches may result in the forced application of expensive, inflexible approaches by regulatory agencies.

REFERENCES

1. Environmental Protection Agency, Region VI, September 1975, "Water Quality Impacts of Uranium Mining and Milling Activities in the Grants Mineral Belt, New Mexico." EPA 906/9-75-002, Dallas, Texas.

2. Pickens, J.F., J.A. Cherry, G.E. Grisak, W.F. Merritt, and B.A. Risto, September-October 1978, "A Multilevel Device for Ground-Water Sampling and Piezometric Monitoring", Ground-Water Vol. 16, No. 5, p. 322-327.

3. Rouse, Jim V., March 1977, "Geohydrologic Conditions in the Vicinity of Bunker Hill Company Waste-Disposal Facilities" U.S.E.P.A. National Enforcement Investigation Center, EPA-330/2-77-006, Denver, Colorado 46 p.

4. Ross, Lawrence W., September 1973, "Removal of Heavy Metals from Mine Drainage by Precipitation", EPA-670/2-73-080, Environmental Protection Agency, Washington, DC 64 p.

7

Effect of Longwall Mining on Ground Permeability and Subsurface Drainage

by B. N. Whittaker, R. N. Singh, and C. J. Neate,
Department of Mining Engineering,
University of Nottingham,
Nottingham, United Kingdom

SUMMARY

The paper briefly reviews mining subsidence characteristics associated with longwall mining and discusses the implications of subsidence on surface and subsurface drainage pattern changes. Both surface subsidence and subsurface subsidence aspects are discussed. Investigations are described into ground permeability changes between the surface and the mining horizon. Instrumentation and investigation techniques to study ground permeability changes are described and the results of United Kingdom studies presented and discussed.

LONGWALL MINING SUBSIDENCE

Longwall extraction involving caving of the roof strata is the prevalent underground method in European Coalfields. The caving of the roof strata behind the longwall extraction produces controlled subsidence of the ground between the mining horizon and the surface. The amount of subsidence occurring at the surface can be predicted from knowledge of the principal mining dimensions namely depth below surface, width of longwall and extracted seam height together with knowledge of the geological conditions. The prediction method used in British Coalfields is based on an empirical design procedure established over several years from precise levelling observations in different mining conditions covering a depth range of 100 to 1000 metres below the surface (1). It applies entirely to longwall mining type of extractions and allows accurate predictions to be made of anticipated subsidence both in extent and amplitude in addition to the calculation of surface ground strain and tilt. An example of the general characteristics of a surface subsidence trough above a longwall mining extraction is shown in Figure 1.

The creation of a subsidence trough at the surface can itself introduce a change in surface drainage pattern especially for thick extractions at relatively shallow depths. Rib pillars are frequently left between successive longwall extractions in order to reduce surface subsidence and the magnitude of surface ground strains. The method of using pre-designed ratios of width of longwall to width of rib pillar between faces has been employed over many years with considerable success in European Coalfields as a means of controlling subsidence in areas where surface drainage is critical, for example under low-lying agricultural land close to a major tidal river, and under major inland water courses such as rivers and canals.

LONGWALL SUBSIDENCE AND SUBSURFACE DRAINAGE ASPECTS

If the surface ground strains, especially in the tensile zone, are sufficiently high and the surface rocks brittle then cracking and opening of fissures can occur which can affect surface and subsurface drainage patterns. It is generally thought that the depth below surface of such subsidence cracks which have a direct connection with the surface, is limited in extent and does not affect major surface water bodies such as the sea or large lakes but small ponds have been known to be drained by such subsidence cracks opening at the

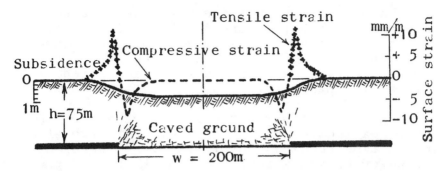

Figure 1. General characteristics of subsidence trough and surface ground strain due to longwall mining of coal seam in shallow conditions. (The subsidence parameters have been calculated using the National Coal Board Subsidence Engineer's Handbook method).

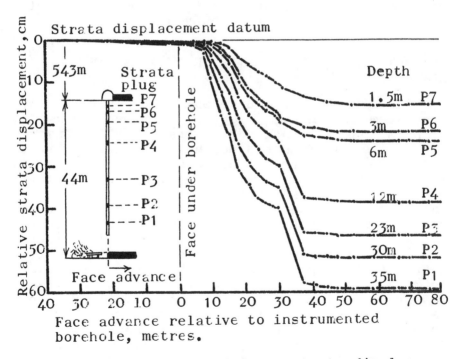

Figure 2. Development of inter-strata displacements in an instrumented borehole located in the path of an approaching longwall extraction. (The illustration has been taken from King, Whittaker and Batchelor (1972)).

pond's base although this greatly depends upon the type of geological formations. The likelihood of cracks appearing at the surface greatly decreases with deeper workings since the ground strain effects are more widely spread with a significant reduction in their magnitude.

The caving process of the roof beds behind the longwall extraction creates a zone of broken strata which in time becomes consolidated. Consequently the zone of broken strata immediately behind the longwall face is one which is likely to encourage flow of water towards the working horizon, providing an aquifer (or other source of water) is within the zone of influence. This is vitally important to the safe working and success of all underground mining operations. The present investigation has been directed towards examining the zone of influence of mining operations on changes in ground permeability and potential subsurface drainage pattern changes.

CHARACTERISTICS OF SUBSIDENCE IN PROXIMITY OF EXTRACTION HORIZON

Figure 2 shows the development of inter-strata displacements in the immediate roof beds overlying a longwall face 587 metres below the surface (2). The instrumented borehole was drilled vertically downwards from a horizon 44 metres above the longwall which was to subsequently undermine the borehole and had seven strain wires P1 to P7 anchored at the depths shown in Figure 2. The borehole was located centrally within the path of the approaching 200 metres wide longwall extraction. The strata displacements are relative to a datum at the borehole mouth, that is a horizon 44 metres above the longwall extraction. The most important feature of the results shown in Figure 2 is the zone of major strata movement recorded between 10 to 40 metres behind the longwall face. Also of importance is the progressive decrease in the amplitude of relative vertical strata displacements from the mining horizon. The results also show a progressive change in consolidation from the working horizon. It was viewed important to investigate the influence of such subsidence on

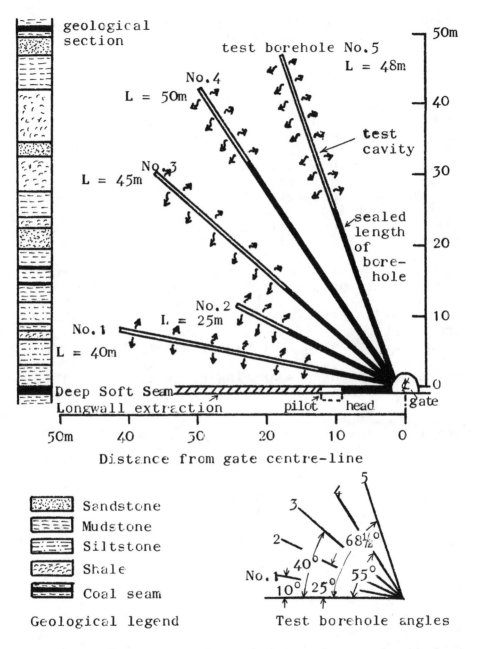

geological section

50m

test borehole No.5
L = 48m

No.4
L = 50m

test cavity

No.3
L = 45m

sealed
length
of
bore-
hole

No.2
L = 25m

No.1
L = 40m

Deep Soft Seam
Longwall extraction   pilot   head

gate

40

30

20

10

0

50m   40   30   20   10   0

Distance from gate centre-line

Sandstone
Mudstone
Siltstone
Shale
Coal seam

Geological legend

Test borehole angles

No.1   10°   25°   40°   55°   68½°

Figure 3. Illustrating positions of test boreholes
at experimental site in Deep Soft Seam, East
Midlands Coalfield and their location in relation
to the Longwall extraction.

changes in permeability of the strata within this
zone close to the working longwall face.

RESEARCH OBJECTIVES

The main objective of this work was to investigate the zones of increased permeability resulting
from undermining by a longwall extraction.
Within this investigation also came the need to
establish the base permeability of the rock types
overlying the longwall extraction and to ascertain
the change in permeability resulting from progressive undermining. It was firstly required to design a scheme of instrumentation which permitted
these changes to be investigated. Having established the investigation technique it was a major
aim to study how the subsidence resulting from
longwall mining affected the strata permeability.

Two major sites were selected for the study.
The first permitted the strata permeability change
to be investigated in close proximity to the mining horizon, whilst the second concentrated on
permeability changes arising close to the surface
and well within the critical area of extraction.

STRATA PERMEABILITY CHANGES IN PROXIMITY OF THE
LONGWALL FACE

The site chosen for the investigation was in
the East Midlands Coalfield, in the Deep Soft
Seam.   The retreating longwall face was 220 metres
long and had an extracted seam height of 0.81metre
whilst the depth below surface was 628 metres.

Figure 3 shows the general location of the test
boreholes in relation to S34's face.   The gate
from which the boreholes were drilled had been
formed previously for the extraction of S32's
longwall advancing face, immediately to the right
of S 34's, see Figures 3 and 4.   A small pillar
of coal was left between the gate and the pilot
heading as shown in Figure 4.

A section of the roof strata above S34's face
is shown in Figure 3 and this consists mainly of

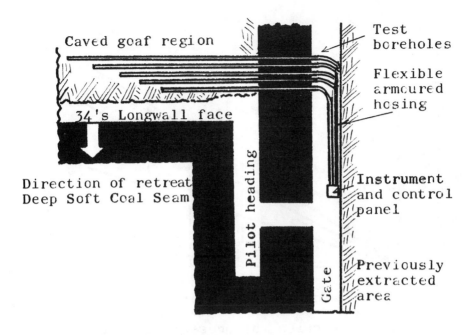

Figure 4. Showing location of test boreholes and instrumentation/test panel

shale, siltstone, mudstone and sandstone within the 50 metres above the Deep Soft Coal Seam. Figure 3 also shows the positioning of the test boreholes and their respective lengths.

The test boreholes were drilled 60 millimetres diameter. The first borehole was completed when the face was still 55 metres from the borehole plane. The five boreholes were drilled in the same vertical plane. Each test cavity was formed by pumping cement grout into the borehole mouth; cement was pumped against an increasing head until cement began to return via a 19 millimetre diameter breather tube. A second tube had also been placed in position leading to 3 metres beyond the end of the breather tube and was to be used later for pressure testing of the test cavity. A flexible seal was positioned between the end of the breather tube and the test cavity to prevent any tendency for cement grout to continue filling the borehole beyond the end of the breather tube.

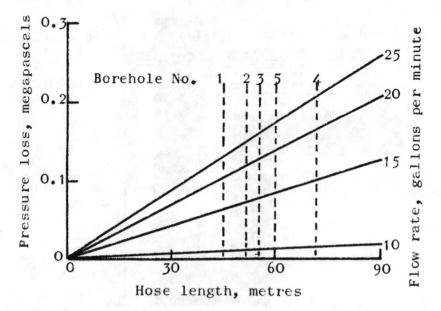

Figure 5. Correction for pressure loss in connecting hosing (Deep Soft test station)

Figure 4 shows a general layout of the test boreholes in relation to the face-end. Flexible armoured hosing connected each borehole mouth to the instrumentation panel which was conveniently located for access some distance outbye of the face line.

STRATA PERMEABILITY TESTING PROCEDURE

Each borehole was pressure tested using water when the face was at different positions in relation to test boreholes. The pressure testing equipment consisted of an assembly similar to that shown in Figure 12. The inlet water pressure was 6.3 megapascals and this was reduced by an in-line reducing valve. Due account was taken of the pressure loss resulting from hydraulic connections and Figure 5 shows the nonogram for this correction for a given flow rate and length

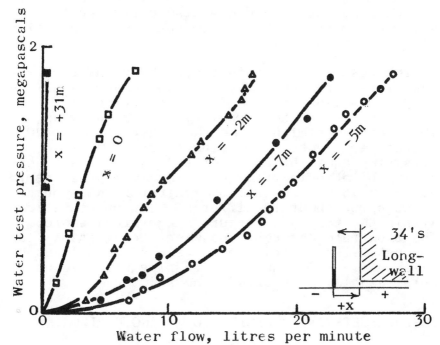

Figure 6. Borehole No.3 flow characteristics

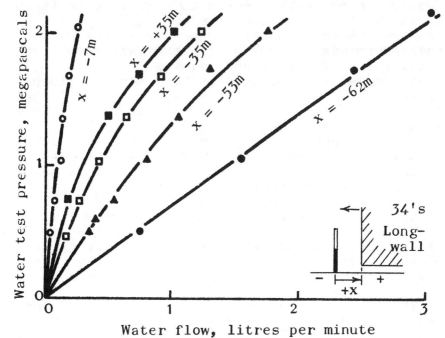

Figure 7. Borehole No.5 flow characteristics.

of hose. Static head was also corrected for by using the vertical height to the central position of the test cavity.

The test procedure involved observing the flow rate for increments of testing pressure usually up to 2 - 3 megapascals. Two flow meters were incorporated in the circuitry, one reading up to 100 litres per minute and the other up to to 20 litres per minute. Testing firstly involved attaining equilibrium saturation within each test cavity by allowing flow under maximum pressure for at least 15 minutes and thereafter flow as observed at up to about 12 different test pressure levels within the testing pressure range given above. The flow rate was observed when steady state flow was established during each test and usually took less than 2 - 3 minutes. Testing all five boreholes usually took about 3 hours.

TEST RESULTS IN PROXIMITY TO MINING HORIZON

Figures 6 and 7 show typical test results for two of the boreholes tested at different positions of longwall face advance. The results presented in Figure 6 show the flow characteristics before the ground was undermined together with test data showing the effect of undermining. The flow characteristics indicate the formation of widening cracks along the test cavity as the longwall face gradually undermined the test section. Figure 7 shows a test section which was only slightly affected by undermining; these results indicate that the ground became more impermeable before moving to a phase of increased permeability some distance after undermining. Comparing the results given in Figures 6 and 7, it is inferred that the ground associated with borehole No.3 became significantly affected by caving whilst the test section of borehole No.5 was virtually intact during undermining. The pressure-flow curve variation was due to opening and closing of minor fissures/cracks.

The degree of variation in flow in two of the test boreholes is clearly illustrated in Figures 8 and 9 which show flow rate plotted against longwall face position. In the case of Figure 8

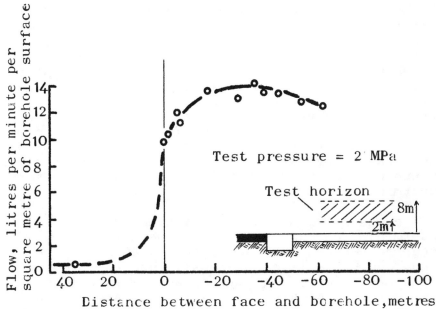

Figure 8. Relationship between flow characteristics of borehole No. 1 and face position

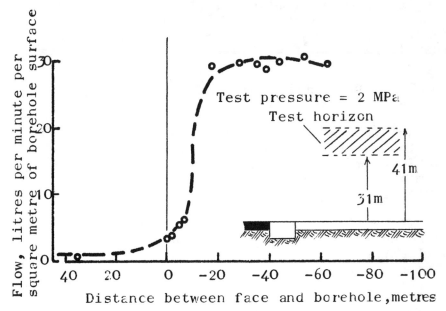

Figure 9. Relationship between flow characteristics of borehole No. 4 and face position

which shows the test horizon covering a band 2 to
8 metres above the seam, the results show that the
strata were significantly affected immediately
after undermining.   In the case of Figure 9 which
represents data from a test horizon covering 31 to
41 metres above the longwall extraction, the strata
were not greatly affected until about 15 metres
after undermining.   In the latter case, a bed of
sandstone and appreciable thickness of shale formed the strata test horizon and it appears that the
sandstone behaviour during undermining may have
accounted for the relatively high flow rate after
undermining.

    The results show that the maximum effect of
undermining on change in ground permeability
occurred between the face line and 40 metres behind, and there is a progressive upward movement
of change in permeability behind the face line.
The test results also generally indicate opening
and closing of cracks and bed separation cavities
during the undermining phase.   After 40 metres
behind the face line there is an indication of
increasing consolidation of the strata taking
place.   The results and discussion here are in
general agreement with the strata displacement
results given in Figure 2.

STRATA PERMEABILITY CHANGES CLOSE TO THE SURFACE AND ABOVE LONGWALL EXTRACTION

    The site selected for this part of the invest-
igation was located in the Yorkshire Coalfield in
the Swallow Wood Seam at Wentworth where the coal
seam is 2.1 metres thick and 54 metres below the
surface.

    Figure 10 shows the position of the instrument-
ed borehole in relation to the approaching longwall extraction (190 metres long) at the time the
borehole was drilled.

    The instrumented borehole was 96 millimetres
diameter and drilled 42.7 metres deep.   This
depth was judged to give an adequate thickness of
strata between the base of the hole and the underlying Swallow Wood Coal Seam (at 54 metres) which

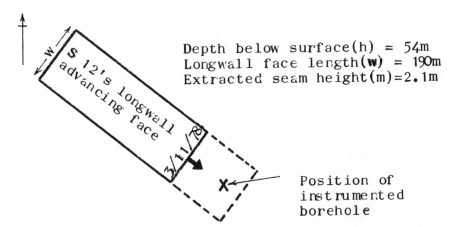

Depth below surface(h) = 54m
Longwall face length(**w**) = 190m
Extracted seam height(m)=2.1m

Position of
instrumented
borehole

Figure 10. Location of instrumented borehole in relation to longwall face position (Wentworth site)

was to be undermined by S12's longwall face. A section of the strata at the borehole is given in Figure 13 and as can be seen the beds are mainly Coal Measures formation types which are well known for their relatively high impervious properties. The thickness of cover between the borehole base and the Swallow Wood Coal Seam was further increased by the 1.4 metre thickness of cement grout seal used at the base of the borehole to secure the first strain wire.

Figure 11 shows the instrumented borehole used at the Wentworth Test Site. Four permanent resin seals were located as shown. The seal was formed by firstly lowering a fairly tight-fitting multideck platform of fibre/foam discs secured to a steel framework, and thereafter Celtite-Selfix M100 resinous injection grout pumped to rest on the upper surface of this flexible temporary seal. The general procedure involved firmly securing the flexible temporary seal in position at the desired depth by clamping the 19 millimetre diameter plastic tubes (for subsequent testing) at the surface rig. Each temporary flexible seal was located in position by special insertion rods which were uncoupled from the seal prior to pumping the M100 grout onto the temporary seal. The grout produced a seal which was about 3 metres in length and

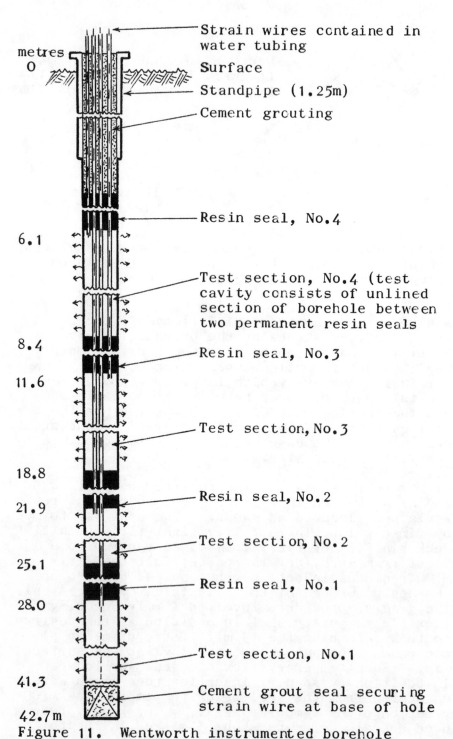

Figure 11. Wentworth instrumented borehole

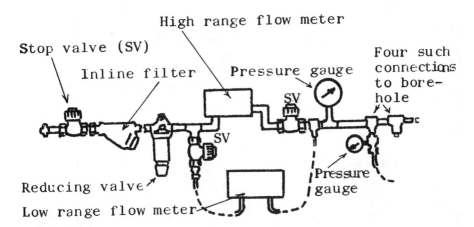

Figure 12. General hydraulic circuitry used at Wentworth instrumented borehole

proved effective in sealing different sections of a borehole which contained an increasing number of plastic tubes and was to be subsequently affected by undermining. Mechanical seals were judged to be inadequate for such geotechnical and mining conditions. Each seal was established as a separate operation and the resinous grout allowed to cure (about 2 - 3 hours) before the next seal operation was carried out. This method of providing a borehole with several sealed sections has been successfully applied in boreholes down to a depth of 70 metres and where six seals have been installed in a 100 millimetre diameter unlined hole. Strain wires were secured to the base of each resinous grout seal, and brought to the surface via the water pressure testing tube. Resin seal No.1 plastic testing tube contained two strain wires, one connecting to the base of the seal and the other to the base of the hole. The upper section of the borehole was grouted to a depth of 6.1 metres to test section cavity No.4. Each strain wire was tensioned and observations made of displacement with an extensometer.

The testing arrangement is shown in Figure 12. A rotameter was used to measure low flow rates up to 1 litre per minute. A constant test pressure of 2 bars (at the borehole mouth) was used throughout the testing programme.

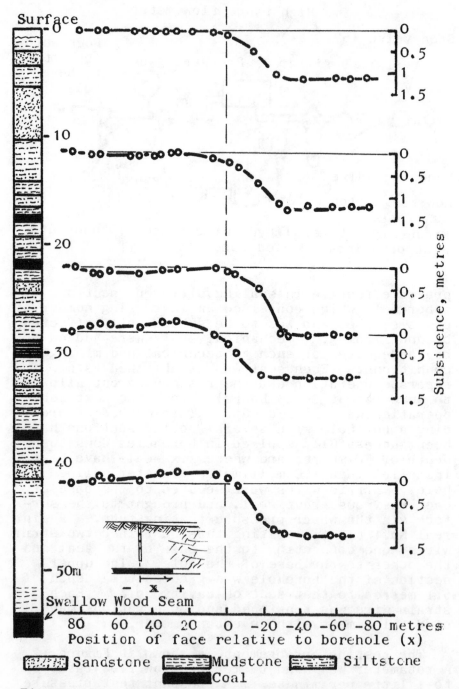

Figure 13. Surface subsidence and sub-surface subsidence characteristics, Wentworth borehole

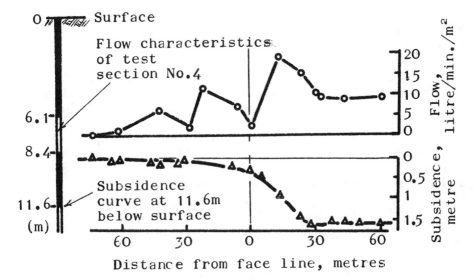

Figure 14. Flow characteristics of test section No.4 in relation to sub-surface subsidence arising from undermining, Wentworth instrumented borehole

Surface levelling was carried out to determine the progressive subsidence of the borehole mouth and also the seal positions within the borehole since strain readings relative to the borehole mouth were observed also.

TEST RESULTS IN PROXIMITY TO SURFACE

The surface subsidence curve for the borehole is shown plotted in Figure 13 together with the subsurface subsidence curves as determined using the strain wires. Some uplift of the strata ahead of the face line was recorded at the lower horizons. Subsidence showed a more marked change at the lower horizons as depicted by the more distinct step characteristic of the subsidence profile.

Figure 14 shows test results for the uppermost test section (No.4) and it demonstrates that discernible change in the flow characteristic was taking place at some 50-60 metres ahead of the face line and this increased in marked steps implying opening and closing of near-surface cracks/fissures. The flow curve settled to a consistent value at about 35 - 40 metres behind the face line.

The testing condition has been assumed to be equivalent to a constant head test and the following equations have been used for determination of in situ permeability of the strata. These equations represent Horslev's approach (3) and they have been discussed elsewhere (4) and (5) regarding application to estimation of in situ permeability of bedded and jointed rock structures.

$$k = \frac{q}{F.\,Hc} \qquad \ldots\ldots (1)$$

$$F = \frac{2\,\pi\,\ell}{\log_e(2\,m\,\ell/D)} \qquad \ldots\ldots (2)$$

combining (1) and (2)

$$k = \frac{q.\,\log_e(2\,m\,\ell/D)}{2\,\pi\,\ell.\,Hc} \qquad \ldots\ldots (3)$$

Where,
k = coefficient of permeability normal to hole
kp = coefficient of permeability parallel to hole
q = flow rate
F = shape factor of test cavity ($\ell > 4D$)
Hc = constant pressure head of water applied during test (above any original ground water value)
ℓ = length of test cavity
D = borehole diameter in test cavity
m = $(k/kp)^{0.5}$

The authors have adopted a value of $k/kp = 10^6$, this being consistent with an earlier paper by the present authors (5) and has been discussed in detail previously.

Values of in situ permeability have been determined using these equations and a detailed presentation of the results is given in Figure 15 which shows the ratio of subsequent permeability/base permeability plotted against longwall face position. These results indicate that the upper ten metres of the strata section (which contained a bed of sandstone, see Figure 13) experienced the

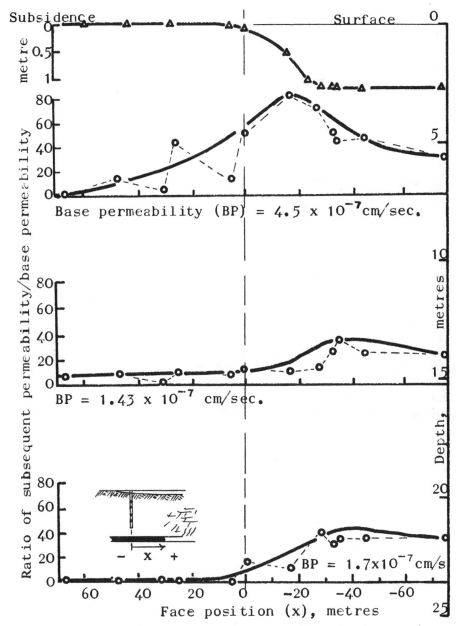

Figure 15. Illustrating comparison of change in ground permeability of strata overlying a longwall extraction (Wentworth instrumented borehole)

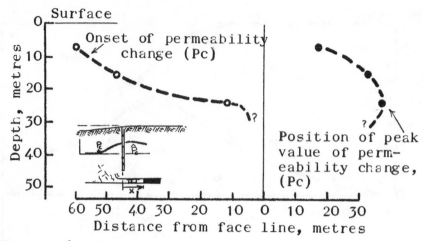

Figure 16. Position of onset and peak value of
permeability change of strata overlying a longwall
extraction due to undermining

greatest change in permeability. It is considered that the main factor responsible for this feature is the close proximity with the surface even
though sandstone was present which would have also
contributed to this degree of change. All the
test curves indicate a tendency towards decreased
change in permeability after 35 - 40 metres behind the face line.

Figure 16 has been plotted using data from
Figure 15 and it indicates that onset of permeability change occurs significantly ahead of the
face line with the upper test horizon when compared with the lower test horizons. A similar
trend is indicated with the position of the peak
value of permeability change.

GENERAL DISCUSSION OF RESULTS

The testing procedure and equipment described
in the paper proved satisfactory for investigating
ground permeability changes resulting from longwall mining operations. The instrumentation
scheme was sufficiently sensitive to monitor small
changes in permeability. The results permit the
onset of permeability change arising from mining

Table No. I

In situ strata permeability data

Site	Test section	Test section position, metres	Strata type	In situ permeability (k) centimetres per second	
				Base value	Maximum value
Deep Soft	1	2-8*	M Slt Sh	1.5×10^{-4}	1.4×10^{-3}
Deep Soft	2	8-11*	Slt M	1.1×10^{-5}	1.5×10^{-3}
Deep Soft	3	13-29*	M C Sh	1.4×10^{-4}	4.5×10^{-4}
Deep Soft	4	30-41*	Sh M Sd	5.7×10^{-6}	1.3×10^{-3}
Deep Soft	5	25-45*	M Sh Sd	5.2×10^{-6}	4.9×10^{-5}
Wentworth	1	28-41**	C M Sd Slt	1.0×10^{-9}	NA
Wentworth	2	22-25**	C M Sd Slt	1.7×10^{-7}	2.1×10^{-6}
Wentworth	3	12-19**	Slt M C	1.4×10^{-7}	6.6×10^{-6}
Wentworth	4	6-8½**	Sd	4.5×10^{-7}	2.3×10^{-5}

* measured vertically above coal seam; ** measured below surface
C = coal, M = mudstone, Sh = shale, Slt = siltstone, Sd = sandstone
NA = not available

proximity to be readily evaluated. Values of in situ permeability have been calculated for the experimental sites described in the paper, and Table I presents the base and maximum values of coefficient of permeability (k) for each of the test horizons studied.

In the case of the Deep Soft Coal Seam Experimental Site the ground was found to have a discernible degree of permeability before being disturbed by current longwall mining, see Table I. This is probably due to previous mining. The effect of current mining operations was to produce appreciable change in ground permeability especially in the test zones near to the mining horizon.

The strata tested can be described as virtually impermeable before undermining in the case of the Wentworth Site, but after undermining change in ground permeability was sufficient to promote minor flow in the case of the upper horizon but the lower horizons were not so affected. The presence of impervious beds within the strata sequence plays a major role in such mining situations.

CONCLUSIONS

1. The instrumentation and testing procedure proved successful for studying ground permeability change resulting from undermining by a longwall extraction.

2. The main zone of appreciable change in in situ permeability was found to lie between the face line and 40 metres behind the face.

3. Appreciable in situ permeability change was observed to occur up to 40 metres above the extraction horizon.

4. Changes in ground flow properties of the strata were found to be of a stepped characteristic and this is thought to be due to opening and closing of cracks and separations.

5. Significant change in ground permeability

was observed close to the surface above a long-wall extraction in shallow mining conditions.

ACKNOWLEDGEMENTS

The authors acknowledge the generous financial and practical support given by the National Coal Board to this Project. Special thanks are due to several mining engineers, surveyors and geologists within the National Coal Board for excellent co-operation and help given to the authors during the field studies. Thanks are also due to the technical staff of the Mining Department, Nottingham University for valuable design contribution to the instrumentation used in this project.

REFERENCES

1. — Subsidence Engineers' Handbook, Production Department, National Coal Board, London, 1975.

2. King, H. J., Whittaker, B. N. and Batchelor, A. S. The Effects of Interaction in Mine Layouts, Fifth International Strata Control Conference 1972, Paper No. 17, 11 pp.

3. Horslev, M. S. Time lag and soil permeability in ground water measurements. U.S. Corps of Engineers Waterways Exp.Stn.Bulletin 36, 50pp,1951.

4. Hoek, E. and Bray, J. W. Rock slope engineering. The Institution of Mining and Metallurgy, London, 309 pp, 1974.

5. Whittaker, B. N. and Singh, R. N. Design aspects of barrier pillars against water-logged workings in coal mining operations. Symposium on Water in Mining and Underground Works, SIAMOS 1978, Granada, Spain. Vol.1, pp 675 - 692.

8

Coping with Mine Drainage Regulations

by Roy E. Williams,
Professor of Hydrogeology and Director of
the Mineral Resources Research Institute,
University of Idaho, Moscow, Idaho, USA,
Joe Baldwin,
North Dakota Water Commission,
Bismarck, North Dakota, USA,
and Dale R. Ralston,
Associate Professor of Hydrogeology,
College of Mines and Earth Resources,
University of Idaho, Moscow, Idaho, USA

ABSTRACT

As of May 1, 1979, only one set of basic regulations
govern the control of mine drainage. These regulations
are at the federal level and they stem from the passage
by Congress of the Water Pollution Control Act amendments
of 1972 (Public Law 92-500). That Act was amended further
in 1977 but the 1977 amendments did not change the basic
intent of the 1972 Act. The regulations that govern the
discharge of acid mine drainage as of July 1, 1977, are the
result of what Public Law 92-500 refers to as "The Best
Practicable Control Technology Currently Available". The
regulations and the control technologies for several categories of industries, including ore mining and dressing,
were derived from studies which produced so called "Development Documents" for the industries in each category.
Public Law 92-500 provided for enforcement by either state
or federal agencies depending on several variables. The
enforcement agency theoretically applies the effluent
guidelines limitation values to a company depending on the
category it fits into. The up-to-date status of the regulations for any industry at any time can be obtained from
a publication called "The Environment Reporter".

The Surface Mine Control and Reclamation Act of 1977 also provides for additional regulation of the mining industry. However, mine drainage from coal mines must meet the guidelines of Public Law 92-500 and the additional regulations are relatively insignificant with respect to mine drainage.

The Resource Conservation and Recovery Act of 1976 ultimately may result in some form of regulation for mine drainage, but we are of the opinion that it will be relatively insignificant compared to the effect of Public Law 92-500.

Two types of activities are involved in coping with regulations governing mine drainage. One set of activities requires a great deal of paper shuffling and filling out forms to comply with the National Pollutant Discharge Elimination System permits in order to comply with the appropriate effluent limitations guidelines under Public Law 92-500. Since the Best Practicable Control Technology Currently Available for most industrial categories consists of lime and settle, this procedure is fairly straight forward. It assumes that the company involved has elected to treat its mine drainage and meet the effluent limitation guidelines in that fashion.

The second category of activity is extremely technical in nature and considerably more challenging. It involves technological attempts to minimize the production of mine drainage, thereby eliminating or minimizing the mine drainage to be treated in order to achieve compliance with Public Law 92-500 by lime and settle. This paper deals primarily with the second category of activity. It discusses the technological approaches we use to minimize the production of mine drainage so that treatment via lime and settle can be avoided. The approach requires delineating and altering the ground water flow systems that produce the acid mine drainage.

INTRODUCTION

In October, 1972, the 92nd Congress of the United States passed the Federal Water Pollution Control Act Amendments of 1972. The purpose of the Act was to extend earlier legislation in the areas of protection and maintenance of the quality of the environment. Designated Public Law 92-500 (PL 92-500), the amendments apply to discharges from the mining, milling, and metallurgical industries by way of Sections 301, 302, and 304, under Title III - "Standards and Enforcement, Effluent Limitations". These sections state that by July 1, 1977, the best practicable control technology currently available must be applied to waste effluent, and that by July 1, 1983, the best available technology economically achievable must be applied to point source discharges.

The Effluent guidelines for Best Practicable Control Technology Currently Available for selected mining categories are as follows:

"The quantity of pollutants or pollutant properties discharged in mine drainage from mines operated to obtain copper bearing ores, lead bearing ores, zinc bearing ores, gold bearing ores, or silver bearing ores or any combination of these ores from open-pit or underground operations other than placer deposits shall not exceed the following limitations:

	Effluent Limitations	
Effluent characteristic	Maximum for any 1 day	Average of daily values for 30 consecutive days shall not exceed --
Milligrams per liter		
TSS	30	20
Cu	.30	0.150
Zn	1.5	.75
Pb	.6	.3
Hg	0.002	0.001
pH	Within the range 6.0 to 9.0	----

Permits issued to companies in these categories must comply with the guidelines except for unusual circumstances.

The mining industry historically has been a source of waste water with low pH and high concentrations of dissolved and suspended solids. In many instances this water was discharged directly into streams with no treatment to remove dissolved metals or suspended solids. With the implementation of PL 92-500, most operating mines have constructed settling ponds and installed water treatment facilities (mostly liming facilities) to meet effluent guidelines. However, some mines were abandoned or closed prior to adoption of effluent guidelines. These mines continue to discharge poor quality water to surrounding streams. In some cases they constitute field laboratories available to study the production of acid mine drainage with an eye to reducing or eliminating it at its source.

Numerous examples of this situation exist in metal mining areas of the northwestern United States. Sceva (1973) notes areas in Oregon, Idaho, and Washington where inactive mines contribute dissolved metals such as iron, manganese, copper, and zinc to nearby drainages. High concentrations of dissolved iron and aluminum pose a major water quality problem in the vicinity of Cooke City, Montana, where two inactive gold mines are located (Sonderegger and others, 1975). Poor quality water discharging from one of the mining areas drains into nearby Yellowstone National Park. Twenty-five areas in Colorado affected by acid mine drainage have discharges high in iron and sulphate as well as other trace elements (Wentz, 1974; Moran and Wentz, 1974). Abandoned mines constitute an important area of need with respect to eliminating or minimizing acid mine drainage.

ACID MINE DRAINAGE AT THE BLACKBIRD MINING DISTRICT

The Blackbird Mining District borders the Big Horn Crags Recreational Area on the south and lies east of the Central Idaho Primitive Area. The remainder of this paper discusses the production of acid water in the district as a means of illustrating a complex technological approach to coping with regulations governing the release of acid mine drainage.

Discharge high in dissolved metals and of low pH originates from the inactive Blackbird Mine, the principal mine in the district. Poor quality water discharging from the copper-cobalt mining area flows into Panther Creek, a tributary to the Salmon River which has been designated a Wild and Scenic River by the U.S. Congress. This study was conducted by University of Idaho personnel with funding from the Surface Environment and Mining program of the USDA, Forest Service. The Idaho Bureau of Mines and Geology (IBMG) provided field vehicles throughout the course of the field study. We present it here to illustrate the approach we believe necessary to minimize the production of acid mine drainage as an alternative to brute force treatment of point source discharges with lime.

Purpose and Objectives

The objective of any such study is to delineate alternatives for water quality control with respect to mine related features and to evaluate and recommend techniques to minimize water quality problems in future mining activities with minimal cost.

The specific objectives of this study were to:

i.   Determine the relationship between ground-water recharge, movement, and discharge, and acid production in underground workings and surface waste features in the Blackbird mining area.

ii. Determine the relationship between surface and ground-water quality for surface waste features and stream drainages.

iii. Determine the relative contributions of poor quality water from the various sources in the mining area by a quantitative analysis of flow and metal loads.

iv. Recommend procedures for reducing acid production from present surface and underground mining features, and recommend solutions to potential problems of acid production from future mining operations.

This study is discussed in greater detail by Baldwin, Ralston and Trexler (1978).

Description of the Blackbird Mining District

The Blackbird Mining District is located approximately 25 miles west of Salmon, Idaho, and lies within the U.S. Geological Survey's Blackbird Mountain 1:62,500 quadrangle. The mining area is drained by Blackbird and Bucktail Creeks, both tributary to Panther Creek in the Salmon River drainage. The Panther Creek drainage basin includes Blackbird Creek which drains an area of about 23 square miles and Bucktail Creek which drains an area of about 1.7 square miles. Table I presents precipitation data for the area.

Geology of the Blackbird Mining District

The geology of the Blackbird Mining District is dominated by Pre-cambrian metamorphic rocks of the Belt series (Anderson, 1947). South of the district, these impure quartzites are overlain by Tertiary age Challis Volcanic rocks while they form discordant contacts with granitic intrusive rocks contemporary with the Idaho Batholith to the north. Border facies between the metamorphic and intrusive rocks are common to the area. These metamorphic rocks have a regional scale folding system striking east-west with moderate dips to the north and east (Anderson, 1947, p. 26).

Structure

Structure in the Blackbird Mining District is dominated by several open north plunging major folds with associated drag structures. Superimposed on the large folds are smaller scale folding features of generally the same orientation. Northwest trending joint and fault systems have provided avenues for the emplacement of the ore deposits with post ore shearing contributing to the complexity of the mining situation. Cobalt and copper are the ore minerals and pyrite is associated with them.

Location and Character of the Mine

The headquarters and mill for the Blackbird Mine are located on Blackbird Creek at its confluence with Meadow Creek (Figure 1). Levels of most recent mining are located above the main complex from a main mining level at an elevation of 6850 feet to the open pit operation located at 7800 feet. Mining extends below the open pit into the Bucktail Creek drainage.

Table I   Total monthly precipitation in inches at Cobalt, Idaho, for the period January 1961 through December 1977.

	October	November	December	January	February	March	April	May	June	July	August	September	Annual
61-62				0.47	1.66E	0.49-	0.68	2.80	1.84-	1.33	0.91	0.07-	
62-63	1.42	2.04-	1.62	0.65-	2.59	0.79	3.17	1.36	5.21	0.62	0.35	1.11-	
63-64	2.61	1.69	0.73	2.54-	0.71	0.77	3.36				0.97	0.49	
64-65	0.29			2.56	0.29	0.10							
65-66	0.00-	1.03	1.01	1.44	1.39					0.00-	0.76	1.63	
66-67	0.78	0.88	0.99	1.69	0.61	1.89	3.36	0.93	2.91	1.65	0.24	1.48	17.41
67-68	2.98	0.47	0.99	0.72	1.69	0.86	1.07	1.42	2.29	1.99	3.34	2.48	20.30
68-69	0.76	3.24	1.27	2.58	0.39	0.63	1.09	0.99	2.52	1.76	0.13	0.68	16.04
69-70	0.99	0.64	1.52	2.75	0.40	1.85	1.08	1.65	3.42	1.35	0.49	2.68	18.82
70-71	1.76	2.06	1.50	3.33	1.10	1.70	3.25	2.54	1.56*	0.88	0.77	0.68	21.13
71-72	1.02	1.65	2.78	2.21	1.77	2.03	1.30	1.01	2.12	0.67	1.61	1.65	19.82
72-73	0.84	1.08	1.19	0.91	0.05	0.91	1.34	0.72	2.00	0.93	0.97	2.58	13.52
73-74	0.92	2.85	2.23	1.89E	0.83	2.89	0.59	1.63	0.43	0.74	1.45	0.18	16.63
74-75	0.75	0.87	1.17	3.26	1.02	1.18	2.65	1.88	1.65	3.30	1.80	0.32	19.85
75-76	3.20	1.32	2.80	2.20	1.61	1.24	1.83	1.56	1.77	1.07	2.00	1.90	22.50
76-77	0.33	0.34	0.29										
Mean	1.33	1.39	1.44	2.00	1.07	1.30	1.91	1.54	2.35	1.36	1.13	1.40	
No. of Months	14	13	14	13	15	13	13	12	11	12	14	12	
Percent Annual	7.3	7.6	7.9	11.0	5.9	7.1	10.5	8.5	12.9	7.5	6.2	7.7	

Mean Annual Precipitation 18.22 inches.

- missing values during month
E estimated values during month
* accumulations during month

Mine Workings and Methods

The Blackbird Mine complex consists of 12 levels, 8 portals, an open pit, 3 major waste piles and a tailings pile (rich in pyrite), a mill and concentrator, and support facilities. The principal entrance to the mine is at 6850 feet of elevation, marked on various maps as the 6850' level (Figure I). This level opens to the main yard which contains the crusher bin, shops, offices, concentrator, etc. This level extends about 9600 feet into the mountain. About 2,200,000 tons of ore have been mined above this level including 758,000 tons from the open pit mine (Davis, 1972, p. 33). No ore has been mined below this level, although there is a winze to the 6600' level. Above the 6850' level on the south side of the mountain are the 7100', 7200', 7300', and 7400' levels. The St. Joe Shaft is between the 6850' and the 7100' portals. Two portals on the northern side of the mountain are situated below the existing open pit mine. These are the 7117' and the 7265' levels. The 6850' level passes beneath these two levels and continues to the northwest some 1200 feet.

Mining in the underground portion of the mine occurred from drifts following the lenticular and tabular ore bodies. As a result, much of the rock mined in drifting was of mill grade and waste rock was reduced to a minimum. Ore bodies were removed by room and pillar methods and block caving of overhead stopes. Sand fill recovered from the coarse fraction of the milling operation was returned to the mined areas to provide support for continued mining operations or to support abandoned areas. Backfill with tailings was not practiced between the years 1960 to 1967. The movement of equipment, personnel, ore, and waste rock between different levels in the mine was conducted through vertical openings, manways, and ore passes to the main work levels. Plates IA and IB (end of paper) show cross sectional and plan views of the Blackbird Mine workings. The mining operation in the open pit area removed a large volume of rock from an extensive ore zone and created a depression of 11 acres. Waste rock from this operation was dumped into two waste piles (Figure I).

Future plans are uncertain but the mine probably would be reopened if the acid mine drainage problem can be resolved and compliance with PL 92-500 achieved economically.

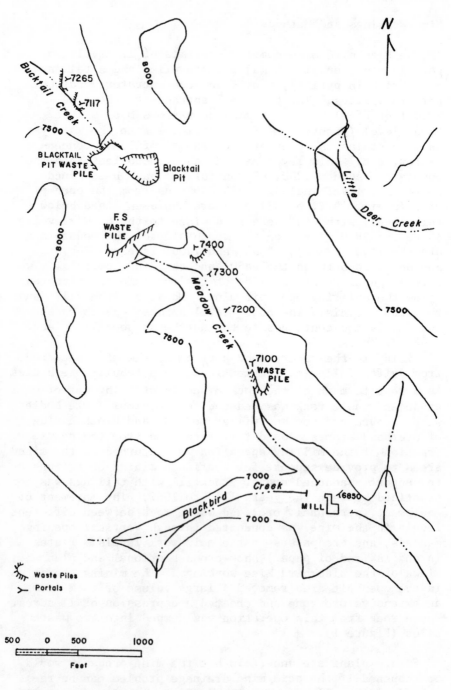

Figure I   Blackbird Mine facilities.

The Acid Mine Drainage Problem at the Blackbird Mine

As early as 1628, references to acid mine drainage were made relative to the coal mining industry (Hawley, 1972). The following statement referred to a coal region in North America (Hawley, 1972, p. 5):

> "I have reason to believe (that) there are good coals (here) also for I have observ'd (that) the runs of water have the same color as that which proceeds from the coal mines in Wales."

Modern-day acid mine drainage has been noted and studied in coal mines in the eastern U.S. for many years (Ohio State University Foundation, 1971). However, articles on acid mine drainage problems in western hard rock mines are relatively uncommon in the literature. Mines of this type which contain pyrite often produce poor quality water with a low pH and a variety of metal ions. The chemistry of acid mine drainage and conditions favorable to the production of poor quality water are well established.

Production of acid water is common to mining situations where pyrite and other metal-sulphides become exposed to atmospheric conditions. Upon exposure to the atmosphere, sufficient oxygen and water are present to initiate the cycle. The oxidation of pyrite occurs according to the following process (Stumm and Morgan, 1970, p. 540-542):

$$FeS_{2(s)} + 7/2\ O_2 + H_2O \rightleftharpoons Fe^{++} + 2SO_4^= + 2H^+ \tag{1}$$

Although the initial oxidation of pyrite may take place in a dry environment according to the equation

$$FeS_{2(s)} + 3\ O_2 \longrightarrow FeSO_4 + SO_2,$$

there is almost always sufficient moisture in mine waste piles and mine workings to favor reaction (1). The ferrous iron from reaction (1) is oxidized to ferric iron by:

$$Fe^{++} + 1/4\ O_2 + H^+ \rightleftharpoons Fe^{3+} + 1/2H_2O \tag{2}$$

Hydrolysis of the ferric ion produces ferric hydroxide and releases additional acidity:

$$Fe^{3+} + 3H_2O \rightleftharpoons Fe(OH)_3 \downarrow + 3H^+ \tag{3}$$

The pale-yellow to orange ferric hydroxide is known as "yellow boy" among miners. This insoluble precipitate coats stream bottoms and forms thick sludges in adits.

The sum of reactions 1, 2, and 3,

$$FeS_{2(s)} + 15/4\ O_2 + 7/2H_2O \rightleftharpoons Fe(OH)_3 \downarrow + 2SO_4^= + 4H^+ \quad (4)$$

shows that 4 moles of H^+ are released for each mole of FeS_2 oxidized; few other natural weathering reactions produce this amount of acidity.

Various studies (Smith, 1971; Singer and Strumm 1970) on the importance of ferric iron in the oxidation of FeS_2 have shown that the following reaction accounts for the principle method of breakdown of the pyrite:

$$FeS_{2(s)} + 14Fe^{3+} + 8H_2O \rightleftharpoons 15\ Fe^{++} + 2SO_4^= + 16\ H^+ \quad (5)$$

When ferric iron is the oxidizing agent, reactions 2 and 4 determine the rate of oxidation of FeS_2. Reaction (2), the oxidation of ferrous to ferric iron appears to be the rate determining step. The rate of this reaction is a function of hydrogen ion concentration, decreasing with pH down to about 4.5. From pH 4.5 to 3.5 the relationship of Fe^{++} and O_2 concentration changes and below pH 3.5 reaction (2) is very slow and independent of pH.

At pH of 3.5 or less, bacteria such as <u>Ferrobacillus</u> <u>ferrooxidans</u> <u>F.</u> <u>Sulfooxidans</u>, and <u>Thiobacillus</u> <u>ferrooxidans</u> accelerate the rate of conversion of Fe^{++} to Fe^{3+}. Singer and Strumm (1970, p. 1122) note such bacteria may accelerate reaction (2) by a factor of 10^6 or more.

Wentz (1974, p. 20) describes the above reactions for a situation where oxygen laden water at a near neutral pH infiltrates mine waste containing pyritic material:

"The FeS_2 is oxidized, probably by molecular O_2 at first (reaction 1), thus releasing Fe^{++} and lowering the pH. In addition large amounts of SO_4 are produced. Some of the Fe^{++} is oxidized abiotically to Fe^{3+} (reaction 2) which in turn also oxidizes FeS_2 (reaction 4). As the pH and the amount of available O_2 decrease, reaction 1 becomes less important. Moreover, the abiotic rate of reaction 2

also decreases, thus limiting oxidation of FeS_2
by Fe^{3+}. However, at this point (about pH 4.5-5)
the iron bacterium *Metallogenium* becomes important
and catalyzes reaction 2 until a pH of about 3-3.5
is reached. Below this value, the *Ferrobacillus-*
Thiobacillus group takes over the catalysis. It is
these later organisms which are responsible for the
pH's of less than 3 seen in nature. And, because
of the inefficient nature of the Fe^{++} to Fe^{3+} oxidation, these organisms also contribute to the dis-
position of large amounts of $Fe(OH)_3$ (reaction 3)."

In addition to the formation of water with low pH and
high iron, acid produced from the oxidation of pyrite may
also dissolve other minerals which by themselves do not
contribute to the formation of acid waters. The disolution
of the sulphide copper mineral chalcopyrite is an example
(Davis, 1972, p. 8):

$$CuFeS_2 + 2\ Fe_2(SO_4), + 2H_2O + 3\ O_2 \rightleftharpoons CuSO_4 + 5FeSO_4$$

$$+ 2H_2SO_4 \qquad\qquad (6)$$

Sources of Recharge to Mine Workings
in the Blackbird Creek Drainage

A significant amount of the total discharge from the
mine is due to recharge to mine workings which has been induced by the mine itself. Identification of recharge areas
is prerequisite to reduction or elimination of recharge
from surface waters. Mine-related surface features which
allow surface water to recharge underground workings directly include raises intersecting ground surface, surface
disturbed areas and abandoned open pits. Raises intersecting the ground surface should be covered to prevent direct
surface water recharge. However, some raises at Blackbird
were sealed inadequately or not sealed at all. Some raises
connect only two levels but some connect several levels.
An unrestricted flow path is created in the case where a
raise extends from the ground surface to a working level
with little offset between levels. Four such flow paths
were identified based on observed discharge from raises on
the 6850 level at the Blackbird. Plate I shows that these
raises do extend from the 6850 level to the surface. Plate
I also shows that the 706 vent raise (706VR) extends from
the 7100 level to the ground surface. A circular opening

about 20 feet in diameter marks the intersection of this raise with the ground surface. This opening lies near the bottom of a small draw which carries runoff water to acid forming minerals in the mine during spring months.

Surface water also may enter underground workings through mining-modified ground-water flow systems. At the Blackbird some 60 trenches and shallow pits were constructed during exploration and mapping of geologic structures in the mining area. Many of these features are located on surface expressions of fault and fracture zones. Water collects in these trenches from precipitation and runoff and infiltrates the fault zones. Many of these zones lead directly to underground workings. We estimate that recharge to underground workings from this source amounts to about 10 percent of the total discharge at station 7 (6850 portal Plate I).

Surface water also reaches underground workings through fractures created by mining at the Blackbird. Removal of ore from workings close to the ground surface causes stress on the overlying material. This stress has resulted in subsidence and produced surface fractures. Surface water from spring snowmelt enters these fractures and discharges to mine workings. This type of recharge to mine workings is estimated to constitute 10 percent of the total recharge at station 7 (6850 portal, Plate I)

An estimated 75,000 feet of surface diamond drilling has been completed in the mining area. This type of drilling is aimed at reaching ore bodies, which usually are more permeable than the surrounding rock. This type of exploration increases recharge to the ground-water flow systems by providing more interconnections between the surface and subsurface.

Recharge from Meadow Creek to mine workings is another potential source of water in the mine. During the course of our underground investigations, it was noted that faults, fractures and raises on the 7100 level northwest of the 7100 portals consistently discharged water to the level while similar structures east of the portal were essentially dry. Figure 2 shows the cross-sectional relationship between Meadow Creek and mine workings in the vicinity of the 7200 and 7100 portals. The workings on the 7100 level northwest of the portal are below creek level. A similar situation exists on the 7200 level, where workings north-

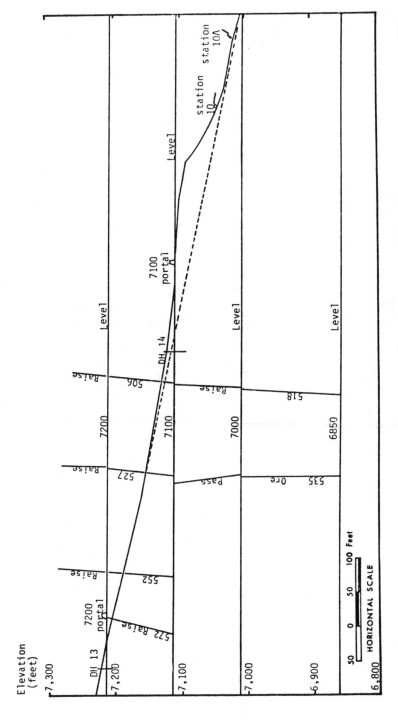

Figure 2. Cross sectional relationship between Meadow Creek and mine workings in the vicinity of the 7100 and 7200 portals.

west of the 7200 portal are below creek level. Faults and fractures connecting mine workings and Meadow Creek provide an avenue for recharge. Vertical distances of up to 275 feet between the 7100 level and Meadow Creek provide ample head to drive ground water down along permeable zones. Northwest of the 7200 portal, raises extend upward and intersect the ground surface. These raises undoubtedly dewater colluvium and fault zones saturated from snowmelt runoff. Rock units in this area dip 30° to 60° NE from Meadow Creek to the mine workings. The amount of water moving in this manner from Meadow Creek to mine workings is difficult to measure. Discharge data show that during the spring runoff period Meadow Creek is a gaining stream; therefore, stream recharge to mine workings could not be detected by this technique. Water level data from piezometers show that this area of the valley floor is a recharge zone. Therefore, the gain in Meadow Creek must result from surface runoff and shallow ground-water flow from spring snowmelt. It is believed that recharge to mine workings from Meadow Creek represents about 5 percent of the total discharge at station 7 (6850 portal, Plate I).

Water reaching the 7200 level (Plate I) normally flows out the 7200 portal but the portal was blocked by a small cave-in until mid-1976. Water ponded up behind the cave-in until it reached a sufficient depth to flow down raises to the 7100 level. One such raise was the 572R, which connects the 7200 and 7100 levels in the vicinity of the 7200 portals (Plate I). This raise is filled partially with ore and water flowing down the raise leaches out metal ions. Underground investigations on the 7100 level showed that this raise normally discharged about one gpm. But when peak spring runoff occurs, this raise discharges about 20 gpm. Analysis of a sample of this discharge showed that the metal load was 8 pounds per day of cobalt, 11 pounds per day of copper, and 5 pounds per day of iron. Later, the cave-in was removed from the 7200 portal and mine drainage flowed out the portal and into Meadow Creek. This maintenance work resulted in a reduction in cobalt, copper, and iron loads at station 7 by 15, 10 and 5 percent, respectively.

Water Quality in Mine Workings in
the Blackbird Creek Drainage

Distinct water types within the Blackbird mine workings can be identified on the basis of water quality differences.

These water quality differences exist because of differences in mineralogy, flow path length and travel time for the various sources of recharge to the mine workings. Mine-created flow, water discharging from raises, ground water (water from flooded levels below 6850), and diamond drill hole water all have differing water-quality characteristics.

Water discharging from diamond drill holes can be further subdivided based on whether or not the drill hole encountered an ore body. Table 2 is a summary of water-quality data for various discharge sources in the underground workings. Table 3 presents additional water quality data from various sources.

Surface runoff water was sampled at one point in the mine, the 706 vent raise (706VR) on the 7300 level. The water at this station does not come into contact with sulfide minerals. The water derives from a ground-water flow system in the shallow sediments where the 706VR intersects the ground surface; therefore the water is of good quality.

Water flowing from flooded levels below the 6850 was sampled at station 6827 (Plate I). The source of this water is ground-water from faults and fractures. The high iron concentrations indicate that this water comes into contact with sulfide mineralization; however, average pH of this water is 6.4. The flooded nature of this portion of the mine limits acid production by limiting oxygen availability. Solubility relationships show that at these high pH values, most of the iron exists as Fe(II) or $Fe(OH)_2$.

Water quality data for five diamond drill holes which did not encounter ore are shown in Table 2. The quality of this water is high; very little cobalt, copper, and iron is present. Water discharging from these drill holes follows faults and fractures that do not contain ore or pyrite.

Water discharging from diamond drill holes which penetrate ore bodies is lower in pH and higher in dissolved metals than water from diamond drill holes which do not penetrate ore bodies. The pyrite is associated with ore. Water percolating through the ore bodies dissolves pyrite oxidation products and removes metal ions from the oxidation sites. In addition, active mining of the ore bodies exposes pyrite minerals to atmospheric conditions which enhances the oxidation process. Water from drill holes pene-

Table II. Water quality data for different sources in mine workings in Blackbird Creek drainage. See Plate I for locations. (Metal ion concentrations given in parts per million)

Water Source	pH	E.C.	Co	Cu	Fe	Mn	Mg	Ca	Na	Number of Samples
73707 (706 vent raise-surface water)	6.7		-0.1	-0.1	-0.1	-0.1	0.8	3.6		1
6827 (Pierce Winze-ground water)	6.4	770	2.1	-0.1	162.0	3.8	23.4	10.3	7.8	14
Diamond Drill Holes (Ore bodies[a])	4.5		17.7	1.2	242.0	11.1	45.1	21.4	9.9	5
Diamond Drill holes (No ore bodies encountered)	5.0		1.2	0.2	0.4	2.4	2.3	1.5	2.8	5
5 Raises	2.6	2500	23.3	46.9	518.0	25.0	118.0	15.4	4.7	37
6835 (Drainage from back part of 6850)			3.2	1.3	4.2	1.3	6.9	2.0	2.7	1

[a] Ore body has been actively mined

-0.1 less than 0.1

Table III. Ground-water quality in the Blackbird Creek drainage during the 1976 field season. (Concentrations are dissolved metal ions in parts per million, except as noted.)

Sample Station Number	pH	E.C.	Co	Cu	Fe	Mn	Mg	Ca	Na	Number of Samples
DH4	5.6	430	7.1	1.2	10.7	2.3	23.1	60.7	16.0	6
13	3.0	500	27.4	26.6	4.9	2.9	31.1	21.8	4.1	1
DH3S	3.9	940	50.5	64.0	5.4	50.0	35.7	3.1	10.2	7
DH3D	6.2	255	3.9	3.1	4.3	2.9	8.3	33.4	8.4	7
10B	3.7	720	7.7	39.9	7.1	2.0	33.0	20.3	4.3	11
DH2	4.0	1110	1.2	1.4	92.3	1.4	11.4	132.0	23.9	7
DH1	3.1	950	14.6	1.6	243.0	4.4	25.4	77.8	19.7	7
100[a]	4.7	760	6.7	1.3	31.6	4.7	82.0	235.0		3
101[a]	3.1	960	7.3	2.3	34.8	3.5	84.8	190.0		3

[a] Concentrations are total metal ions in parts per million.

trating ore bodies which have been mined is higher in dissolved metals and has lower pH than other drill holes. Five samples were taken from diamond drill holes where an ore body was encountered but had not been mined. The quality of this water was intermediate between the previous two water types.

A total of 37 water samples were collected from raises discharging water to the 6850 level (Table 2) during the 1976 field season. This water displayed the lowest pH and highest metal concentrations of any of the water types identified in underground discharge points. This water type results from the most favorable conditions for production of acid water. Large amounts of ore-rich materials in raises, stopes, and drifts are exposed to atmospheric conditions and oxidation products are removed by water. Increased flow through mine workings during spring runoff flushes oxidation products from areas not normally in contact with water. Numerous pools of acid water also collect in the mine during low flow periods. The influx of water during spring runoff flushes out these pools, adding additional poor quality water to the system.

The chemical processes of acid production are identical for both underground and surface situations. One variable which favors increased acid production in underground workings is greater exposure of sulfide minerals to atmospheric conditions. Stopes, drifts, cross-cuts, ore chutes, and raises all expose ore material to oxygen. The major limiting factor on acid and heavy metal production from underground workings at the Blackbird mine is the lack of water to carry away oxidation products; the Blackbird is a relatively "dry" mine by most standards.

Variations in metal ion concentrations for underground workings are very similar to variations observed at surface waste features. Figures 3 and 4 show metal ion and discharge variations for the 6850 and 7400 portals for 1976. Discharging raises on the 6850 level show similar metal ion variations with flow. As with surface waste features, runoff water entering mine workings flushes away accumulated oxidation products resulting in increased metal loads from underground discharge points during high runoff. Oxidation products begin to accumulate as soon as the spring runoff water recedes. This accumulation process continues until a surge of water again passes through the mine, transporting the acid salts away. Runoff from late summer thunder-

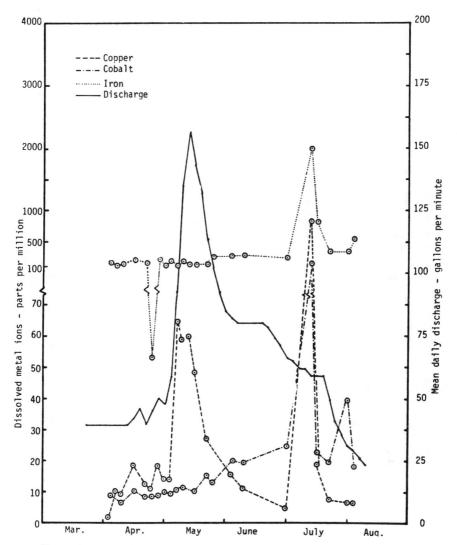

Figure 3.   Dissolved cobalt, copper, and iron concentrations at station 7 (6850 portal) for 1976.

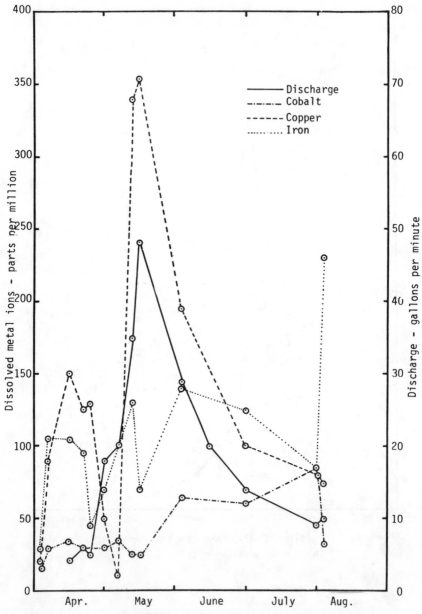

Figure 4.   Dissolved cobalt, copper, and iron concentrations at the 7400 portal for April to August, 1976.

storm activity may transport metals from the mine during the low-flow period. This process caused the peak in metal-ion concentration in mid-July on Figure 3. Figure 4 shows that a peak in metal-ion concentrations occurred at the 7400 portal during mid-April of 1976. This peak resulted from the first introduction of snowmelt into the mine workings during the 1976 runoff period. The discharge hydrograph for the 7400 portal (Figure 4) shows that only a very small volume of water was necessary to bring about high metal ion concentrations during mid-April. Total metal-ion concentrations increase with downstream position as each source contributes its share of acid and metal ions. Farther downstream, dissolved metal-ion concentrations begin to decrease, indicating that dissolved metals begin to form precipitates but remain in suspension and are transported out of the mine. The precipitation of dissolved metals results from the addition of relatively good quality water from diamond drill holes downstream of station 6824 (Plate I).

Water discharging from the 6850 and the 7400 portals represents the majority of all point source acid discharge from underground workings in the Blackbird Creek drainage. Table 4 gives metal loads for various periods from 1969 through 1976. Sample collection was not conducted during winter months but projected water quality and quantity parameters show that approximately 3,000 pounds of copper and cobalt would have been produced at the 6850 portal for 1976. The data show that the St. Joe portal contributes about 1 percent of the metal load from the three portals for the period April 3 to August 3, 1976. The data for the 6850 portal and the 7400 portal are not comparable directly for the various years of record because of differences in analytical techniques, but variations in metal loads are evident for different years. The amount of water available to transport metals from the mine is probably the major factor which determines total metal loads from year to year. Water produced by mine waste dumps containing pyrite are also a source of acid drainage at the Blackbird mine. Water in drill holes monitored during the 1976 field season show a decreasing head potential with depth at key location. Ground water is therefore moving downward in those areas. Figure 5 shows the interpreted ground-water flow system in the vicinity of the waste pile at the 7100 portal. The figure shows that the water table intersects land surface at the lower portion of the waste pile, resulting in the spring discharge which was monitored at station 10 shown

Table IV. Metal load production from underground workings in the
Blackbird Creek drainage. (Metal load is total metals
except as indicated.) (See Plate I for portal locations)

Station	Period	Metal Load (lbs)		
		Co	Cu	Fe
7 (6850 portal)	2/25 - 9/30/69	3,600	3,400	7,200
7	6/21 - 11/01/71	1,300	1,000	22,600
7	8/04 - 12/31/74	900	300	4,500
7	5/19 - 7/31/75	2,200	5,300	11,700
7	4/03 - 8/03/76[a]	1,600	2,100	21,000
7	1976 Water year[a]	3,100	3,300	
9(St.Joe portal)	4/03 - 8/03/76[a]	60	160	180
15(7400 portal)	2/15 - 9/30/69	2,300	3,200	2,500
15	7/21 - 11/02/74	300	400	200
15	4/13 - 8/03/76[a]	1,000	6,000	1,500

a Metals are calculated as dissolved metal ions

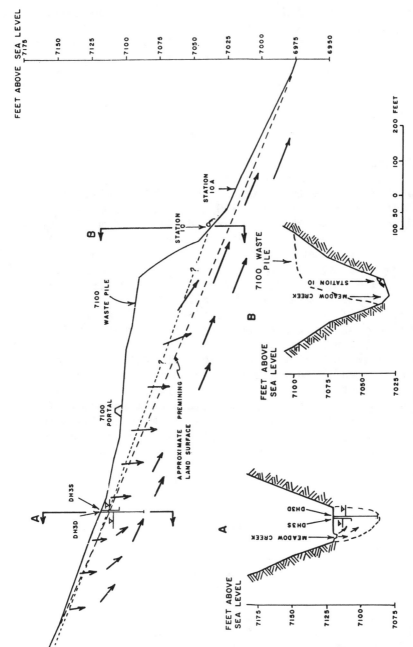

Figure 5. Meadow Creek stream profile in the vicinity of the 7100 waste pile.

in the Figure. This discharge probably represents only a
small portion of the total quantity of ground water moving
through the mine waste and valley fill material. Additional ground water probably moves down gradient at depth.
This ground-water underflow discharges to Meadow Creek in
the form of poor quality water.

CONCLUSIONS AND CORRECTIVE MEASURES FOR
ACID MINE DRAINAGE AT THE BLACKBIRD MINE

Total Discharge

Total discharge from the Blackbird Mining area for the
1976 water year was about 5,900 acre-feet, with about
5,800 acre-feet of this discharge deriving from Blackbird
Creek and about 100 acre-feet from Bucktail Creek. In
Blackbird Creek, acid drainage totaled about 420 acre-feet
from Meadow Creek and 63 acre-feet from the 6,850 portal
for the 1976 water year; the remaining 5,320 acre-feet
was good-quality water from Blackbird Creek above the
Blackbird mill and small tributaries. Only about 50 acre-
feet of the 420 acre-feet measured at Meadow Creek is
actual acid mine drainage from point discharge sources; the
remaining 370 acre-feet is good-quality water from snowmelt runoff and Meadow Creek above the uppermost Waste
Pile. The entire 100 acre-feet of discharge measured in
the Bucktail Creek drainage is acid mine discharge. This
gives a total of 213 acre-feet of acid mine drainage from
point discharge sources in the Blackbird Mining Area for
the 1976 water year. These point source discharges will
require NPDES permits and unending legal obligation by any
company that reopens the mine which is the only known
domestic source of cobalt.

Discharge-Metal-Ion Relationships

Stream discharges and water quality are closely inter-
related in the Blackbird Mining Area. Discharge-metal-ion
relationships show that heavy metal concentrations occur:
(1) low during winter months, (2) increase sharply during
the initial spring runoff period, (3) are very low during
the latter part of the spring runoff, and (4) rise gradually during later summer months. As much as 75 percent of
the total annual metal production occurs during April and
May.

Acid Production: Underground Workings

Acid production from underground workings is controlled by: (1) oxygen, (2) distribution of pyrite, (3) moisture in the mine atmosphere, (4) availability of water to transport oxidation products, and (5) mine characteristics (Trexler and others, 1974) (Williams, 1975). An additional variable may be the presence of iron bacteria which facilitate the oxidation of Fe^{2+} to Fe^{3+}. Variables 4 and 5 can be managed to reduce or eliminate acid mine drainage from the underground workings.

Several raises in the Blackbird Creek drainage intersect the ground surface and receive direct recharge from surface runoff and ground-water discharge from shallow ground-water flow systems recharged by snowmelt. Recharge to mine workings also occurs in areas where Meadow Creek flows above workings on the 7100 and 7200 levels. Oxidation of sulfide ore minerals takes place continuously. Flood events flush the oxidation products out of the mine. In the Bucktail Creek drainage, the 7265 and 7400 levels are hydrologically connected with flow systems associated with the Blacktail Pit. Workings at the 7117 level are isolated from these flow systems. Mine workings at higher elevations produce greater quantities of discharge than do workings at lower elevations in the mountain.

Acid Production: Surface Waste Features

Acid production from surface waste features is governed by the following variables: (1) oxygen, (2) availability of pyrite and other heavy metals, (3) moisture in the waste material, (4) availability of water to transport oxidation products, (5) physical location of the waste feature, and (6) presence of iron bacteria. Variables 4 and 5 may be managed to reduce acid drainage from surface waste features.

Certain piles near the Blackbird mine produce water with significantly lower iron concentrations and lower total iron loads than waste piles located at lower elevations in the Meadow and Bucktail Creek drainages. Waste features located at lower elevations are recharged by acid water with high metal-ion concentrations and low pH values. Acid production from tailings and waste rock deposited in and near stream channels is a significant source of acid water and heavy metals in the Meadow Creek drainage.

Corrective Measures

Reduction of acid production from surface and underground mine and waste structures can be accomplished by
initiating various maintenance procedures. Future mining
activities should incorporate hydrological variables in
mine planning and surface waste site selection procedures.
Prevention of acid mine drainage is much less difficult
than curing acid mine drainage.

Underground Workings

Field investigations have shown that mine characteristics and availability of water to transport oxidation products out of the mine are factors which can be controlled
to reduce acid mine drainage.

Mine Characteristics

All raises intersecting the ground surface should be
carefully inspected for signs of recharge from both surface and ground water. This inspection should include in
particular raises: 506R, 527R, 598R, 607R, 619R, 622R,
663R, 669R, and the 706VR. Any additional raises intersecting ground surface which are not shown on mine diagrams should also be inspected for signs of recharge. Many
raises have been sealed against direct surface water recharge in the past three years. Water seeping into the
raises from saturated soils and colluvium may be prevented
by grouting around the outside of the raise to a depth of
8 to 10 feet. This recommendation applies in particular
to raises located in areas where ponding or direct surface-
water flow exists. Raise 706VR has not been sealed and
the raise is forming an increasingly large pit as sloughing occurs along its sides.

Mine characteristics contributing to recharge to mine
workings in the Bucktail Creek drainage are difficult to
correct. One solution is to seal the bottom of the Blacktail Pit to eliminate direct recharge to the 7400 and 7265
levels. However, water would then collect in the pit and
seepage through the pit walls would occur unless the walls
also were sealed. Seepage through the pit walls would
probably leach heavy metals from the ore zones. Metal
production might even be increased if this procedure was
used. The above problems could be avoided if the Blacktail Pit were filled to an elevation of about 7,520 feet

(an expensive alternative), whereupon surface water would drain out of the pit area and down the Blacktail Pit waste pile (Figure I).

Availability of Water to Mine Workings

Reducing or redirecting water flow in a mine reduces metal loads discharging from the mine. A first priority should be to grout or cap all flowing drill holes on all levels, especially the 6850 level. This would result in an immediate reduction of 16 acre-feet of water at the 6850 portal.

Maintenance work should be continued on all levels to prevent ponding of water and flooding of ore-filled raises, such as on the 7200 level. During spring runoff ponding occurs on levels which are blocked by cave-ins or excessive accumulations of iron hydroxide precipitates. Water ponds until it flows down raises that normally are dry. Oxidation products are then flushed out of the raises as acid mine drainage. Water discharging from raises to the 7100 and 7200 levels should be traced back to its origin and appropriate steps taken to reduce this flow. Water should be prevented from flowing through stopes or raises containing oxidized ore where production of acid salts is inevitable. In many cases this would involve erecting and sealing a bulkhead at the entrance to the stope or raise, while in other cases merely cleaning out the drainage ditch on the level to allow water to flow freely along the level would suffice.

Diversion of discharge to central flow points within the mine workings would help to eliminate flushing of accumulated oxidation products or contamination of good-quality discharge sources. Discharge from the 7400 portal could be diverted down the Brown Bear shaft (Plate I) and down raises to the 6850 level. Diversion of this flow down the Brown Bear shaft would not result in any additional metal leaching since the shaft is fully timbered. Such a diversion would be a temporary solution since the timbering in the shaft will deteriorate with time. This discharge and water flowing to the shaft from other levels could be directed to the 6850 level down raises which do not contain oxidized ore. The drainage system on the 6850 level could handle this increased discharge if flowing drill holes on the 6850 level were capped. There should be no net increase in discharge at the 6850 portal since the annual discharge from the drill holes is about equal to flow on the 7400 level. As an additional advantage in this diversion, discharge from the 7400 portal would no longer be available to leach metals from waste piles and mine debris in the Meadow Creek drainage, resulting in decreased metal production from this source. Decreased metal production should be especially apparent during low flow periods when the 7400 portal is the major source of poor quality in the upper Meadow Creek drainage.

A second major diversion would direct water from the upper Bucktail Creek drainage down through a bore hole to the 6850 level and out of the mine. If this diversion could also include discharge from upper Bucktail Creek, the majority of all water quality problems in the Bucktail Creek drainage could be eliminated. Such a diversion would necessitate enlarging the drainage system on the 6850 level as a maximum flow of about 2 cfs should be expected at the 6850 portal during peak runoff periods. The diversion site on Bucktail Creek should be selected carefully so that all poor-quality water discharging to Bucktail Creek is included. The original plan called for completing a borehole from the 7117 to the 6850 level, but this would not allow for diversion of poor-quality water from the creek. Analysis of the data show that poor-quality ground water enters Bucktail Creek below the 7117 waste pile, from 7000 to 6975 feet elevation. This poor-quality ground water might be diverted at higher elevations in the drainage. However, drill logs show that the water table is about 35 feet below land surface in the 7265 waste pile. A similar depth to water probably exists at station 21 (7117 waste pile). It appears that completing a bore hole from an elevation of about 6975 feet in the Bucktail Creek streambed to the 6850 level would intercept all poor-quality water produced by upstream mining features, including portals and waste piles. This plan would have the drawback of diverting much good quality water during the spring runoff.

Surface Waste Features

Reclamation alternatives for surface waste features in the Blackbird Mining area are more expensive and difficult to initiate than underground reclamation alternatives. Surface waste features are vulnerable to flushing of oxidation products from both the pile surface and within the waste material. Erosion of the waste material by surface water is a problem also. Revegetation research is continuing on the F. S. and upper Blacktail Pit waste piles with encouraging results. This approach deals effectively with erosion and also helps to prevent leaching of acid salts from the waste pile. The development of a mature soil profile and establishment of vegetation eliminates direct action of weathering processes on the waste material. Evapotranspiration losses from vegetation established on the waste pile will reduce the amount of water infiltrating into waste piles. Therefore poor quality seeps and springs originating from waste piles should show a decrease in discharge. Additional reclamation procedures which may be applied to other surface waste features in the area are discussed in the following section.

Considerations for Future Mining Development

The Blackbird Mining area contains the largest known cobalt deposit in the United States. Mining of the deposit will resume when economic conditions become favorable. These economic conditions include assuming legal responsibility for the production of acid mine drainage for the duration, including after abandonment. Water quality problems associated with mining activities can be minimized by applying procedures discussed in previous sections and by considering the following points.

Hydrologic site selection factors should be considered for the location of tailings disposal areas, waste rock storage areas, and low grade ore storage areas planned for future mining activities. Disposal areas for tailings and waste rock are limited by the physical characteristics of the Meadow Creek and Blackbird Creek valleys. These valleys would normally be considered marginal for the disposal of the solid wastes since both have perennial streams and associated ground water flow systems, but there are no alternative sites in the Blackbird Mining Area.

Plans are being considered for two new open pits, two overburden disposal areas, a low-grade ore disposal area, and a tailings disposal area. The potential tailings disposal is located on Blackbird Creek about 500 feet upstream of its confluence with Meadow Creek (Figure 1). About 2 million cubic yards of tailings can be deposited behind a dam built from about 800,000 cubic yards of overburden from the proposed open pit. Water from Blackbird Creek is to be diverted around the tailings pile.

Discharge from underground workings can be expected to increase following the resumption of mining activities. Water for diamond drilling, sand-fill water, and recharge from the Idaho-Dandy open pit will constitute the majority of this increase. Recharge to mine workings from Meadow Creek should decrease with the development of the Brown Bear open pit. Discharge from Meadow Creek will enter the Brown Bear pit and continuous pumping of the pit will be required. Plans call for backfilling deep mine areas with sand fill from the mill. It is suggested by the writers that those workings nearest the surface, both existing and proposed, be sand filled to discourage the entrance of re-charge to mine workings. Sand filling will reduce subsi-dence problems and prevent the development of fracture systems associated with subsidence. Numerous bulkheads have collapsed in the existing workings allowing sand fill to escape from mined-out areas. Bulkheads installed for future sand fill operations should be constructed so as to prevent collapse.

The total volume of acid water presently discharging is small in relation to total discharge from the mining area. Some poor-quality water from the proposed mining area is unavoidable. But treatment costs will be considerably less if this discharge is isolated from good-quality water. Ground water discharge from all surface waste features should be intercepted by the use of cutoff walls and this discharge should be diverted to a water treatment plant.

REFERENCES

1. Sceva, J. E., 1973, Water Quality Consideration for the Metal Mining Industry in the Pacific Northwest: U.S. Environmental Protection Agency Report No. Region X-3, Seattle, Washington.

2. Sonderegger, J. L., Wallace, J. J., and Higgins, G. L., 1975, Acid Mine Drainage Control-Feasibility Study, Cooke City, Montana: Final Report Montana Bureau of Mines and Geology to Montana Department of Natural Resources and Conservation.

3. Wentz, D. A., 1974, Effect of Mine Drainage on the Quality of Streams in Colorado, 1971-72: Colorado Water Conservation Board Water-Resources Circular 21.

   Moran, Robert E., and Wentz, D. A., 1974, Effects of Metal-Mine Drainage on Water Quality of Selected Areas of Colorado, 1972-73: Colorado Water Conservation Board Water-Resources Circular 25.

4. Baldwin, J. A., Ralston, D. R., and Trexler, B. D., 1978, Water Resource Problems Related to Mining in the Blackbird Mining District, Idaho: Completion Report, U.S.F.S. Cooperative Agreement 12-11-204-11, College of Mines, University of Idaho, Moscow, Idaho.

5. Anderson, A. L., 1947, Cobalt Mineralization in the Blackbird Mining District, Lemhi County, Idaho: Economic Geology, V. 42, No. 1, p. 22-46.

6. Davis, F. T., 1972, Water Pollution Abatement Program for the Blackbird Mine of the Idaho Mining Company: Unpublished report prepared by Hazen Research, Inc., Golden, Colorado, for the Idaho Mining Company, Box 514, Cobalt, Idaho 83229.

7. Hawley, John R., 1972, The Problem of Acid Mine Drainage in the Province of Ontario: Special Projects Section - Mining Industrial Wastes Branch, Ministry of the Environment, 135 St. Clair Avenue West, Toronto, Ontario, Canada.

8. Ohio State University Foundation, 1971, Acid Mine
    Drainage Formation and Abatement: Document PB
    199 835, National Technical Information Service,
    Department of Commerce, Washington, D.C.

9. Stumm, Werner, and Morgan, J. J., 1970, Aquatic Chem-
    istry; an Introduction Emphasizing Chemical
    Equilibria in Natural Waters: New York, Wiley-
    Interscience, 583 p.

10. Smith, E. E., 1971, The Chemical System, in Acidic
    Mine Drainage Formation and Abatement: Washing-
    ton, (U.S.) Environmental Protection Agency
    Grant 14010 FPR, DAST-42, p. 35-42.

    Singer, P. C., and Stumm, Werner, 1970, Acidic Mine
    Drainage: The Rate Determining Step: Science,
    v. 167, p. 1121-1123.

11. Trexler, Bryson D., Jr., Ralston, D. R., Renison, W.,
    and Williams, R. E., 1974, The Hydrology of an
    Acid Mine Drainage Problem: Proceedings #18,
    Symposium on Water Resources Problems Related to
    Mining. American Water Resources Association.

12. Williams, R. E., 1975, Production and Disposal of
    Wastes from Mining, Milling, and Metallurgical
    Industries: Miller-Freeman Publishing Company,
    San Francisco, California.

    Williams, R. E. and Mink, L. L., 1975, Settling Ponds
    as a Mining Wastewater Treatment Facility: Idaho
    Bureau of Mines and Geology, Pamphlet 164,
    Moscow, Idaho.

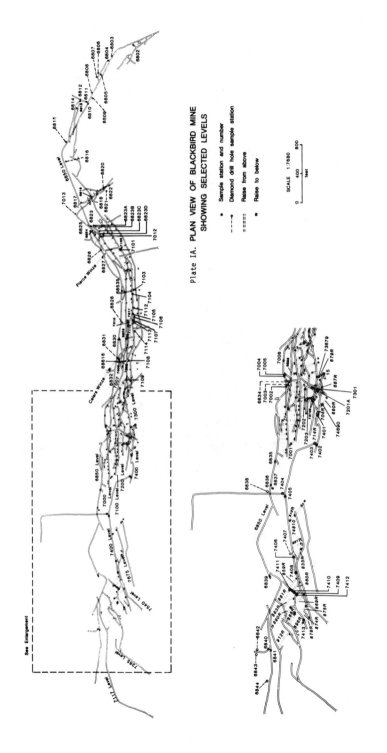

Plate IA. PLAN VIEW OF BLACKBIRD MINE
SHOWING SELECTED LEVELS

• Sample station and number
• Diamond drill hole sample station
= = = = Raise from above
■ Raise to below

SCALE 1:7680

0   400   800
         feet

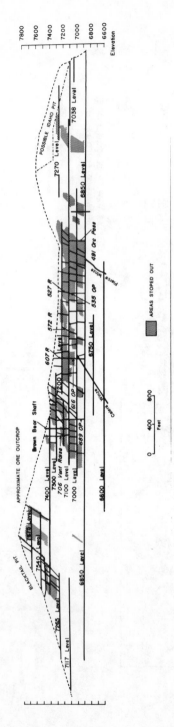

Plate IB. Cross sectional view of Blackbird Mine workings.

SECTION 2

Drainage Control for Surface Mines

9

Dewatering of Mines—A Practical Analysis

by Lloyd G. Venburg,
Principal Ground-Water Geologist,
International Engineering Company, Inc.,
San Francisco, California, USA

INTRODUCTION

Methods of controlling ground water must be devised during the planning of mining activities because ground water in pervious rocks can adversely affect the development of a mining operation. To create an effective dewatering system, the economic, environmental and legal aspects of selected dewatering methods should be investigated concurrent with mine design and planning.

The following benefits may be derived from an efficient dewatering system:

- Slope stability in an open cut mining operation.

- Elimination of caving and upheaval in vertical shaft excavations and reduction of hydrostatic pressure from artesian aquifers, which may underlie mining areas.

- Proper alignment of diversion channels with minimal infiltration of water into mining slopes.

- Fewer legal and environmental restrictions and a reduction in the number of sump pumps, water treatment equipment and other facilities.

USE OF AVAILABLE DATA TO IDENTIFY PROBLEMS IN MINE HYDROLOGY

With minor adjustments in the exploration program, invaluable information can be made available to the ground-water geologist without excessive additional costs. With accurate visual and geophysical logs, recorded water level data and data from the drilling operation, potential aquifers and the extent of ground-water problems can be identified.

The geohydrologist can often determine the extent of ground-water problems by reviewing existing exploration boring logs. Unfortunately, exploratory borings are usually drilled to delineate and evaluate ore bodies, and insufficient attention is given to logging and classifying unconsolidated materials and water-bearing rocks. With minimal additional expense, exploratory borings can be used to show depths of unconsolidated sediments, classification and lithology of bedrock, zones of caving or heavy mud loss and water production from an air drilling operation.

Generally, exploratory holes are also logged by geophysical methods. Ideally, these should include temperature, flow meter (spinner) and radioactive tracer logs in addition to caliper, spontaneous potential, resistivity, gamma ray, neutron and other borehole geophysical logs selected for individual site investigations.

Investigative costs can be reduced if exploratory borings are converted to piezometers. A monitoring network can then be established, with water levels recorded regularly, and water samples can be collected for laboratory analysis.

Supplemental data may be obtained from government documents, private papers, geologic reports, local well logs, pumping records, meteorological and river stage data, maps, seismological reports, environmental investigations, and other bulletins pertaining to the area. The ground-water geologist can use these data to identify possible problems concerning the mine hydrology and to proceed with selection and preliminary design of water control systems while mining feasibility studies are being conducted.

FIELD INVESTIGATIONS, DATA ANALYSES AND OFFICE STUDIES

Preliminary assessments can only be confirmed through field investigations. The ground-water geologist may have considerable data to substantiate the hydrologic character- istics of a formation; however, all potential aquifers, possible barriers, conditions of ground-water occurrence, areal effects of ground-water lowering, piezometric fluctu- ations, water quality and other subsurface geologic fea- tures must be identified. The intensive field investigative program should include pumping tests, water level monitor- ing, geologic mapping of the area and surface geophysical surveys to define the depth and nature of the bedrock.

A pumping test consists of pumping a well and observing the effect in several piezometers spaced at varying dis- tances from the well. Siting of these piezometers will usually be determined in the field by the ground-water geo- logist and will be based on assumed transmissivity of the aquifer, planned length of pumping test and other factors such as possible fault zones, the strike or dip of forma- tions, the location of streams and possible ground-water barriers. The effects of barriers on drawdown are illus- trated in Figure 1.

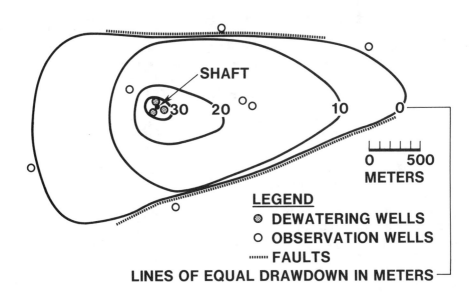

Figure 1. Effect of barriers on drawdown

If an aquifer is pumped at a constant rate, the cone of influence extends outward with time. This cone expands until natural or surface recharge of the aquifer equals the pumping rate (see Figure 2). This may occur within a few hours or days, but, if the aquifer is extensive, the process may continue for years. Precise measurements of pumping rates, water levels in pumping and observation wells and water recovery must be made to produce meaningful data from the pumping tests. The geohydrologist usually conducts several pumping tests early in the mining program to define hydrologic characteristics.

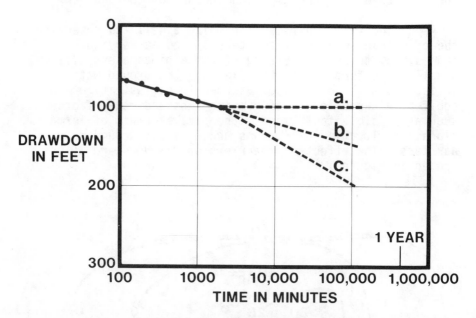

a. Cone of influence intercepts source
b. Cone of influence does not intercept source
c. Cone of influence intercepts hydrologic barrier

Figure 2. Time-drawdown curves

Research has produced usable formulae and analytic methods for evaluating the pumping test results and hydrologic investigations (1). Equilibrium formulae, often modified to reflect site conditions, are used to obtain coefficients of transmissivity and storage if steady-state flow conditions are obtained. More commonly, nonequilibrium formulae are used when equilibrium can not be attained or if radial flow to the well is unsteady on short-term tests.

After data are compiled and evaluated, conceptual designs
of dewatering systems can be confirmed or rejected. With
relatively complete investigative data, the ground-water
geologist can describe the hydraulic characteristics of the
aquifer, compute transmissivities and storage coefficients,
estimate specific capacities and predict infiltration
quantities and drawdown. Also, the viability of water
control can be evaluated.

Concurrent with or subsequent to data evaluation, the
environmental, legal and economic constraints that may influence the dewatering selection process are studied. Pollution, water disposal, effects of large-scale mining with-
drawals of ground water, possible saline water intrusion
into potable aquifers, subsidence, the effect of groundwater lowering on domestic and animal habitats and many
other environmental aspects of dewatering must be considered.

The ground-water geologist and the engineer must work
closely to analyze all factors and to implement the most
feasible and economic system. In addition to evaluating
the effects of dewatering, the types and availability of
the following materials and installation equipment must be
considered: drilling rigs, well point systems, pumps, pipe,
well screen, bentonite, cement, water treatment equipment,
power, sand and gravel and other materials.

WATER CONTROL SYSTEMS

Practical and economical results can be achieved with the
selection of one or more of the water control systems that
have been used successfully by the mining and construction
industries for many years. Pre-drainage may be considered
infeasible and mine sumping systems may be installed particularly at open cut mines. Treatment and surface impoundment of sumped water may be required to allow for settlement
of suspended solids or precipitation of iron, manganese and
other elements.

Conventional and vacuum wellpoint systems are commonly
used to dewater unconsolidated sediments. Wellpoints that
are 1-1/2 to 2 inches in diameter and 2 to 5 feet in length
are attached to riser pipes and installed in a line or ring
at spacings generally ranging from 2 to 8 feet. These
risers are connected to a common header; they are pumped by
one or more wellpoint pumps, which are a combination of

centrifugal and vacuum pumps and are generally capable of lowering water levels 15 to 20 feet. For greater lifts, multi-stage wellpoint, jet eductor or deep well systems are effective. Often, well point systems are prescribed to allow placement of compacted earth core or cutoff trenches for diversion or tailings dams, to provide stable slopes along diversion channels or to contribute to ground-water lowering when used in conjunction with a deep well system. A two-stage wellpoint system is shown in Figure 3.

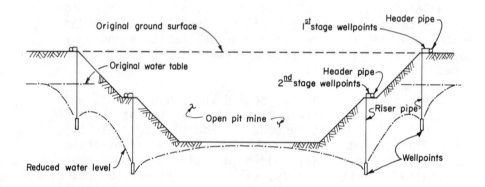

Figure 3. Two-stage well point system

Water control in unconsolidated sediments can also be accomplished by installing slurry trenches. A vertical walled trench is excavated by a backhoe, dragline, trenching machine or clamshell. Bentonite slurry is pumped in the trench to replace the excavated material and to provide support for the trench walls (see Figure 4). The slurry level should not be over 1 or 2 feet below ground level and several feet above the existing static water level. Backfill is usually composed of excavated materials, imported select soils and slurry and consists of a thoroughly mixed, well graded, homogeneous mass that is free from boulders.

Backfill is usually placed by a bulldozer. This method is feasible in areas underlain by silts, sands and gravels; however, excavation may be difficult if boulders are present.

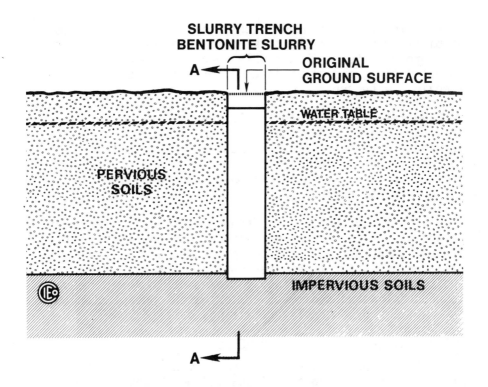

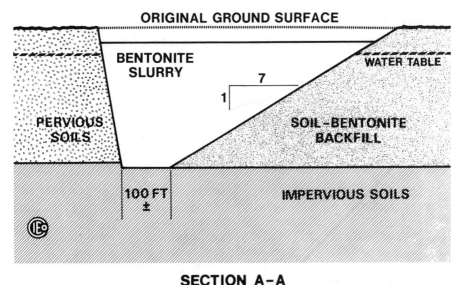

SECTION A-A

Figure 4. Slurry trench with bentonite slurry

Freezing has been used successfully for many years to stabilize ground for the sinking of mine shafts and to control ground water. This highly specialized procedure requires design, installation and operation by experts in freezing techniques.

Chemical or cement grout is often used to provide an impervious wall in pervious soils and to seal fractured and jointed rock. This method is most effective and economical for water control in localized areas or in mine shaft operations. Extensive grouting may prove uneconomical in a large mining operation.

Wellpoint systems, slurry trenches, freezing and grouting methods, along with sumping systems, horizontal and vertical drains, sheet piling and logging, can be usable and practical procedures for mine water control. Many of these methods, however, are confined to zones of localized seepage, to unconsolidated sediments or for water control along diversion dams or channels or tailings dams (2).

WATER CONTROL SYSTEMS - DEEP WELLS

Installation of deep wells is the most common method for pre-drainage, and properly installed wells and pumps can provide effective water control. Homogenous and free-draining sediments, stratified permeable layers and fractured rock zones can be penetrated by wells from the surface or from working levels in the mine. If pressure relief is of prime importance, relatively few wells may be required. A successful system may include a combination of two or more water control methods, such as deep wells and sumping systems or slurry trenches and pressure relief wells.

Well drilling procedures have advanced from hand excavation methods used over 4,000 years ago to the efficient use of modern equipment. The advantages and disadvantages of current drilling methods are described in greater detail in other documents (3).

Reverse rotary drilling is advantageous in unconsolidated formations containing few boulders because it allows for large hole diameters of 24 to 36 inches. Gravel filters for stabilizing formations can be placed in the annular spaces around the well screens, which usually range from 6 to 16 inches in diameter. Bentonitic drilling muds or other drilling additives that tend to plug formations and gravel filters are not necessary in most cases.

Wells with diameters less than 16 inches are drilled by standard rotary methods, often with roller type rock bits. Bentonite, organic polymers or other additives are added to the drilling fluid to lubricate bits, remove cuttings from the hole, reduce fluid loss and prevent hole cavings; however, time to develop wells increases if these additives are necessary.

Air rotary drilling equipment is commonly used to drill water wells in consolidated materials. These drilling rigs use compressed air in lieu of drilling muds, and many rigs are equipped with conventional mud pumps and air compressors for drilling either unconsolidated or consolidated materials.

The water well industry employs air rotary drills equipped with the down-the-hole or pneumatic hammer. This equipment has a rapid rate of penetration because the method involves both rotary and percussion drilling procedures. Deep wells drilled by air are usually less than 10 inches in diameter as air requirements for large-diameter deep wells are excessive. The ground-water geologist may specify drilling of test wells by this method to measure water production during drilling.

Well design criteria must be carefully established. Well size and depth, casing and screen materials, screen length and slot size, gravel filter specifications, grouting and well development procedures must be determined.

Chemical and bacterial laboratory analyses of water sampled during pump testing should be studied during well design. Water may corrode casings and screens if improper materials are installed and if the water has a low pH or contains hydrogen sulphide, high total dissolved solids, chloride or excessive dissolved gases. Also, well plugging can result from carbonates, iron, manganese and bacteria. Well treatment is necessary to control incrustation, and well construction materials should withstand acidizing, chlorination and treatment with biocides and other chemicals. Stainless steel, plastic, monel or brass are used instead of iron or steel screens and casings to counter corrosion. A typical dewatering well is shown on Figure 5.

Severe abrasion from sand produced by wells can ruin pump impellers and bearings. Screen slot sizes and filter gradation must be specified for unconsolidated or poorly cemented sand formations. If bentonite muds are used, polyphosphates may be required to disperse clay particles. Pumping, jetting and surging methods are used for well development. Completed wells should be sterilized by chlorine compounds.

The geohydrologist and engineer can use information from pumping tests to determine the head and capacity requirements for selecting pumping equipment. A variety of pumps made of various alloys and engineered to meet diverse hydrologic conditions are available in the United States, and manufacturers' performance charts should be consulted prior to choosing pumping equipment. Vertical turbine or submersible pumps are selected for large dewatering projects, and irrigation turbine pump settings of 1000 feet are common in California's San Joaquin Valley.

Capital cost items that are included in the budget for a typical well dewatering system may include the following:

- Drilling costs
- Mud pit excavation
- Well casing
- Grouting
- Test pumping
- Power
- Labor, including supervision
- Mobilization and demobilization of equipment, including freight
- Cost of obtaining a water supply, including supply pump and hose
- Pumps and discharge pipe, including installation
- Front end loader, crane, welder, tools, light plant, air compressor and transportation
- Miscellaneous items including taxes, licenses and permits

- Surface casing
- Well screen
- Gravel filter
- Well development
- Fuel, oil and grease

DISCHARGE SYSTEM

Any large-scale dewatering program must be within the limitations imposed by government and private agencies. Discharging into streams in the area may be illegal or may not be feasible, and selection of alternative methods of water storage or aquifer augmentation may be necessary. These methods may be costly and subject to controls.

If water is impounded, the height and construction of the dam are subject to rigid governmental specifications. Land acquisition, pumping equipment, water lines, roads and construction costs and materials must be considered and budgeted. If water is potable or supports plant life, it may be disposed economically by supplying agriculture or industry with water from the mining operation.

Recharge wells, galleries, shafts, pits or basins can counter the effects of extensive lowering of the water table or can be used to dispose of water. Recharge or injection systems have been used effectively by cities and industry for waste disposal, aquifer recharge and water storage, to prevent salt water intrusion and for disposal of brines.

Injection wells or systems may become plugged due to one or more of the following physical and chemical factors (4):

● Air entrainment, a condition in which gas bubbles are trapped, may plug voids more effectively than silts and clays.
● High levels of suspended solids can plug recharge wells and galleries.
● Chemical changes can occur in water as it is withdrawn from an aquifer; minerals, including iron, may precipitate as a result of aeration.
● Iron or sulfate bacteria and other micro-organisms can be introduced into the aquifer or transmitted by the recharge water.
● Clay colloids may swell in the aquifer.
● Chemical reactions can occur between the ground water and the recharge water; insoluble products may precipitate.

Extensive geologic and hydrologic research of the area must be undertaken before injection or recharge is considered. Geologic structures, aquifers, areal seismicity and possible fracture gradients should be studied. Monitoring networks, bacteriology, the need for water treatment and potential sites and aquifers must be evaluated extensively; and the environmental and legal aspects of reinjection must be appraised. Ideally, recharge or injection systems should be recommended initially on an experimental basis or should be prescribed for areas where injection has proven effective and economical. The chemical, physical and biological quality of the native ground water and of the reinjected water should be monitored regularly at pumping, reinjection and observation well sites. A typical reinjection well is shown on Figure 5.

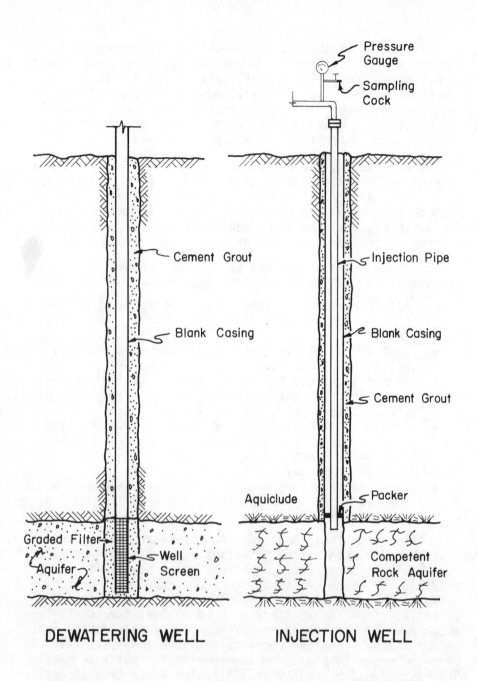

Figure 5. Typical dewatering and reinjection wells

OPERATION AND MAINTENANCE

Costs for operating and maintaining a system of dewatering wells can be budgeted and may include amounts for power, labor, equipment and replacement parts. These can be projected for the duration of mining activities.

Well treatment and rehabilitation costs should also be included because well screens, pumps and formations may be clogged by bacteria, iron, manganese and other elements. If regular inspections and maintenance are not performed, well production declines. Acidization, treatment with polyphosphates, biocides, surging, jetting and over-pumping methods may effectively rehabilitate the well. These procedures are more effective if they are performed by specialists during regular preventative maintenance programs. The ground-water geologist and engineer can devise procedures and suggest schedules for well and pump inspection based on water quality analyses, existing well records and manufacturers' recommendations.

CONCLUSION

Geologic and soil formations at the mine site will dictate the type and application of water control systems. The ground-water geologist can review existing data, prescribe testing procedures and specify methods for dewatering open cut or underground mines. These methods have their respective advantages, disadvantages and limitations; but, with an understanding of the geologic and hydrologic conditions at the mine site, a practical and feasible method of water control can be selected.

REFERENCES

1. Bentall, Ray, Ed., Methods of Determining Permeability, Transmissibility and Drawdown. Geological Survey Water-Supply Paper 1536-I. U.S. Government Printing Office, Washington, D.C., 1963.

2. U.S. Army Engineers Waterways Experiment Station, Dewatering and Groundwater Control for Deep Excavations. TM 5-818-5/NAVFAC P-418/AFM88-5, Ch. 6. U.S. Army, Washington, D.C., 1971.

3. Johnson Division, VOP Inc. <u>Ground Water and Wells:</u>
<u>A Reference Book for the Water-Well Industry</u>. St. Paul,
Minnesota, 1975.

4. Sniegocki, R. T., <u>Problems in Artificial Recharge</u>
<u>Through Wells in the Grand Prairie Region, Arkansas</u>. Geo-
logical Survey Water-Supply Paper 1615-F. U.S. Government
Printing Office, Washington, D.C., 1963.

5. Ferris, J. G. <u>et al</u>., <u>Theory of Aquifer Tests</u>. Geological Survey Water-Supply Paper 1536-E. U.S. Government
Printing Office, Washington, D.C., 1962.

6. Todd, David K., <u>Ground Water Hydrology</u>. John Wiley &
Sons, Inc., New York, N.Y., 1959.

7. West, S. W., <u>Disposal of Uranium-Mill Effluent by Well</u>
<u>Injection in the Grants Area, Valencia County, New Mexico</u>.
Geological Survey Professional Paper 386-D. U.S. Government Printing Office, Washington, D.C., 1972.

8. Marsh, John H., "Design of Waste Disposal Wells",
<u>Ground Water: Journal of the Technical Division, National</u>
<u>Water Well Association</u>. Vol. 6, No. 2, March-April 1968,
Urbana, Illinois, pp. 4-8.

10

Drainage Control and Mine Dewatering at Faro Open Pit Mine

by Randy S. Lopaschuk,
Geological/Geotechnical Engineer,
Cyprus Anvil Mining Corporation,
Faro, Yukon Territory, Canada

ABSTRACT

There have been many problems associated with drainage control and mine dewatering since mining started at the Faro open pit mine. Drainage and dewatering programs have been mainly implemented in three areas of the mine: the Faro Creek diversion ditch outside of the pit limits, the Faro Valley, and the bottom of the open pit. These programs utilize a system of ditches, pipelines, sumps, pumps and inclined drainholes. This paper describes the application of these methods of dealing with water problems at the mine.

INTRODUCTION

Cyprus Anvil Mining Corporation operates an open pit lead-zinc-silver mine and a 10,000 tons per day concentrator at Faro, Yukon Territory, Canada. Since mining began in 1968 there have been problems associated with drainage control and mine dewatering and these problems have increased as the open pit has expanded and deepened. This paper discusses the problems encountered and the solutions that have been applied to enable effective mining operations to continue.

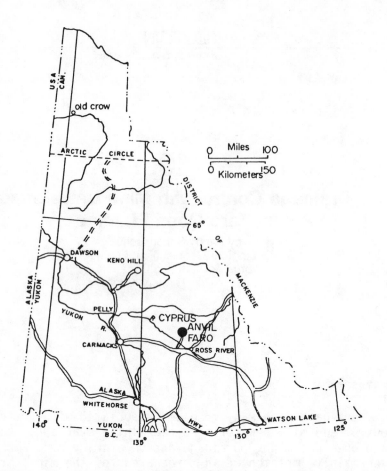

Figure No. 1 - Location of Cyprus Anvil Mine, Faro, Yukon Territory

Location and Climate

The Faro orebody, approximately 120 air miles northeast of Whitehorse, is located east of Rose Mountain and northeast of Mount Mye in the Anvil Range in the east central Yukon (see Figure No. 1).

Temperatures at the minesite range from minus fifty degrees Fahrenheit at mid-winter minimum to plus eighty-five degrees Fahrenheit at summer maximum. Freezing conditions persist from mid-September until early May. Snowfall accounts for one-half of the mean annual precipitation of 15 inches and the maximum snowfall cover ranges up to fifty inches in late March.

Geology

The Faro deposits consist of three nearly horizontal, strataform, stratabound, massive pyritic lead-zinc sulfide zones. Zones 1 and 3 are separate parts of the Large Faro deposit vertically offset by faulting and related intrusions, while the Small Faro deposit (Zone 2) forms a completely separate unit.

The Large Faro deposit is the present area of concern regarding mine dewatering as Zone 2 has not yet been developed. This deposit is lenticular in plan and cross-section with a 5,000 foot length, 1,600 foot width and 150 foot average thickness. Zone 1 is overlain by 90 feet of overburden and 100 to 160 feet of waste rock, while Zone 3 is overlain by 100 feet of overburden and approximately 400 feet of waste rock.

The Faro sulfide bodies are stratabound successively by a thin quartzite which is in sharp contact with "bleached" muscovite schists which grade outward into normal biotite-muscovite ± andalusite schists with irregular interbands of graphite. The schists are overlain conformably by blocky, green calc-silicate phyllites. The dominant foliation in the schists and phyllites, dipping approximately 20 degrees to the southwest, is roughly parallel to the lithological contacts.

The deposits have been intruded by post-ore dykes associated with the Anvil batholith. At the northwest end, sulfides abut against white, heavily altered, medium-grained quartz monzonite. The fault separating Zones 1 and 3 has been intruded by a hornblende-biotite diorite dyke swarm.

PROBLEMS RELATED TO WATER IN THE PIT

Water presently flows into the pit from the Faro Creek valley and from groundwater seepage at the rate of approximately 400 U.S. GPM. Undesirable pit operating and design conditions, as well as other problems, resulting from this incoming water are:

In the Mine

1) Saturation of the east wall of the pit, resulting in unstable slopes and decreased slope design angles, necessitating additional stripping requirements.

2) Excessive slurry consumption because of extensive wet blast hole loading conditions. It costs twice as much to load a wet hole with the appropriate explosive as it does to load a dry hole. Also re-drilling is often necessary because the wet holes cave fairly quickly.

3) Water glaciates across haul roads in the pit bottom in the winter, necessitating constant maintenance and resulting in slippery roads with frequent chuckholes. During spring thaw, this ice buildup turns to deep mud. These roadway conditions result in increased maintenance and downtime on haulage equipment.

4) The water flow necessitates construction and maintenance of ditches along pit ramps. Ice and debris accumulation around these ditches frequently widens the ditch area such that it produces single lane traffic on ramps, thereby increasing truck cycle times and lowering productivity.

5) In the winter, frozen material build-ups occur in truck boxes and in shovel buckets. This causes extra expense due to longer loading times and smaller than normal truck loads.

In the Mill

1) If the ore is very wet, it may be necessary to stockpile it before crushing in order that it will dry. If the ore is stockpiled for too long, oxidation

occurs which creates problems in the concentration process.

2) Sloppy wet ore spills off conveyors, blocks screens and chutes, quickly blocks return rollers and causes overall cleanup problems.

3) In the winter, ice in the ore causes problems in the coarse and fine ore bins.

These problems can be greatly reduced if proper drainage control and dewatering methods are used to cut down the flow and accumulation of water in the pit. Increased safety of the pit slopes and cost savings in operations will result from a comprehensive mine dewatering program. Because of these reasons, Cyprus Anvil reassessed its dewatering programs with the aid of consultants in 1975 and improved and added to them for future improvements in pit water control.

HISTORY OF DEWATERING

The Faro orebody lies with its long axis approximately perpendicular to the Faro Creek valley. Initial mining in the upper part of the orebody took place on the northwest slope of the valley. While mining was confined to this slope, water was not a major factor as it could be conveyed by ditches down the slope to Faro Creek.

As mining approached the Faro Creek, it became necessary to divert the water flow. A route was chosen to carry the flow to the east, outside of the proposed final pit limits, and discharge it into the north fork of Rose Creek. To attain sufficient elevation for the ditch to maintain grade above the pit limits, the point of diversion had to be made nearly a mile upstream from the edge of the pit. The initial ditch, while not completely water tight, diverted most of the surface flow away from the mine. Construction of this Faro Creek diversion ditch was the first major drainage control measure implemented at the mine (see Figure No. 2).

FARO CREEK DIVERSION DITCH

·Faro Creek has been diverted around the Anvil open pit by means of a sidehill cut channel. The diversion ditch was constructed using a backhoe and piling the excavated

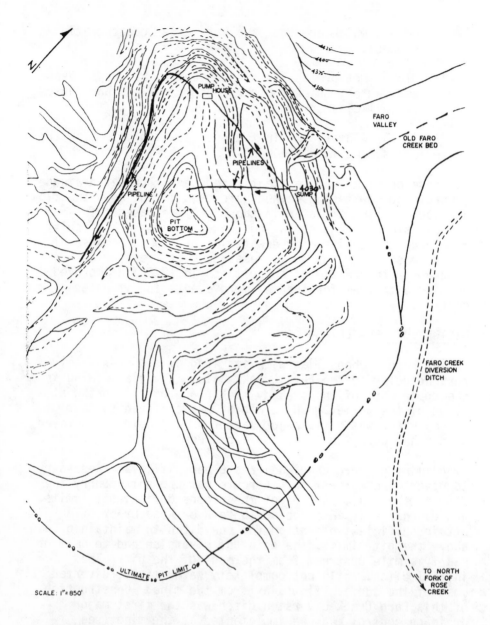

Figure No. 2 - Open pit plan showing components of mine dewatering system

silty soil as a low dyke on the downhill side of the ditch. A rockfill dyke was later constructed along the downhill side of the diversion ditch adjacent to the soil dyke, increasing the height of the dyke. During the spring run-off, the water flow in the diversion ditch rose above the portion of the ditch confined by silty soil, and flowed against the adjoining rockfill dyke causing significant leakage. The ditch was mainly excavated in silty sand containing gravel, cobbles and small boulders. The silt content is sufficiently high to provide a relatively impervious seal, but the ditch does leak to some extent. However, the Faro Creek diversion ditch does not provide a significant portion of the groundwater seepage entering the pit. (1)

Initially, the diversion ditch simply discharged down a hillside after it was past the ultimate pit limits. The outflow cut its own series of channels down the hillside to connect with Rose Creek. This outflow area eventually became responsible for three problems:

1) Heavy, erratic erosion of the hillside.

2) Formation of a large alluvial fan in Rose Creek.

3) Higher than normal suspended solids in Rose Creek.

The construction of a channel with favourable gradients, alignment, cross-sectional configuration and outflow conditions between the existing outflow of Faro Creek diversion ditch and Rose Creek was necessary to prevent further excess erosion and siltation in that area. The new channel alignment was selected based on the following merits:

1) Flows will be carried a safe distance from existing dumps.

2) The channel will have the maximum amount of bedrock exposure.

3) Gradients will be minimized to prevent excess erosion and subsequent siltation of Rose Creek.

4) The channel will discharge into a large, flat settling area, causing decrease in flow velocity and subsequent settling out of suspended solids prior to entry into Rose Creek.

The channel was designed to accommodate flows from a 20 year flood, or 200 cubic feet per second.

The Relocation of the Faro Creek Diversion Ditch

A decision was made in 1978 to extend the final pit limits of the northeast corner and east wall of the pit for slope stability and ore recovery reasons. The establishment of new ultimate pit limits meant that a portion of the existing Faro Valley diversion ditch would have been too close to, or within, these pit limits. Therefore, it was necessary to relocate this section of the ditch. The ditch had to be relocated back into a hillside and a deep cut had to be made to keep the new section on grade with the remaining old sections of the ditch. The relocation route was 2,000 feet long with a 0.9% grade and designed cut slopes of 1.5:1 dropping to a 12 foot horizontal bottom. Bulldozers and scrapers were used to construct the ditch and 100,000 cubic yards of glacial till and rock were removed.

The ditch was constructed almost completely in sands and gravels, except for a 400 foot section where bedrock was encountered along the base of the ditch. The ditch was very permeable and it was thought that too much water would seep out of the ditch and eventually end up in the pit through subsurface flow. To rectify this, it was decided to cut the ditch one foot below grade and then add a silty, clayey fill to provide a more impermeable bottom. The fill was then compacted with a self-propelled, smooth drum compactor. However, leakage from the ditch still presented a big problem because water was escaping along the over-burden/bedrock contact in the section of the ditch that had encountered bedrock. This water was entering the pit along the exposed overburden/bedrock contact and eventually interfering with mining operations and causing wet blast-holes on the east wall of the pit.

To prevent this water from entering the pit, it was decided to line 600 feet of the diversion ditch along the section where the water was escaping. A 32 foot wide, flexible, three-ply, reinforced, 30-MIL, polyethylene liner was installed to stop the leakage.

GROUNDWATER DRAINAGE OF THE FARO VALLEY

Problem

Figure No. 2A - Part of the relocated Faro Creek Diversion Ditch cut into the hillside above the pit.

Figure No. 2B - Water entering the pit along the overburden/ bedrock contact.

The northeast slope of the Anvil pit intercepts bedded granular and clayey soils in the vicinity of the Faro Creek valley. As exposed in the pit face, this alluvial material occupies two distinct ancient channels over a lateral extent of 1,000 feet and a vertical extent of 200 feet in the west channel and 100 feet in the east channel. Waste dumps are situated on top of the valley fill a short distance from the pit limits. The stability of this northeast slope is severely affected by surface and subsurface water conditions.

The ore supply for three mining phases and the ore haulage ramp corresponding with these phases lie directly beneath this alluvial slope. It was feared that production could be interrupted periodically by small mud flows or indefinitely if a large failure occurred. In addition to being a serious threat to continued production, this situation presented a definite hazard to men and equipment working beneath this slope.

Surface Water

Most of the surface water from the Faro Valley drainage area is controlled by the unlined sidehill diversion ditch above the pit limits. Seepage from this ditch and surface run-off between the diversion point and the pit limits have contributed to approximately 350 U.S. GPM of surface flow entering the pit. In the past, the small surface flow of water that existed in the Faro Creek valley downstream of the diversion point flowed through a porous rockfill dam placed upstream of the pit area and entered the pit along the original Faro Creek bed. As the pit excavation encroached on the Faro Creek location, a sump was excavated in the creek bed upstream of the rockfill dam, and surface flows were pumped into the diversion ditch. This sump pumping is still continued to prevent the surface water from entering the pit and from becoming recharge for the Faro Valley groundwater flow.

Surface run-off from the pit slopes and waste dumps is significant during spring break-up and after heavy summer showers. Instantaneous flows in excess of 1,000 U.S. GPM have been recorded during these periods.

Groundwater

Subsurface water in the Faro Valley flows through bedded sand and gravel layers in the area of two ancient stream channels and collects in a ditch at the 4030 elevation. This ditch was constructed along a wide bench approximately half way down the pit wall. Initially, the ditch was un- lined, but because of excessive leakage, it was later lined with a three foot diameter, half-circular metal flume.

At the pit face, the main groundwater flow is between the bedrock/overburden contact and the 4110 elevation with smaller flows stratified above impermeable silt and clay layers upwards to the 4170 elevation in the west channel and the 4115 elevation in the east channel. Accumulated subsurface flows in excess of 350 U.S. GPM have been measured in weirs in the 4030 ditch.

During November and December, 1975 and January, 1976, five rotary test holes were drilled through the waste dumps and overburden into bedrock to determine soil density and internal stratigraphy. Multiple piezometer installations were located in these holes to determine groundwater conditions and to monitor the effectiveness of a proposed dewatering system.

From the borehole investigations, the alluvium appeared to be mainly bedded gravels and sands with varying amounts of silt. Zones of varved clay and clayey sand-gravel occur but cannot be readily projected from hole to hole. A "marker bed" of white granitic gravel indicated an apparent bedding dip of 10 degrees toward the pit. The bedrock surface dips at 2 to 5 degrees toward the pit. (2)

The piezometer readings indicated a groundwater flow within the alluvium channels along the alluvium/bedrock contact to a depth of 50 to 80 feet with a gradient of 6 to 9 degrees toward the pit. There appeared to be no general perched water table except locally near the present creek bed. The springs observed at the face above the 4115 elevation were presumed, therefore, to be small, isolated flows not connected with the main piezometric surface. The piping observed at the bedrock/overburden contact indicates that the piezometric surface steepens as it approaches the pit.

Slope Stability

Numerous slump failures have occurred in the Faro Valley overburden slopes. On August 14, 1975 an estimated 25,000 BCY of saturated mud flowed out of the area, isolating a 15 cubic yard electric mining shovel for almost two days and disrupting ore development as the mud flowed into the pit bottom.

The concern was that the surface run-off could initiate large scale failures by two mechanisms. Sloughed material and mud flows could cause blockage of the groundwater outflows, thereby increasing the piezometric head to the point of instability. Also, continued sloughing could eventually cause the waste dumps and possibly the Faro Creek diversion ditch to be undercut.

The failure mechanism, due to excessive groundwater, appeared to be undermining by piping in granular soils, followed by collapse of overlying silty and clayey soils. These initial block failures, by removing weight from the passive block, by steeping the slope, and possibly by obstructing groundwater outflow, could initiate large scale (1-3 million BCY) wedge-type failures. (2)

With the groundwater level that was present in 1975, the entire slope had a very marginal factor of safety. A 20 foot increase in the piezometric head, or continued block failures, would have surely precipitated a large failure.

Solution

A long term solution to this problem was required due to the magnitude and seriousness of the situation. Four possible alternatives for stabilizing the slope were investigated:

1) Flatten the slope and remove weight from the active block by mining the waste dumps from the valley floor.

2) Intercept the groundwater before it reaches the pit face by installing inclined drain holes.

3) Install a screen of vertical well points behind the pit crest to intercept groundwater.

4) Place a sand and gravel filter blanket across the exposed sediments to control groundwater.

Solution I

Flattening the slope would have involved the removal of approximately 500,000 BCY of waste dumps from a zone 600 feet wide behind the pit crest. This would not have improved the stability of the blocks which were being undermined by piping, but the probability and seriousness of a large scale wedge failure would have been reduced. Failures of a magnitude similar to the August 14th. slide could still occur.

Solution II

Inclined, self-draining holes with slotted casing could be used to intercept groundwater behind the excavated pit slope, thereby preventing piping and subsequent block collapse. The holes would be collared in bedrock on the 4030 bench and driven 500-600 feet into the basal sands and gravels along the bedrock contact. Five or six holes would be drilled into each channel from locations on either side of the channel.

The advantages of inclined drains are:

1) Maximum penetration of water-bearing strata.

2) Effectiveness would not be seriously affected by small failures.

3) The system would be virtually maintenance-free.

Solution III

A screen of vertical wells would be installed behind the pit limit to intercept the groundwater flow. The system would have the following characteristics:

1) Number of Wells - 10

2) Spacing - 100 feet

3) Finished Diameter - 8 inches

4) Depth per Well - 200 feet

5) Screen Length per Well - 20 feet

6) Pumps - 10 H.P. submersible, 100 U.S. GPM discharge

The major disadvantages of a vertical well screen are:

1) In case of a partial slope failure, one or more of the wells may be destroyed.

2) Due to the irregular bedrock and associated ground-water profile, it would be difficult locating wells for maximum dewatering efficiency.

3) High operational and maintenance costs are anticipated to ensure reliable and continuous operation during cold weather.

4) Minimum (vertical) penetration of water-bearing strata.

Solution IV

The forces of water seepage at cut slopes can be controlled by filter blankets. This would require a properly graded, 10 foot thick, sand and gravel filter sheet, lain against a properly trimmed slope with an additional 10 foot thickness of suitable rip-rap to serve as a stabilizing buttress and insulation blanket. The filter prevents piping while allowing the slope to drain freely.

The disadvantages of this solution are:

1) The lack of suitable equipment access to the slope.

2) The necessity of placing the filter and buttress material on the trimmed slope before any slumping occurs.

3) The source of suitable filter material.

4) The difficulty of placing the filter material on a 350 foot long, 30 degree slope.

Waste dump material could not be crushed and screened for the filter, nor could it be used as rip-rap due to its high clay content and weathered condition.

An evaluation of the four alternative solutions indicated that a system of inclined drains was the most effective and economic method of preventing large scale slope failures in the Faro Valley alluvium.

THE INSTALLATION OF DRAINHOLES IN THE FARO VALLEY

After the locations were chosen for the drainholes, the following aspects were considered pertaining to their installation as suggested by the consultants on the project, Piteau & Associates. (3)

1) Inclined drains should be collared in stable areas where it is unlikely that either sloughing or complete slope failure could occur and cut off the drains.

2) The inclined drains should be orientated in such a way that at least 50 feet of rock is penetrated before encountering overburden.

3) The inclined drains should be orientated or inclined in such a way that the drains do not come within about 15 feet of daylighting at any point along the drain.

The drilling of the inclined drains was performed utilizing an Aardvark Model 125 track mounted drilling machine. Six thousand feet of drilling was carried out, distributed among ten holes of approximately equal length.

Some site observations were attempted while the drilling was in progress to obtain a more complete picture of the internal stratigraphy of Faro Valley. It was difficult to determine the exact location of the overburden/bedrock contact while drilling because of the schistose or weathered nature of the bedrock in the area of the contact and because the drill cuttings were usually ground very fine, making them difficult to identify. Correlating the drilling rate with changes in soil and rock type was not particularly successful and it was also difficult to obtain accurate flow measurements during drilling because water was sometimes used while drilling. However, areas where the rate of flow suddenly increased were evident.

After each inclined borehole was drilled, it was lined with 1.5 inch O.D. slotted plastic pipe (the first ten feet of pipe at the collar of the hole was not slotted).

Analysis of Data

After all the inclined drainholes were installed and a sufficient amount of flow data was collected, correlations were attempted between the Faro Valley piezometer data and the drainhole discharge data. The inclined drains were installed to lower the piezometric level in the Faro Valley overburden and analysis of the data was important to determine the success of the project.

The piezometer data was analyzed by Piteau & Associates by plotting and evaluating raw data and then performing a cumulative sums (cusums) analysis on the data (3). Piteau defines the cusums technique as "a rapid and precise method of determining trends above or below a particular reference value and of ascertaining both the magnitude and location of the variations." In this case, the mean piezometric elevation for each piezometer was used as the reference value.

Piteau mentions that "the results of the cumulative sums analyses provide another way of viewing both the seasonal fluctuations of piezometric levels within the slope and the effects of installing inclined drains. Underneath each plot of raw data in Figure No. 3 is the resulting cusums plot and Manhattan diagram for the piezometric elevation. It can be seen that the raw data plot better illustrates the absolute values of the seasonal fluctuations and the exact time at which these fluctuations occur. The cusums analysis more accurately defines the current mean values of the data trends and the relationship of these trends to the overall mean."

Fluctuations of the piezometric levels appear to be seasonal, with levels increasing through the fall and peaking in November or December and the lowest levels occurring in the spring, usually during April or May. Seasonal fluctuations prior to installation of the inclined drains ranged from about 7 to 16 feet.

Since installing the inclined drains, the typical fall increase has been curtailed. A piezometric level drawdown occurred almost immediately, within 1 to 2 weeks after installation of the drains. This drawdown ranged from 2.2 to 31.2 feet. Most piezometers averaged 7 to 14 feet of drawdown. (3)

The total amount of water collected from all inclined drains is approximately 70 IGPM or 100,000 IGPD. Installation of the inclined drains appears to have effectively stopped or significantly reduced the typical seasonal increase in piezometric levels. Since the drains were

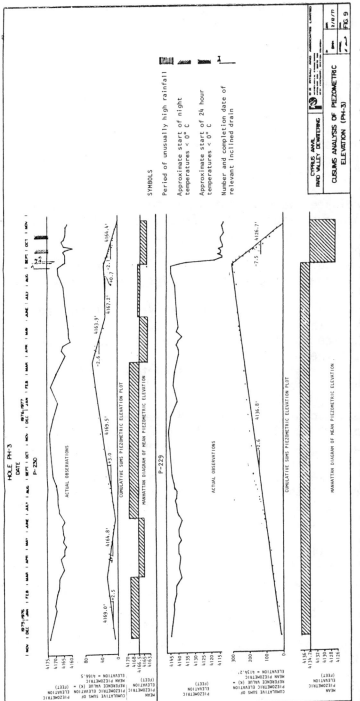

Figure 3 – Cusums Analysis of Piezometric Elevation. Note large decrease in piezometric elevation after drainholes were installed in September, 1977.

installed in September, 1977, no major failures have taken place in the Faro Valley alluvium.

REDIVERSION OF THE WATER IN THE 4030 DITCH

An alternative to the metal flume that carried the Faro Valley water out of the pit along the 4030 bench was needed. The reason for this was that the existing drainage system along the 4030 ditch was in an area of questionable slope stability and also it was not located on a final pit wall, thus eventually requiring relocation of the ditch when the mining phase approached this area.

Any new drainage system adopted had to provide adequate control of both subsurface and surface water. Therefore, it was advisable to continue collecting the water on the 4030 bench level below the Faro Valley because this location was just below the bedrock/alluvium contact and much of the groundwater seepage surfaced at or before this contact.

The alternative to draining the Faro Valley water around the east side of the pit, as it was done, was to drain it to the west. This could be achieved either at a constant bench elevation until the water was out of the pit, or else drained into the existing sump in the northwest corner by the pit pumphouse (see Figure No. 2).

A pipeline was constructed using 8 inch Series 40 poly-ethylene pipe from the 4030 bench below Faro Valley to the pit pumphouse sump in the northwest corner of the pit. It was decided to use a pipeline for diverting the water rather than a ditch and metal flume because it would provide much more flexibility in the course chosen for diversion and it would be easier to maintain (there would be no overflows or ice buildups as with the flume). (See Figure No. 4)

A sump was drilled, blasted and dug in bedrock on the 4030 elevation for use in collecting the water to be diverted down the pipeline. The sump was located so that it could best intercept all the drainage out of Faro Valley. The easiest place to collect all the water would have been just east of the inclined drainhole locations, but this was not an acceptable location because of the slope instability found immediately below on the north pit wall. Even a small failure here could ruin a sump and the escaping water could seriously affect the remaining stability of this section of the pit wall. The sump was constructed on a stable section

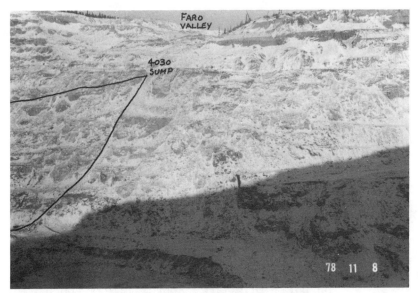

Figure No. 4 - Location of pipelines carrying water from the Faro Valley area to the pit bottom pumphouse.

Figure No. 5 - Water collected in the pit bottom (25 million U.S. gallons, Sept./78). All this water has since been pumped out of the pit using the new pumping system of the 4030 bench below Faro Valley and water was ditched into it from both the east and the west. A concrete dam was constructed to decant water from the sump and the pipelines were anchored in the concrete. Two pipelines were connected to the sump so that if one got blocked or frozen up the other could be opened up and used. The pipelines were designed so that the sump drained by gravity feed and no sump pumping was necessary. Approximately 300 U.S. GPM flow down the pipeline to the pit bottom sump. This amount will triple during spring runoff.

PIT BOTTOM DEWATERING

Problem

In 1975, plans for a final drainage system for the Faro open pit were proposed because the mining phase had reached the stage where the pit bottom was encountering the regional water table. Up until this time, approximately 400 U.S. GPM were being pumped from the bottom of the pit through an old exploration adit. This old pumping system did not have the capability of lifting the water over the existing pit wall and it was only because of the existence of the adit that dewatering was possible. Recirculation of water between the adit and the pit was thought to have existed, contributing to the water control problems in the pit bottom. These problems combined with the fact that the adit was scheduled to be mined out in early 1977, necessitated installation of an alternate dewatering system to prevent flooding of the pit bottom. If flooding had occurred, the ore supply would have been cut off (see Figure No. 5)

Solution

There was a large flat area (300 feet by 400 feet) in the northwest corner of the pit that could accommodate a sump and pumphouse for use in a new dewatering system. This was an advantageous location because the pit wall surrounding the area was final and the area itself would not be mined out and would be accessible during all the successive mining phases. It was decided to install the main components of an in-the-pit dewatering system at this location.

The solution of installing deep wells outside the ultimate pit perimeter to lower the water table in the pit area was rejected because of the cost and because of the size and depth of the pit. (The open pit will eventually reach 1,000 feet in depth and will be 4,800 feet long by 3,000 feet wide).

The pit bottom dewatering system included:

1) Two pumps and motors

2) Two pipelines

3) Four submersible sump pumps

4) One transformer

5) Two electric switch gears

6) Sump

7) Construction of a protective building around the pumps, the motors and the valve system

8) Steamer

9) Miscellaneous parts - valves, couplings, elbows, flow meters, electric heaters, etc.

An analysis of the above items was done to, hopefully, come up with the most efficient system.

When considering the selection of pumps and motors, the following criteria were applied:

1) Capable of handling fines in the water

2) Pump at a minimum of 270 feet total dynamic head

3) Pumping rate of 400 U.S. GPM

4) Minimum delivery time

5) Minimum power consumption

6) Durability

7) Parts' availability

8) Minimum cost

After evaluating different pumps, a horizontal six inch standard centrifugal double stage pump with a V-belt drive was chosen because:

1) It could handle fines up to 0.5 inches.

2) It met the requirements for head and quantity of water.

3) It had a low R.P.M. (1,750 R.P.M.), thus minimizing the wear on the impeller.

4) A similar pump had already been used successfully in the pit.

5) The 75 H.P. motor and the V-belt would allow versatility in the pumping rate and in the total dynamic head.

After selecting the necessary pumps for use in the dewatering system, the choice and location of the pipelines had to be determined. The system incorporated two pipelines (one attached to each pump) that were self-draining, easily accessible and of minimum exposure to blasts and other mining activities. Three possible solutions were considered for the location of the pipelines and a decision analysis was done on the three alternatives to determine the best solution.

The pipeline route that was used was recommended mainly because of the lower head over which the water was pumped in comparison to the other possible routes. The lower head allowed the utilization of polyethylene pipe, resulting in greater manoeuverability as compared to steel pipe, and also of smaller pumps at lower R.P.M., resulting in lower power consumption and less maintenance.

The two pipelines were constructed of six inch Series 160 polyethylene pipe and were both 2,900 feet long. The pipelines run from the pumphouse at the 3790 pit elevation up the pit wall to a wide bench at the 4030 elevation and along this bench until out of the pit area where the water is discharged (see Figure No. 2).

The pumping operation is variable with high pumping rates in the springtime and lower rates in the winter. To eliminate the irregular operation of the pumps, to keep a

Figure No. 6 - Pit bottom pumphouse - this structure houses the pumps, motors, valve system and flow meter.

Figure No. 7 - Pumps used in the pit bottom dewatering system (75 H.P. standard centrifugal double stage pumps).

constant flow through the pipeline, thus preventing freezing, and to facilitate the settling of the fines and protect the pumps, it was necessary to have a sump near the pumphouse on the 3790 bench. A 25 foot by 15 foot by 9 foot concrete sump was constructed with a capacity of 25,000 gallons. The sump had to be waterproofed to prevent recirculation of water back into the pit bottom.

An insulated and heated metal building on skids was constructed to protect the major components of the dewatering system from flyrock and freezing. This structure houses the pumps, motors, valve system and flow meters.

In the event of a forced shutdown in mid-winter and a failure of the automatic draining system to function properly, freezing of the pipelines would occur. A steamer is, therefore, available for use in case of a freeze-up and it has proven to be a practical method of thawing out a frozen pipeline in very cold weather.

Basically, the main components of the pit bottom dewatering system are the pumphouse, pipelines and sump. This pumping system was justified and necessary to keep a dewatered pit bottom to ensure a continuous ore supply to the mill.

FUTURE DEWATERING PLANS

The Faro Creek diversion ditch, the inclined drainholes in Faro Valley and the pit bottom pumping system all combine to provide an adequate dewatering program for the mine, but continual upgrading of the system is necessary. New testing is being carried out to find efficient methods for continuing advanced dewatering in the bottom of the open pit. Plans include drilling 12 to 15 inch diameter holes, using the production blasthole drill rigs, in which submersible pumps can be installed. Pumping tests will be done to gain further knowledge of the necessary well spacings and depths required to ensure a dewatered ore phase before mining begins.

Development of the Small Faro Deposit (Zone 2) will start in 1979 and drainage control measures are being prepared in co-ordination with the mine design.

Mine dewatering of the Faro open pit is an on-going necessity and research and testing will be carried on to ensure adequate control of water problems.

ACKNOWLEDGEMENTS

The writer would like to thank D. Gregoire, Chief Engineer, and D. Hanson, Exploration Geologist, of Cyprus Anvil Mining Corporation for their contributions to this paper based on their past involvement in mine dewatering of the Faro open pit mine.

REFERENCES

1. MORRISON, K. I., "Inspection Report, Anvil Mines - Water at Pit," Ripley, Klohn & Leonoff, File VA1711, August 22, 1972

2. DICK, R. C., "Results of Test Holes Drilled for Stratigraphy and Groundwater Observations in Faro Valley Overburden," Piteau, Gadsby, Macleod Limited, 75-055, February 27, 1976

3. STEWART, A. F. and PITEAU, D. R., "Report on Drainhole Installation and Related Monitoring for Groundwater Drainage of Faro Valley," Piteau & Associates, January, 1978

11

Horizontal Drains—Their Use in Open Pit Mine Dewatering

by Ben L. Seegmiller, Principal,
Seegmiller Associates,
Salt Lake City, Utah, USA

INTRODUCTION

Horizontal drains are one method which may be used for open pit mine dewatering. These devices consist of horizontal holes which usually, but not necessarily, have slotted PVC screen or pipe placed in them. They are used to drain slope embankments or water-storing strata behind an impervious embankment. Further, they may be used underground to assist drainage galleries or shafts placed adjacent to an open pit. Horizontal drains are thought to have first been used in 1939 by the California Division of Highways to drain water induced slope instabilities along highway cuts. Since that time, a number of advances in the method have been made. Most notably the innovations have been in the drilling and emplacement equipment and in the perforated pipe or slotted screen inserts.

The primary purpose of this paper is to describe horizontal drains and their applications and usage in open pit mine operations. The paper begins with a description of a typical drainage system. Next, the procedures for emplacement are described and then advantages and disadvantages are outlined. A brief overview of current costs is then presented followed by a description of a case history which concludes the paper.

SYSTEM DESCRIPTION

Drain Characteristics

Slotted 1½-in. nominal diameter PVC(schedule 80 polyvinyl chloride pipe) screen with machined joints is placed inside holes approximately 4-in. in diameter. The slots vary in size with the smallest being 0.010-in. and the most typical being 0.020-in. The holes are drilled just above the toe of a bench embankment at a slight upward angle, as shown in Figure 1, and at an average length of about 500 feet. A short hole would be 300-ft in length and a long hole would be 700-ft or more in length. The most typical length is 400 to 600-ft. The slotted PVC screen which is placed inside the embankment usually has an unslotted or solid section of pipe placed at the beginning of the hole. A collection system, consisting of larger diameter plastic or steel pipe, usually runs along the toe of the bench and receives water from the solid pipe via a rubber connecting hose.

Drainage System Purpose

There are two distinct purposes for dewatering an open pit mining operation. First are the operational problems that water creates. Water tends to hamper the movement and control of the mining equipment, it increases the unit weight of the material to be removed from the pit and it can cause processing problems in the concentration plant. Second are the slope instability problems. Water reduces the effective strength in the embankment or slope materials and thus, unstable pit walls may be created. It also causes horizontal thrust forces in tension cracks, thereby reducing the factor of safety against slope failure. Horizontal drains may be used alone or in combination with other methods, such as vertical wells or drainage galleries, to lessen or eliminate the adverse affects of water.

Typical Applications

Any dewatering application in an open pit mine is usually worthy of investigation for potential horizontal drains. However, some cases are natural applications. Such a case is the condition where an alluvial sand and gravel overlies bedrock. In this case the top of the bedrock may be old topographic surface which is a relatively impermeable unconformity. Groundwater tends to flow along the interface and exit into the pit just above the contact. Drains may be collared either just above or below the contact. When they

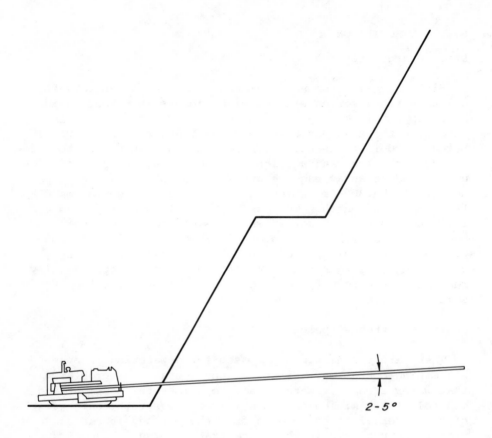

2-5°

Figure 1.   Horizontal Drain Emplacement.

are collared below the contact, they are angled upwards to
pass through the contact at some distance inside the embankment. Another primary application would be in saturated soil
or soft rock materials. In these cases, as in all cases, it
is very important to be sure the source of the water is being
considered and that means are taken, if possible, to lessen
or eliminate the recharge. One other application that deserves
special mention is the case of a water-bearing strata behind
an impervious barrier in the pit slope. The water-bearing
strata may be creating adverse stability affects even though
it is not exposed in the pit. A very closely related condition is a water-filled tension crack located in or beyond
the pit crest. Horizontal drains can serve to tap these
water reservoirs and reduce their adverse affects.

EMPLACEMENT PROCEDURES

Initial Considerations

In order to arrive at the best possible horizontal drainage system, full consideration should first be made of the
applicable geological and hydrological conditions. The
existence of various joint systems, which act as primary
water conduits, should be studied in terms of their spacial
orientations, continuities, spacing and infilling materials.
Usually it is best to lay out a horizontal drain, assuming
that some leeway does exist in the orientation, so that it
intersects as many joints as possible. The permeabilities
of the various rock or soil units should also be examined.
Typically, it may be more desirable to place more drains in
a particular rock or soil material than another, owing to
their different water flow and storage capacity characteristics.

Hole Drilling

Equipment. The first known equipment used for horizontal
drains was called a "Hydrauger". It consisted of a light-
weight air driven rotary drill mounted on a small frame. A
hand operated ratchet level was used to advance the bit into
the slope embankment. A pilot hole about 2-in. in diameter
was originally drilled and then reamed to 6-in. Perforated
steel pipe was then inserted by hand or with the aid of jacks.
Today two commercial drilling machines are available to both
perform the drilling operation and place the PVC screen.
The first unit is the "Hole-Gator" which uses a hollow stem
auger to bore a hole in soil or soft rock materials. The

slotted screen is pushed through the hollow stem, which is then withdrawn, leaving the horizontal drain in place. The second unit is the "Aardvark" which has the ability to drill holes in soft or hard rock materials with drag, tricone or hammer bits. Once the hole is drilled to the desired depth, the bit may be dropped(usually in the case of drag or tricone bits) and the slotted screen is inserted through the rods. A unique patented locking piston allows the Aardvark to suc- cessfully place drains even under the adverse conditions where running sands are present. After screen insertion, the rods are withdrawn over the drain. The drainage system is completed by attaching a collector line to the drain to carry the water away from the slope.

Hole Sizes. The first 15-20 ft of the drain hole is us- ually drilled at 5-in. diameter to accomodate a solid piece of surface casing or pipe. The surface pipe is unslotted and serves to transport the water from the slotted drain to a surface collection system. Auger bits are on the order of 4-in. diameter while drag bits are $4\frac{1}{2}$-in. diameter. Tricone bits vary from 3 3/4 to 4 1/4-in. in diameter. Down-hole hammer bit diameters are typically 4 1/4-in.

Drilling Rates and Hole Completion. These important fac- tors obviously depend on the length of hole and the materials drilled. An example of what may be expected under good con- ditions is 900 ft of drilling in 8 hours, as has been expe- rienced in Wyoming uranium mines, where the drains were placed in medium hard sandstones. Drilling of 200 ft of hole in 8 hours would be considered slow and/or difficult drilling conditions. The completion of a 100 ft long hole would be considered average if done in 6 hours in hard or difficult lithologies and 1 hour under soft or easy conditions. A 500 ft horizontal drain would require from 2 to $4\frac{1}{2}$ days for completion depending on the rock and drilling conditions.

Drain Length

The length of the drain must be such that it reaches the desired water bearing strata. Further, it must reach that strata and effectively solve the problem for which it was originally intended. Obviously, if severe drilling diffi- culties are encountered, the hole may not reach the desired depth and a lessor length will have to suffice. A general rule of thumb that may be followed in the absence of a more definitive basis is that the length of the hole should vary from H/2 to H, where H is the height of the pit slope. In other words, the length of drains for a 500 ft high slope should vary from a minimum of 250 ft to a maximum of 500 ft.

Spacing

Determination of the optimum spacing could, theoretically, have a geological/hydrological basis, but in practice the spacing is usually determined by trial and error. In general, drain spacings range from 10 to 100 feet. Beyond 100 ft, they seldom provide the desired drainage, while at spacings of less than 10 ft, they may not be cost-effective. The permeability conditions obviously will have a pronounced effect on the optimum spacing. As shown in Figure 2, the draw-down curves in a direction perpendicular to the drains could vary considerably depending on the permeability. Effective drainage could only be achieved with closer spaced drains where the permeability is relatively low. The trial and error procedure generally employed consists of the following: A large spacing such as 100 ft is chosen and several drains are emplaced as shown in Figure 3. The rate of flow from the drains is measured and recorded. Then a point midway between two of the drains is selected and another drain is completed. If there is interference between the drains, i.e., if the flow on the adjacent drains lessens more than usual, then the drains may be too close. If no interference is noticed, then the spacing is again decreased by half. The procedure is continued until definite interference is noticed.

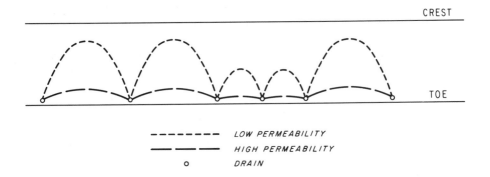

Figure 2. Draw-down Curves Between Drains.

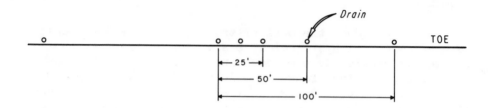

Figure 3. Horizontal Drain Spacing.

At that point the spacing is increased slightly until only
slight interference takes place. The spacing would, in
general, be considered optimal for that portion of the pit.
Other areas, which have differing geological and hydrological
conditions, may also have differing optimum drain spacings.
In any case, the trial and error procedure has been found in
practice to yield the best method of determining drain spacing.

Drain Performance

The completed drainage system should consist of the drains
themselves, a collector system and monitoring piezometers, as
shown in Figure 4, for example. The ultimate performance of
the complete drainage system obviously is the success in getting rid of the water affecting pit operations and causing
slope instabilities. In the shorter term, however, two methods to gauge drain performance are available. The first
method involves the decrease in flow from the drains as a
function of time. If the dewatering operation is successful,
it should be expected that the amount of water flowing from
the drains over a period of time decreases as the amount of
water in the slope embankment decreases. An example of the
decrease in flow that could occur is shown in Figure 5. In
this case a flow of 100 gpm was initially experienced but
quickly decreased to about 20 gpm after only one day. After
one year the flow had decreased to about 10 gpm which was
the static flow for this drain. Other drains under other
conditions will have their own characteristic flow decrease

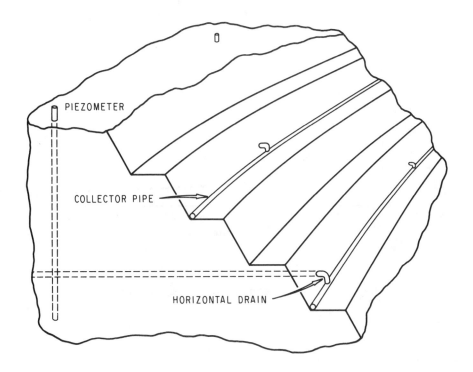

Figure 4.   A Complete Horizontal Drainage System.

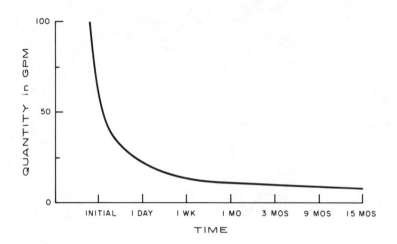

Figure 5.   Horizontal Drain Flow Rate.

curves.   However, they should show a marked decrease in flow
rate with time, if the drains are to be considered sufficient
in number and effectiveness.   The second method of gauging
performance is to use piezometers with which direct measurements of the water pressure in the slope may be made.   As an
example, consider the slope embankment shown in Figure 6.
Prior to placement of the horizontal drain, the majority of
the failure plane was under the phreatic surface as would be
noted in the piezometer reading.   After placing the drain,
a distinct drop in pressure would be recorded with the piezometer, indicating the successful lowering of the groundwater below the failure plane.   Use of piezometers represents
a very easy and quick method to measure changes in the groundwater table.   Such changes indicate whether or not a successful or unsuccessful drainage effort has been completed.

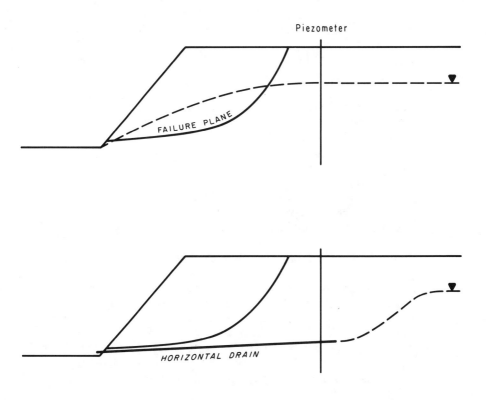

Figure 6.   Groundwater Table Location Before and
After Horizontal Drain Emplacement.

ADVANTAGES AND DISADVANTAGES

The advantages of horizontal drains are many and may be enumerated as follows:

1 - Drains are quick and easy to install
2 - There are no moving parts
3 - No power is required
4 - They work by gravity
5 - Little or no upkeep required
6 - Corrosion proof system
7 - They present a flexable system
8 - System life is long
9 - The relative cost is very low

Disadvantages are few, but may be listed as follows:

1 - Usually an existing slope is required. However, the drains have been installed from underground galleries and from inside vertical shafts.

2 - The water flows by gravity to the lowest point in the system and, therefore, usually at least one pump is required to remove the water from the pit.

COSTS - 1979

The costs of a drainage system will obviously vary with the geological and hydrological conditions. However, some ranges of figures may be specified:

Typical Drain	Cost Per Linear Foot	
	Soft Rock	Hard Rock
Minimum	$3.00	$4.50
Maximum	$6.50	$12.00
Average	$4.25	$7.00
Underground (Overhead)	$16.00	$20.00

CASE HISTORY

General Background

   The Yerington Pit is located approximately 2 miles west
of Yerington, Nevada and is in an open pit disseminated copper mine. An alluvial blanket more than 300 ft thick covers
the underlying rock, which is predominately quartz monzonite.
The contact forms a relatively impermeable barrier causing
water to flow along old stream channels into the west end of
the pit, just above the alluvial-bedrock interface. In 18
years of mining, vertical wells had been the primary dewatering tool and in most cases were successful. However, the
seepage water above the alluvial-bedrock contact had not been
successfully removed, even though considerable effort had been
expended in drilling and pumping numerous vertical wells.
The great interest in dewatering in the west end of the pit
was brought about by four adverse factors: (1) the water
was a hindrance to mine equipment operation; (2) the wet
material represented additional weight to be hauled by truck;
(3) screens in the mill became plugged when wet ore was processed and (4) slope stability problems were aggravated by
water pressure affects. In 1971, the use of horizontal drains
was tried as an alternative method of dewatering.

Procedures

   The procedures used to implement the horizontal drainage
system may be numerated in order as follows:

   1 - Geologic and seismic survey data were initially used
       to determine the shape of the alluvial-bedrock con-
       tact, specifically, the old stream channel locations.

   2 - Drain holes, which would intersect these channels and
       intercept a maximum amount of water, were planned.

   3 - An Aardvark was used to drill some 33 holes complete
       with 1½-in. diameter PVC screens. The holes were
       inclined upward at 2-3°. They had optimum spacings
       of approximately 75 ft and had lengths which averaged
       approximately 300 feet. In the alluvium, the lengths
       ranged from 230-400 ft while in the bedrock, lengths
       were in some cases only 100 ft, but up to a maximum
       of 520 feet. An emplacement rate of 300 ft per day
       of completed system was achieved.

4 - A collection system was constructed which would pipe the water from the individual drains to one central pump station, where the water was removed from the pit.

Results

The end results of the project were that the visible saturated zone and related seepage were completely eliminated. Further, the movement of a two bench failure which had developed in the alluvium, due to adverse water pressures, was completely stopped within the first two days the drains were operational. Mining equipment operation and efficiency improved and down-time in the mill due to screen plugging was essentially eliminated.

Costs

Two different contractual agreements were used during the drain emplacement project. The first was an equipment lease basis and the second was a complete contract basis. The resulting direct drain costs were $2.94 per linear foot for the equipment lease basis and $4.85 per linear foot for the contract basis. Operator costs for the equipment lease basis probably added approximately $1.50 to the cost, for a total of $4.44 per linear foot.

Summary

The case history presents the results of a complete horizontal drainage project. Costs were probably higher at the time (1971) than they perhaps should have been, but the project had been approached on a research basis. The success is attested to by the immediate results which were produced and the fact that, on another pushback in 1972 in the same area of the pit, mine management again successfully used horizontal drains to dewater. Costs during the second phase were reduced approximately 50¢ a linear foot. A series of photographs dipicting various aspects of the case history is presented in Figures 7 through 13.

Figure 7. West End of Yerington Pit Showing Saturated Zone Immediately Behind Mining Equipment.

Figure 8. Aardvark Drilling Drainage Hole.

Figure 9.   Tricone Bit and PVC Screen.

Figure 10.   Completed Horizontal Drain.

Figure 11.   Horizontal Drain, Rubber Connecting Pipe
             and Water Collector System.

Figure 12.   Water Collection System Dischargimg to Pump
             Sump Intake.

Figure 13.   Slope Failure Whose Further Displacement
            Was Stopped By Horizontal Drainage System.

SECTION 2

Drainage Control for Surface Mines

12

Open Pit Dewatering at Pine Point

by Keith J. Durston, Mine Engineering Superintendent,
Pine Point Operations, Cominco Ltd.,
Pine Point, Northwest Territories, Canada

[Hydrogeology section by K. U. Weyer,
Research Scientist, National Hydrology Research Institute,
Environment Canada, Calgary, Alberta, Canada]

INTRODUCTION

Ground dewatering during open pit mining is a common practice. It is usually necessitated by the practical considerations of mining equipment and methods and because of geotechnical reasons.

Operating in a location experiencing relatively long and cold winters produces additional problems. This is the situation at the Pine Point Operations of Cominco Ltd. It is not unique but, as mining frontiers advance further north, the experience gained at Pine Point becomes of increasing interest to those involved in these developments.

This paper is not intended to be a text on hydrogeology or aquifer investigation but rather a description of dewatering procedures used successfully at an unusual northern open pit mining operation.

GENERAL

The open pit lead and zinc mine owned by Pine Point Mines Limited and operated by its majority shareholder, Cominco Ltd., is located near the southern shore of Great Slave Lake at latitude 60° 49' North and longitude 114° 28'

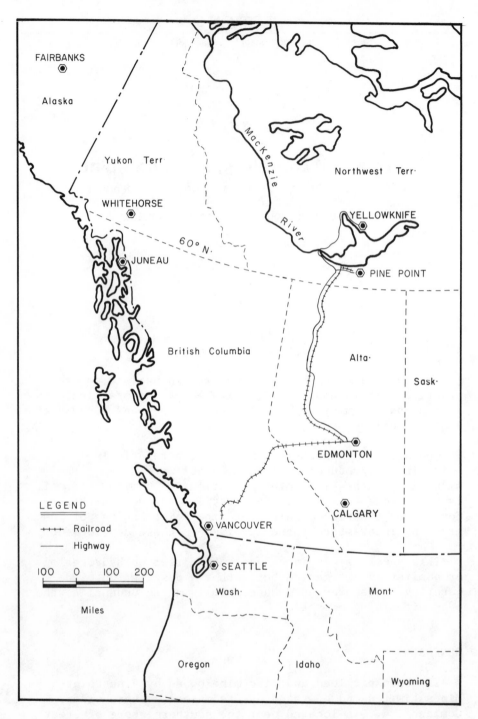

Figure No. 1   Location Map

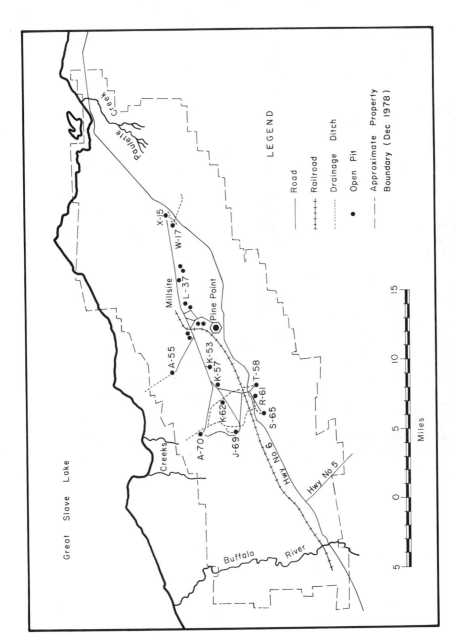

Figure No. 2   Property Map of Pine Point Mines Limited

West (Figure No. 1).

Mining involves the open pit extraction of relatively small, isolated orebodies (Figure No. 2). The pits are generally circular or elliptical in plan with lateral dimensions ranging from 400 to 3,000 feet and depth averaging 175 feet below surface, with a maximum depth to date of 327 feet in one pit. Production started in 1965 and has attained a level of about 11,000 tons of ore and 20,000 tons of waste rock and overburden per day. The strip ratio is increasing and has resulted in the recent acquisition of a dragline to supplement existing truck and shovel stripping capability. Small scale underground mining was performed close to the millsite between 1970 and 1977 and will be resumed at that location and in other areas west of the millsite when economic conditions permit.

Mining activity started in the then known area of ore reserves close to the millsite and has progressively moved further from this area as these reserves were depleted and mineral exploration activity proved reserves in other areas of the mine property. Constraints imposed by production equipment logistics, mill head grade requirements, and varying metallurgical properties necessitate the operating of as many as six open pits at any time. Simultaneous mining of pits scattered over a relatively large area produces unusual operating problems. These are compounded when most of these pits require dewatering installations and drainage ditch systems.

NATURAL ENVIRONMENT

Surface Topography and Vegetation

The mine property is located in an area which is generally low lying and poorly drained. The ground slopes gently towards the south shore of Great Slave Lake, about six miles north of the millsite. The change in surface elevation over this distance is from about 700 to 515 feet above mean sea level. Low gravel ridges, muskeg areas, swamps, and shallow lakes cover the area.

Surface expressions of karstic features include intermittent creeks, natural springs, and sinkholes.

The active mining area, some 20 miles east-west and five miles north-south, lies between the Buffalo River to the west and Paulette Creek to the east. These rivers, together with the Little Buffalo ten miles further east, form distinct surface drainage systems. Other systems are generally poorly defined.

The area lies within the boreal forest and vegetation consists of stunted spruce and pine with birch and aspen occurring on the gravel ridges. Open areas of scrubby willows, sedges, and grasses are common. Trees seldom attain commercial quality. Very slow growth rates reflect the harsh environment.

Climate

Relatively long winters and short, dry summers are experienced. The annual number of frost free days averages 80 and sustained periods of below minus 30 degrees Celcius air temperatures occur from December to March. Light northerly winds are common throughout this period.

Annual precipitation is low, averaging about 13 inches of water equivalent. Much of this is in the form of snow which, during the spring thaw in late April or in May, flows over the frozen ground to seasonal creeks and towards Great Slave Lake. Ice on the major lakes and rivers breaks up and is carried down the Mackenzie River in June.

The climate is classed as semi-arid.

Geology

Surface outcrops are very rare in the region. Over-burden, consisting of sandy glacial till with occasional gravel beds and areas of varved clays and cemented fine sands which are known locally as "hardpan", varies from 10 to 150 feet in depth. This material is often overlain by an organic, peaty layer of muskeg varying in depth from one to ten feet. Localized areas of permafrost have been encountered in the overburden but are not common.

General geology is shown in Figures No. 3 and No. 4. Lead and zinc mineralization of the Mississippi Valley type occurs within the Devonian formations. The ore deposits are associated with a barrier reef complex in this formation and host rocks are medium to coarse grained recrystallized dolomites. Rock types within the formation also include

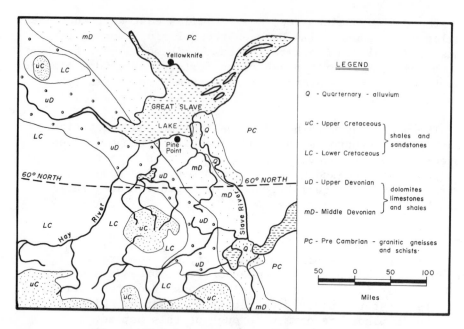

Figure No. 3   Regional Geological Map

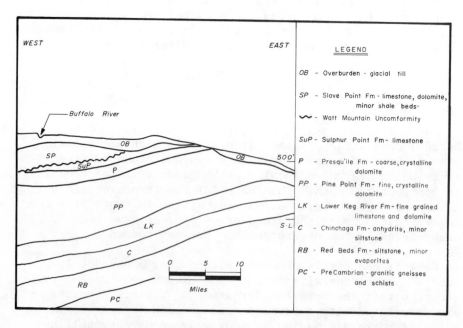

Figure No. 4   Generalized Geological Section

limestones, shales, and mud and sand seams. Karstic features
such as sinkholes, solution channels, and cavities are
widespread. Sinkholes are filled with sands and various
brecciated material and often contain ore grade mineralization.

Strata dip gently to the southwest, folding is minor,
and major fracture zones reflecting tectonic movement in
the basement have been identified. Distinct bedding planes
and vertical fracturing are common.

Detailed descriptions of the geology of this area have
been published (1).

Hydrogeology (by K. U. Weyer)

The natural groundwater table in the Pine Point area
varies in depth below surface from a few feet to about 60
feet.

Perched water is common within the overburden in the
"hardpan" areas. The abundant small lakes are usually
shallow and often have fine clay bottoms. These and the
areas of perched groundwater are often unaffected by major
ground dewatering programmes.

Studies of regional groundwater flow are active (2, 3). It
appears that flow through the aquifers of the Devonian formation is from south to north with a major area of recharge
being the Cretaceous formations of the Caribou Mountains
150 miles to the south of the mining area (Figure No. 3).
Significant discharge and recharge zones have been identified
along the Buffalo River in zones of faulting and significant
fracturing and in other areas.

The lithology of the Pine Point complex varies considerably and continuous separate aquifers are difficult to
identify. The overall formation is considered an extensive
major aquifer. The gently dipping strata result in varying
aquifer conditions across the mining property. The aquifer
is considered unconfined to the east and increasingly confined to the west where overlying shale and clay beds
occur. Artesian flows have been encountered in the western
and northwestern parts of the property. Natural springs
occur in these areas.

The porosity of the limestones and dolomites themselves
is relatively low. Groundwater flow is considered to be
mainly along solution channels, bedding planes, and fracture

zones. Aquifer characteristics determined by pumping tests are described later.

Chemical analyses of natural spring water and of deep well pump discharges have indicated two distinct "types" – salty and sulphur water (2, 3). The range of analyses of groundwaters near the open pits is shown in Table No. I. Their differing chemical and isotope characteristics reflect different groundwater flow systems. To the south of the mining property limestones and dolomites are underlain by evaporite beds of salt and gypsum. These are absent in the vicinity of the ore deposits. Natural discharges of salty water and brines containing up to 340 grams per litre T.D.S. and with specific conductivities greater than 80,000 micromhos per centimetre have been found in some areas within the region (2).

Table No. I
Range of Analyses of Pumped Groundwater (2, 3)

pH	7.0 – 8.0
Suspended solids	0 – 200
Total dissolved solids (T.D.S.)	1300 – 4300
Hardness, as $CaCO_3$	1000 – 2000
Dissolved anions	
– chloride	20 – 300
– sulphate	1000 – 1500
Dissolved cations	
– calcium	150 – 500
– magnesium	75 – 200
– sodium	20 – 100
– potassium	2 – 10
– copper, iron, lead, zinc	less than 0.1
Total copper, iron, lead, zinc	less than 1.0 each
Specific conductivities	
– salty water	3000 – 6000
– sulphur water	1000 – 2000

Note: All values are parts per million, except for specific conductivities, which are in micromhos per centimetre, and for pH.

The temperature of pumped groundwater appears to be consistent through the seasons and varies throughout the mining area from about two to five degrees Celcius.

DEWATERING SYSTEMS

Most of the orebodies occur below the natural groundwater table and within the major aquifer. Without dewatering, mining would be difficult and hazardous in the summer and probably impossible in the winter.

Dewatering, or the localized depression of the groundwater table, is accomplished by pumping with deep well pumps located in wells drilled around the perimeter of each open pit. These pumps operate continuously and develop a cone of drawdown in the groundwater table centred on the pit. Upon completion of mining, the pumps are removed and recovery of the water table occurs. The rate of drawdown and of recovery depends on several factors, including the pumping rate, the ultimate drawdown depth, the local hydrogeological conditions, and the proximity of other dewatering operations.

Observation of surface drainage systems such as lakes and creeks and of localized areas of perched water within the overburden indicates that drawdown has very little effect on these. This water results from natural precipitation. Small lakes immediately adjacent to pits having active deep well dewatering systems often show no significant change in water levels during the dewatering programme. Surface run-off and drainage systems are diverted from active pit areas and this water is usually collected in the pit perimeter ditches which serve the well discharges.

With the area being semi-arid, the accumulation of surface precipitation within open pits does not produce significant operating problems and special facilities are not required to handle these small quantities of water. Water formed during the spring thaw and resulting from infrequent light summer rain showers usually percolates though the pit floor to the depressed water table.

In-pit sump pump operations are sometimes used during final pit mining when the depressed water table is reached and economic considerations, or production schedules, preclude the drilling of additional wells.

Development

Perimeter dewatering systems were initiated on the advice of Legette, Brashears and Graham of New York in the late 1960's (4). Papers on the development of open pit dewatering at Pine Point have been written by Calver and Farnsworth, and by Vogwill (5, 6).

Perimeter deep well dewatering systems have been successfully used for pits within the unconfined aquifer. Future mining developments will be within the confined aquifer on the western part of the property and underground below the natural water table. These will require modification of aquifer investigation methods and of dewatering system design and implementation.

Design

Aquifer characteristics in the areas of planned open pit mining are determined by performing pumping tests.

Procedures have been previously described by Brashears and Slayback, Calver and Farnsworth, and Vogwill (5, 6, 7). Basically, controlled pumping is performed in a test well and resulting changes in elevation of the groundwater table monitored during drawdown until a storage depletion trend is attained and during recovery after cessation of pumping. The total cost of performing a 14 day pumping test is approximately $15,000 (Can.), excluding well drilling costs.

Data are analyzed using the straight-line method of Cooper and Jacob (8) and the distance-drawdown method of Thiem (9). Use of these techniques assumes that the aquifer conforms to certain basic hydraulic and geological properties. Many of the pit dewatering programmes have been in areas of unconfined aquifer conditions and designs based on test results have resulted in satisfactory dewatering performance. Analysis of pumping test data from areas of partially and fully confined aquifers is modified to take into account leaky artesian conditions. Field data are matched to a type curve and values for well functions and leakage factors obtained (6).

The purpose of the analyses is to obtain local values for the transmissivity and storage coefficient of the aquifer. From these, water table drawdown can be determined for various rates of deep well pumping. Total drawdown and rate of drawdown are matched against the mining production schedule for the pit.

The number of wells required to perform the dewatering programme is calculated, considering the following factors:

1. average well yield, related to
   (a) initial test well drilling and pumping test experience, and
   (b) practical and economic considerations of maintaining an inventory of pumps of various capacities;

2. loss of 10 percent of the wells because of ground collapse; and

3. 80 percent effective pumping rate because of interruptions from power failures, pump failures, and general maintenance requirements.

Factors 2 and 3 result from experience gained during the dewatering of eleven pits since 1968.

Aquifer characteristics obtained from pumping tests performed to date are shown in Table II.

Table No. II
Aquifer Characteristics in Open Pit Areas
as Determined by Pumping Tests

Pit	Transmissivity (U.S. gpd/ft)	Storage Coefficient
J-44	60,000	0.025
N-42	54,000	0.016
O-42	72,000	0.035
M-40	50,000	0.016
X-15	35,000	0.006
W-17	69,000	0.050
T-58	77,000	0.001
R-61	37,000	0.001
K-57	50,000	0.001
K-62	68,000	0.050
J-69	70,000	0.050
A-70	68,000	0.002

Note: U.S. gpd/ft = U.S. gallons per day per foot

After the number of wells has been determined, well locations relative to the final pit rim are chosen. Factors considered during well siting include:

1. location of sinkholes. Collapse material within these usually consists of boulders and rock fragments within

a matrix of sand, gravel, and clay. To maintain well holes in this material, casing and well screen would be required. The cost of such well construction compared with non-cased holes in relatively competent limestone and dolomite, and the relatively low yield of wells in such material, precludes siting them within sinkholes.

2. existence of patterns of anisotropy within the regional aquifer characteristics. These are often indicated during the pumping tests; two lines of observation holes, usually perpendicular to each other, are used during the test. Directions of preferential ground-water flow are also often indicated during investigation of the geological environment. Lineation of fracture patterns, fault zones, and facies types indicate such directions. Well holes are sited within zones that will provide maximum yield.

3. possibility of drawdown interference between adjacent wells. The extent and shape of the drawdown cone for any well varies according to the local aquifer properties and, of course, the duration and rate of pumping. Experience at Pine Point has indicated that a minimum spacing of 300 feet between well holes is effective in producing drawdown over the lateral extent of most pits without producing significant interference between wells. A few widely spaced wells seldom produce the required drawdown unless the water table has already been significantly lowered by pumping at an adjacent pit.

4. the design location of the final pit rim and the perimeter drainage ditch. Location of the latter depends on local surface topography. In most areas this is relatively flat and, together with the frequent occurrence of swamps and small lakes, makes ditch layout very critical. Flow rates must be such to ensure that discharged water does not freeze during the long, cold winters. Well holes are located at least 185 feet from the pit rim and sufficiently close to the drainage ditch that discharge pipe lengths are not excessive. The 185 feet accommodates a pump service road 25 feet wide, an allowance for minor pit design changes, and for possible slumping of the overburden. Typical arrangements are shown in Figures No. 5 and No. 6.

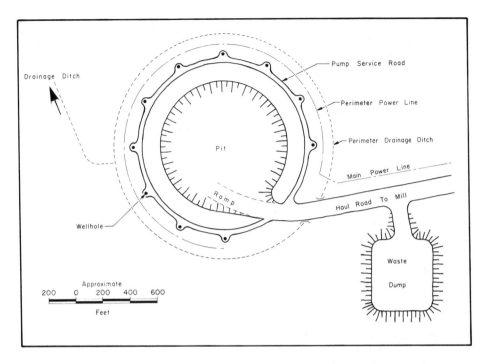

Figure No. 5   Typical Well and Ditch Arrangement

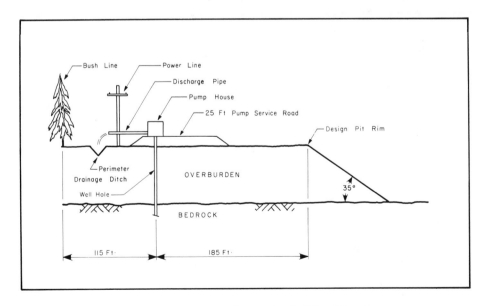

Figure No. 6   Section of Typical Pit Rim Arrangement

5.   the total pit perimeter length. On small, deep pits
     it has been necessary to drill a double ring of wells
     on surface and, in some cases, to supplement these
     during pit mining with wells drilled on the outer edge
     of the in-pit ramp.

Well depths are usually between 400 and 500 feet, depending
on the ultimate pit depth. Experience has shown that drilling
to 200 feet below the pit bottom elevation results in
sufficient penetration of the aquifer to give well yields
compatible with pumps sized to fit the wells and to achieve
the desired drawdown at the pit centre.

Well Drilling

Well drilling is contracted and, to minimize the effect
of mobilization costs, sufficient drilling is performed in
a single annual programme to satisfy the next year's pit
development and mining. Since 1968 annual well drilling
footage has averaged 8,000 feet.

Initially, wells were drilled 12 1/4 inches in diameter.
Pumps were in the size range of 40 to 100 horsepower.
Problems with crooked wells and the need to use larger
pumps led to larger wells. All wells are now drilled
14 3/4 inches in diameter. This size is believed to be
the optimum after considering typical well yield, relative
drilling costs, and hole stability. Dependence on a few
large diameter wells is avoided.

The development of drilling methods has been described
by Vogwill (6). Current practice is to drill a 14 3/4 inch
hole through the overburden, which averages 50 feet in
thickness, and 20 feet into the bedrock. This hole is then
reamed to 17 inches in diameter and 16 inch steel casing
installed. The hole is then drilled to its final depth,
using a 14 3/4 inch tricone bit. No casing or well screen
is installed.

The hole is drilled to about 150 feet, well into the
water table, using up to 300 U.S. gallons per minute of
water. Drilling mud is used only through the overburden
and only when this is composed of unconsolidated material
that would otherwise collapse. Beyond about 150 feet, air
is introduced at up to 1,200 cubic feet per minute at 250
pounds per square inch. Water from the circulating pump is
reduced according to the quantity of water made naturally
within the hole. Drilling foam (soap) is injected when

necessary to assist in cuttings removal.

On completion of drilling, the hole is flushed until clear water is produced, usually after one to two hours. Secondary development of wells was attempted early in the dewatering programme but is no longer considered necessary. The dolomites and limestones are well fractured and vuggy.

The rig used successfully for the past eight years has been an Ideco H-25 with a dual stage 70-95 foot Cardwell telescoping derrick. Collaring on bedrock is slow because of the lack of pulldown. Every attempt is made to drill vertical holes and contracts have been let on an hourly rather than footage rate. Close technical control is supplied by Cominco personnel. The drill string configuration used to ensure straight holes includes a 9 inch diameter drill sub, shock sub, and rib collar between the bit and the 6 inch drill pipe. The shock sub and rib collar, with 11 1/2 inch ribs, are each 10 feet long.

Average drill performance for a 500 foot hole with 60 feet of casing and a move of 300 feet between set-ups is:

Move, rig up, and tear down	8 hours
Install casing, including welding	2 hours
Drill	14 feet per hour
Blow out hole	2 hours

1978 drilling costs were $26 (Can.) per foot. Including site preparation and rig mobilization from central Alberta, the overall cost was $35 per foot for a 12 hole, 6,000 foot programme.

Pump Roads and Pads

For access for well drilling and for the installation and maintenance of pumping equipment, a 25 foot wide road is built to each well site. This, and an approximately 100 foot square pad at the well site, is constructed from nearby gravel sources or, in their absence, from waste rock from the nearest pit or waste dump. Three to four feet of material is usually required to construct a service road across the often wet and soft ground surface.

This work is performed by mine production crews, or by a local contractor when development areas are distant from active mining areas.

Pumps

Several different types of submersible and lineshaft pumps have been used. Consideration of purchase, installation and operating costs over the past 12 years has resulted in the selection of the two types now in use. Details of these are summarized below:

1. Lineshaft pumps--

    Peerless Pump Division of F.M.C. Corporation, 7-stage, 12HXB bowl assembly pump with a 125 horsepower Westinghouse vertical hollow shaft motor, 3/60/575, 1,800 revolutions per minute with a non-reverse ratchet. Oil lubricated lineshaft complete with inner column. Also, similar pumps with 150 and 200 horsepower motors.

2. Submersible pumps--

    TRW Pleuger Canada Ltd., P104 2-stage pump with Pleuger 100 horsepower, 3/60/575, 3,450 revolutions per minute, water filled wet stator submersible motor. Also, similar 3-stage pumps with 130 and 150 horsepower motors.

It has been found that to best suit location conditions where the majority of wells yield 800 to 1,200 U.S. gallons per minute and the total dynamic head averages 250 feet, pumps in the range of 100 to 150 horsepower are required. A few wells are drilled within open pits and water is discharged through lengthy 8 inch lines. For these, several 200 horsepower Peerless lineshaft pumps are maintained.

In the past, sump pump arrangements for final bench mining have involved installing a well pump in a pump stand fabricated on the property from 16 inch well casing. Discharge to surface was through an 8 inch steel line installed along the edge of the driving ramp and, where possible, up and over the completed benches to the pit rim. Recent practice has been to use sump pumps manufactured by Flygt Ltd. with a flexible rubber discharge line about 200 feet long, connected to a steel line. These pumps can be readily moved within the pit as operating conditions dictate and do not require to be set vertically within a pump stand. For shallow pits, the flexible line can be quickly lowered over the pit rim. This is both faster and safer than the previous practice of installing steel pipe lines. Performance characteristics required for sump pumps are usually low volume and high head.

Pump Installation and Maintenance

In recent years, an average of 50 to 60 wells have been operating at five or six separate open pits. Between 10 to 20 new installations and 20 to 30 removals for pump or riser pipe maintenance are necessary per year.

This work is performed under the supervision of one mine shift boss by the following crew:

- one mobile crane operator
- two pump installation men
- two supply and general labour men
- one maintenance and general labour man

The repair and replacement of pump parts is performed within the mine machine shop and requires the full time services of one repairman. One electrician is employed full time for installation and routine maintenance. This does not include the installation of power lines and transformers or major repair work such as rewinding motors.

For a new pump installation, the pump, 8 inch riser pipe for submersibles, or inner and outer pipe column and shafting for lineshaft pumps, motor or switchgear shack, and surface discharge pipe are delivered from the millsite storage yard to the wellhead by the two supply men. For this they use a 5-ton flatbed truck equipped with a hydraulic lifting boom. The crane operator and two installation men assemble and install the well pump and pipe. The 8 inch riser pipe and the outer column for lineshaft installations are supplied in 20 foot lengths of standard schedule 40 pipe with threaded couplings.

Average installation time for the three man crew for a pump set at 400 feet is six hours for a submersible and 18 hours for a lineshaft pump. An extra man is usually required when installing the latter type.

A daily pump check, involving the operating condition of every well pump and the lubricating reservoir for lineshaft pumps, is performed by the maintenance and general repair man. This usually takes about five hours per day. Polar

35 oil (Imperial Oil Limited) is used for lineshaft lubrication. For the remainder of the eight hour shift, this man performs routine maintenance and cleaning of recovered pipe and shafting.

The pump crew work a 5-day, Monday to Friday, steady day shift schedule. On afternoon and night shifts and on weekends, the operating status of each pump is checked visually by the mine production shift boss. A system of operating status coloured lights, described later, is mounted at each wellhead. Electrical problems are reported to the shift electrician for immediate attention. Other problems are noted in the shift log book and in the event of major problems in critical operating areas, the pump crew and shift boss are called out on overtime. These occur infrequently.

The shift boss is also responsible for checking the condition of drainage ditches and culverts. This is especially important during the period of high surface run-off in the spring.

It has been found that the Peerless lineshaft pumps can operate continuously for about three years. Replacement of bowl assemblies and bearings can extend their useful life by one to two years. The most frequent maintenance required involves the replacement of the inner or outer column, or of the shafting. This can be caused by wear from shaft misalignment or from sand in the discharged water or by corrosion from the water. The frequency of such maintenance varies considerably from six months to two years. Vertical mounted motors are very dependable and serve several successive pump installations.

Pleuger submersible pumps have been used for the past three years. The need for pump maintenance has been insignificant to date. As with lineshaft pumps, the frequency of replacement of riser pipe through wear or corrosion varies considerably. Electrical problems with the pump motor or the jacketted cable have been few. Electrical repairs to the submersible motor require return to the Canadian assembly plant.

Occasionally, corrosion of the riser pipe causes a pump to be dropped to the well bottom. Use of a fishing tool, designed and fabricated on the property, has been very successful in recovering these pumps.

Power Supply

Power is supplied to each pit at 12,500 volts. At appropriate locations around the pit perimeter, 450 KVA transformers are located. Each transformer supplies power at 550 volts to four well installations via jacketted ground cable.

For lineshaft installations, the wellhead is covered by a pump shack formed from 10 foot diameter multi-plate culvert. The shack is fitted with a removable metal roof with an access hatch to allow servicing of the well installations by crane. It houses the motor and electrical switchgear. Motor generated heat keeps the area sufficiently warm and frost-free in the winter and simply leaving the door and roof hatch open in the summer keeps it cool enough to prevent switchgear malfunction because of rising ambient temperatures.

For submersible installations, the switchgear is housed in a small wooden enclosure adjacent to the wellhead.

A coloured light system is mounted on each pump shack or switchgear enclosure. Each light indicates the status of the pump: red - operating, orange - timing device activated, green - not operating and attention required, no light - inactive. This system enables a quick, visual check to be made at any time from the top of the open pit access ramp by production personnel.

All switchgear, in addition to standard motor control relays, is equipped with automatic, timed, restart relays. These operate following power outages and are timed to minimize peak start-up loads and to allow the complete draining of discharge pipes and riser pipes to occur before motors are restarted. Check valves are not installed in the riser pipes and surface discharge pipes are installed for gravity drainage to ensure that all pipes drain when the pumps stop. This is necessary to prevent freezing of lines during winter. Switchgear for pumps at each pit is usually timed for delayed automatic restarting at two minute intervals.

Drainage Ditches

Drainage ditches serving individual well discharges are excavated around the perimeter of each pit. These lead to main surface drainage ditches that direct the water to the nearest natural surface drainage system (Figure No. 6).

Currently, about 25,000 feet of perimeter ditch, discharging into 100,000 feet of main surface drainage ditch, is in use. These ditches service five operating pits. Between 10,000 and 20,000 feet of new ditch is excavated each year. This work is seasonal and is performed by a local contractor.

Ditch size is designed to accommodate the anticipated maximum flow from the area served and varies from four feet wide and four feet deep to eight feet wide and five feet deep. The surface topography generally has a gentle grade sloping to the north towards Great Slave Lake and major cuts are seldom required. Through experience it has been found that a ditch grade of 0.3 percent or greater and a surface flow rate of not less than 2 1/2 feet per second is sufficient to prevent freezing during the long winters.

Ditches are usually excavated in the muskeg and overburden by a three cubic yard capacity backhoe mounted on wide pad tracks. In soft, swampy areas a backhoe mounted on a low ground pressure, all terrain vehicle is used. Recent excavation costs have ranged from $1.50 to $2.00 (Can.) per cubic yard.

Recharge and return flow to the karstic limestone from drainage ditches is not usually a problem. Precipitation of carbonate and sulphate minerals from the water appears to seal the ditches (2). Clay and fine material from the overburden and muskeg also tends to restrict seepage. Occasional gravel zones within the overburden are by-passed and to date all gravel ridges encountered have been distant from active mining areas. No lining or artificial sealing of ditches has been practised.

Regular, unlined multi-plate steel culvert is used under mine roads since most ditch systems are only used for pit drainage for three to four years. On completion of mining in each area, ditch and culvert systems are left to help in the general removal of spring surface run-off. They are usually dry during the summer and winter months. Those culverts under the public highway which primarily serve discharge from several pit areas and will have long operating lives have recently been replaced with asphalt lined multi-plate culverts. It was found that after 5 or 6 years discharged groundwater had significantly corroded the previous unlined culverts.

Costs

Dewatering costs are a significant portion of the direct open pit mining costs at Pine Point, comprising 16 percent of the total in 1978 (Table No. III). A summary of those dewatering costs is shown in Table No. IV and is typical of recent years.

The scope of the dewatering programme in 1978 is summarized below:

Average number of pumps operating	46
Maximum number of pumps operating	57
Ratio of submersible to lineshaft pumps	1:1
Average pumping rate (U.S. gallons per minute)	46,300
Average operating horsepower	5,280
Well drilling (feet)	6,000
Number of well sites prepared (roads and pads)	12
New drainage ditch excavated (feet)	19,500
Existing drainage ditch cleaned (feet)	11,000
Number of 100 foot long culverts installed	3
Personnel - staff	3
- pump crew (excluding electricians and mechanics)	6

In addition to the practical operating reasons for dewatering before mining, such as the potential problems of increased tire wear and frozen muck piles in winter, the increased costs of drilling and blasting wet rock are important. Blasting costs, per ton broken, when water resistant explosives are used are approximately three times those resulting from using ANFO type explosives for dry blasting. Operating under wet conditions with the aid of sump pumping also decreases overall mining productivity.

WATER TABLE AND DEWATERING MONITORING

Water table elevations are measured weekly in active pit dewatering areas and once or twice per year at various sites throughout the mining property.

Fisher M-scopes are used to measure water levels in test holes drilled within active pits by production blasthole

Table No. III
Distribution of 1978 Direct Mining Costs

	Percent
Drilling and blasting	10
Loading, hauling and dozing	54
Haulroad maintenance and construction	5
Dewatering	16
Stockpiling at millsite	10
Supervision	5
	100

Note: General mining parameters:
- waste moved - 7.5 million tons
- ore moved - 3.3 million tons
- average haul distance to millsite - 6.3 miles

Table No. IV
Distribution of 1978 Dewatering Costs

	Percent
Electrical power	57
Electrical maintenance	3
Ditches and culverts	4
Pump roads and pads	5
Well drilling, including mobilization	12
Pump installation	4
Pump maintenance	9
Design, monitoring and supervision	6
	100

Note: These do not include the costs of pumps, switchgear, transformers, or power line installation.

drills. When inactive well holes are available at a pit
and are considered beyond the immediate influence of
nearby active pumping wells, continuous water level readings
are obtained by installing Stevens Type F automatic recorders.
Analysis of the charts obtained from these recorders allows
assessment to be made of the changes in water levels resulting
from power interruptions or changes in pump performances.

Individual pumping rates are measured monthly or whenever
significant changes occur in a rate as determined by visual
inspection of the discharge and by changes in the pump
motor power demand.

The evaluation of pumping rates and changes in the water
level at each active pit is used to assess dewatering
progress and as the basis for changes in system capacity
and design.

Water levels measured regularly in exploration diamond
drill holes throughout the property allow regional water
table contour maps to be maintained. These indicate the
regional drawdown and recovery resulting from changes in
the pit dewatering systems.

Pump discharge water is sampled at the start of dewatering
of each pit area and at six month intervals thereafter.
Samples are usually taken downstream from the junction of
a pit perimeter ditch and the main drainage ditch. They
therefore represent the combined water flows of each of the
wells in a pit dewatering system. Additional samples are
taken in the natural drainage systems that receive well
discharge water. Analysis of these samples permits the
quality of discharged water and its effects on natural
surface waters to be monitored.

DEWATERING PERFORMANCE

Generally, pit dewatering systems have achieved the
anticipated results in water table drawdown in most areas.
Experience gained early in the dewatering programme has
resulted in the incorporation of the factors discussed
previously in the design of individual pit dewatering
systems.

Drawdowns and recoveries experienced at various open
pits are summarized in Table No. V. Significant regional
drawdown effects have been observed and have influenced the

Table No. V

Water Table Drawdown and Recovery at Open Pits

Pit	Avg. Distance From Pumps to Pit Centre	Average Pumping Rate	Duration of Pumping (months)	Drawdown at Pit Centre	Recovery to Dec. 31/78	Remarks
J-44	590	6,700	Nov/68–May/72 (42)	102	36	Maximum recovery of 46 feet shown by Nov/72. Increased millsite pumping has since lowered water table 10 feet.
O-42	730	3,200	Nov/68–June/72 (43)	68	10	Recovery ceased in late 1972 because of effect of millsite pumping.
N-42	550	1,600	May/68–Mar/69 (11)	74	10	Same as above.
M-40	730	1,300	June/72–Oct/74 (28)	56	0	Drawdown assisted and then maintained by millsite pumping.
X-15	1,440	3,400	July/68–Dec/73 (66)	95	—	Drawdown assisted by W-17 pumping. Center to centre distance X-15 to W-17 is 5,000 feet.
X-15	—	0	Jan/74–Oct/77 (46)	+ 59	—	
X-15W	750	1,800	Nov/77–Dec/78 (13)	+ 28	—	

Table No. V – Continued

Pit	Avg. Distance From Pumps to Pit Centre	Average Pumping Rate	Duration of Pumping (months)	Drawdown at Pit Centre	Recovery to Dec. 31/78	Remarks
W–17	950	18,000	Oct/71–Aug/77 (70)	224	–	Drawdown additional to 29 feet produced by early pumping at X–15. Maximum pumping rate was 23,000 U.S. gallons per minute (Aug/77).
W–17	950	14,000	Aug/77–Dec/78 (16)	0	41	Reduced pumping maintained for drawdown effect at X–15W.
T–58	–	0	Jan/76–Mar/77 (15)	23	–	Result of R–61 pumping. Centre to centre distance T–58 to R–61 is 4,200 feet.
T–58	800	7,400	Apr/77–Dec/78 (20)	+ 86	–	Pumping rate 9,650 U.S. gallons per minute in Dec/78. Drawdown assisted by R–61 pumping.
R–61	800	4,675	Jan/74–Dec/78 (60)	136	–	Pumping rate 9,100 U.S. gallons per minute in Dec/78. Drawdown assisted by T–58 pumping.

Table No. V - Continued

Pit	Avg. Distance From Pumps to Pit Centre	Average Pumping Rate	Duration of Pumping (months)	Drawdown at Pit Centre	Recovery to Dec. 31/78	Remarks
K-57	680	6,100	July/71–Aug/75 (48)	152	75	Recovery initially effected by K-62 pumping and then by T-58, R-61 and J-69.
K-62	–	0	July/71–May/75 (46)	50	–	Result of K-57 pumping. Centre to centre distance K-62 to K-57 is 6,800 feet.
K-62	800	6,400	June/75–Oct/76 (16)	+ 79	80	Recovery in 1978 only 15 feet because of effect of pumping at T-58, R-61 and J-69.
J-69	–	0	July/71–Oct/77 (75)	47	–	Result of pumping at A-70, K-62, T-58 and R-61.
J-69	800	12,000	Nov/77–Dec/78 (13)	+ 93	–	Pumping rate 15,000 U.S. gallons per minute in Dec/78.
A-70	870	9,925	Feb/76–Sept/77 (19)	98	72	

Notes:
(1) Distances, drawdowns and recoveries in feet.
(2) Pumping rates in U.S. gallons per minute.
(3) Inter-pit drawdown effects determined from regional water table contour maps.
(4) Refer to Figure No. 2 for relative open pit locations.

drawdown in various groups of pits, viz. X-15/W-17, R-61/T-58/S-65, K-57/K-62/J-69/A-70, and O-42/N-42/J-44 (Figure No. 2). Within the constraints of production equipment availability and millfeed metallurgy, mine production has been scheduled to take maximum advantage of the regional dewatering effects in adjacent pits.

The regional drawdown effect of deep well pumping in the townsite for domestic water and the millsite for process water has been observed at the open pit and underground mining operations within about 15,000 feet of the mill and townsite.

In recent years dewatering performance in the western part of the property in areas of semi-confined groundwater conditions has indicated some inadequacies in pumping test procedures and analysis. Slower than anticipated drawdown has resulted from changes in storage characteristics and the effect of regional groundwater flow during prolonged dewatering. Modifications to pumping test procedures, more rigorous pre-dewatering hydrogeological investigation, and better observation and analysis of early dewatering performance are planned.

ENVIRONMENTAL EFFECTS OF DEWATERING

Dewatering operations at Pine Point are assessed and monitored by the Water Resources Division of the Federal Government's Department of Indian and Northern Affairs. Controlling legislation includes the Northern Inland Waters Act and Fisheries Act.

The quantity and quality of discharged water, changes in the natural surface drainage system, and changes in groundwater levels and flow patterns are monitored. Regional environmental surveys have been commissioned by Cominco Ltd. and the results of these supplement observations made by Government officials.

Effects of the dewatering operations on local fauna and flora appear to be minimal and are not reasons for major concern. The region is very sparsely inhabited and there are no other well pumping operations for domestic or industrial water supply in the area.

SUMMARY

Open pit dewatering by localized drawdown of the groundwater table has been practised successfully for 12 years at
Pine Point. Deep well pumping discharge rates have increased
from 20 million to 60 million U.S. gallons per day during
that period. Pumping has been predominantly from an unconfined, relatively thick, laterally extensive aquifer.

In the future, mining will be increasing in areas of semi-
confined and confined groundwater conditions. Dewatering
system design will require more rigorous hydrogeological
investigation and it is anticipated that total pumping rates
will increase. The latter could attain 100 million U.S.
gallons per day by 1985. Limitations in power supply and the
increasing cost of locally generated power will increase this
already significant portion of the mining cost. Improvements
in present techniques and implementation of new mining and
dewatering techniques will be investigated.

ACKNOWLEDGEMENTS

The author gratefully acknowledges Pine Point Mines
Limited and Cominco Ltd. for approval for publication of this
paper and specifically thanks S. Hoffman, E. Mehr and
K.U. Weyer for general review and discussion, G. Riseborough
for the draughting of figures and B. Babiuk and O. Affleck
for the typing of the manuscript. Previous papers (3, 5, 6,
7) and internal reports (2, 4) have been used during the
preparation of this paper and are acknowledged in the
references listed below. The reader is referred to these
for additional information on the subject.

REFERENCES

(1) Skall, H., 1975, The paleoenvironment of the Pine
     Point lead-zinc district, Econ. Geol., V.70.

(2) Weyer, K.U., 1978 and 1979, Investigation of ground-
     water flow in the Pine Point region - Reports for the
     years 1977/78 and 1978/79, unpublished reports on a
     joint research project between the Hydrology Research
     Division of Environment Canada and Pine Point Mines
     Limited.

(3) Weyer, K.U., Krouse, H.R., and Horwood, W.C., 1978,
     Investigation of regional geohydrology south of Great
     Slave Lake, N.W.T., Canada, utilizing natural sulphur
     and hydrogen isotope variations, Isotope Hydrology
     1978, Volume 2, Special Publication, International
     Atomic Energy Agency, Vienna.

(4) Brashears, M.L., 1968, Groundwater conditions and
     dewatering of ore pits at Pine Point, N.W.T., Canada,
     Legette, Brashears and Graham Report to Cominco Ltd.

(5) Calver, B., and Farnsworth, D.J.M., 1969, Open-pit
     dewatering at Pine Point Mines, C.I.M. Bulletin, V.62,
     No. 692.

(6) Vogwill, R.I.J., 1976, Some practical aspects of open
     pit dewatering at Pine Point, C.I.M. Bulletin, V.69,
     No. 768.

(7) Brashears, M.L., and Slayback, R.G., 1971, Pumping
     test methods applied to dewatering investigations at
     Pine Point Mines, N.W.T., Canada, A.I.M.E. Annual
     Meeting, New York.

(8) Cooper, H.H., and Jacob, C.E., 1946, A generalized
     graphical method for evaluating formation constants
     and summarizing well-field history, Am. Geophys. Union
     Trans., V.27, No. 4.

(9) Thiem, G., 1906, Hydrologische methoden, (see Wenzel,
     L.K., 1936, The Thiem method for determining permeabi-
     lity of water-bearing materials, U.S.G.S. Water Supply
     Paper 679-A).

13

The Design of
Mine Dewatering Systems in Poland

by Jacek S. Libicki, Chief Geologist,
Poltegor,
Wroclaw, Poland

INTRODUCTION

Poland belongs to the group of countries that has relatively rich deposits of useful minerals. So mining and
minerals processing are among the most developed branches of
the national economy.

Because of the geological character of the ore deposits,
and especially their various depths, both underground mining
and surface mining are widely developed. (Figure No. 1)

Bituminous coal and copper, lead, and zinc ores are primarily extracted from underground mines. In total, underground
production of all minerals reaches 250,000,000 tons per year.
Of this total about 200,000,000 tons is bituminous coal.
Underground mining is expected to increase by about 50
percent in the next 15 years.

Lignite, sulphur, stowing sands, and various clays as well
as stones and aggregates for many purposes are extracted from
surface mines. The total amount of useful minerals mined by
surface methods is about 500,000,000 tons per year, and this
requires removal of more than 200,000,000 cubic meters of
overburden. In these totals lignite, with production of
40,000,000 tons per year and removal of 130,000,000
tons of overburden, is number one. Although the total

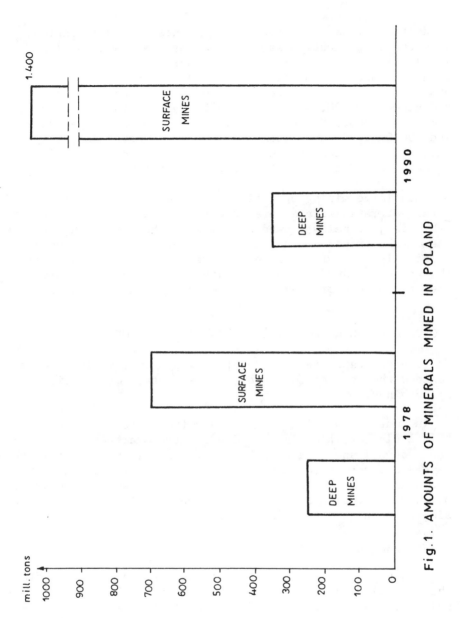

Fig.1. AMOUNTS OF MINERALS MINED IN POLAND

production of sands, gravels, and stones for constructions is greater, production is from so many small and shallow local operations that it is less important. In addition, with the fast development of lignite surface mining, annual production is expected to reach 80,000,000 tons in 1985 and about 140,000,000 tons in 1990-1995. This will require removal of 300,000,000 cubic meters of overburden per year and 700,000,000 cubic meters per year of overburden, respectively. Also the depth of surface mining operations will have increased to 300 meters during that time.

Such large mining operations are almost always conducted in water saturated strata--everywhere in Poland the groundwater table is just below ground level--make the dewatering of mines one of the principal challenges in mining operation design. Especially in surface mining, where the mined seam as well as the whole overburden has to be drained in advance of mining operations, the problem of dewatering is a major factor.

GEOLOGICAL AND HYDROLOGICAL CHARACTERISTICS OF POLISH MINES

To understand the mine dewatering systems, it is necessary to know the natural conditions and structure of deposits being mined.

In underground mines, the strata that determine the hydrologic situation in the mine are the seams and the footwall and hanging wall beds. This is because only these layers are cut by the mining operations; less important are the beds laying above. In surface mines, however, the whole overburden section is cut through, and all formations play a similar role in water conditions of a mine.

Underground Mines

Bituminous Coal. Poland's bituminous coal is mined (1) from the Carboniferous formation at the depth of 300 to 800 meters below ground level. (Figure No. 2) This formation is constituted of sandstones and shales (with coal seams) of a total thickness of several hundred meters. Carboniferous beds (Figure No. 2) are covered by the Triassic, Tertiary, and Quaternary formations, but sometimes directly by Quaternary Age sands. The amount of water inflow to mines is dependent on the amount and intensity of fractures occurring in the hanging wall formations and also on the character of rocks overlaying the Carboniferous series. The permeability

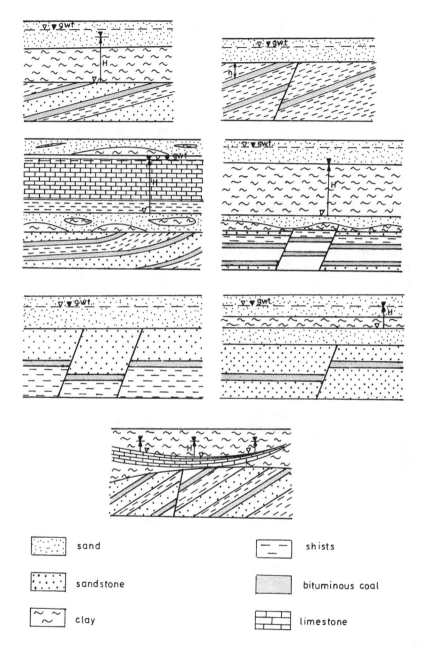

Fig. 2. TYPICAL HYDROGEOLOGICAL SECTIONS OF BITUMINOUS COAL
DEPOSITS MINED BY UNDERGROUND MINES.

coefficient of Carboniferous sandstones is in the 0.005 to 1.0 meter per 24 hours range, and water inflows are between 1 cubic meter per minute (minimum) and 25 cubic meters per minute (maximum) in any mine.

Copper Ores. The copper ores occur in Poland in the Permian limestones and dolomites (1), which are overlain by Triassic sandstones and Tertiary formations represented by sands, clays, and lignite seams. The Quaternary series have been deposited on the top. The ore bearing limestones and dolomites—from which at the depth of 700 to 1,000 meters below ground level the ore is mined—have coefficient of permeability of 0.03 to 0.85 meter per 24 hours. Their permeability depends on how much the junctions and cavities have been filled with secondary material. The inflow of water to particular mines is 3 to 20 cubic meters per minute, and it is mostly a result of the character of rocks overlaying the limestone-dolomite series.

Zinc and Lead Ores. These ores are found in Poland in dolomite and limestone formations of the Triassic Age (Figure No. 3), which constitute the gentle synclinal forms. This formation is a very saturated aquifer due to fractures and cavities of karstic origin. The permeability coefficient of these strata is 1 to 24 meters per 24 hours. This aquifer is fed with water percolating from Quaternary sands of river valleys. The inflow of water to the 150-meter deep underground mines is between 20 and 100 cubic meters per minute. The local inrush of water sometimes reaches 50 cubic meters per minute from one face.

Surface Mines

   The hydrogeological conditions in surface mines are very important and their detailed investigation is required for proper operations design. This knowledge is of equal importance for the mined beds, the overburden, and the underlaying beds.

Lignite. All deposits of lignite in Poland are of the Tertiary Age and could be roughly divided into three hydrogeological groups (Figure No. 4):

   First group—one flat lignite seam (impermeable), 6 to 15 meters thick, covered by 25 to 75 meters of overburden, of which 70 to 80 percent are Tertiary and Quaternary clays and 20 to 30 percent are sands of the same age (in the form of

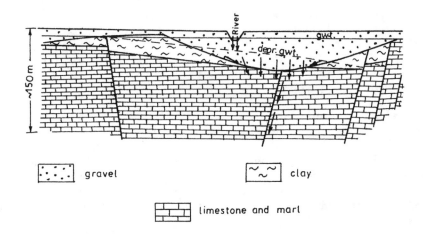

gravel

clay

limestone and marl

Fig. 3. HYDROGEOLOGICAL SECTION OF LEAD AND ZINC DEPOSITS
MINED BY UNDERGROUND MINES.

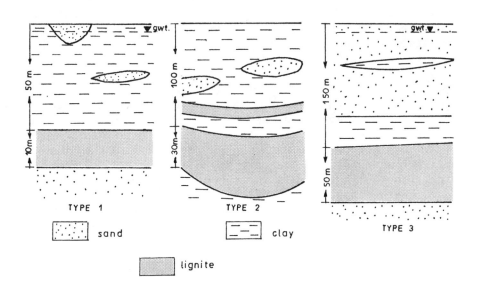

TYPE 1

TYPE 2

TYPE 3

sand

clay

lignite

Fig. 4. TYPICAL HYDROGEOLOGICAL SECTION OF LIGNITE DEPOSITS
MINED BY SURFACE MINES.

closed lenses or erosion troughs). The lignite seam is underlain by saturated sands, 20 meters to 50 meters thick,
containing subartesian water under pressure of 3 to 8 bars,
and characterized by the permeability coefficient of 3 to 5
meters per 24 hours. The groundwater inflow to these mines
is 30 to 100 cubic meters per minute.

Second group--multiseam basins in which overburden, the
underlaying beds, and the intercalations consist of clays
(70 to 80 percent) and of sands (20 to 30 percent) in the form
of closed lenses. The sands' lenses contain static groundwater under pressure depending on the depth. Thickness of
lignite seams is 5 to 40 meters, the depth of mining reaches
160 meters; groundwater inflow to these mines is 30 to 40 cubic
meters per minute.

Third group--one or two lignite seams, 20 to 70 meters
thick, are covered with sandy overburden, 100 to 200 meters
thick and underlain with fine sands. Where lignite is
deposited in tectonic trenches, the seams adjoin highly permeable limestones of Jurassic Age. The coefficient of
permeability of overburden is 8 to 20 meters per 24 hours;
of Jurassic limestones about 10 meters per 24 hours; and of
Tertiary fine sands 1 to 3 meters per 24 hours. The natural
groundwater table is just below ground level and so the
hydrostatic pressure reached 30 bars; the inflow of groundwater to these mines, when drawdown reaches 300 meters depth,
is about 400 cubic meters per minute.

Sulphur. The sulphur deposit is found (1) in the Miocene
limestone beds (Figure No. 5). The upper part of overburden
consists of the saturated Quaternary sands, 5 to 20 meters
thick, being in contact with the large river Vistula; the
lower part consists of the Tertiary clays, 50 to 70 meters
thick. The sulphur occurs in fractured and saturated limestones characterized by coefficient of permeability of 40
meters per 24 hours. The limestones are underlain by fine sands
(permeability coefficient 3 to 4 meters per 24 hours), 20 to
70 meters thick, where groundwater is under pressure of 3 to
8 bars. The inflow of groundwater to the mine is about
30 cubic meters per minute and TDS of these waters is in the
5 grams per cubic decimeter range.

Stowing Sands. As stowing sand--for backfilling of underground
mine openings under cities--the Quaternary sands with a grain
size of 0.25 to 0.50 millimeter are used. The deposits of
these sands are always connected with river valleys (Figure
No. 6). Thickness of these deposits (and the depth of mining

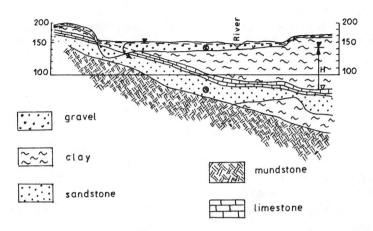

gravel

clay

sandstone

mundstone

limestone

Fig.5. HYDROGEOLOGICAL SECTION OF SULPHUR DEPOSITS MINED
BY SURFACE MINES.

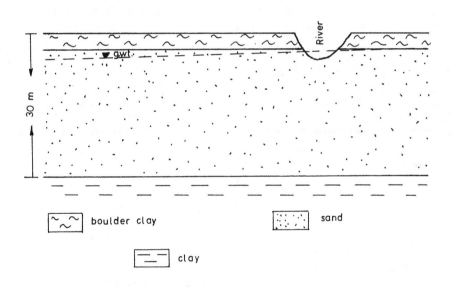

boulder clay

sand

clay

Fig.6. HYDROGEOLOGICAL SECTION OF STOWING SAND DEPOSITS
MINED BY SURFACE MINES.

operations) is 20 to 40 meters, and the sands are covered with thin topsoil only. Permeability coefficient of sands is 15 to 25 meters per 24 hours and the free groundwater table should be lowered 15 to 30 meters for mining operations. The groundwater inflows to these surface operations are 20 to 60 cubic meters per minute.

Clays. Clays mined for various ceramic and industrial purposes are found most often in small deposits of Tertiary or Quaternary Age. The thickness of overburden is almost always within 3 meters and the depth of operations does not exceed 30 meters. Groundwater occurs in small closed lenses of sand, and the inflow to particular mines does not exceed 1 to 2 cubic meters per minute.

Rocks and Aggregates. These operations (generally small) are conducted mostly in unsaturated beds. In the quarries, where operations are being conducted below groundwater table, the inflow of water coming from fractures does not exceed 3 cubic meters per minute. The gravel pits below the groundwater table are operated with dredging equipment.

MINING OPERATION SYSTEMS

To better understand the design of mine dewatering systems, it is necessary to know the extraction methods used. These, together with hydrogeological conditions, influence the design of mine dewatering systems.

Underground Mines

The production level of the main workings is generally accessible by vertical shafts that are 100 to 1,000 meters deep and 4.0 to 8.5 meters in diameter. Shaft sinking in soft ground is mostly done by hand, with blasting in hard rocks. The casing is installed simultaneously or in sections. In saturated beds the drawdown of groundwater by wells equipped with submersible pumps or a solidification or freezing is used. Close to the shaft bottom, chambers (among them the chamber for the pumping station) and water reservoirs (galleries) are driven. When ready, the galleries for the first mining are driven with the use of blasting and mechanical loading equipment. These headings are the most hazardous in difficult hydrogeological conditions.

Various methods of extraction are used in bituminous coal mining depending on:

- Depth of operations.
- Thickness of the coal seam to be mined.
- Roof and floor conditions.
- Inclination of coal seam.
- Minability of coal.
- Gas occurrences.

The seams up to 3 meters thick, flat or with small inclination, are mined with 200- to 250-meter longwalls and roof caving, when there are no special requirements to protect the land surface. Where a seam is dipping more than 30°, the "step by step" method with a dry backfilling is employed; the operation progresses from lower to upper levels.

The thick seams (above 3 meters), flat or gently inclined, formerly were mined by the room and pillar method. Recently the longwall method has been used. The seam is mined in 3.5-meter thick benches, using hydraulic backfilling or caving with an artificial roof; the operation progresses from the upper to lower benches. The steep and thick seams are always mined with the use of hydraulic backfilling.

In underground copper, zinc, and lead mines, the room and pillar method, with various modifications, is used. Blasting and caving are generally employed; backfilling is occasionally required to protect sensitive buildings on the surface above from subsidence.

Surface Mines

Lignite, sulphur, stowing sands and clays, as well as overburden of these deposits, are loose soils. So these useful minerals and the overburden are mined with bucket-wheel and bucket-chain excavators. The material is directly loaded on belt conveyors or sometimes on railway cars. Blasting is rarely necessary in these deposits; but, in quarry operations, blasting, shovels, draglines, and loaders and trucks for haulage are widely in use.

The stowing sands, clays, and rock deposits are covered with only a thin topsoil overburden. In these mines the extraction of the useful mineral begins right after removal of the topsoil (which is stored for further reclamation). However, in lignite surface mines (and also in the sulphur mine), where overburden is 30 to 130 meters thick, the large operations to make the "opening cut" (to uncover the lignite seam) have to be executed. The volume of overburden (clays and sands) to be removed, and transported outside the mine, in these operations ranges from 30,000,000 to 120,000,000 cubic meters. This requires two to four years. When the lignite seam is uncovered, simultaneous lignite mining and overburden removal begins. And when mining faces extend a fair distance, the backfilling of waste into the open pit can start. This operation--consisting of several overburden working levels and one to three working levels in lignite-- moves through the deposit in a parallel or fan-shaped system. The output of one open pit, working as above, is 2,000,000 to 20,000,000 tons per year of lignite and 10,000,000 to 50,000,000 cubic meters per year of waste. During the next two years, a mine with an output of 40,000,000 tons per year of lignite and 120,000,000 cubic meters per year of overburden from one pit will be completed.

Such a magnitude of operations, with their depth, lithology of rocks, and the fact that mining extends deep below the groundwater table, make it necessary to have the dewatering system ready in advance.

DEWATERING SYSTEMS DESIGN AND THE DESIGN REVISION

In Poland, the design of mine dewatering systems is done by specialized design and consulting companies. They are:

- The Central Design Office in Katowice, for underground mining of bituminous coal.
- The Cuprum in Wroclaw, for underground mining of ores.
- The Poltegor in Wroclaw, for all surface mines.

The large mine dewatering systems are designed in three phases:

(i)   Feasibility studies are made for new mines. In these studies, estimate of expected groundwater inflow must be made and general ideas of multialternative technical solutions should be presented and compared from the financial and technical point of view. Also the out- lines of the required hydrogeological investigation needed for a detail design should be proposed. These feasibility studies are submitted for revision and approval by the company that intends to invest in and develop the deposits.

(ii)   Preliminary design should contain the general description
       of the entire dewatering system in one (maximum two)
       alternative. The inflow of groundwater and the size of
       the depression cone outside the mine should be calcu-
       lated; the dewatering arrangements should be sited and
       selected and the technology of their construction de-
       tailed. The required equipment and installations should
       be listed as should the number and the specifications
       of the staff to be employed; the environmental impacts
       and control measures, therefore, have to be presented.
       In conclusion, the investment and operational costs,
       as well as the timetable of system construction, should
       be elaborated. The preliminary design must be approved
       by the Ministry that supervises the mining company or,
       in the case of a large operation, by the State Commission
       for Economical Planning. From the standpoint of environ-
       mental protection, the preliminary design of a dewater-
       ing system must also be approved by local authorities.
(iii) Technical designs are made for particular installations
       or units (i.e., draining wells, monitoring wells,
       pumping station, sedimentation pond, etc.); they should
       contain the detailed location of every element and the
       technology of its construction, which is used by the
       construction company. These designs must be approved
       by the mining company with participation of the con-
       struction company, if different.

   The above designs are made on the basis of Geological
Reports prepared by the geological company that does the
field prospecting. These Geological Reports (also containing
the resources assessment) must be approved by the National
Geological Administration. For this approval, the design
office's opinion, with a statement that the scope of investigation is sufficient for system design in the related phase,
is required. Other data for dewatering system design
includes the requirements of mining extraction design as well
as the environmental authorities' requirements.

   The most significant data are:

(i)   Lithologic, tectonic and stratigraphic characteristics
       of the strata within the whole basin and in its
       surroundings.
(ii)   Thickness and extent of aquifers.

(iii) Hydraulic contacts between particular aquifers and between aquifers and surface water (i.e., lakes and rivers).
(iv) Permeability and specific yields of aquifers.
(v) The requirements by mining technology, area, and depth of the groundwater table drawdown.
(vi) Time of drawdown required by mining operations.
(vii) Requirements regarding location, quantity, and quality of mine drainage discharge.

The data mentioned in (i) to (iv) should be estimated while making the hydrogeological prospectus and investigation and should be included in the officially approved Geological Report mentioned above. The data mentioned in (v) and (vi) must be provided by the extraction system designers and the data from (vii) should be given by local water and environmental authorities.

METHOD OF HYDROGEOLOGICAL AND HYDROLOGICAL CALCULATIONS

The goal of the calculations made for dewatering systems design is to obtain:

- Inflow of ground and precipitation water with time.
- Shape and time of depression cone development.
- Output of particular elements.
- Spacing between draining elements.
- Time needed to draw down the groundwater table.

Depending on the size of the dewatering system and the time of dewatering, the calculations, based on the assumption of steady or unsteady flow, are applied (4). In both the above cases, for small and simple systems, the analytical solutions of formula derived from classic Dupuit and Theiss equations are used. For large and complicated systems the modeling methods are used (4). Until the beginning of the 1970s, methods based on hydraulic (i.e., Hele-Shaw) and electrical (EHDA or pattern integrator) analogy were used. Recently the numerical methods have prevailed. These methods deal with Boussinesque equation solved on plane with a regular or irregular discreteness. For calculations, the finite element or finite difference method with iteration (i.e., Gauss-Seidel or Galerkin) are applied. The programs are written in Fortran 1900 language, and Polish third generation computers, ODRA 13 series, are used.

Depending on quality and credibility of input data (received mostly from hydrogeological investigations), the results show ± 10 to 20 percent differences compared with the actual results. For systems with 10 to 400 cubic meters per minute inflow, this could be assumed satisfactory.

Also quite good results can sometimes be obtained with the use of very simple calculations based on analogy to the existing systems proved under similar conditions.

DEWATERING METHODS AND ARRANGEMENTS

In underground mines the main methods of protection against uncontrolled inrush of groundwater are:

- Protective and safety pillars and shelves.
- Moving and sealing of surface waters.
- Sealing of workings.
- Construction of insulating benches.
- Drilling of horizontal drainage holes in advance of the face progress (to 100 meters long).
- Execution of drainage holes to drawdown the groundwater or reduce its pressure.
- Vacuum draining holes constructed where quicksand is found.
- Construction of sealed stoppings.

For continuous removal of water inflow, pumping stations, with 120 percent of reserve in pumps and water reservoirs to hold a 16-hour inflow, are constructed in the lower level of the mine.

Cost of dewatering provisions in underground mining is rather low; it is within 2 percent of total investment and operational costs.

In lignite surface mines, where the size and scope of dewatering systems is the largest, the following procedures are used:

(i)   Drainage wells (Figure Nos. 7 and 8) are drilled from the surface and equipped with submersible pumps; the diameter of wells is 300 to 1,000 millimeters, and their depth is 50 to 350 meters. The output of these wells, depending on aquifer thickness and permeability, is 0.5 to 6.0 cubic meters per minute. In the well casing,

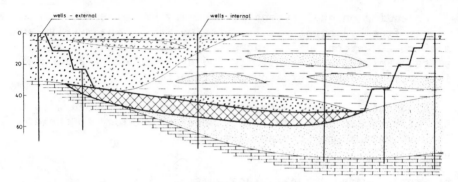

Fig.7. SCHEME OF DEWATERING SYSTEM OF ADAMÓW SURFACE
LIGNITE MINE.

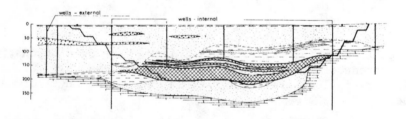

Fig.8. SCHEME OF DEWATERING SYSTEM OF BEŁCHATÓW SURFACE
LIGNITE MINE.

the lower part (about 10 meters long) serves to keep the sand grains coming through, the filter section (which consists of perforated pipes wrapped with gauze and surrounded with gravel packing) and the upper pipe part, could be distinguished. The drainage wells are located around the mine and in internal galleries; the spacing between wells in galleries is in the 80- to 150-meter range, and the distance between galleries is 200 to 600 meters.

(ii) Underground drainage galleries are drifts in the lignite seam at about 200-meter spacing. The seam is accessible through the pits or declines. The drainage system for the overburden is the holes drilled from the surface. To drain the under seam aquifer, holes are drilled from galleries. Both types of drainage holes discharge groundwater to the galleries by natural forces. The water runs through the galleries to the underground pumping station and from there is pumped out onto the land surface. According to regulations, pumps must have 120 percent of reserve and must be fed with energy from two independent sources; water reservoirs must have enough volume to contain two hours inflow (Figure Nos. 9 and 10).

(iii) Impermeable diaphragms are constructed where the open pit cuts the very permeable layers which have contact with rivers or lakes; these screens are excavated with shovels or drilling equipment specially designed for excavations to 30 meters deep and 0.3 to 0.8 meter wide; the sealing medium is mostly a mixture of special cement and clays or chemical components.

(iv) Horizontal holes from the slopes as well as drainage holes which channel groundwater from upper to lower aquifers are used as supplementary procedures.

(v) Dewatering trenches are excavated within the open pits to catch rainwater and the remaining groundwater missed by the above procedures. The water flows through these trenches to pumping stations; the trenches on the permanent slopes are lined and on periodic slopes are made without a casing. The width of the bottom of the trenches is 0.6 to 1.0 meter, their slope inclination is 1:1.5 to 1:2.0; their depth is 1.0 to 2.0 meters and their longitudinal dipping is 1 to 2 meters per thousand.

(vi) Pumping stations are located in the lowest parts of open pits as stable or shiftable units, and, according to Polish regulations, must have 50 to 100 percent of reserve in pumps and reservoirs for 4-hour retention of

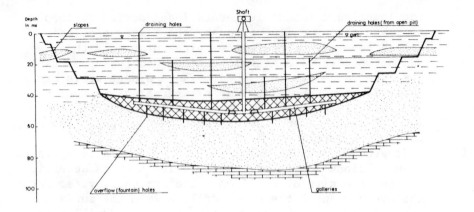

Fig.9. SCHEME OF DEWATERING SYSTEM OF KONIN SURFACE
LIGNITE MINE.

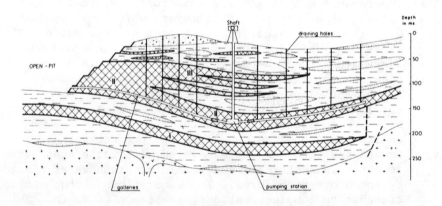

Fig.10. SCHEME OF DEWATERING SYSTEM OF TURÓW SURFACE
LIGNITE MINE.

total inflow. The inflow is calculated as 24-hour amount with probability coefficient p = 10 percent. (Figure No. 11)

(vii) Sedimentation ponds are used to purify mine drainage from mineral and organic suspension, because this contains 100 to 1,000 ppm of suspended matter. In the sedimentation ponds of 1- to 3-day retention time, the reduction of suspended matter concentration is effected in a natural sedimentation process, down to 50 ppm. Recently, to improve the effect (below 30 ppm) and to reduce the size of sedimentation ponds in mines, with inflow of 50 to 200 cubic meters per minute, flocculents and also the grass filter process are being introduced.

In surface lignite mines, the combination of all or some of the above technical means is used. In surface sulphur mines, only wells and supplementary procedures are used. In stowing sand and clays surface mines only, the procedures described in items (v), (vi), and (vii) are used.

For the newly developed lignite mines, the dewatering systems begin operation one or two years before the heavy machines start to remove the overburden. During current operations the dewatering system advances the slopes of the open pit by about one year.

In surface mines of other useful minerals, such advance time is shorter.

In Poland, the cost of surface mine dewatering systems is a factor in about 10 to 25 percent of total investment and operational cost of lignite mines. In other surface mines, except sulphur, the percentage is much smaller.

CONCLUSIONS

1. In all mining operations, below the groundwater table, the proper design of dewatering systems is an indispensable condition of undisturbed work.
2. The proper design of mine dewatering systems is directly dependent on the sufficiency and correctness of hydro-geological recognition.
3. In the underground mines and in open pits dug in hard rock, the aim of a dewatering system is to protect people and mine workings against flooding.

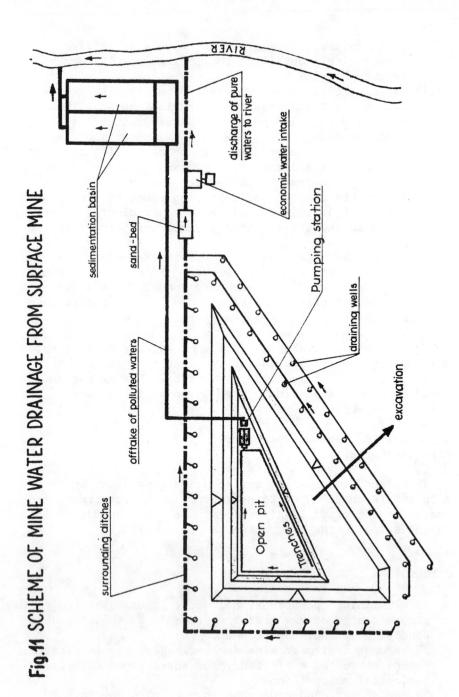

Fig.11 SCHEME OF MINE WATER DRAINAGE FROM SURFACE MINE

sedimentation basin

sand - bed

surrounding ditches

offtake of polluted waters

RIVER

discharge of pure waters to river

economic water intake

Pumping station

draining wells

excavation

Open pit

trenches

4. In the surface mines operated in loose grounds (sands, clays, mud), the proper dewatering of overburden, of useful mineral, and underlying beds is an indispensable factor in keeping the slopes stable, as well as excavator output and safety.
5. The design of mine dewatering systems should take into consideration the wide scope of environmental protection requirements, especially the quantitative and qualitative protection of ground and surface water.

REFERENCES

1. Mining Guide Book. Volume 2. Katowice 1975.

2. Jacek Libicki. Hydrogeological Conditions of Lignite Deposits in Poland and Criteria for Dewatering System Selection. Second International Symposium, Dubrovnik 1978.

3. Jacek Libicki. Technology of Mine Dewatering Systems. Guidelines for Design. Poltegor 1972.

4. Zbigniew Burzyński, Lech Jarodzki. Model Forecast of Hydrogeological Processes in Mine Dewatering Design. Surface Mining No. 4-5. 1975.

5. Henryk Janiak. The Impact of Lignite Mining on Surface Water and Means for Its Control. Second U.S.-Polish Symposium Ksiaz, Poland, 1978.

14

Case Examples of Open Pit Mine Drainage

by D. L. Pentz, Vice President,
Golder Associates,
Kirkland, Washington, USA

ABSTRACT

The methods of optimizing slope angles of open pit mines are limited. Reduction in the natural groundwater pressures is perhaps the most significant method available to the mine designer. For similar modest values of risk of failure of large slopes overall savings on the order of five to ten degrees are possible. This paper cites two cases with widely different properties where the effect of underground galleries have been measured. The difference between depressurization and drainage is demonstrated in materials which have overall permeability of 10^{-6} cm/sec and 10^{-2} cm/sec, respectively.

DRAINAGE AND DEPRESSURIZATION IN OPEN PITS

Introduction

This paper is intended to draw upon experience gained in two predominantly copper deposits to illustrate the difference between drainage and depressurization of rock masses forming the slopes of open pits. The importance of determining the hydraulic characteristics of a rock mass before embarking on large-scale engineering programs will be emphasized.

The concept of effective stress in materials forming

the earth's crust has been well established in both practice and in the laboratory and is an important factor in the practice of soil mechanics, rock mechanics, and reservoir engineering. Reduction in effective stress will decrease the available strength of the rock mass subjected to shear forces.

We may demonstrate deterministically (Refs.1,2 and 3) that significant increases in either slope angle and/or slope height can be achieved by reduction in water pressures present in a slope. If we wish to be more rigorous, we can express such changes probablistically in the form of risk/uncertainty analyses. In one of the cases to be briefly discussed here, as an example, some reference is made to this approach.

In the mining industry we are primarily concerned with extracting minerals with the maximum economy. In the case of open pits, we must mine the mineralized rock such that the total waste rock, which is necessary to remove, is kept to a minimum. The slopes of an open pit should be cut at as steep angles as possible consistent with efficient mine operating considerations.

If for a moment we ignore the complex issue of cost of failures and financial risk analyses in optimizing a decision process (i.e., a mine design), we can usefully turn our attention to how we may improve the strength of a slope. Since modern day soil mechanics became discernible parts of civil and mining engineering practice, it has been demonstrated that slope angles of soil or rock slopes may be steepened substantially by reducing the pore or groundwater pressures. An increase in the effective strength may be effected by other means such as cable bolting (Ref.4). The author's opinion on this method of optimizing slopes has been stated elsewhere (Ref.5). Suffice it to say here that the geological conditions where such methods of rock reinforcement should be applied are limited, but, in any case, reduction in groundwater pressures and cable reinforcement are not mutually exclusive. The primary technical and operating advantage of groundwater pressure reduction as a mechanism for increasing strength, and thus slope angles, is that changes in operating costs or mineral prices can still be accomodated by employing significant changes in the mine schedule; without losing the capital investment in the drainage or depressurization system.

Summary of Theory

If a borehole, well, or underground opening is placed beneath the water table, a gradient is set up in the rock mass. Water commences to flow from the material immediately surrounding the opening. This loss of water is made up by so-called storage effects, and the water left behind expands due to the pressure reduction. At the same time, the formation consolidates or undergoes compaction due to the increased effective stress. As the material immediately surrounding the opening is depressurized, so the material further away is "stressed," a hydraulic gradient is set up, and flows will be initiated towards the "depressurized" zone and then subsequently into the opening or "drain." The rate at which the depressurized zone expands will depend on the ratio of the permeability to the storage coefficient of the material. The storage coefficient may be related to the stiffness of the material; thus low stiffness and low permeability will lead to an extremely low rate of expansion of the depressurized zone. An example of a material with these properties would be clay. On the other hand, a fractured andesite with high permeability and relatively high stiffness will allow the zone of depressurized rock to expand very quickly. Once the depressurized zone reaches the phreatic surface, water will begin to drain from the material at this elevation. With time, the entire volume of water which occupied the drainable porosity of the rock mass will pass into the opening. The drainage of the rock mass may thus be divided into two phases: depressurization and subsequent drainage and lowering of the phreatic surface. A simple diagrammatic representation of these processes is shown in Figure No. 1.

In the two case histories summarized in this paper, it will be demonstrated that essentially complete depressurization has occurred in one (Twin Buttes), with the phraetic surface still remaining at approximately its original position. In the other case (Bougainville-Bulk Sampling Adits), the other results demonstrated that depressurization and drainage occurred almost simulataneously.

ALTERNATIVE METHODS OF OPEN PIT DRAINAGE OR DEPRESSURIZATION

The mining engineer or geologist is faced with essentially three alternative methods:
1. Toe drains
2. Perimeter and in-pit wells
3. Underground galleries.

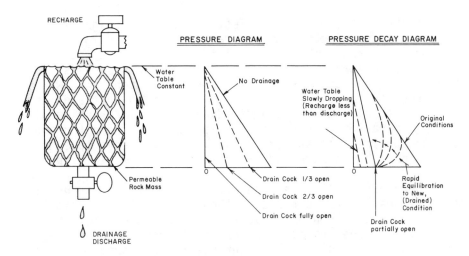

Figure No. 1,   DRAINAGE AND DEPRESSURIZATION MODEL

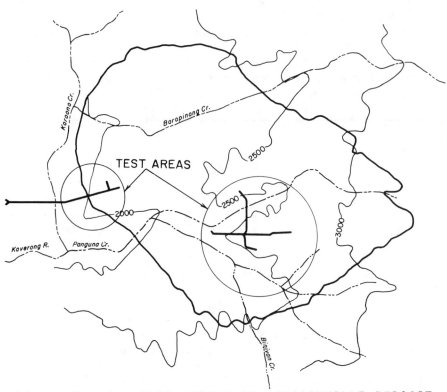

Figure No. 2,   PLAN SKETCH OF BOUGAINVILLE DEPOSIT
                 AREA

The first and last categories have the advantage of being effectively passive, that is, gravity driven and thus after construction require minimal maintenance. If the rock mass is highly permeable and the hydraulic barriers such as faults are say hundreds of feet apart, then perimeter wells may present a practical solution. However, both toe drains and in-pit wells suffer the disadvantage of interfering with mining operations and require replacement as the pit expands. The toe drains also suffer from a further disadvantage that they cannot be constructed prior to mining the pit slope.

Underground galleries have often been favored for use in high slopes by the author even though the initial capital cost is relatively high because of the efficiency of the system. The possibility also exists to couple an underground gallery system with a surface run-off sump collection system.

The example of the Twin Buttes Mine quoted below indicates that where a real commitment and case is made for optimizing pit slopes, then a drainage gallery system will ensure that an effective depressurization program can be carried out.

Finally, it should be pointed out that while a drainage gallery has many advantages, this does not preclude the use of toe drains and wells in addition. Also, for local potential instability, toe drains have proved to be very successful in halting slides along highways and in some open pits (Ref. 1).

CASE HISTORY A - BOUGAINVILLE FEASIBILITY STUDY

Prior to making a decision on the investment associated with the Bougainville Copper Deposit in Papua and New Guinea, a large scale diamond drilling and bulk sampling program was carried out to determine the nature and limits of the grade distribution (Ref. 6). Associated with this study a large geotechnical program was carried out to evaluate a variety of factors including slope angles. The geotechnical study utilized diamond drillholes for mineral evaluation purposes and some additional special purpose engineering holes. Simple probe tests (inflow) were performed to evaluate permeability in a variety of holes over specified lengths (1 to 2 meters). The majority of the groundwater information was, however, obtained from instrumentation of two bulk sampling adits; the Pan Adit and the Western Adit (see Figure No. 2). The effect of driving these adits on the preexisting groundwater conditions was monitored by measuring the discharge at the portal and several additional points within the adits and by also measuring the response of open holes and sealed piezometers. The piezometers were set in the line of the adits and on either side of centerline of the adits prior to construction.

The Bougainville deposit is characterized by a high frequency of jointing in intrusive and extrusive rocks (andeoite and diorites, granodiorites are the predominant rock types). Typically, the rock fractures have a frequency from 10 to 70 fractures per meter and associated high porosity (see Figure No. 3, Ref. 7). The fracturing shows some directional concentrations but this did not preclude joints being measured in exposures in any orientation. The majority of joints were however, measured at angles of greater than 60 degrees. The joints exposed in the test regions of the two adits were open and fresh for the most part. In addition to the joints, the rock mass at Bougainville was found to be interspersed by some predominantly steeply dipping clay filled faults. The results from the two adits may be summarized as follows:

Pan Adit

1. Full drainage occurred almost instantaneously, i.e., there was no discernable depressurization phase. Steady state was reached within 2 to 3 weeks at any point which was monitored.

2. The zone of rock which was drained to approximately the elevation of the adit extended beyond the immediate confines of the underground openings (see Figure No. 4).

3. When clay filled structures were penetrated as mining progressed, sudden responses in piezometric head (see Figure No. 5) were measured accompanied by sudden increases in inflow in the adit.

4. A maximum rate of some 100,000 gallons per

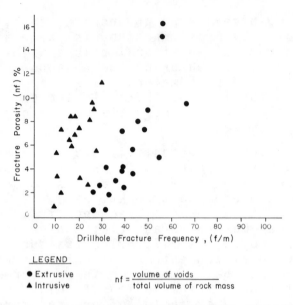

Figure No. 3, RELATIONSHIP BETWEEN FRACTURE FRE-
QUENCY AND FRACTURE POROSITY AT
BOUGAINVILLE MINE

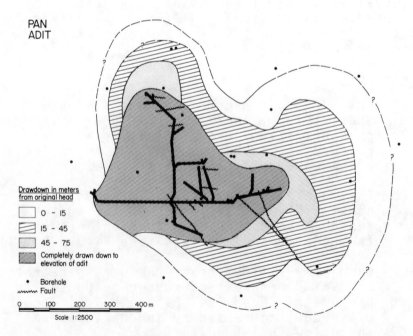

Figure No. 4, PLAN VIEW OF PRESSURE DROPS AS
RESULT OF PAN ADIT

hour was measured at the portal (this is
equivalent to 22 gallons per foot of adit).

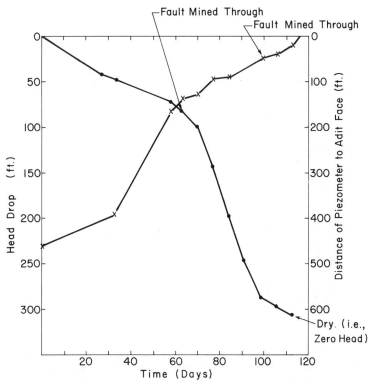

Figure No. 5, TYPICAL PAN ADIT PIEZOMETER RESPONSE

Western Adit

1. The Western Adit showed similar general
    response to that of the Pan Adit except
    there was more marked response to semi-im-
    permeable structures (see Figure No. 6).

2. The significant lateral influence of the
    adit in one type section (see Figure No.
    7 and No. 8) was restricted to some 150
    meters on either side where R_U* values
    (Ref. 8) dropped in excess of 75 percent.
    Beyond this distance the response was re-
    stricted to less than 16 percent.

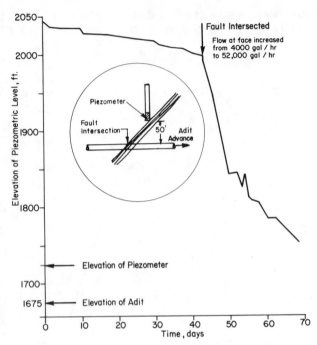

Figure No. 6,   WESTERN ADIT - EFFECT OF INTERSECT-
ION OF FAULT ON PIEZOMETRIC HEAD

3. The maximum flow rate which was recorded
    over the test section was some 45,000
    gallons per hour immediately after traver-
    sing the fault referred to in Figure No. 6.

General

The results from the adit tests at Bougainville indicated variable permeabilities. The
values ranged from 10^{-2} to 10^{-5} centimeters per
second.

CASE HISTORY B - TWIN BUTTES, EAST PIT

At a recent meeting of AIME (Refs. 9, 10, 11,
12) a series of papers was presented describing
an extensive program of depressurization of a
clay rich rock slope and subsequent slope stability analyses. These presentations are being
prepared for publication elsewhere and thus it is
not intended to duplicate that description but
rather to provide only a brief overview of the

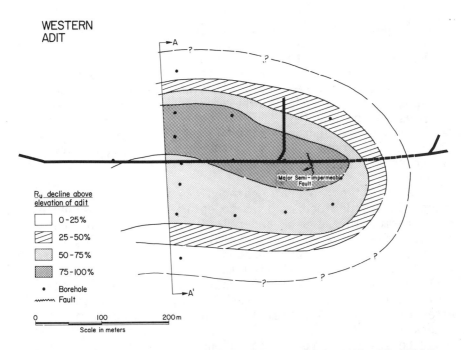

WESTERN ADIT

R_u decline above elevation of adit

- [ ] 0-25%
- [/] 25-50%
- [▨] 50-75%
- [▦] 75-100%
- • Borehole
- ⌇⌇⌇ Fault

Major Semi-impermeable Fault

0   100   200m
Scale in meters

Figure No. 7,   PLAN VIEW OF R_u DECLINE IN TEST SECTION OF WESTERN ADIT

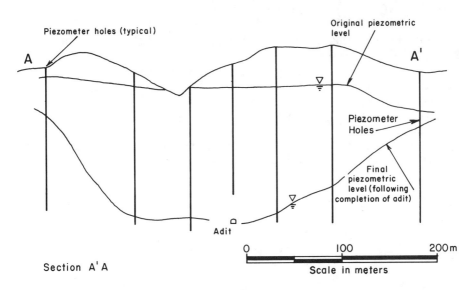

Piezometer holes (typical)

Original piezometric level

A   A'

Piezometer Holes

Final piezometric level (following completion of adit)

Adit

Section A'A

0   100   200m
Scale in meters

Figure No. 8,   SECTION THROUGH TEST SECTION OF THE WESTERN ADIT

CASE EXAMPLES OF OPEN PIT MINE DRAINAGE **333**

salient characteristics of the project.

The east slope of the East Pit of the Twin Buttes Mine in Arizona is geologically characterized by a paleozoic sequence (typically limestones, siltstones) containing the ore and separated by a major fault zone from the waste mesozoics (arkoses and porphyries). This fault zone contains several well defined semivertical clay filled structures and in some 200 feet wide zone. Overlying the bedrock is an alluvium cap which exceeds some 400 feet in vertical thickness.

As a result of several geotechnical and mining considerations, it was decided in 1975 to optimize the slope angles to be formed in the weak and relatively impermeable mesozoics. After several unsuccessful attempts at using toe drains, an extensive underground adit system was driven with some 72 piezometers installed in predominantly surface drilled vertical holes in a manner such that the project could be monitored from a standpoint of reduction in groundwater pressures. A system of installing pneumatic piezometers was developed (Ref. 13) such that up to 4 piezometers could be installed to depths of up to 900 feet.

A total footage of approximately 3,400 feet of underground gallery was mined specifically for this purpose with additional 25,500 feet of fan drilling (installed with slotted PVC pipe) (Figure No. 9).

The program was carried out in stages with each stage being planned based on the monitored results of the piezometers. The flow from the underground openings was also monitored which, for example, averaged some 0.13 gpm/feet through the 21-02 crosscut (see Figure No. 9). Flows from the fan holes drilled from the 21-05 crosscut showed in some cases flows as much as 25 gallons/minute which after typically two months dropped off to fractions of a gallon per minute in the majority of holes.

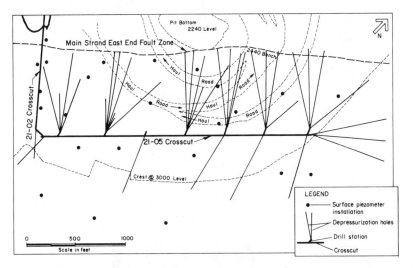

Figure No. 9,   PLAN OF DEPRESSURIZATION UNDER-
                 GROUND LAYOUT

The groundwater pressures response of the rock mass and primary conclusions may be summarized as follows:

1. The pressure drops range from 11 to 100 percent averaging 67 percent. The percentage drop in R_u values is demonstrated through time in Figure No. 10. The gallery itself caused the greatest pressure response.

2. A series of so-called "rubble zones" - - high permeability features which were found to be several hundred feet in extent. When a fan hole penetrates such zones, the effective size of the hole was increased thus enabling much larger zones to be depressurized.

3. The overall permeability of the material was found by modeling the response of piezometers and flow into the adit to be approximately 10^{-6} centimeters per second.

4. The water table is still at or near the surface since the underground system is removing water only at a slightly faster rate than it is being replenished by

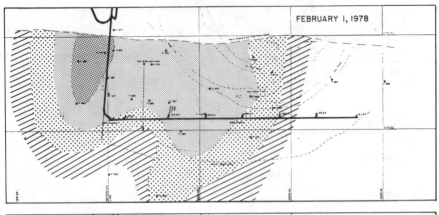

FEBRUARY 1, 1978

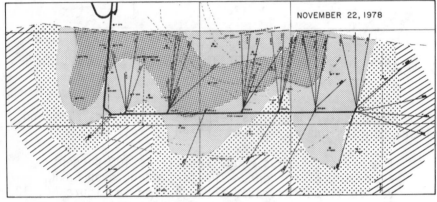

NOVEMBER 22, 1978

R_U Decline Above 2100 Level

▦	76% – 100%
▨	51% – 75%
⣿	26% – 50%
▧	6% – 25%
☐	0% – 5%

Figure No. 10, R_U PLOTS – FEBRUARY 11, 1978
NOVEMBER 22, 1978

rainfall and infiltration. Accordingly, very slow
pressure drops are continuing to be noted, as shown
typically in Figure No. 11.

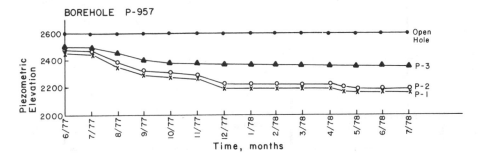

Figure No. 11, TYPICAL PIEZOMETER RESPONSE TO
ADIT SYSTEM

5. The results were incorporated in full risk/uncertain-
    ty analysis incorporating a rigorous statement of
    our uncertainty in all hydrological, geological and
    strength factors. A typical result is shown on
    Figure No. 12 to demonstrate the effect of a depress-
    urization system on a particular slope. If in this
    case a slope of 30 degrees is selected, an improve-
    ment of 26 percent in reliability due to the depress-
    urization program has been achieved. Alternatively,
    if a risk of failure of 12 percent is accepted, then
    the slope angle can be increased from 27 degrees to
    to approximately 35 degrees.

CONCLUSIONS

This paper is intended to emphasize the positive effect
of depressurization and drainage on rock masses forming pit
slopes. For the same degree of risk significant improvements in overall slope angles are possible. Indeed, the
higher risk which a mine may be prepared to accept, so the
possible benefit of drainage or depressurization systems
will increase.

The rock mass must be investigated from a geological and
hydrological point of view prior to installing any system.
The hydrological monitoring system should be tailored for
the specific requirements and should be used to control
the location and nature of the system.

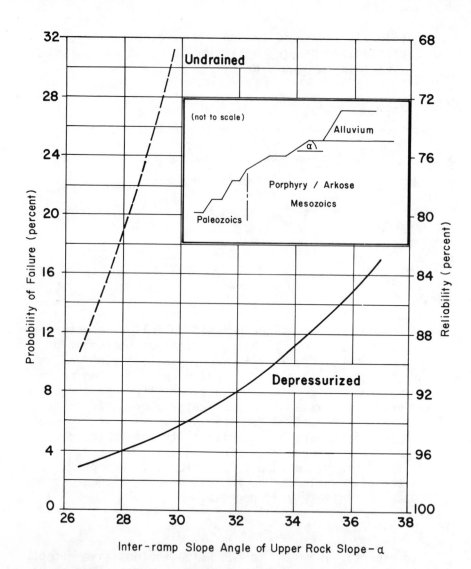

Figure No. 12, TYPICAL RESULT OF RISK SLOPE
ANALYSIS OF EAST PIT

Finally a plea is made to those geologists and engineers involved in exploration and feasibility studies of mineral deposits to maximize the information gathered from boreholes and bulk sampling adits so that substantially more reliable data may be obtained for evaluating ore as opposed to mineral reserves.

ACKNOWLEDGMENTS

I wish to acknowledge the Conzinc Rio Tinto Company, and in particular, M.R.L. Blackwell, for his help during the Bougainville Copper Feasibility Studies and also to the staff past and present of Anamax Mining Company for permission to use the data presented on Twin Buttes.

REFERENCES

1. Brawner, C.O. 1974. Rock Mechanics in Open Pit Mining. In Advances in Rock Mechanics: Proceedings of the 3rd Congress of the International Society for Rock Mechanics, Denver, V.1, pp. 755-773. Washington, D.C,: National Academy of Sciences.

2. Hoek, E. and J. Bray. 1977. Rock Slope Engineering. Rev. 2nd Ed. London: The Institution of Mining and Metallurgy.

3. Sharp, J.C. and T. Maini. 1972. Fundamental Considerations on the Hydraulic Characteristics of Joints in Rocks. In Proc. Symposium on Percolation Through Fissured Rock, International Society for Rock Mechanics, Stuttgart, pp. T1-F1-T1-F15.

4. Seegmiller, B. 1974. How Cable Bolt Stabilization may Benefit Open Pit Operations. Mining Engineering, V. 26, No. 12.

5. Pentz, D. and P. Hodges. 1976. Geotechnical Factors in Open Pit Mine Design. In Site Characterization: 17th U.S. Symposium on Rock Mechanics, Snowbird, Utah, V. 81, pp.A113-A120.

6. Stephenson, H.H. ed. (1973). Bougainville - The Establishment of a Copper Mine. Kilda, Australia: Construction, Mining, Engineering Publications.

7. Ashby, J. 1979. Personal Communication.

8. Bishop, A.W. and N. Morgenstern. 1960. Stability Coefficients for Earth Dams. Geotechnique, V. 10, No. 4, pp. 129-150.

9. Miller, I. and G. Deardorff. 1979. Bedrock Geohydrology of East End Fault Zone Slopes at Twin Buttes. Paper presented at the AIME Annual Meeting, New Orleans, Feb. 18-22.

10. Pentz, D. and P. Hodges. 1979. Summary of Objectives and Achievements of Slope Design at

Twin Buttes. Paper presented at the AIME Annual Meeting, New Orleans, February 18-22.

11. Byrne, J. and D. Pentz. 1979. Stability Analysis and Mining Implications for Twin Buttes. Paper presented at the AIME Annual Meeting, New Orleans, February 18-22.

12. Rippere, K. and Charles Barter. Engineering Geology of the East End Fault Zone Slope Desing Program at Twin Buttes.

13. Deardorff, G.B., A.M. Lumsden and W.M. Heffer-on. 1979. Pneumatic Piezometers: Multiple and Single Installations in Vertical and Inclined Boreholes. Paper submitted for pub-lication.

15

Ground Water Flow Systems in Idaho's Western Phosphate Field

by Dale R. Ralston,
Associate Professor of Hydrogeology,
College of Mines and Earth Resources,
University of Idaho, Moscow, Idaho, USA,
Michael R. Cannon, Hydrologist,
U.S. Geological Survey, Helena, Montana, USA,
and Gerry V. Winter, Hydrogeologist,
Hydrometrics, Helena, Montana, USA

ABSTRACT

Complex ground water flow systems and hydraulically connected surface water systems occur within the southeastern
Idaho phosphate field. Factors such as the geologic, topographic, hydrogeologic, chemical, and climatic characteristics of the area largely control the occurrence, movement
and quality of water in these flow systems through alteration
of existing characteristics. At certain mine sites the water
resource systems have the potential to interfere with mining
operations through mine pit flooding and through pit and
waste dump stability problems. Potential hydrogeologic
impacts from mining and potential hydrologic limitations to

mining are often difficult to predict because of the many variables involved.

Hydrogeologic studies in the southeastern Idaho phosphate field show that there are definite relationships between geologic, topographic, hydrogeologic, and climatic factors and existing ground water flow systems. The ore-bearing Phosphoria Formation effectively separates ground water flow in the Thaynes and Dinwoody formations from the underlying Wells Formation. Considerable ground water discharge occurs from the lower member of the Dinwoody Formation. Stream flow is commonly lost into the upper member of the Wells Formation. Analysis of existing mine sites shows that relationships exist between the water resource systems which occur at a mine site and the potential hydrologic impacts from mining. Hydrologic limitations to mining are also related to the water resource systems which occur at the mine site.

Ground water flow system theory and observed water resource systems relationships were used to develop conceptual models that identify water resource systems at mine sites and evaluate mine sites for potential hydrologic impacts and mining limitations. The conceptual models can be used to interpret flow systems at existing or proposed mine sites. Such analyses will facilitate environmental management with minimum costs to industry and also provide important inputs for mine management. The models yield highly reliable results when used as specified.

INTRODUCTION

Statement of the Problem

Southeastern Idaho encompasses a large portion of the western phosphate field. The Idaho phosphate deposits contain about 80 percent of the ore reserves of the western phosphate field, or about 35 percent of the United States reserves (U. S. Department of the Interior, U. S. Department of Agriculture, 1977). Phosphate ore is mined by open-pit methods along outcrops of the Meade Peak member of the Phosphoria Formation, where it has been exposed through folding, faulting, and erosion (Fig. 1).

Water resources within the phosphate field exist in complex ground water and surface water flow systems. These

Figure 1. Location of Phosphoria Formation outcrops in the southeastern Idaho phosphate field (after Ralston, et al., 1977).

complex water resource systems have developed over geologic time, through the interaction of many environmental factors. Factors such as the geologic, topographic, hydrogeologic, chemical, and climatic characteristics of the area influence the occurrence, movement, and quality of the water resource systems.

Mining activities within the phosphate field alter the existing environmental characteristics and therefore will, or have the potential to, impact the water resource systems. The water resource systems also have the potential to hamper mining operations in certain areas through pit flooding and through pit and waste dump stability problems.

An expected future increase in mining activities increases the potential for impacts of the water resource systems. It is evident that a thorough understanding of the many inter-related factors which control the water resource systems is necessary before potential mining impacts can be predicted and assessed. A definite need exists for a systematic method of identifying water resource systems at mine sites and eval-uating mine sites for potential hydrologic impacts. Accurate identification of water resource systems allows more efficient environmental management with less cost to industry. It also provides important inputs for mine management.

Purpose

The purpose of this paper is to present conceputal models of water resource systems of the southeastern Idaho phosphate field that can be used to systematically identify water resource systems at mine sites and evaluate mine sites for potential hydrologic impacts. The conceptual models are to be based on ground water flow theory and on observations of existing flow systems and mining impacts. The models can be used to evaluate present and potential mining impacts on the water resource systems and also to predict potential limita-tions to mining imposed by the water resource systems. The evaluation method should be of benefit to both mining inter-ests and resource administration.

Description of the Phosphate Mining Region

Several important major valleys and ridges occupy the central portion of the western phosphate field in Idaho. These ridge and valley systems trend predominantly northwest-southeast. The ridges in the study area are from 5 to nearly

40 miles long and from 1 to 10 miles wide. Elevations of ridge tops range from 7,000 feet to nearly 10,000 feet. The valleys as a rule are narrower and shorter than the ridges and range in altitude from about 5,800 to 7,500 feet.

Average annual precipitation in the study area ranges from about 15 inches or less at the lower elevations, to more than 35 inches on the higher ridge tops. In the southern and eastern portions of the study area, an average of 54 percent of the annual precipitation falls between November 1 and April 30, mainly as snow (U.S.D.A. Forest Service, 1978, p. 57). Snow accumulations on the lee (northeast) side of ridges may create drifts up to 30 feet or more in depth.

Geologic Setting

Rocks exposed in the study area range in age from Precambrian to recent; however, the marine sedimentary rocks of Carboniferous, Permian and Triassic age are of primary importance to the phosphate mining industry. Phosphate ore is mined from the Meade Peak member of the Phosphoria Formation, which is of Permian age. Hydrogeologic descriptions of pertinent formations in the study area are presented in table 1.

The geology of the study area is extremely complex. The general northwest-southeast linear trend of the mountains and valleys can be attributed to major thrusting and deformation during the Laramide Orogeny of Cretaceous age. Structure of the study area is dominated by major northwest-southeast trending synclines, anticlines, and associated faults. Subsequent erosion formed many valleys along the anticlinal fold axes. Normal faulting of the region during late Tertiary and throughout the Quarternary further complicates the structure. Quarternary basalts blanket a portion of the study area and form the Blackfoot lava field in the vicinity of the Blackfoot Reservoir. Most valleys of the study area contain Quarternary deposits of colluvium and alluvium.

WATER RESOURCE SYSTEMS OF THE PHOSPHATE AREA

Introduction

Hydrogeologic investigations conducted at three separate mine sites reveal relationships between specific geologic

Table 1. Hydrostratigraphic columnar section in the investigated areas in southeastern Idaho (after Ralston et al., 1977).

	Formation	Member	Thickness feet	Lithology	Hydrogeologic Characteristics (Permeability)	Hydrogeologic Classification
Triassic	Thaynes	Upper	900-1200	Limestone and sandstone with some shale siltstone layers	moderate to high	Aquifer
Triassic	Thaynes	Middle	2000	Limestone facies interbedded with greater portion of siltstone and shale	low to moderate	Aquifer
Triassic	Thaynes	Lower	2000	Limestone facies interbedded with greater portion of siltstone and shale	low to moderate	
Triassic	Dinwoody	Upper	900	Interbedded limestone and siltstone with discontinuous shaly zones	moderate for limestone and siltstone, low for shale and silt	Aquifer
Triassic	Dinwoody	Lower		Calcareous shale and siltstone with few thin limestone beds.		
Permian	Phosphoria	Rex Chert Unit	120- 150	Chert and cherty limestone, thick bedded	permeable when fractured	Aquifer or Aquitard
Permian	Phosphoria	Meade Peak Unit	150- 200	Phosphatic shale, mudstone and phosphatic rock. Some limestone and siltstone	low to semi-permeable	Aquiclude
Carboniferous	Wells	Upper	50	Siliceous limestone	Moderate	
Carboniferous	Wells	Middle	1500	Sandy limestone, sandstone	high	Aquifer
Carboniferous	Wells	Lower		Limestone, mostly sandy and cherty	moderate to high	
Carboniferous	Brazer	Upper	200	Black and white laminated	very low	
Carboniferous	Brazer	Middle	1000	Thick bedded limestone	high	Aquifer
Carboniferous	Brazer	Lower	600-1000	Thin bedded limestone	high	

units and ground water flow systems. In each area the
Thaynes and Dinwoody formations were found to support significant ground water flow systems. It was also determined
that the Phosphoria Formation does not support any major
ground water flow systems; however, the underlying Wells
Formation does support flow systems (Ralston and others,
1977). Winter (1979) demonstrated that the "phosphate sequence" of sedimentary rock units (Dinwoody, Phosphoria and
Wells formations) exhibit similar hydrogeologic properties
over a large area. Winter's study included measuring stream
gain or loss over the "phosphate sequence" and locating
springs with respect to geologic controls.

The hydrogeologic characteristics of the specific units
combine with structural, topographic and climatic factors
to control the flow systems in the area. It is important
to understand how these factors interrelate to form the
complex water resource systems found at mine sites.

Hydrogeology

The sedimentary sequence of the Dinwoody, Phosphoria, and
Wells formations forms the basic stratigraphy at all mine
sites within the study area. Colluvium and alluvium are
also important at some sites.

The Dinwoody Formation of Triassic age consists of an
upper member and a lower member. Winter (1979) identified
25 springs discharging from the Dinwoody Formation in eastern
Caribou County. Of these 25 springs, 20 were discharging
from the lower member. Stream gain-loss studies indicated
that flow increased at most sites across exposures of the
Dinwoody Formation because of ground water discharge into
the stream. Hydrogeologic investigations suggest that both
members of the Dinwoody Formation will support ground water
flow systems throughout the study area, provided that recharge
is available to the formation. The cross section of the
Little Long Valley Mine presented in figure 2 shows that the
stream in the valley receives most of its baseflow from a
ground water flow system in the Dinwoody Formation on
Rasmussen Ridge. Similar springs issue from the Dinwoody
Formation at most mine sites.

The Phosphoria Formation of Permian age consists of the
Rex Chert Member (the Cherty Shale Member is included as
part of the Rex Chert Member) and the Meade Peak Phosphatic
Shale Member. The Rex Chert Member generally has very low

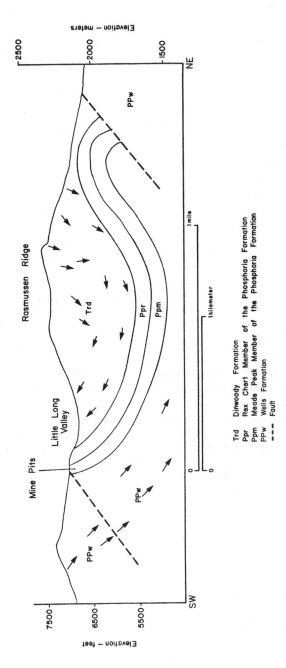

Figure 2. Generalized geologic section of the Wooley Valley Mine area (after Mohammad, 1977).

Trd   Dinwoody Formation
Ppr   Rex Chert Member of the Phosphoria Formation
Ppm   Meade Peak Member of the Phosphoria Formation
PPw   Wells Formation
---   Fault

hydraulic conductivity except where it has been significantly altered by fracturing and jointing. Aquifer tests conducted at the Lower Dry Valley Mine site by Vandell (1978) demonstrated that highly fractured zones within the Rex Chert can yield significant quantities of water; however, these zones are discontinuous features that are not widespread. Winter (1979) concluded that the Rex Chert and Meade Peak members of the Phosphoria Formation do not support any major ground water flow systems in the study area. His conclusion was based on the limited number and size of springs that discharge from the Phosphoria Formation. Streams generally do not gain or lose across exposures of the Phosphoria Formation due to the low hydraulic conductivity of the formation. Studies at specific mine sites support the hypothesis that the Phosphoria Formation does not support any major ground water flow systems in the study area. Figure 2 shows that the Phosphoria Formation separates the flow system in the Dinwoody Formation from a deeper flow system in the Wells Formation in Little Long Valley.

The Wells Formation of Pennsylvanian age is divided into an upper member and a lower member. Both members of the Wells Formation support major ground water flow systems in the study area. Sections of the Wells Formation exhibit high hydraulic conductivity and readily accept recharge. Stream gain-loss measurements made by Winter (1979) showed that stream flow is always lost to some degree, if not entirely, across exposures of the upper member of the Wells Formation. Several large springs in the study area issue from the Wells Formation or from the underlying Brazer Limestone. These springs have relatively constant discharge, suggesting a regional ground water flow. A ground water flow system in the Wells Formation accounts for the lack of streamflow in Dry Valley near a mine site in that area (Fig. 3). Large springs occur in Slug Creek Valley at the end of this flow system.

Quarternary deposits of colluvium and alluvium support ground water flow systems in the study area. Major valleys contain aquifers within alluvium which play important roles in ground water-surface water relationships.

Structure

The geologic structure of the study area is dominated by folds and faults. Structural features have greatly influenced the devlopment of ground water and surface water flow

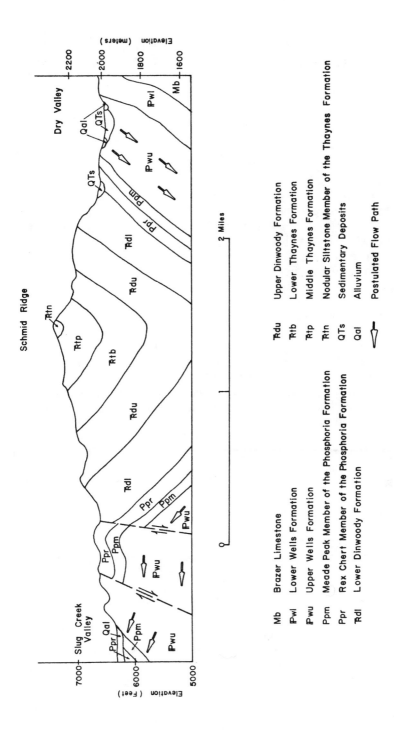

Figure 3. Postulated Dry Valley-Slug Creek Valley ground-water flow system

Mb   Brazer Limestone
Pwl   Lower Wells Formation
Pwu   Upper Wells Formation
Ppm   Meade Peak Member of the Phosphoria Formation
Ppr   Rex Chert Member of the Phosphoria Formation
Rdl   Lower Dinwoody Formation

Rdu   Upper Dinwoody Formation
Rtb   Lower Thaynes Formation
Rtp   Middle Thaynes Formation
Rtn   Nodular Siltstone Member of the Thaynes Formation
QTs   Sedimentary Deposits
Qal   Alluvium
⇨   Postulated Flow Path

systems. Major surface drainages are generally parallel to fold axes or follow fault structures. Stream valleys generally occur within the eroded cores of anticlines and ridges generally follow synclinal axes.

Structural features control to a large extent the location of ground water recharge and discharge areas. Ground water entering a geologic formation tends to follow bedding planes because hydraulic conductivity is higher parallel to bedding than across bedding planes. Valleys in the study area often lie on anticlinal axes, which provides a structural avenue for ground water to flow from one valley to another under ridges. Recharge to permeable rock outcrops on ridges may also follow fold structures and discharge in distant valleys. Fault structures affect the location of many springs. Figures 2 and 3 show how structure controls ground water flow in Little Long Valley and Dry Valley.

Topography and Climate

Topography and climate greatly influence flow system development in the study area. Basically, the topography is dominated by ridge and valley systems which trend northwest-southeast. Wind patterns cause snow to accumulate on the eastern and northern slopes of these ridge systems. Snow drifts on ridges may accumulate to more than 30 feet in depth and be as long as six miles (U.S.D.A. Forest Service, 1978). Eastern and northern ridge slopes and other lee slopes accumulate a large snowpack; therefore these areas are major recharge areas for ground water and surface water flow systems.

Summary of Water Resource Systems

Definite patterns of surface water and ground water flow are evident in the southeastern Idaho phosphate field. These ground water and surface water flow patterns are largely controlled by geology, hydrogeology, topography, and availability of recharge.

Precipitation on lee slopes supports flow in small surface channels and recharges ground water flow systems in the Thaynes, Dinwoody and Wells formations and in colluvial deposits. Ground water within saturated colluvium moves down slope forming local flow systems. These local flow systems discharge as small springs or seeps. Many of these local ground water flow systems dry up during summer months.

Recharge which enters the Thaynes and Dinwoody formations forms local and intermediate ground water flow systems. Recharge comes mostly from direct precipitation and from discharge by small local ground water flow systems. Ground water within these formations moves down gradient following bedding planes and fault structures. Discharge from the flow systems is to springs and streams where bedding planes and faults intercept land surface. Some of the ground water within these flow systems moves across bedding planes into the lower member of the Dinwoody Formation. Further cross bedding flow is virtually prevented by the relatively low hydraulic conductivity of the Phosphoria Formation. Ground water commonly discharges along the Dinwoody-Phosphoria contact in the form of springs and increased stream flow (Winter, 1979).

The Meade Peak member of the Phosphoria Formation supports no significant ground water flow systems. The Rex Chert member may support localized flow systems where it is highly fractured. The Phosphoria Formation forms an effective hydrologic barrier between flow systems within the Thaynes and Dinwoody formations from those within the Wells Formation and Brazer Limestone. A possible exception to this is where considerable displacement has occurred due to faulting.

The Wells Formation supports major ground water flow systems within the study area. Evidence suggests that these flow systems are regional in extent. Recharge to regional ground water flow systems in the Wells Formation occurs from precipitation, streamflow loss, and downward percolation from alluvial valley aquifers. The high mountains and valleys, which receive the greatest precipitation, are the principal recharge areas for regional flow systems. Discharge from regional flow systems is controlled largely by topography and structure. The Snake River Valley and the Bear River Valley are probably primary discharge areas for regional ground water flow systems.

Alluvial material in valleys contain large quantities of ground water. Surface water and ground water flow systems within alluvial materials readily interact. Some stream reaches within valleys lose to underlying alluvium while other reaches gain water from the alluvium.

MINING AND WATER RESOURCE SYSTEMS

Environmental Factors Which Control Water Resource Systems

The flow systems indigenous to the phosphate field of southeastern Idaho are the result of the interaction of the many physical factors actively at work within the environment. These include geologic, topographic, hydrogeologic, climatic and chemical factors. Identification of these environmental factors and determination of their influence on flow system processes is important to the development of flow system models of the phosphate mining areas. Impacts of mining on water resource systems can only be predicted if the relationships between environmental factors and flow system development are understood. For example, potential impacts of mining on a ground water flow system can be predicted only if it is known how changes in geologic, topographic, and hydrogeologic factors affect a ground water flow system, because mining alters these factors.

Geologic factors greatly influence the location and development of ground water and surface water flow systems. Some of the geologic factors which affect the development of flow systems are: 1) areal extent and thickness of rock units, 2) dip of rock units, 3) orientation of rock units relative to topography, 4) folding of rock units, 5) fracturing and faulting, and 6) outcrop patterns.

Topographic factors influence the geometry of a basin and the development of local, intermediate, or regional flow systems. Some of the topographic factors which affect the development of flow systems are: 1) regional slope of valley flanks within a basin, 2) amount of local relief, 3) relative size of basins, and 4) orientation of valleys and ridges.

Hydrogeologic factors within a basin directly affect ground water flow rates, flow capacities of rock units, and location of major flow systems. Hydrogeologic factors include: 1) hydraulic conductivities of rock units, 2) relative hydraulic conductivities parallel and perpendicular to bedding planes, 3) specific yield or storage of rock units, and 4) fluid potential within rock units.

Climatic factors include: 1) precipitation, 2) wind velocity and direction, and 3) evaporation and evapotranspiration potential.

Chemical factors of primary importance to water quality include: 1) available nutrients, radioactive elements, and heavy metals in the rock, soil, and water, 2) chemical stability of earth materials, and 3) pH balance between ground water and earth materials.

Mining Factors Which Affect Water Resource Systems

Mining activities alter or have the potential to alter the existing geology, topography, hydrogeology, biology, and chemical equilibrium within a basin. Changes to these factors will, in turn, affect the water resource system. Potential impacts to water resource systems include changes in the occurrence, movement, and quality of ground water and surface water flow systems. The development of pits and waste dumps are the mining factors which have the greatest potential to affect water resource systems because they create the largest changes in geology, topography, and hydrogeology.

Excavation of mine pits necessarily alters the geology and topography. Factors of pit construction include: 1) areal extent, 2) depth, 3) wall slopes, 4) location relative to geologic structure and 5) location relative to topography (Mohammad, 1977).

Construction of waste piles involve several factors that may affect the occurrence, movement, and quality of flow systems. These include: 1) areal extent, 2) thickness, 3) slopes of waste dump surfaces, 4) hydraulic conductivity of waste rock, 5) location relative to topography, 6) location relative to geologic structure, and 7) chemical stability of waste rock to leaching (Mohammad, 1977).

CONCEPTUAL MODELS OF WATER RESOURCE SYSTEMS

Introduction

The conceptual, qualitative models presented in this section are based on ground water flow systems theory and on the regional, intermediate, and local flow system relationships outlined previously. The factors found to exert the greatest influence on flow systems within the study area are variations in topography, geology, climate, and hydraulic conductivity of geologic formations. Combinations of these factors are used to determine the ground water flow systems which are most likely to occur at any given mine site. The models are valid only for areas which contain the "phosphate sequence" of sedimentary rock units in well defined ridge and valley systems such as those found in the southern and eastern portions of the study area. The models cannot be used to reliably predict ground water flow systems in areas which are dominantly fault controlled and show no definite ridge and valley systems.

Assumptions

Several assumptions are necessary for application of these models to ground water flow systems. It is assumed that the relative hydraulic conductivities of the geologic units are consistent over the study area; the Thaynes and Dinwoody formations exhibit moderate hydraulic conductivity, the Phosphoria Formation exhibits low hydraulic conductivity, and the Wells and Brazer Limestone formations exhibit high hydraulic conductivity. The hydrogeologic study on ground water flow systems in the phosphate sequence conducted by Winter (1979) indicates that this is a valid assumption.

It is assumed that relationships between the environmental factors of geology, topography, hydrogeology and climate, and ground water flow system development are the same wherever the same combination of factors exists. Analysis of six existing mine sites in the area indicates that areas which have similar environmental characteristics have similar ground water flow systems. Ground water flow system theory also supports this assumption.

It is assumed that relationships between water resource systems, mining factors, and hydrologic impacts are similar, wherever the same combination of factors exists. Analysis of six existing mine sites in the area indicates that a given hydrologic impact is caused by a given combination of mining factors and water resource system factors. For example, a mine pit may reduce the flow of a spring issuing from the Dinwoody Formation if the mine pit intercepts the ground water flow to that spring.

Mine Type Designation

The following steps are outlined to select the mine model that best fits a given situation.

Step 1. Is the mine site located within a definite ridge and valley system? Answer: Yes or No. If the answer is no the models do not directly apply. If the answer is yes, continue.

Step 2. From figure 4 select the topographic location of the mine site on the major ridge system. Choices are 1) ridge top, 2) ridge flank, or 3) ridge bottom. Selection should be made based on the location of the mine pits. If the bottom of the mine pit will be no more than about 300 feet below the top of the major ridge, it is classified as "ridge top". Do not classify a mine as ridge top unless it is at the crest of a major ridge or unless it occupies a secondary ridge and the bottom of the mine pits will be substantially above adjacent valley floors. Mines are classified as "ridge bottom" if mine pits will extend below the elevation of the adjacent valley floor. All mine sites located between ridge top or ridge bottom are classified as "ridge flank".

Step 3. From figure 4 select the local topographic condition of the major ridge slopes. Choices are: A) broken ridge slopes and B) smooth ridge slopes. Broken ridge slopes are characterized by numerous valleys, small ridges, and knolls which interrupt the major slope of the ridge. These topographic irregularities are in the order of 100 to 300 feet in relief.

Step 4. From figure 4 select the geologic configuration of the rock units at the mine site. Choices are: A) dip with slope and B) dip contrary to slope. Geologic configuration should be chosen with respect to the location of the mine pits on the ridge. If geologic formations are slightly overturned and the Wells Formation or Brazer Limestone is located at the top of the ridge, choose dip with slope (A). If the geologic units are horizontal and the Dinwoody Formation is located upslope from the mine pits, choose dip contrary to slope (B).

Step 5. Slect the slope aspect of the mine site. This should be the slope aspect of the major ridge slope. Choices are: A) north and/or east facing, and B) south and/or west facing.

Step 6. The mine site should now have a one digit, three letter code which designates a specific mine type. An example is 2ABB. This particular designation means that the mine pits will be located on a ridge flank with broken local topography, the formations dip contrary to the topographic slope, and the slope faces either south or west or both. Cannon (1979) presents a detailed description of each mine site classification.

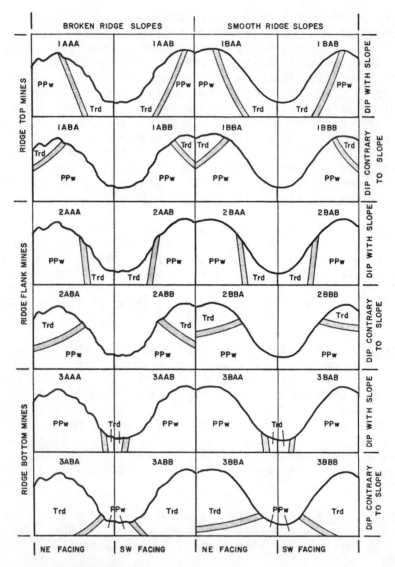

Figure 4. Diagrammatic section for each mine type.

Discussion of Model Predictions

A general ranking of each mine site is given in table 2 for: a) potential for discharge of various types of flow systems into the pit and the associated limitations on mining, b) potential mining impacts on springs which supply baseflow for perennial streams and c) potential for waste dump erosion and instability from water movement through the dump (assuming the waste dump has not been vegetated and is located downstream from the pits). Table 2 shows that mines located at ridge bottoms have the greatest potential for intersecting large flows of ground water. Ridge top mines have the greatest potential for waste dump erosion and instability.

In general, the models should predict ground water flow systems at proposed mine sites with a high level of reliability. However, all models are simplifications of real systems. Local folds or faults may cause variations in flow from that predicted.

CONCLUSIONS

1. Definite relationships between environmental factors and development of water resource systems have been observed in the study area. Past hydrogeologic studies have shown that relationships exist between geologic formation type and ground water flow systems. This study demonstrates that additional relationships exist between topographic, geologic, and climatic factors and flow system development.

2. Relationships between existing water resource systems, mining activities, and water resource impacts have been observed. The degree of hydrologic impacts from mining is related to the size (local, intermediate, or regional) and types (ground water or surface water) of flow systems encountered at the mine site. Hydrologic limitations to mining are dependent primarily on the size and types of flow systems intercepted by mine pits.

3. Conceptual models have been developed which can be used to identify water resource systems at existing and proposed mine sites in the southeastern Idaho phosphate field. The models delineate ground water flow systems based on the geologic structure, topographic configuration, topographic location, and climatic conditions of the mine area. These

Table 2. Rank of Mine Types for Various Parameters

RANK	PARAMETER					
	Potential for discharge of ground water flow systems into pits				Potential for impacts to springs which supply base flow to perennial streams	Potential for waste dump erosion and instability from water movement through dump
	Local	Intermediate	Regional	Limitations to mining		
HIGH	3ABA 2ABA 3BBA 2BBA 3ABB 2ABB 3BBB 2BBB 2AAA 2AAB 2BAA	3ABA 3BBA 3ABB 3BBB 2ABA 2BBA 2ABB 2BBB	3ABA 3BBA 3ABB 3BBB 3AAA 3BAA 3AAB 3BAB	3ABA 3BBA 3ABB 3BBB 3AAA 3BAA 3AAB 3BAB 2ABA 2BBA 2ABB 2BBB	3ABA 3BBA 3ABB 3BBB 2ABA 2BBA 2AAB 2BBB	1BAA 1AAA 1BBA 1ABA 2BAA 2AAA 2BBA 2ABA 1BAB 1AAB 1BBB 1ABB
MEDIUM	2BAB 3AAA 3BAA 3AAB 3BAB			2AAA 2BAA 2AAB 2BAB		2BAB 2AAB 2BBB 2ABB
LOW	1ABA 1BBA 1AAA 1BAA 1ABB 1BBB 1AAB 1BAB	All Others	All Others	1AAA 1ABA 1BAA 1BBA 1AAB 1ABB 1BAB 1BBB	All Others	3AAA 3BAA 3AAB 3BAB 3ABA 3BBA 3ABB 3BBB

models may be utilized both for environmental management and mine planning.

REFERENCES CITED

Cannon, M. R., "Conceptual Models of Interactions of Mining and Water Resource Systems in the Southeastern Idaho Phosphate Field", University of Idaho, M.S. Thesis, 106 p., 1979.

Mohammad, O. M. J., "Evaluation of the Present and Potential Impacts of Open Pit Phosphate Mining on Ground Water Resource Systems in Southeastern Idaho Phosphate Field", University of Idaho, Ph.D. Dissertation, 166 p., 1977.

Ralston, D. R.; Mohammad, O. M. J.; Robinette, M. J.; and Edwards, T. K., "Solutions to Water Resource Problems Associated with Open Pit Mining in the Phosphate Area of Southeastern Idaho", Completion Report for Groundwater Study Contract No. 50-897, U. S. Department of Agriculture, Forest Service, 125 p., 1977.

U. S. Department of the Interior and U. S. Department of Agriculture, "Final Environmental Impact Statement, Development of Phosphate Resources in Southeastern Idaho", FES 77-37, 4 volumes, 1977.

U.S.D.A. Forest Service, "Environmental Statement and Land Management Plan, Caribou National Forest", Diamond Creek Planning Unit, 370 p., 1978.

Vandell, T. D., "Analysis of the Hydrogeology of the Phosphoria Formation in Lower Dry Valley, Caribou County, Idaho", University of Idaho, M.S. Thesis, 116 p., 1978.

Winter, G. V., "Ground Water Flow Systems of the Phosphate Sequence, Caribou County, Idaho", University of Idaho, M.S. Thesis, 120 p., 1979.

16

Artesian Dewatering Operations at Morwell Open Cut

by C. J. Fraser, Geotechnical Engineer,
Fuel Department,
and H.A. Pitt, Engineer,
Operations Planning, Coal Production Department,
State Electricity Commission of Victoria,
Melbourne, Australia

ABSTRACT

Morwell Open Cut is a brown coal project in the Latrobe Valley of South Eastern Australia. At the site, large scale dewatering of underlying aquifers is carried out to maintain the stability of the open cut floor. There are two extensive aquifers that contain groundwater under pressure and a continuous pumping program is required to lower the artesian pressures to safe levels. On a mass basis, the amount of artesian water pumped is about twice the coal won.

This paper briefly describes the hydrogeology of the situation, the requirements to prevent excessive floor heave, the dewatering operations, surveillance procedures, and pump and bore installations.

The problems and consequences of the dewatering operations are also reviewed. These include the dependence of the coal winning operations on the continuous dewatering of the aquifers and the extensive subsidence of the sediments of the Latrobe Valley resulting from the regional drawdown effects.

INTRODUCTION

Morwell Open Cut is a brown coal project located in the Latrobe Valley of Victoria, Australia (Figure 1). The brown coal is excavated to supply fuel to the Hazelwood Power Station (1600 MW) and Morwell Power Station (135 MW) which provide much of Victoria's base load electricity. Coal production from the open cut is currently running at about 16 million tonnes per annum.

Overburden at the site is generally less than 20 m deep and development is to the full depth of an upper coal seam ranging between 100 m and 120 m thickness within the open cut. Bucket wheel dredgers and one bucket ladder dredger operating on faces up to 25 m in height are used to supply coal via conveyors to bunkers of limited capacity. Overburden is transferred to an external dump. The dredgers move along parallel operating benches loading onto movable face conveyors. The open cut has been developed with multiple parallel operating faces to the west and is now going through a pivot operation to swing the development to the south-west.

The initial opening up of the site commenced in the 1950s. By 1960 bores were established in the open cut and dewatering of an underlying aquifer commenced, initially with free flow bores, but later with pumping bores as the depth of the excavation increased. It was required to lower the pressure of the artesian groundwater to maintain

stability against excessive floor heave as done at the
Neyveli lignite mine, India (Vogt (1)). However, by 1969
the development was approaching the base of the coal seam
and floor heave together with uncontrolled flows of artesian
water emerging through tension cracks in the base were
experienced. Subsequent investigations revealed the
significance of a deeper and more extensive aquifer. Since
1969 water has been extracted from both aquifers peaking
for a short time in 1973 at 1350 1/s (refer appendix for
units). Currently, the mass of artesian water pumped is
about twice the mass of coal won.

It is postulated that, if the pressure of the artesian
waters is not maintained at a safe level, excessive floor
heave would result, flooding by water and sand slurry would
occur and large batter movements could develop due to the
loss of toe support.

This paper describes the artesian dewatering operations
at Morwell Open Cut and discusses the methods used, the
requirements for stability, and the problems associated
with the dewatering program.

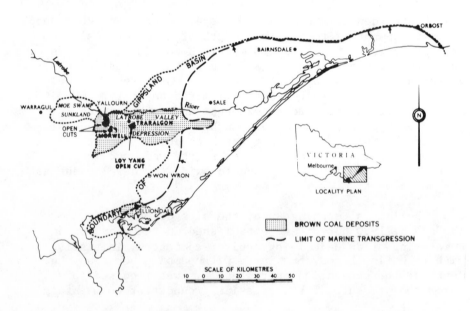

Figure 1 - Gippsland Basin and Locality Plan

GEOLOGY

The Latrobe Valley depression comprises up to 700 m of Tertiary sediments including thick brown coal seams at shallow depth, together with occasional basaltic flows. The depression exists at the western end of the Gippsland Basin (Figure 1) which is one of the coastal artesian basins of Australia. The stratigraphy and structure of the Latrobe Valley coal measures have been described by Gloe (2). The stratigraphy is complicated by numerous splits in the depositional sequence and later major structural events.

In the Morwell area, the Tertiary sequence lies unconformably on a Mesozoic basement. The sequence commences with the Hazelwood Formation which comprises up to 150 m of sediments interbedded with minor basalt flows. The sediments include clays and sands with up to 45 m of gravels towards the base.

The Hazelwood Formation is overlain by the Morwell Formation which includes two major coal seams separated by an interseam of clay and sand. The lower coal seam, named the Morwell 2 seam, is about 50 m thick in the area of the open cut. The upper coal seam (Morwell 1 seam) has a maximum thickness of 165 m just south of Morwell township, but, due partly to tilting and erosion, gradually thins to the south and west. It is this coal seam that is excavated by the Morwell Open Cut. The interseam separating the two coal seams has a thickness of approximately 30 m.

The sequence is terminated with the Haunted Hill Gravels. This deposit consists of sands and clays of Pliocene age that unconformably overlie the Morwell Group. It is less than 20 m thick in the area of the open cut. The stratigraphy of the site is shown in Figure 2.

The coal seams are strongly jointed with near vertical joints that fully penetrate the seams. The orientation of the joints clearly indicates their tectonic origin. They are often open and infilled with sand or clay.

HYDROGEOLOGY

Two major aquifer systems occur below the open cut as shown in Figure 2. The M1 aquifer is a near continuous sand layer of about 15 m thickness in the interseam separa-

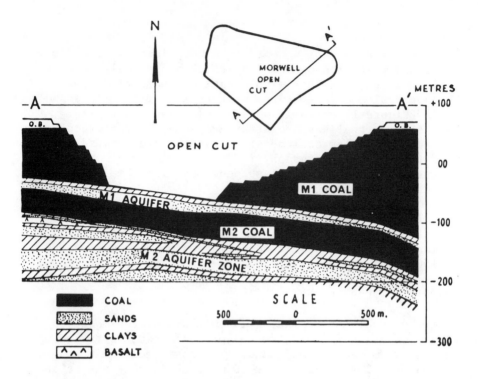

Figure 2 - Morwell Open Cut Section

ting the Morwell 1 and Morwell 2 coal seams. A clay layer
separates the aquifer from the base of the Morwell 1 seam.
The deeper M2 aquifer system occurs in the Hazelwood
Formation as a series of lensoidal sand layers immediately
below the Morwell 2 coal seam. The M1 aquifer extends up
to 11 km to the western outcrop of the coal measures. To
the north the interseam disappears at a distance of about
5 km whereas to the east it has not been traced due to
rapid deepening of the strata. The M2 aquifer is less
defined, but it is thought to be in hydraulic connection
with the basal aquifers that exist as a complex leaky aquifer
system throughout much of the Latrobe Valley.

Before open cut operations commenced the piezometric
surface of the M1 aquifer was at about +60 m AHD which is
very close to ground surface. In fact, it is on record
that as early as 1913 artesian flows were obtained from
deep bores in topographically low areas. This was possible
as it has been found that the artesian pressures increase
with depth.

The recharge source to both aquifers is not precisely known. However, indications are that they are both recharged from the hills at the western edge of the Latrobe Valley and possibly from the Moe Basin through the Haunted Hills. This inference is made from the relationship between piezometric surface and distance from centre of pumping shown in Figure 3. Carbon dating of the waters supports this boundary source and also suggests that the aquifers obtain leakage from deeper aquifers and drainage from consolidating aquitards.

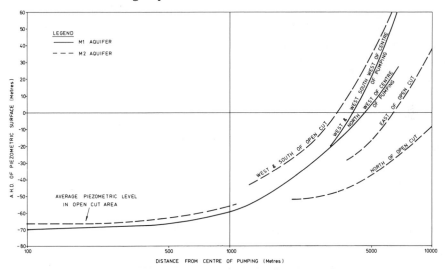

Figure 3 - Drawdown-Distance Relationships

The temperature of the artesian waters is high and the geothermal gradient is several times greater than world average. The average temperature of the water pumped from the M1 and M2 aquifers is $46^{\circ}C$ and $55^{\circ}C$ respectively. The waters are of reasonable quality with total dissolved solids averaging about 400 mg/l for both aquifers, but they can be highly corrosive to mild steel.

The M1 aquifer sands are reported by Barton [3] to be poorly sorted, positively skewed mature sediments with a mean particle size in the coarse sand range. The sands are predominantly clear, detrital quartz. Experience has shown the M2 aquifer sands to be of a similar nature. Pump tests done during the late 1960s indicated that the transmissivity of the M1 aquifer is 325 m^2/day and the storage coefficient is 1×10^{-3}. The average M2 aquifer parameters determined from a controlled recharge test in 1973 are transmissivity equal to 1700 m^2/day and storage coefficient equal to

3×10^{-4} (Golder, Brawner and Assoc (4)).

REQUIREMENTS FOR STABILITY

To prevent catastrophic floor heave, it is required that the water pressure in the aquifers below the open cut be less than the equilibrium pressure of the aquifer. The equilibrium pressure is that pressure which just balances the weight of the overlying sediments. Consequently, as the depth of the open cut is increased, the weight of overlying sediments is reduced, and the required amount of aquifer depressurisation is increased. It is assumed that the weight of the overlying sediments of clay and coal provide the reactive force required for stability as shown in Figure 4. The shear strength of the material separating the aquifer and open cut base cannot be relied upon for assistance because of the large floor area and the presence of near vertical joints that penetrate the full thickness of the coal seams.

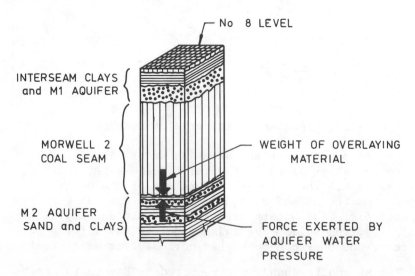

Figure 4 - Equilibrium Forces

To maintain stability, it is required that the artesian pressure at every location be lower than the corresponding equilibrium pressure. The critical location is where the weight of the overlying sediments is a minimum (deepest part of open cut) and aquifer depressurisation should be centred on that location to minimise pumping.

A factor of safety is applied to the determination of the equilibrium pressure to allow for uncertainty in the assessment of the forces involved. The factor of safety against floor heave is defined as -

$$\text{Factor of safety} = \frac{\text{Weight of material overlying aquifer}}{\text{Force exerted by aquifer water pressure}}$$

A system of "target", "security" and "emergency" piezometric pressures developed by Brown (5) and extended by Hutchings and Guest (6) is used to assist the operating staff in maintaining the stability of the current critical area and provide a code to the status of that stability. For each condition a different factor of safety is used which corresponds to a different probability of failure.

The following values are used:

Stability Condition	M1 Aquifer		M2 Aquifer	
	Factor of Safety	Probability of Failure	Factor of Safety	Probability of Failure
Target	2.0	0.005	1.30	0.005
Security	1.37	0.05	1.20	0.05
Emergency	1.16	0.20	1.06	0.20

The "target" piezometric levels are those below which it is aimed to maintain the aquifer piezometric levels during normal operations. These levels provide a buffer below the "security" levels to allow for pump outages. The "security" level is the highest level at which floor stability is deemed safe. If the "security" levels are exceeded, local emergency action is taken to reinstate pumps. Finally, if the "emergency" levels are exceeded then serious disruption to coal winning operations is likely and general emergency procedures are invoked to re-establish safe piezometric levels.

The "target" level for the M1 aquifer is simply selected as the lowest point in the open cut and the "target" factor of safety for the M2 aquifer is the optimum value determined with respect to cost of failure. The factors of safety for the "security" condition were selected so that the actual factor of safety would be unity if the uncertainty of measurement of the water pressure, the material thickness, and the material density were to take their worst case. The "emergency" factors of safety provide a probability of failure of approximately 20% (Hutchings and Guest (6)).

Under present conditions with the M2 aquifer at its "target" level and if all pumping ceased, it would take about 45 minutes to reach the "security" level and 10 hours to reach the "emergency" level. The times are estimated using the method suggested by Golder, Brawner and Assoc (4). For partial outages the times are significantly increased.

DEWATERING OPERATIONS

Before the project started, it was realised that the artesian pressure in the M1 aquifer would require lowering as the eventual base of the open cut was to be within 15 m of that aquifer. In 1960 the piezometric surface of the aquifer was more than 120 m above the base (-63 m AHD).

Artesian dewatering commenced in 1960 when four free-flow bores were drilled on No 1 coal level. By mid 1965 the piezometric surface had been reduced from +60 m AHD to about +15 m AHD by a succession of free flow bores as described by Gloe (7). The total flow from the aquifer peaked at 167 1/s in 1964. In 1965 the open cut was developed to No 4 level which is at about +10 m AHD.

During this initial period, widespread heaving, up to 2.5 m in places occurred in the floor. With the full development of No 4 level and a pilot opening to No 5 level in 1966 detailed surveys showed that an additional heave of 1.7 m occurred during the year (Gloe, et al (8)). Also, considerable uncontrolled flow of artesian water through the floor of the No 5 level opening indicated the possibility of further heaving. Four additional free flow bores were established on No 5 level and by the end of 1966 the piezo-metric surface was reduced to +5 m AHD. Nevertheless, at that time it was decided to advance the dewatering program with pumping bores and abandon the free flow concept in an endeavour to avoid further heave.

When the No 5 level and a temporary pump sump on No 6 level were developed in early 1967 the piezometric surface had been lowered by pumping, but the pressure was still too high and the first pilot bore drilled on No 6 level flowed and some heaving occurred. Pumping continued and by mid

1968 the piezometric surface below the open cut was at
about −23 m AHD.

In mid 1968 development of No 7 level commenced with a
pilot opening and similar conditions to those experienced
on No 6 level were encountered. The elevation of the
opening was −30 m AHD. As the opening was extended,
uncontrolled flow of hot artesian water broke through a
number of fissures and cracks in March 1969. The flow
gradually increased to an estimated rate of 115 l/s with
the total artesian flow being 340 l/s. At that time the
piezometric level in the M1 aquifer was −35 m AHD.

Prior to the occurrence of uncontrolled flow on No 7
level, two attempts to dewater the M2 aquifer were unsuccessful because the bores encountered poor aquifer sands.
However, by this stage the M1 aquifer dewatering operations
had lowered the piezometric pressure of the M2 aquifer to
approximately +25 m AHD by upward leakage. In November 1969
a bore drilled from No 7 level into the Morwell 2 coal seam
produced a free flow of 45 l/s. The head in the bore was
greater than that in the overlying M1 aquifer as was the
water temperature. The water was derived from the M2
aquifer through cracks and fissures in the coal. A bore
was immediately drilled from No 5 level into the M2 aquifer.
Free flow from this bore quickly led to a lowering of
pressures and the cessation of the uncontrolled flow on
No 7 level by December 1969. During the period of
uncontrolled flow, heave of the base amounted to 1.5 m.

In 1970/71 four additional free flow bores were
established in the M2 aquifer from No 7 level. The total
flow from the aquifer reached 265 l/s in early 1971 and the
piezometric level was lowered by about 10 m in the vicinity
of No 7 level. By this stage it was realised that much
greater flows would be required from the M2 aquifer to
establish a safe piezometric level prior to further
deepening (Gloe, et al (8)).

The flow from the M2 aquifer was steadily increased by
the introduction of pumping bores. In early 1973 the flow
had reached 700 l/s but the piezometric surface had only
been lowered to −30 m AHD. The dewatering program had
called for a level of −48 m AHD before the No 8 level
(bottom level) was opened up (Brown (5)).

After 1969 the piezometric surface of the M1 aquifer
steadily declined along with the pumping rate. When the

No 8 level was opened up in mid 1973 the piezometric surface
of the M1 aquifer was at about -61 m AHD and the flow rate
was 200 1/s. In an endeavour to meet the target level set
for the M2 aquifer the pumping rate from that aquifer was
increased. By late 1973 the piezometric surface was
slightly above that required and the flow averaged 1000 1/s
with peaks in excess of 1100 1/s. Although the target level
for the M2 aquifer was not quite achieved prior to the
opening up, no major problems were experienced with the
development of No 8 level.

The M1 aquifer flow and level continued to decline
until 1976 when the flow rate was 130 1/s and the piezometric
surface was at -62 m AHD. Since that time a relatively
steady flow rate has been maintained and the level has
continued to fall slowly. Over the same period the flow
from the M2 aquifer was maintained at about 1000 1/s until
1975 when the piezometric level stood at -55 m AHD. Since
then there has been a small, but steady, decline in pumping
rate and a correspondingly small decline in aquifer pressure.
The current pumping rate averages 860 1/s.

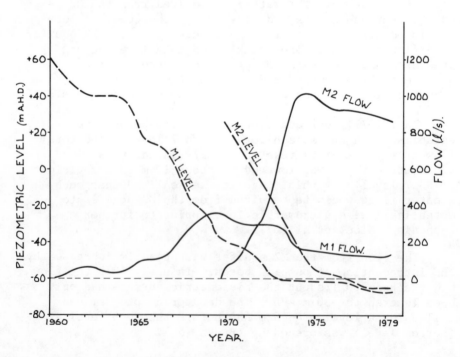

Figure 5 - Piezometric Levels and Flows

The history of piezometric levels and flows from the
two aquifers is shown in Figure 5. Figure 6 shows the
relationships between piezometric level and flow.

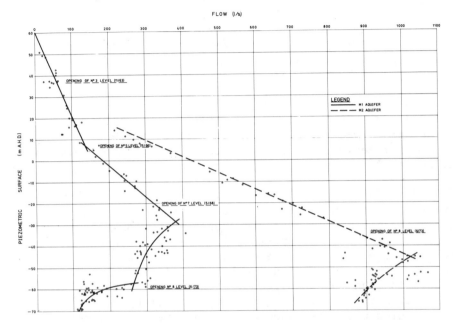

Figure 6 - Relationships Between Piezometric
Level and Flow

From Figure 6 the four major episodes through which
the dewatering operations have passed can be readily seen.
The initial episode embraces the period of free flow from
the M1 aquifer and shows a linear relationship between
piezometric pressure and flow. The second episode also
experienced a linear relationship and encompasses the
period that pumping from only the M1 aquifer was carried
out. The third episode commenced with the dewatering of
the M2 aquifer and continued until stable conditions had
been reached and the open cut was developed to its full
depth. During this episode there was a slight reduction in
flow from the M1 aquifer (less leakage from M2) and
piezometric levels dropped. At the same time, there was
a positive linear relationship for the M2 aquifer as with
the M1 aquifer during the second episode. The final
episode is one of consolidation of dewatering operations
from both aquifers and it is characterised by reductions
in pumping rates and stable equilibrium pressures being
maintained.

PUMPS AND BORES

The free flow bores used during the early stages of the dewatering operations for both aquifers were mostly completed using 150 mm diameter steel casing open to the top of the aquifer. A valve at the surface discharged to a V-notch weir for control and measurement. With these bores, problems were often encountered with aquifer collapse due to sand removal.

When pumping bores were introduced, sand had to be excluded and there was experimentation with drilling and screening techniques. Resin bonded gravel screens of 400 mm diameter were used in the early stages along with welded steel bore casing.

After incidents of steel casing failures caused by the corrosive artesian waters, asbestos cement (AC) bore casing with a special coupling was developed in conjunction with a local manufacturer as reported by James Hardie and Co (9). Problems were also encountered during drilling. These included aquifer contamination by drilling mud, loss of circulation, and bore collapse. Consequently, the reverse circulation rotary drilling method was introduced in 1970. Difficulties were also encountered in developing sands through the resin bonded screens and some screen collapses occurred. Current bore construction methods make the use of resin bonded screens impractical and wire wound stainless steel screens are now used as standard (Scott (10)).

Currently, bores are constructed as shown in Figure 7. The procedure is to first drill a pilot hole of 125 to 150 mm diameter and obtain samples of the aquifer sands for screen design. The pilot hole is overdrilled by the reverse circulation method at 1000 mm diameter into the last clay above the aquifer sands. AC casing of 575 mm i.d. is then set into the clays and also supported from the surface. The space behind the casing is generally backfilled with gravel. Drilling is continued through the casing at 560 mm diameter to about 2 m below the last sand. The screen assembly consisting of 406 mm o.d. mild steel pipe with wire wound screens and centralisers is set into the aquifer.

Most bores are gravel packed behind the screens with 4-5 mm standard gravel. In such cases the screens have a 3 mm slot opening. Where natural packing is suitable, generally in the M1 aquifer, slot openings are 1-2 mm. The length of screens varies between 6 m and 14 m.

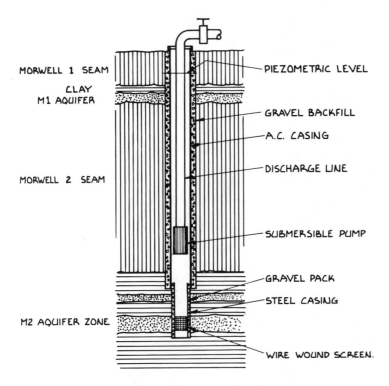

MORWELL 1 SEAM

CLAY
M1 AQUIFER

MORWELL 2 SEAM

M2 AQUIFER ZONE

PIEZOMETRIC LEVEL

GRAVEL BACKFILL

A.C. CASING

DISCHARGE LINE

SUBMERSIBLE PUMP

GRAVEL PACK

STEEL CASING

WIRE WOUND SCREEN.

Figure 7 - M2 Aquifer Pumping Bore

Piezometric level observation bores are generally
drilled at 150 mm diameter and a slotted 63 mm diameter
galvanised iron pipe installed. Key observation bores in
the M2 aquifer tap a thin sand seam near the top of the
aquifer zone as this is the one that is important to
stability.

Submersible motor pump combinations are used in the
pumping bores. "Small" units have 70 or 90 kW motors with
pumps rated at 75 1/s at 80 m head. "Large" units use
185 kW motors rated at 150 1/s at 85 m head. The pump units
are very reliable, most outages being due to power supply
problems. However, pump failures caused by sand ingestion
or motor thrust bearing breakdown do occur. Currently,
with good maintenance and bore construction practices, pump
lives are in excess of 30 000 hours.

The submersible pumps deliver to a surface collection
system leading to buffer tanks at the base of the open cut.
Most bores deliver to the tanks via gravity pipelines, but
a pressure pipeline is required from those bores at the

lowest parts. The buffer tanks allow sand to settle and dissolved CO_2 to dissipate. Water in the tanks is pumped to the power station cooling pond or directly into the open cut fire protection network with high head centrifugal pumps.

The location of the pumping bores and the key observation bores operational in 1978 is shown in Figure 8. At that time there were four M1 aquifer pumping bores with only two in regular use. These bores were equipped with the "small" pumping units. The M2 aquifer had 13 operational pumping bores with eight in regular service. These were a mixture of "small" and "large" pumping units. The large number of pumping bores on standby is required to enable rapid reinstatement of the required flow whenever an outage occurs.

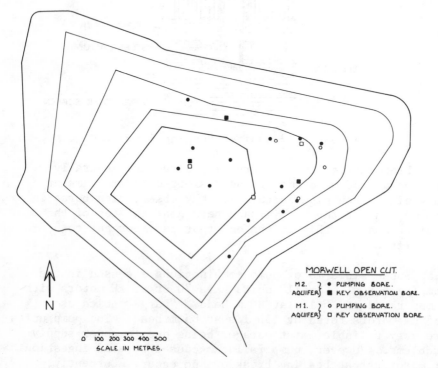

MORWELL OPEN CUT.

M2. } AQUIFER } • PUMPING BORE. ■ KEY OBSERVATION BORE.
M1. } AQUIFER } ○ PUMPING BORE. □ KEY OBSERVATION BORE.

0 100 200 300 400 500
SCALE IN METRES.

N

Figure 8 – Location of Bores

Each aquifer has three key observation bores to monitor the piezometric surfaces. The bores are carefully selected for location and response to changes in pumping rate. The average level from the key bores in each aquifer is used as a measure against the "target" piezometric level.

A large number of observation bores are located in and
around the open cut. These are used for a variety of
purposes, but mostly to provide back-up to the key bores
and for studying the wider effects of the dewatering operation.

SURVEILLANCE

Monitoring of the dewatering operations is conducted
on a routine basis. The piezometric level of the six key
observation bores is monitored by continuous recorders.
The pumping bores are inspected every shift and flows
measured on a weekly basis. The piezometric level of
several less important observation bores located within the
open cut is also measured on a weekly basis and all other
bores within the open cut on a two or three-monthly basis.

Outside the open cut, a network of regional observation
bores is established. These tap either the M1 and M2 aquifer
close to Morwell Open Cut, but beyond, where the stratigraphy
changes, a variety of aquifers (mostly basal) are monitored.
The frequency of readings on the regional bores is either
two monthly or three monthly depending upon distance from
the centre of pumping.

The target flows and levels are routinely adjusted
every six months. This is done to take account of critical
areas created by the advance of the working faces and the
success in achieving previously set target levels.

Whenever an emergency condition arises, close monitoring
is carried out until flows are re-established.

FACTORS ASSOCIATED WITH DEWATERING OPERATIONS

Pumping is required to be continuous to ensure that
safe piezometric levels in the aquifers are maintained at
all times. If interruptions occur, the piezometric levels
in the aquifers rise rapidly. This could cause failure of
the open cut floor if flows are not re-established rapidly.
Outages due to pump failures, interruptions to the power
supply and occasional bore failures make it difficult to
maintain a constant pumping rate.

The State's generation system is arranged such that
under a system emergency, Morwell Power Station, together

with Morwell Open Cut and some other loads, are isolated completely from the rest of the State. This provides a secure overall power supply for the pumping bores as well as the many other important loads of the system.

The most common source of outage is in the open cut electrical distribution system where brief interruptions in the power supply cause the pump motors to stop. Most of these stoppages are of short duration and are overcome quickly. There are several such occurrences each month. If an outage is widespread many man-hours of work can be required to reinstate the pumping.

The worst such occasion was in November 1977 when a major coal fire in the open cut burnt power cables. During the fire, the flow rate from the M2 aquifer dropped to 230 l/s for more than one hour and was less than 50% of normal flow for more than 12 hours. It took about 27 hours to re-establish normal flow. During that time the piezometric level in the M2 aquifer rose by about 10 m. Fortunately, the levels were very low beforehand and the "security" level was not exceeded. It was estimated later that it would have taken three days to reach the "emergency" level under the prevailing conditions. The M1 aquifer bores were not greatly affected.

The work force responsible for the operation of the artesian system and rainfall and surface water pumping is usually six men with many others involved on a part-time basis and during emergencies.

Another factor associated with the dewatering operations is the regional subsidence caused by the widespread drawdown in the aquifers. The effect of open cut operations on large scale earth movements in the Latrobe Valley are fully discussed by Gloe (11) and Hutchings, et al (12). However, those caused by artesian dewatering are briefly discussed here.

A lowering of the piezometric pressure in the aquifers results in an increase in the effective stress in the strata. This in turn leads to consolidation of the coal seams and clayey interseams. The effects of drawdown in the basal aquifers can be seen to extend to the east of Traralgon (Figure 9). Survey data indicate that subsidence contours have a similar pattern with 0.2 m being recorded up to 15 km from the open cut and more than 1.6 m being recorded at Morwell township.

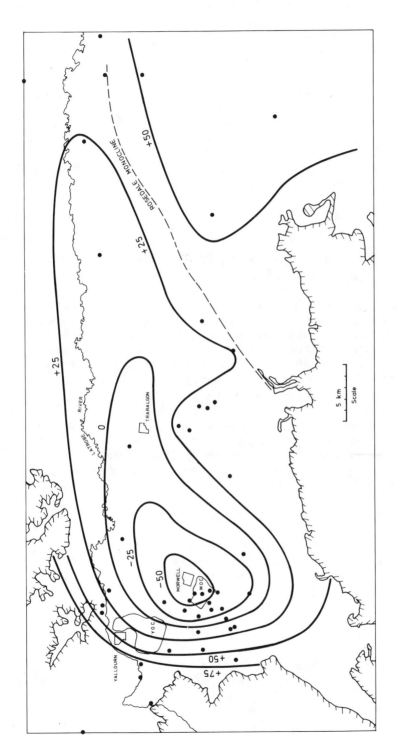

Figure 9 – Regional Piezometric Surface of Basal Aquifers

In order that the regional drawdowns are reduced to a minimum, an endeavour is made to keep the centre of pumping (centre of mass from operating bores) as close as possible to the critical area. This minimises the required flow. Currently, the working faces are passing through the deepest zone and the critical area is at the toe of the bottom cut. New pumping bores have been established on the floor as close as possible to the toe. By minimising the amount of pumping the rate of regional drawdown is reduced. This slows the rate of subsidence, keeps costs to a minimum, and helps to preserve the water as a resource.

CONCLUSIONS

Artesian dewatering is required at the Morwell Open Cut to ensure the stability of the floor against heave. Because of the hydrogeological situation and the importance of the open cut to the State's energy supply the dewatering operations are given special attention. A sophisticated system of pumping bores is operated on a continuous basis with operating personnel motivated to overcome all outages promptly. A large number of pumping bores are maintained on standby and a secure power supply is provided to assist in maintaining the required pumping rate.

Dewatering commenced in 1960, but large scale pumping did not start until 1970. It was not until 1975 that stable piezometric pressures were reached. Since then it has been possible to slightly reduce the pumping rate whilst maintaining stable piezometric levels. It is anticipated that this trend will continue even though the floor area of the open cut is steadily increasing.

The major problems associated with the artesian dewatering operations are those caused by the need for continuous pumping and the regional subsidence resulting from the dewatering.

ACKNOWLEDGEMENTS

This information is published with the permission of the State Electricity Commission of Victoria. The contributions made to the work described here by many of our colleagues in the Commission and Golder, Brawner and Associates, Vancouver, is most willingly acknowledged.

REFERENCES

1   Vogt, W.   Stage and Development of the South Indian Neyveli Lignite Project.   Braunkohle, 27(5), May 1975.

2   Gloe, C S.   The Latrobe Valley Coal Measures. Contribution to Tertiary Section of the Geology of Victoria, Geol Soc Aust, July 1974.

3   Barton, C M.   The Morwell Interseam "Sands". J Geol Soc Aust, 17(2), 1971 : 191-204.

4   Golder, Brawner and Assoc.   Impact of a Power Outage on the Heaving Safety of the Floor of Morwell Open Cut.   Report to SECV prepared by Golder, Brawner and Associates, Vancouver, Report No V75068, October 1975 (unpublished).

5   Brown, A.   Factors of Safety for Heaving Stability, SECV, Fuel Department, Report No DD58, January 1973 (unpublished).

6   Hutchings, R and Guest, J.   Morwell Open Cut Artesian Dewatering - M1 and M2 Aquifer Equilibrium Pressure Levels 1976 to 1994.   SECV, Fuel Department, Report No DD108, March 1976 (unpublished).

7   Gloe, C S.   The lowering of the Artesian Water Pressure Surface in the Vicinity of the Morwell Open Cut. Memoirs IAH Congress 1965, Vol VII, Hannover, 1967 : 193-196.

8   Gloe, C S, Waghorne, E, Brown, A and James, J P. Earth Movement Investigation - Morwell Open Cut, Review of Underground Water Operations and Investigations.   SECV, Planning and Investigations Department, Internal Report, July 1971 (unpublished).

9   James Hardie and Co.   Dewatering the Brown Coal Open Cuts.   Supplement to J Inst Eng Aust, 45(2), December 1973.

10   Scott, A.   A study of the Performance of Water Well Screening Systems.   Master of Engineering Thesis, Uni NSW, Sydney, 1977 (unpublished).

11   Gloe, C S.   Land Subsidence Related to Brown Coal Open Cut Operations, Latrobe Valley, Victoria, Australia.

Proc 2nd Inter Symp on Land Subsidence, Anaheim, California, 1976.

12   Hutchings, R, Fajdiga, M and Raisbeck, D. The Effects of Large Ground Movements Resulting from Brown Coal Open Cut Excavations in the Latrobe Valley, Victoria. Proc of Conf on Large Ground Movements and Structures. University of Wales, Inst of Sci and Tech, Cardiff, 1977.

APPENDIX

AHD	=	level in metres relative to the Australian Height Datum which is mean sea level
1 m	=	3.281 ft
1 mm	=	0.04 inches
1 l/s	=	15.8 gpm (u.s.)
1 m^2/day	=	80.5 gal/day/ft (u.s.)
1 mg/l	=	1 ppm (approx)
1 kW	=	1.341 horsepower

17

Computation of and Experience on Lignite Opencast Mine Drainage

by Rolf H. Hofedank,
Geophysicist/Senior Hydrologist,
Otto Gold Consulting Engineers,
Cologne, Federal Republic of Germany

1. INTRODUCTION

The planning of an openpit drainage represents a complex problem. Aside from hydrology and hydrogeology, the investigative phase requires the application of geology, pedology, climatology, meteorology, hydraulics of open channels, geophysics, chemistry and mathematics (statistics, theory of probabilities, modelling), including programming. In the planning stage, cost and time calculations, fluid hydraulics in pipes, soil mechanics, and the thorough knowledge of materials are added.

In an openpit drainage there is no hydrological or hydrogeological problem which does not appear in some other connection as well. On the other hand, no other problem concerning water, aside from those having to do with the drainage of mines, needs such a large number of different sciences for its solution.

No project implies the application of all the above mentioned disciplines to the same degree. Some will be used only as a secondary aid; this applies - to give you one example - to the statistical calculation of the recurrence probabilities of heavy rainfalls of the flood frequencies of rivers, if the client or government entities can provide the statistics.

The following will provide an overall idea of the individual operations which experience has shown to be the most important required in the planning of an openpit drainage, up to and including claims.

Finally, using the example of a lignite field in India, the influence of a variable geohydraulic factor - i.e. the leakage - on the drainage of an openpit will be established and the possibilities available at present for its investigation described. Since this influence can also appear in other openpit mines, it is of particular interest generally speaking.

2. CALCULATIONS AND MEASUREMENTS IN CONNECTION WITH THE PLANNING OF THE DRAINAGE OF OPENCAST COAL MINES

2.1 Ground Water affecting the Mine

Calculation of the ground water outflow at the beginning of mining operations and over the long run.
Assessment of the risk of bottom heave.

- Work involved

Evaluation of the existing (hydro)geological data
Determination of drilling programmes
Core description
Evaluation of grain-size distributions of borehole samples
Measurements of ground water levels
Flow measurements at springs and artesian wells
Localization and design of pump wells and monitors
Execution and evaluation of pump tests
Interpretation of geophysical borehole logs and of air borne geophysics
Interpretation of data obtained from geophysical ground methods
Determination of water chemism

- Information obtained

Natural directions and velocity of ground water flow

Permeabilities, transmissivities, storage coefficients, leakage factors, drainage factors, piezometric heads, etc. of the aquifers and the overburden, coefficients of possibly impervious layers and of coal

Hydraulic coefficients (see above) of foot wall
Water contents and transmissivity of wash-out channels

Potential water flow from recharge boundaries (e.g. wash-out channels, permeable faults, water courses adjoining the mine)
Impact of barrier boundaries
Impact of other conditions failing to conform with the so-called ideal aquifer (anisotropy of hydraulic conductivity, sloping aquifer, wedge-shaped aquifer etc.)
Possible chemical agressivity of the ground water.

Protective Measures

Well fields for pre-drainage
Vacuum-dewatering system by well points
Slurry curtains
Drainage ditches for shallow aquifers
Relief wells in the foot wall
(Computation based on ground water models; all measures must take into consideration soil mechanical factors)
Computation of costs and of time requirements.

2.2 Surface Water affecting the Mine

Calculation of the maximum flow rates and their super-position into high-water peaks at the mine rim and within the region of the outside dumps.

- Work involved

Evaluation of climatic data and meteorological statistics
Evaluation of topographic maps
Evaluation of geological and pedologic maps
Execution and evaluation of possible further hydrological measurements
Determination of solid matter in the water, in particular during floods
Determination of the water chemism, also during floods.

- Information obtained

Size of catchment areas of the water courses crossing or touching the mine
Descending gradients of catchment areas
Roughness of ground surface (e.g. vegetation, etc.) in the river catchment areas
Branching of water courses draining the catchment areas
Dependence of precipitation on topographic height
Portion of precipitation seeping into ground
Evaporation-precipitation ratio
Run-off coefficients of catchment areas

Velocity of surface drainage
Flow velocity in the water courses
Water retention capacity of creek and river beds
Intensity, duration and percentage of occurrence of
"critical precipitation"
Abrasive effects of water under normal conditions and
during floods
Possible chemical agressivity of the surface water under
normal conditions and during floods.

Protective Measures

Diversion canals
Protective dams
Water retention basins
River diversions
River development
Pumping stations
(Some of the computations use computer programmes; all measures must take into consideration soil mechanical factors)
Computation of costs and of time requirements.

2.3 Ground Water and Precipitation in the Mine

Computation of the precipitation representing a danger for the mine.

- Work involved

    see items 1) and 2)

- Further Calculations

    Calculation of the mine aperture and the geometry of the
    bottom of the mine, i.e. of the accumulated quantity of
    precipitation and the corresponding water level including
    ground water seeping into the mine
    Water from the inside dump consists of ground water and
    precipitation
    Determination of the maximum tolerable pump down time.

Protective Measures

Ditches on berms and benches on the inside dump and on the
foot-wall
Lifting and removal of water using sump pumps and dredges
Computation of costs and of time requirements.

2.4 Possible Environmental Impact of the Mine

Active : Contamination of surface and ground water, lowering of the ground water level in the vicinity of the mine, etc.

Passive: Seepage of contaminated water or salt water - e.g. sea water - into the depression cone.

These factors are to be taken into consideration when planning the protective measures.

2.5 Possible Impairment on Existing Ground and River Water Intakes

e.g. intakes for water supply or irrigation purposes.

2.6 Expansion of Exploitation of Other Water Resources or Exploration and Development of New Resources

(applicable only when required by 2.5)

Depending on the phase in which the project is, the stress might be on different types of work. Because of the contracts to be signed individually and the conditions to which these contracts with clients must be adapted, no subdivision was made into types of study 5 to 1 or into the pre-feasibility study, feasibility study and detailed planning. -

As an example of one of the numerous problems which arise, and using for this example the lignite openpit mine in the Cuddalore Basin in India, the possible changes in leakage with time are discussed. This problem may also arise in the U.S.A. when enlarged openpit mines will be operated from the 80s onward.

3. Ground Water Leakage in a Lignite Opencast Mine in India

3.1 General Geological Data

The lignite reserves are in the south of India, in the Neyveli-Basin situated in the federal state of Tamil Nadu, approximately 17 miles from the Bay of Bengal and some 110 miles south of Madras. The opencast mine has been operated by the NEYVELI LIGNITE CORPORATION LIMITED (NLC), Neyveli, since 1957 (1).

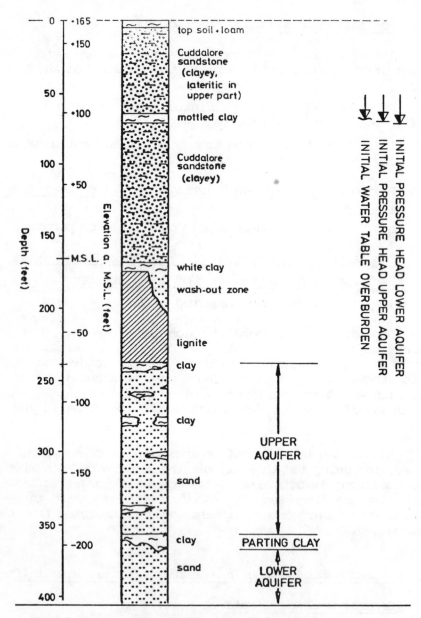

Figure 1: Neyveli Lignite Mine, Tamil Nadu, India
General Section of Strata / Pressure Head Conditions
after SUBRAMANYAM and VENKATESAN, 1969

The schematic stratigraphic log (Fig. 1) shows that below a soil layer with a thickness of about 7 feet, there are highly consolidated clayey sands down to a depth of 160 feet (Cuddalore Sandstone, Mio-Pliocene). These layers constitute the overburden. The underlying lignite seam has a thickness of approx. 50 feet. It is partly affected by washout channels which are filled with fine sand. The lignite seam is followed by a clay bed, 3 feet thick, which, however, disappears in several places. Next comes a series of beds consisting of unconsolidated sands and gravels which have been investigated by drillings to a depth of about 650 feet. These beds consist mainly of medium and coarse sands. The total thickness of the sands and gravels is unknown since there are no deep boreholes in the centre of the Cuddalore Basin. However, the deepest point is expected to have a thickness over 1100 feet. Numerous clayey lenses of varying thicknesses, some of which covering large areas, are intercalated with sands and gravels.

The ground surface of the opencast mine as well as the sequence of strata as described above incline in a south-eastern direction.

3.2 Hydrogeological Conditions

Fig. 1 shows the original pressure heads within the lignite deposit.

The overburden on top of the lignite constitutes an unconfined aquifer which is fed by precipitation and water courses.

The lignite overlies a partly interrupted clay layer under which further aquifers are encountered. There is an "upper" aquifer of some 90 feet and a considerably thicker "lower" aquifer which is likely to extend to the bottom of the basin. An intercalated clay layer reaching a thickness of approx. 8 feet on an average forms a hydraulic separation.

Both water-bearing layers are confined as they are expected to be under the prevailing geological conditions. Prior to pumping, the piezometric surface of the aquifers was approx. 160 feet above the lignite base which equals approx. 100 feet a.MSL. The phreatic surface of the unconfined aquifer is partly above and partly below the piezometric surface of the confined aquifers.

The nearest rim of the main recharge area for both aquifers is situated northwest of the mine at a distance of about 3.5 miles. Extending mostly over a somewhat higher and hilly region, the recharge area covers a southwest-northeast striking plane at least 35 miles long and 4 miles wide on an average (Fig. 2) (2).

Consistent with the dip of the layers, the ground water within all the mentioned aquifers flowed in a southeastern direction prior to pumping. However, during pumping, the equipotentials changed in such a way that the northern part of the mine receives the ground water from the north and, consequently, the western part from the west.

3.3 Ground Water Control Pattern/Calculation of Transmissivity

Lignite exploitation in deep surface mines requires extensive investigation of the hydraulic properties of all the layers involved. This must be conducted prior to and during the mining operations. In actual fact, the overburden did not need to be drained. On the other hand, the pressure head of the aquifer immediately below the lignite had to be relieved, since after the mining of lignite at the latest, the excess pressure of 160 feet would inevitably have caused a bottom heave or water outflow, thus endangering the stability of the mine slopes (Fig. 3).

When ground water control operations were started in 1961 the mine was a 5700 feet long strip. Along the two small sides and the long side opposite of the face, it was surrounded by production wells designed to drain the aquifer between the parting clay and the lignite. One "upper" and one "lower" aquifer piezometer were installed at about 1000 feet from one end of the long well row. The upper piezometer fully penetrated the aquifer, while the lower one only penetrated about 80 feet into the very thick lower aquifer. The two piezometers will again be dealt with later in this paper. These two and up to 27 other piezometers, which are situated in the surroundings of the mine, were used for the initial tests and for the execution of further calculations during the mining operations.

As the mining operations advanced, some wells within the area of the two aforementioned piezometers remained active to protect the inside dump. As for the other wells,

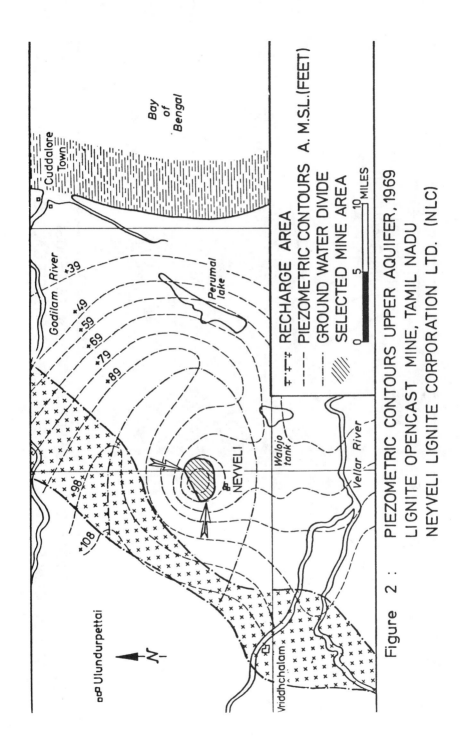

Figure 2 : PIEZOMETRIC CONTOURS UPPER AQUIFER, 1969
LIGNITE OPENCAST MINE, TAMIL NADU
NEYVELI LIGNITE CORPORATION LTD. (NLC)

RECHARGE AREA
PIEZOMETRIC CONTOURS A.M.S.L.(FEET)
GROUND WATER DIVIDE
SELECTED MINE AREA

0   5   10 MILES

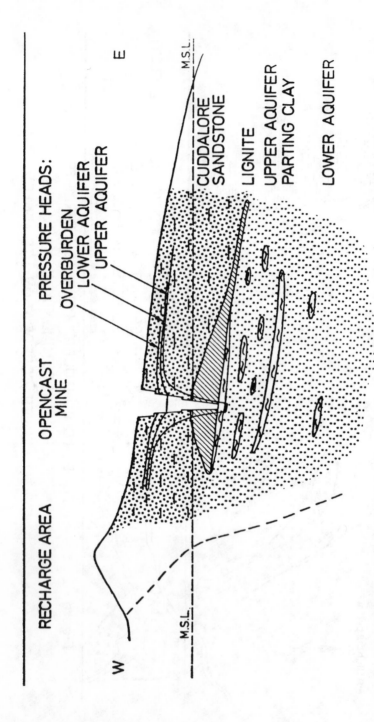

Figure 3 : SCHEMATIC CROSS SECTION OF LIGNITE DEPOSIT AND
PRESENTATION OF HYDROGEOLOGICAL CONDITIONS (CUDDALORE BASIN/TAMIL NADU)

they followed the face in the array described above. This was also the reason why on the first bench of the inside dump it was necessary to sink wells.

NLC decided, as mentioned above, to relieve the pressure head only of the aquifer directly underlying the lignite. The number of active wells varied between 30 and 50; the total production ranged from 30,000 to 60,000 US gallons/minute.

The geologists of the NEYVELI LIGNITE CORPORATION (NLC) based their calculations of the transmissivity of the upper aquifer on the values obtained from the initial pump tests. Later on, they based them on the changes in the total pump rate as they occurred during the subsequent years of mining operations. They used the THIEM formula (drawdown-distance semi-log) for steady-state conditions, applying the principle of superposition (3).

In doing so, they did not consider aquifer properties that might deviate from those of the ideal aquifer. For instance, the resulting transmissivities were also marked by leakage, for it was only the upper aquifer which had to be pumped. This is also why the NLC geologists quite correctly speak of an "Apparent Transmissivity". Obviously, the almost steady-state conditions that could be observed after several weeks of pumping permitted the application of an evaluation method related to the steady-state conditions. The values thus obtained served as a basis for NLC to develop a drainage of the mine for many years.

3.4 Decrease in the "Apparent Transmissivity"

Already in the first years of pumping, the continuous evaluation of the measuring data revealed the following particularity: remaining relatively constant between 1961 and 1964, the apparent transmissivity declined steadily after this phase. While the values obtained in 1964 amounted to as much as 135,000 gallons/day/foot, the values measured in 1974 were only around 77,000 gallons/day/foot.
This decrease follows an exponential curve (Fig.4) (4).

Over the years - and as a result of a more advantageous well array -,the total pump rate of the wells could be adjusted to the empirically encountered changed conditions, i.e. it was reduced from 60,000 gallons/minute (1964) to 31,200 gallons/minute (1976). Yet, NLC realized, that a clarification and a quantitative representation of this effect

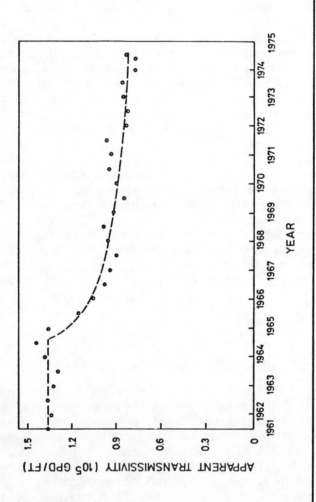

Figure 4 : TIME-VARIATION OF COMPUTED APPARENT TRANSMISSIVITIES
(3 MONTH MOVING MEAN) AFTER INDIAN INSTITUTE OF TECHNOLOGY, MADRAS, 1975

would have been of advantage to allow an effective preliminary planning over several years.

3.5 Computer Models of the INDIAN INSTITUTE OF TECHNOLOGY, Madras

At the request of NLC, the HYDRAULIC ENGINEERS DEPARTMENT of the INSTITUTE OF TECHNOLOGY (IIT), Madras, then conducted a study in 1974 (4). The aim of this study was to clarify the question of whether the change in the transmissivity observed by NLC was statistically significant, whether it could be put in relation to any parameters and which drainage scheme was to be considered the most appropriate in the future.

They recalculated the drawdown curves, the radii of influence and the negative effects of possibly inexact measurements in this area. They also determined the transmissivities on a monthly basis by staggering the average transmissivity over 3-months intervals in dependence on the drawdown difference $\triangle$ s.

The following possible causes for the decreasing transmissivities were investigated:

- Variations in aquifer thickness
- Changes in the formation of new ground water
- Dependence on total pump rate
- Changes in the average pump rate of the individual wells
- Lowering of water level into the pumped aquifer, i.e. transition from confined to unconfined conditions
- Influence of pumping time.

According to the investigation results obtained by IIT, some of these influences are not existing; if any were apparent, they were not able to cause a decrease in the transmissivity to such an extent. Grain size analyses which were executed prior to and after the IIT calculation did not furnish any clear indications either.

However, the results of the pump tests in which we were involved as consultants in 1977 (5) induced us to go into this problem again, paying special attention to the leakage.

3.6 Ground Water Leakage within the Mine Area

We will now deal with two superimposed aquifers which are hydraulically balanced and are separated by a layer of far lower permeability. If water is withdrawn from one aquifer, the water not only comes from this aquifer, but also from the other one. This phenomenon is known as "leakage". The flow rate q (per square unit), which is fed from one aquifer into the other, is proportional to the differential head ($\triangle$p) of the two aquifers and inversely proportional to the hydraulic resistance (c) of the separating layer (6):

$$q = \frac{\triangle p}{c}$$

were

q = flow rate per square unit of the semi-pervious layer (gallons/minute/foot^2)

$\triangle$p = the differential head (feet)

c = the hydraulic resistance of the semi-pervious layer (minutes)

    c = M'/k' where M' = thickness of the semi-pervious layer (feet)

                      k' = permeability (hydraulic conductivity) of the semi-pervious layer (feet/minute)

The influence of the "initial gradient" is neglected (7).

Due to the low values of the k'/k ratio (about 1/10,000) - k is the permeability of the pumped aquifer - horizontal flow components within the separating layer must not be considered in this particular case (8). -

The investigation carried out prior to, after, or during the tests conducted by IIT paid little attention to the leakage factor. The most recent pump tests (1977) therefore concentrated more on the aquifer below the parting clay. They clearly demonstrated that water from the lower aquifer was seeping into the upper one (5).

The following coefficients were obtained:

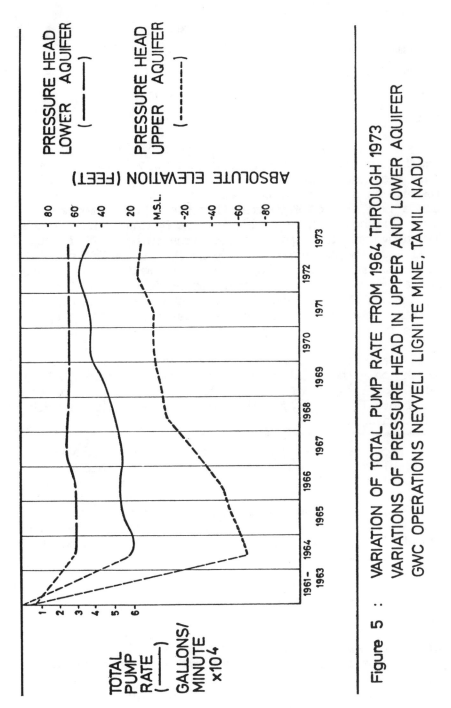

Figure 5 : VARIATION OF TOTAL PUMP RATE FROM 1964 THROUGH 1973 VARIATIONS OF PRESSURE HEAD IN UPPER AND LOWER AQUIFER GWC OPERATIONS NEYVELI LIGNITE MINE, TAMIL NADU

	Upper Aquifer	Parting Clay
Transmissivity T (gpd/ft)	58,000	-
Storage coefficient S (-)	$1 \cdot 10^{-4}$	-
Leakage factor L (feet)	3,900	-
Hydraulic resistance c (min)	-	$3 \cdot 10^{6}$

As can be seen from the storage coefficient the upper aquifer is semi-confined or semi-unconfined, respectively. This fact in itself is not new. The precise water level measurements which NLC had been carrying out regularly since 1961 already supported this view. The hydrograph (Fig. 5) shows the variations of the hydraulic head in the two above mentioned piezometers situated near the first well row. The beginning of pumping operations did not only produce a relief in the upper aquifer (maximum 164 feet), but also in the lower one (maximum 36 feet) (also Fig. 3). This means that with sufficient lateral expansion of the parting clay, the water, in the present case, flows upwards into the pumped aquifer.

Until 1964 - when the opencast had reached its maximum extension - the total required pump rate had increased to 60,000 gallons/minute. At the same time and as can be seen, the hydraulic heads of both aquifers lowered in the well surroundings.

From 1964 onward, however, the hydrograph showed a particularity: the curbing of the total pump rate to approx. 31,200 gallons/minute - already described previously - as well as the increasing distance of the well gravity center from the piezometers caused a rise in the hydraulic head of the upper aquifer; yet, the head in the lower aquifer did not recover again after this date, it stayed at the lower level.

It is possible that due to the fact that this decrease in differential head is higher than expected, the leakage might reduce. This would be very interesting with a view towards clarifying the decrease in the apparent transmissivity which has also been observed since 1964. There is a definite connection between leakage and apparent transmissivity:

As is well known, the vertical leakage entails a flattening of the depression cone which starts near the production well; also the distance-drawdown curve gets flatter (9).

If transmissivity and leakage are calculated separately
in the evaluation of the pressure head measurements as is
the case, for example, with the WALTON time-drawdown method,
the coefficients obtained under ideal conditions will be independent of the distance from the well (6). If, on the
other hand, the leakage is not considered in the calculation,
its influence is included in the coefficient which is now to
be called "apparent transmissivity". The values of the apparent transmissivity are larger than the real T - as is the
case when using the THIEM method. Provided all other conditions remain constant,

$$T_{app.} = f \left\{ T, \frac{1}{L} \right\}$$

where   f   = symbol of the function

         T   = transmissivity (gallons/day/foot)

         L   = leakage factor (feet);
                 L is inversely proportional to
                 the leakage-rate q!

For example, if it is assumed that an intense new formation of ground water has caused the pressure head of the
lower aquifer to rise, this will result in an increase of
the differential head $\triangle$ p and consequently in an increase
in the seeping rate through the parting clay into the upper
aquifer. Although it is assumed that the production rate is
kept at a constant rate, the depression cone will become
even flatter there and the apparent transmissivities obtained according to THIEM will also increase.

The general rule is that if the leakage rate increases
in relation to the pump rate, the apparent transmissivities
will also rise when calculated with the help of piezometric
measurements. Inversely, it can be said that the apparent
transmissivities decrease as soon as the percentage of
leakage of the pump rate goes down.

Because of this relation and the almost constant pressure head in the not directly pumped aquifer, it was decided that all the data indicating decreasing leakage in the
mine since 1964 should be studied again.

3.7 Decrease in Leakage

The transmissivities and leakage factors of the opencast mine in the 60s are not available. A decision could be made if it were possible to determine the amount of leakage in its time-dependent variation based on appropriate piezometer observations and by forming the ratio between differential head and total pump rate. However, based on the assumption that the phenomenon of the pressure head remaining low was not restricted to the surroundings of the piezometers in question, it can only be supposed that as a strong lowering of the differential head $\triangle p$ was registered, the leakage, being considerably influenced by $\triangle p$, decreased likewise.

This conclusion is backed by the results of the pump tests conducted in 1977 in the southeastern part of the mine area. At that time, ground water conditions were only slight-ly affected by ground water control: In the production well located farthest away from the mine at a distance of 1.7 miles, the pressure heads of both aquifers were almost the same before pumping with a difference of only a few inches. Hence, as far as this well is concerned, it can be assumed that the calculated mean leakage coefficient, L = 3900 feet, is not influenced by too strong a ground water flow, but is more or less undisturbed.

For testing the effective leakage properties within the mine proper with regard to the year 1977, the drawdowns in numerous wells and testpoints during the aquifer drainage were controlled mathematically, applying the value L = 3900 feet. A short explanation of the calculations is given below.

We used the DE GLEE formula ((6), also JACOB (8)):

$$s_m = \frac{Q}{2 \pi T} \cdot K_o \left(\frac{r}{L}\right)$$

were

s_m = steady-state drawdown in a piezometer or in a well (feet)

Q = discharge rate of the pumped well (gallons/day)

T = transmissivity (gallons/day/foot)

L = leakage factor (feet)

r = distance from the pumped well (feet)

$K_o \left(\frac{r}{L}\right)$ = modified BESSEL function of the second kind and of zero order (=HANKEL function)

Since it is the steady-state flow which is described by the series, the storage coefficient and the pumping time are not considered as they are important only during the non-steady-state flow.

Since the partial differential equation governing the DE GLEE formula is linear (8), this formula and the principle of superposition can be used to obtain solutions for any number of pumping wells (10).

In the computation, the HANKEL function was replaced by a convergent series (11). If both partial series are only used up to the 10th power, the DE GLEE formula being prepared for superposition is as follows:

$$
s^*_{mn} = \frac{Q_n}{2 \pi T} \cdot \left\{ -(0.5772 + \ln\frac{r_n}{2L}) \cdot [1 + (\frac{r_n}{2L})^2 + \right.
$$

$$
+ 0.25(\frac{r_n}{2L})^4 + 0.0278(\frac{r_n}{2L})^6 + 0.00174(\frac{r_n}{2L})^8 +
$$

$$
+ 0.000764(\frac{r_n}{2L})^{10}] + (\frac{r_n}{2L})^2 + 0.375(\frac{r_n}{L2})^4 +
$$

$$
+ 0.0509(\frac{r_n}{2L})^6 + 0.00362(\frac{r_n}{2L})^8 +
$$

$$
\left. + 0.000159(\frac{r_n}{2L})^{10} \right\}
$$

s^*_{mn} = steady-state drawdown at the testpoint, caused by pump well N^o n (feet)

Q_n = pump rate of well N^o n (gallons/day)

T = transmissivity of the pumped aquifer (gallons/day/foot)

r_n = distance from the pump well N^o n (feet)

L = leakage factor (feet)

The total drawdown, s^*_m, at the testpoint results from the following superposition:

$$s_m^* = \sum_{n=1}^{n=z} s_{mn}^*$$

(z = number of wells)

Coordinates are used in the calculation program so that the drawdown of the pressure head produced by the well field can be calculated for any point desired.

The testing of the effective leakage properties as they appeared in the mine area in 1977 used the 1977 pump rate, Q, and the 1977 r values. The transmissivity, T, and the leakage factor, L, were taken from the pumping tests carried out that same year.

A comparison of the calculated water levels of the upper aquifer with those measured in the mine area showed that there was no conformity at all. The calculated drawdown values proved to be much too low.

The conformity can only be achieved if – with T being constant – the leakage factor is not entered with L = 3,900 feet but with L = 8,000 feet. This reflects a lower leakage (The leakage factor is inversely proportional to the seeping leakage rate).

The consideration of the fluctuations of T obtained from the pump test evaluation (maximum $\pm$ 20 %) and the use of the relation

$$L^2 = T \cdot c$$

(c being the hydraulic resistance of the parting clay) leads to the conclusion that the leakage in the mining area must be lower than the pump tests have shown.

Besides the hydrograph, these calculations provided an additional indication pointing out that the observed decrease in the apparent transmissivity might, at least in part, be a result of the declining leakage.

3.8 Hydrological Model of the Leakage in the Area of the Lignite Deposit – Conclusions

Both WALTON (6) and BOULTON (6) described the pressure

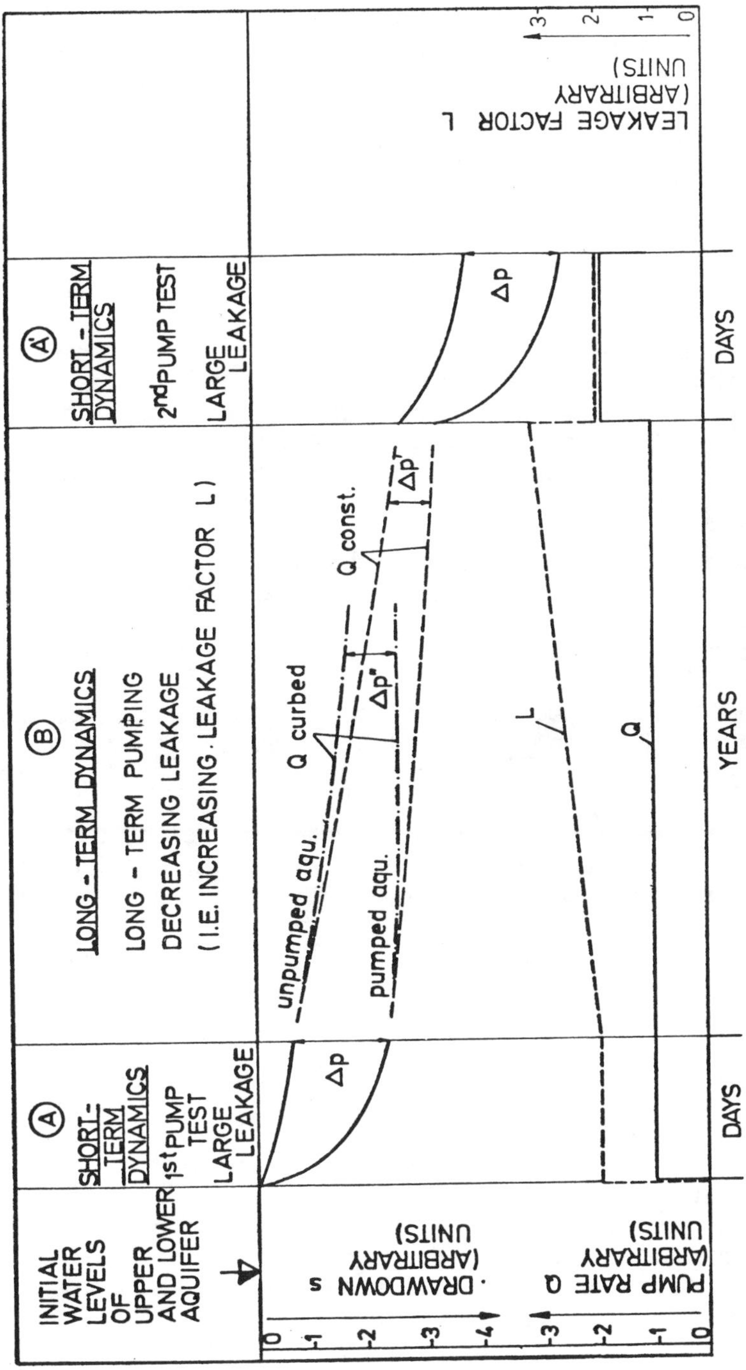

Figure 6 : GROUNDWATER LEAKAGE ACCORDING TO SHORT – TERM
AND LONG – TERM DYNAMICS

conditions in a pumped confined aquifer under the influence
of leakage. WALTON takes the pressure in the unpumped aquifer as being constant; BOULTON, on the other hand, permits
lowering of the water level (secondary cone). This results
in a very important difference: in the first case, the water
level in the pumped aquifer (primary cone) reaches the
steady state after a certain period of time; in the BOULTON
model, however, it reaches a temporary stability and then
sinks continuously until at least one of the cones reaches
a recharging area with sufficiently abundant water.

The reason for the continuous lowering of the water
level is that the secondary cone also spreads out. The same
thing happens with the isolines of differential head and
the isolines of horizontal flow volume within the pumped
aquifer. Because of increasing friction losses in the aquifer, the pressure head in the pump well continues to sink (12).

At a successive decreased discharge, too, the secondary
cone can change to such an extent that the differential head
sinks lower than would be necessary to keep the leakage factor constant. As a result of this, the leakage decreases.

Based on this concept according to BOULTON, the decrease
in leakage in the openpit mine might be explained by the pumping at a high pump rate which occurred over a period of years.-

The results of the pumping tests should now be considered
again.While the effective leakage in an openpit mine may have
decreased down to a small amount due to a strongly decreasing
differential head, non-steady pumping tests carried out directly within the influential reach of the aquifer drainage
may indicate a leakage several times higher. The following
reasoning provides an explanation.

When comparing leakage values calculated from observed
drawdown data, whether obtained through pump tests or from
the aquifer drainage data, the duration of the decrease must
be particularly considered. In general, a difference must be
made between short-term and long-term dynamics. In comparison
to the case described above of long-term drawdown of the water
level in the mine area (Fig. 6, Section B, differential head
$\triangle p'$ or $\triangle p''$), a pump test will show (both in the pumped and
in the unpumped aquifer) drawdowns of completely different
dimensions. For these dimensions, it is almost negligible
whether the pump test started out from the initial water level (Section A), or whether it increased already existing draw-

downs (Section A'; please note the different time units).
In both cases, the leakage resulting from Δp will be considerably greater than the leakage resulting from long-term
dynamics at a smaller $\Delta p'$ value. The same applies to the
$\Delta p''$ value which results when the pump rate is curbed
(Section B).

This explains the difference between the leakage value
obtained through pumping tests and the actual leakage existing in the mine itself. It also explains why the pumping
tests did not also indicate the phenomenon of decreasing
leakage.

The formation of the secondary cone could be abandoned
altogether when making the evaluation according to WALTON,
since the decrease was less than 5% of the entire thickness
of the lower aquifer. The equilibrium observed during the
pumping tests was possibly the same equilibrium which appeared at times in the evaluation according to BOULTON.
Under the conditions prevalent in 1977, it was neither necessary nor possible to continue pumping.

Between 1961 and 1964, when more or less constant "apparent transmissivities" were calculated, the decrease - if
any - in leakage may have remained undiscovered due to the
continuous increase in the total pump rate.

The above results lead to the following considerations:

- When comparing leakage values, the corresponding pumping
  time on which the figures are based must be considered.
- With pumping tests within the mine area, it is possible
  that a higher leakage rate will be calculated although
  the effective leakage is considerably lower.
- Pumping tests where an equilibrium appears can be evaluated according to either WALTON or BOULTON, but a long-
  term prognosis can only be made after pump tests which
  clearly show without a doubt whether in the long run the
  leakage will decrease or not.

For the time being, the planning of the future ground
water control makes allowance for the effect described above
by extrapolating the falling apparent transmissivity into
the future. -

It is not the aim of this paper to establish a quantitative connection between the course of the pressure head
(Fig. 5) and the difference in the calculated numbers of L.
This can only be possible when further pump tests can be
executed. It was only our intention to point out an interesting aspect of mine drainage.

This aspect is all the more important as the experience gained by clarifying the hydrological and hydrogeological causes of leakage decreases might be transferred to
other opencast mines. Thus it might be possible in the
future to avoid overdimensioning of drainage installations.

4.   RESUMÉ

An overall view is first given of what experience has
shown to be the most important operations in the planning
of an openpit drainage. Here we find three main divisions:
protection against ground water; protection against water
at the ground surface; and protection against water within
the openpit. The main objectives to be reached are mentioned
as well as the necessary operations and intermediate results.

Not only must the mine be protected from disrupted natural conditions. The environment too must be protected from
the openpit mine. For this reason, the subjects of environmental protection, protection of human water needs and
claims are briefly mentioned.

As an example of one of the numerous problems which
arise, and using for this example the lignite openpit mine
in the Cuddalore Basin in India, the possible changes in
leakage with time are discussed. It has been proved that
leakage appears during the pressure relief of the upper of
two aquifers under the lignite layer, separated from each
other by a semi-permeable clay layer. Prior to pumping,
both hydraulic pressure heads were approx. 110 feet above
the lignite. Ground water control operations were started
in 1961. Only the upper aquifer was pumped; the pressure
head was sunk down to below the lignite. By 1964, when the
mine reached its greatest expanse, the total required pump
rate rose to 60,000 gallons/minute, but decreased to
31,200 gallons/minute by 1976 (US gallons).

At the same time, the apparent transmissivity of the
upper aquifer, calculated according to the equilibrium
THIEM method, sank from 135,000 to 77,000 gallons/day/foot.

At a constant transmissivity, two things indicated that a decreasing leakage might be present: The lowering of the pressure in the unpumped aquifer remained in its lowered state even after decreasing the total pump rate and in spite of a rise in pressure in the pumped aquifer. Moreover, in the most recent pump tests carried out in 1977 at a distance of 1 to 2 miles beyond the openpit itself, a leakage factor of L = 3,900 feet was calculated (according to WALTON), while at the same time the figure of the mine area was L = 8,000 feet (JACOB/DE GLEE). (Leakage is converse to the leakage factor).

A hydrological model of the lignite deposit area in the Cuddalore Basin based on BOULTON's concepts of the semi-confined aquifer may possibly explain the questions and contradictions through decreasing leakage. In the empirical evaluation of leakage values, a distinction must be made between short-term and long-term dynamics. Pump tests may provide considerably high leakage though real leakage in the mine area will be very low. This leads to the conclusion that caution should prevail when making prognoses based on leakage values obtained through pumping tests.

Conclusive statements and quantitative data can only be made after further pumping tests. Since decreasing leakage would permit a reduction in the required pump rate, cost savings would be possible and could possibly be planned. Similar effects can also be expected during the operation of other openpit mines.

REFERENCES

1.   Vaidyanathan, P. and Balasundar, N.K., "Controlling of Water in an Opencast Mine with special Reference to Neyveli Lignite Mines: South Arcot", Internal Report of NLC Limited, Neyveli, India.

2.   Dr. Otto Gold - Consulting Engineers, Cologne, Germany, "Feasibility Study - Expansion of Mine Capacity - Neyveli Lignite Corporation Limited", 1975.

3.   Balasundar, N.K., "Otto Gold Pump Test, Evaluation of Data and Preparation of Ground Water Control Plans for Mine Expansion Scheme", Internal Report of NLC Ltd., Neyveli, 1978.

4.   Indian Institute of Technology, Madras, "Computer Studies on Mine Water Pressure Control and Optimization of Pump Well System", Report furnished to Neyveli Lignite Corporation Ltd., 1975.

5.   Dr. Otto Gold - Consulting Engineers, Cologne, Germany, "Final Report on the Evaluation of Pump Tests Executed in the Selected Mining Area of Neyveli Lignite Corporation Limited, Neyveli, India", 1978.

6.   Kruseman, G.P. and De Ridder, N.A., "Analysis and Evaluation of Pumping Test Data", The Netherlands, 1970.

7.   Polubarinova-Kochina, P.Ya., "Theory of Ground Water Movement", Translated from the Russian by J.M. Roger De Wiest, Princeton, 1962.

8.   Jacob, C.E., "Radial Flow in a Leaky Artesian Aquifer", Transactions of the American Geophysical Union, 1946, pp. 198-205.

9.   Hantush, M.S. and Jacob, C.E., "Non-Steady Radial Flow in an Infinite Leaky Aquifer", Transactions of the American Geophysical Union, 1955, pp. 95-100.

10. Neuman, S. and Witherspoon, P.A., "Theory of Flow in a Confined Two Aquifer System", Water Resources Research, 1969, pp. 803-816.

11. McLachlan, "Bessel Functions for Engineers", 1934, cited by Don Kirkham in "Discussion" relating ref. 8 of this paper.

12. Hofedank, R.H., "Tests and Considerations on the Flow of Water in Unconsolidated Sediments and in Fissured Basalt" ("Untersuchungen zum Fließverhalten von Wasser in Lockergestein und klüftigem Basalt"), Gießener Geologische Schriften, Gießen, Germany, 1974.

18

Twenty-five Year Experience in Dewatering at Canadian Mining Complex

by O. Garg, Engineering Superintendent,
G. Hétu, Supervisor, Mine Dewatering,
and D. Hindy, Supervisor, Mine Engineering,
Iron Ore Company of Canada,
Schefferville, Quebec, Canada

INTRODUCTION:

The Knob Lake complex of the Iron Ore Company is centered around the town of Schefferville (54° 49' North and 66° 50' West) located in Quebec, Canada. (Figure 1).

In addition to the Schefferville complex, the Iron Ore Company's other mining operation is located at Labrador City in Newfoundland. The terminal and port facilities are located at Sept-Iles in Quebec. The distance between mines in Schefferville and Sept-Iles is 365 rail miles.

For its subarctic location, the mean annual air temperature is -4.9 degrees Centigrade or 23.2 degrees Fahrenheit. The precipitation is high with 340 centimeters or 134 inches of snowfall, and 39.5 centimeters or 15.6 inches of rainfall.

In the Schefferville mining complex, six to seven open pit iron ore mines are operated each year. These mines are spread over a distance of approximately 26 miles from south to north and these deposits are located both in the province of Quebec, and Labrador, Newfoundland.

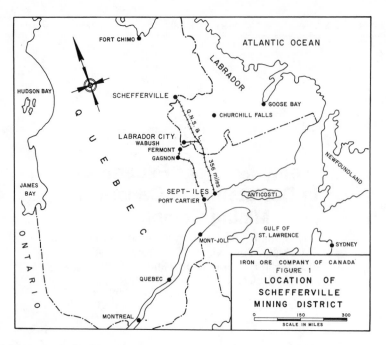

Location of Schefferville Mining District. Figure No. 1.

THE MINING SETUP:

The typical open pit mining setup consists of drilling a
9 7/8 inch diameter hole, blasting and loading the blasted
ore by shovels into the trucks. The equipment presently in
use at Schefferville consists of eight 50R drills, nine
electric shovels with capacities varying from six to thirteen
cubic yards, and twenty-nine 120 ton haulage trucks.

The ore is hauled from the pit to the primary crusher
where it is reduced to -2 inch size in a two stage crushing
operation.

PURPOSE OF DEWATERING:

Since the beginning of the mining operation in 1954, the
regional and local water table had to be controlled in and
around the open pit mines in order to mine efficiently.
(1) & (2).

Drainage control is particularly important because of
the following: (3) & (4).

1. To minimize the moisture content of the ore shipped.

2. To reduce pressure on the ultimate pit walls. (5) & (6).

3. To maintain dry operating conditions in the pit and along the haulage roads.

The first water problems were encountered in the spring of 1955. Dewatering shafts and drifts were tried. However, these were not successful because of caving problems and heavy water inflows. The problem at that time was solved using shallow wells and sumps.

Since that time, improvements in well drilling techniques such as casing of holes have permitted drilling of deeper wells. Although the run off water is still handled in open sumps, groundwater is pumped from deep wells by means of vertical turbine pumps.

TYPICAL MINE DEWATERING SETUP:

A typical mine dewatering setup is outlined taking Redmond Mine, located 10 miles south of Schefferville and presently in operation, as an example. The following dewatering facilities are required to allow mining efficiently in Redmond Mine which is approximately 3500 feet long, 2000 feet wide and 600 feet deep.

To divert the surface runoff water away from the deposit area;

1. The original creek had to be diverted through a ditch on the east side of the pit.

2. A small lake over the ore body had to be pumped out before the mining could commence in 1967.

3. The dyke road is used to divert the surface water away from the pit. The surface water which does get into the pit is handled through a series of ditches and sumps.

When the mining started at Redmond Mine in 1967, the water table was within 30 feet of the original ground surface.

In order for mining operations to proceed efficiently to deeper levels and for slope stability, sixteen wells up to

700 feet deep were drilled all along the perimeter of the mine between 1966 and 1976. In addition, twelve wells were drilled within the pit limits mainly to dewater the ore.

From these 28 inpit and peripheral wells an average of approximately 6400 U.S. Gallons per Minute are being pumped out of the pit throughout the year. This has resulted in successfully lowering the water table by 500 feet from the original water table during the 12 years of the operating life of the mine.

Similar types of the dewatering setup exist in other operating mines.

DEWATERING EQUIPMENT:

The total number of deep wells presently operating in the entire Schefferville area is 47. Approximately 25,000 U.S. Gallons per Minute are pumped from these 47 installations.

Most of the wells are equipped with vertical turbine type of pumps such as 10RM, 10EC and 8BS with varying number of stages. Most of these deep well pumps are equipped with 150 Horse Power vertical hollow shaft type motors.

During the last couple of years, down-the-hole pump and motor installations have been used in some of the deep wells. These include low volume (250 U.S. Gallons per Minute) high head capacity pumps such as the Pleuger 81 model, and low head and higher capacity (600 U.S. Gallons per Minute) model such as the Pleuger 101.

SELECTION OF WELL LOCATIONS:

Because of the highly variable nature of rocks in terms of geological structure, permeabilities and porosities, the location of dewatering wells requires careful consideration. (7) (8) (9) (10).

Table I shows variations in physical properties of three most common rock types which are encountered in mine dewatering and other geotechnical work in the area.

In general, a well location in the Schefferville mining district is determined by using the following criteria:

1. Location of regional recharge and discharge areas.

2. Location and extent of aquifer(s) in the area of the mine.

3. Geological structure and degree of leaching of various rock types.

4. Engineering properties specially variations in permeabilities and porosities of wall rocks.

5. Pit layout and location of other mining facilities in the area.

Table No. I
Physical Properties of Some Typical Rock Types

Rock Type	Mean Bulk Density Pounds/Cubic Feet	Porosity Percent	Permeability Centimeters/ Second
Quartzite (Wishart Formation)	121	15 - 40	5.0×10^{-4} to 5.0×10^{-5}
Ferruginous Slate & Chert (Ruth Formation)	181	10 - 20	1.0×10^{-4}
Chert Breccia (Fleming Formation)	140	15 - 35	8.5×10^{-5}

An example of the complex nature of the geological structure with a series of parallel faults in Timmins 2 mine is shown in Figure 2. The meaning of the abbreviations used in Figure 2 are as follows: - LC = Lean Chert, UIF = Upper Iron Formation, MIF = Middle Iron Formation, LIF = Lower Iron Formation, JSP = Jaspillite, RF = Ruth Formation. This particular well location was chosen to dewater the ore at at depth and to lower the water table in the wall rocks on the east side of the pit. In order to achieve these two purposes, only an inpit well could be drilled.

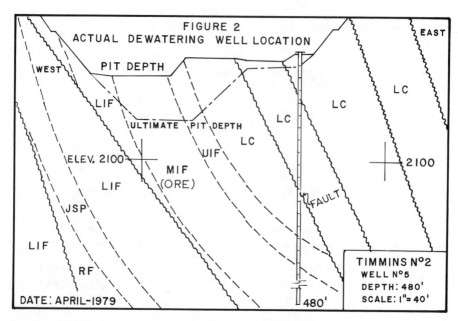

Actual Dewatering Well Location at Timmins 2 Mine. Figure No. 2.

Another example, in terms of having a rather limited choice for a well location, is shown in Figure 3. This part of the Redmond mine is relatively narrow. The water table was only 40 feet from the mining elevation in 1978 in spite of the fact that wells no. 18 and no. 19 were operating in the area.

In order for mining to proceed to deeper levels during 1978 and 1979, additional wells were required. The location of well no. 24 was chosen in 1978 to minimize interference with the operation. However, it could not completely de-water the ore because of the relatively impermeable charac-teristic of the Ruth Formation. Therefore another well (no. 26) was required in early 1979 to complete the mining of ore from the last two lifts or approximately for 75 feet. The mining in this part of the pit was successfully completed in July, 1979.

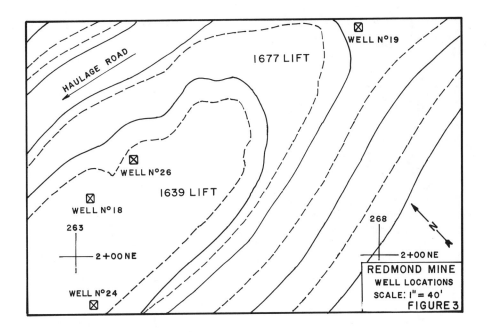

Redmond Mine Well Locations.   Figure No. 3.

WELL DRILLING SEQUENCE:

Having selected the location(s) of dewatering wells, the next step is to drill and develop these wells.

The following is the sequence of drilling and developing a typical dewatering well in the mining area.

1. Installation of starting casing 18 inches in diameter drilled by a rotary production drill.

2. Cementing of well casing using portable cement machine.

3. Drilling of 15 inch diameter hole to required depths of up to 700 feet using the Frank Comet Rig.

4. The installation of pre-slotted casing in the well. In the past, the casing was perforated using a knife after its installation in the hole. It should be mentioned that screen casings were not successful because of their failure due to blast vibrations.

5. Development of well.

6. Installation of pump, motor and pipeline suitable for the well location.

SOME OPERATING PROBLEMS:

Some of the operating problems which are commonly encountered in the mine dewatering work are outlined as follows:

1. Culvert shacks are required to protect pump installations from adverse weather conditions.

2. In case of leaking pipeline during the winter, both ice and snow must be removed to repair the pipeline. However, snow cover over the pipeline is desired to prevent freezing.

3. Draining points must be installed in pre-determined locations to allow line drainage in case of pump or power failure.

4. Build up of snow and ice on the power line causing at times, power failure.

SPECIAL PROBLEMS:

Because of its location and the highly variable rock properties, mining in the Schefferville area presents some special problems. Three of these problems are briefly outlined below.

1. Pumping Due to Regional Water Table Conditions

The necessity to keep the water table lowered by pumping water out from a pit which is depleted during the period when an adjacent mine is in operation. This was the case in Ruth Lake/French/Burnt Creek Mining Complex located 3.5 miles west of Schefferville. During the seven year period between 1970 and 1976 while ore was being mined from Burnt Creek Mine, pumping installations had to be kept operational in two adjacent mines, Ruth Lake and French, which were closed for mining in 1966 and 1970 respectively. In its final stages, French Mine alone had 27 deep well installations and pumped over 19,000 U.S. Gallons per Minute on a continuous basis.

Figure 4 shows the location of Burnt Creek Mine (on the left) and French Mine (on the right).

Location of Burnt Creek (on the left) and French (on the right) Mines. Figure No. 4.

A Floating pipeline and pumping setup at Hematite Lake. Figure No. 5.

In order to maintain the water level at a required elevation in the operating pit such as Burnt Creek, a floating platform equipped with vertical turbine pumps had to be installed in the depleted mines. Because of the volume of water required to be pumped out, this type of installation had to be maintained during the winter months. This was achieved by installing heated culvert pipe around the pump intake to prevent freezing.

Another interesting aspect of dewatering work in the area is the necessity of frequently pumping water from a mine into a booster tank using the high capacity, low head submersible pump and then pumping the water out of the tank using high head, high capacity vertical turbine pumps. Such a setup was used at Ruth Lake and French Mines. This type of setup facilitates better access to the vertical turbine pumps at all times for maintenance purposes.

Figure 5 shows a floating platform equipped with two vertical turbine pumps and a floating pipeline setup in Hematite Lake. Water had to be pumped out of this lake in order to deplete mining of ore from Fleming 3 pit which extended underneath the lake bed.

2. Presence of Permafrost

Another unique aspect of our dewatering work is related to the presence of permafrost up to depths of 375 feet in more northern areas of the operation (11). The runoff water flowing over the impervious frozen ground creates additional handling problems. The common solution used is to install a sump below the depth of thaw and pump the water out of these sumps. Horizontal, low head, high capacity pumps are used to pump water from areas of surface accumulation to the main sump installation.

Two other interesting points related to dewatering in permafrost are:

a) Water due to melting of ice, must be pumped from production blast holes before loading of explosives.

b) While mining to the bottom of permafrost, deep wells are not required. However, the groundwater below the bottom of permafrost is handled by the similar type of deep well pumping installations as described above.

3. Elross Creek Diversion

An unusual dewatering project which has been successfully completed in the area involved the diversion of a major natural stream called Elross Creek flowing through the center of the Timmins ore body. This diversion was required in order to mine the ore underneath. For the diversion channel to be completed at a reasonable cost, available mining equipment had to be used for excavation. The final preparation of the open channel was completed by using tractors and scrapers.

In the area where backfilling was required, special precautions had to be taken to avoid seepage of water through fill. This involved installation of wooden supports on which conveyor belting was laid to allow for differential settling. Impervious rubber liner was installed over the conveyor belting.

Peak flow of up to 110,000 gallons per minute is handled successfully during the spring runoff through the diverted channel.

REMAINING UNSOLVED PROBLEMS:

Although considerable progress has been made in controlling the mine dewatering situation in the area over the last 25 years, several problems remain to be solved. Some of these are:

a) How to model complex geological and hydrological conditions existing in the Schefferville area on computer for the purpose of proposing new well locations. (12)

b) Problems of drilling 15 inch diameter deep wells in the area at a more reasonable cost.

c) Selection of pumps and related equipment suitable for highly variable pumping conditions such as varying head and flow capacity for each installation.

d) How to improve the overall pumping capacity from each mine in spite of operating delays caused by blasting, relocation of pipelines, inspection and change of pumps, etc., in relatively small size pits.

e)   How to train and retain the manpower required to keep
the entire dewatering operations going 24 hours a day, 365
days a year.

ACKNOWLEDGEMENTS

The authors would like to thank the Management of the
Iron Ore Company of Canada for permission to publish this
paper. Suggestions and contributions resulting from discussions with our colleagues in the Operations and Engineering Departments are thankfully acknowledged.

REFERENCES

1. Pfleider, E.P. (1960) Mine Dewatering Study, Knob Lake Group. Consulting Engineer's Report to the Iron Ore Company of Canada, August, 1960.

2. Stubbins, J.B., Munro, P. (1965) Open Pit Mine Dewatering - Knob Lake. CIMM Bulletin, Volume 58, August, 1965.

3. Iron Ore Company of Canada Engineering Manual, Schefferville Mining Division, 1979 Edition.

4. Charbonneau, D., Morrison, D. (1977) Mine Dewatering at Knob Lake. A paper presented at the First Open Pit Operators Conference held in Labrador City in May, 1977.

5. Coates, D.F., McRorie, K. & Stubbins, J. (1963) Analysis of Pit Slides in Some Incompetent Rocks. Trans. AIME, Vol. 226, 1963.

6. Bullock, W.D. (1972) Development of the Burnt Creek - Rowe Mine Complex on the Knob Lake Iron Range. Canadian Mining Journal, November, 1972.

7. Blais, R.A., Zajac, I.S. (1961) Origin of the Soft Ore of the Knob Lake Range. CIMM Bulletin, Volume 54, January, 1961.

8. Nichols, L. (1968) Field Techniques for the Economic & Geotechnical Evaluation of Mining Property for Opencast Mine Design, Knob Lake, Quebec. The Quarterly Journal of Engineering Geology, Volume 1, No. 3, December, 1968.

9. Krishnan, T.K. (1976) Structural Studies of the Schefferville Mining District, Quebec-Labrador, Canada. Unpublished Ph.D. Thesis, University of California, Los Angeles.

10. Sagi, R.S. Drilling Methods Used For Sampling Soft Iron Ore Deposits. CIMM Bulletin, Volume 70, July, 1977.

11. Garg, O.P. (1973) In Situ Physicomechanical Properties of Permafrost using Geophysical Techniques. Proceedings of the Second International Conference on Permafrost. National Academy of Sciences, Washington, D.C. (1973).

12. Garg, O.P. (1976) Application of Geotechnical Studies in Open-Pit Mine Planning. A paper presented at the 11th Canadian Rock Mechanics Symposium held in Vancouver in October, 1976.

19

Drainage Used to Control Movements of a Large Rock Slide in Canada

by John C. Sharp, Consultant/Principal,
Golder Associates,
Maidenhead, Berkshire, United Kingdom

1. INTRODUCTION

The Jeffrey Mine, owned by Johns Manville Canada Inc. is situated at Asbestos, Quebec. It is currently one of the largest open pit mines in Canada and the biggest producer of asbestos fibre in the free world.

The open pit, approximately 1,000 ft. deep, is immediately west of the town of Asbestos. On the south side of the pit are located the major crushing and milling facilities (see general location plan; Figure 1).

During 1970 and 1971, a major rock and overburden slide developed in the south east corner of the open pit. The eventual slide limits are shown on Figure 2. At that time ore was being hoisted via a skipway to the primary crusher located at the pit crest. The lower section of the skipway and the associated ore pass bridge structure were located within the slide area.

In order to maintain an efficient supply of ore as well as to control the movements of a significant volume of material, stabilisation measures consisting primarily of drainage, were adopted.

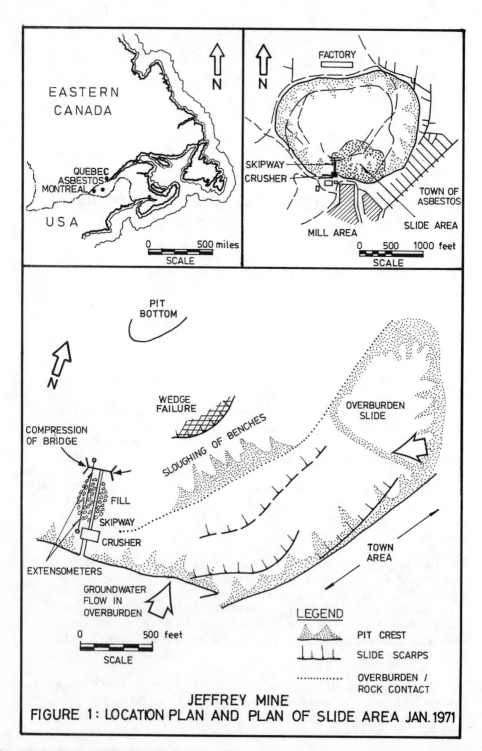

EASTERN
CANADA

QUEBEC
ASBESTOS
MONTREAL

USA

0   500 miles
SCALE

FACTORY

SKIPWAY
CRUSHER

TOWN OF
ASBESTOS

MILL AREA

SLIDE AREA

0   500   1000 feet
SCALE

PIT
BOTTOM

N

WEDGE
FAILURE

OVERBURDEN
SLIDE

COMPRESSION
OF BRIDGE

SLOUGHING OF BENCHES

FILL

SKIPWAY

CRUSHER

TOWN
AREA

EXTENSOMETERS

GROUNDWATER
FLOW IN
OVERBURDEN

0   500 feet
SCALE

LEGEND

PIT CREST

SLIDE SCARPS

OVERBURDEN /
ROCK CONTACT

JEFFREY MINE
FIGURE 1: LOCATION PLAN AND PLAN OF SLIDE AREA JAN. 1971

JEFFREY MINE
FIGURE 2: AERIAL VIEW OF SOUTH EAST CORNER

2. GEOLOGY OF THE SLIDE AREA

The geology of the south east corner of the pit
comprises an ultrabasic rock mass, (serpentinised, peridotite and dunite) which is overlain by some 200 ft. of overburden consisting of silts, sands with gravel layers and
glacial tills.

This geology is shown generally in Figure 3. A major
shear zone dips into the slope and outcrops on the upper
part of the slope. The shear zone consists of highly
fractured serpentinised material up to 500 ft. in width.
The underlying peridotite is also traversed by other, lesser,
generally sub-parallel, shear zones. Fracturing is somewhat
irregular and typical of the host rock of an asbestos ore
body. Fractures are often infilled with asbestos or brucite
fibres and characteristically have a low shear strength.

3. PERMEABILITY CHARACTERISTICS OF THE ROCK AND OVERBURDEN
    STRATA

The rock types comprising the slope have a low mass

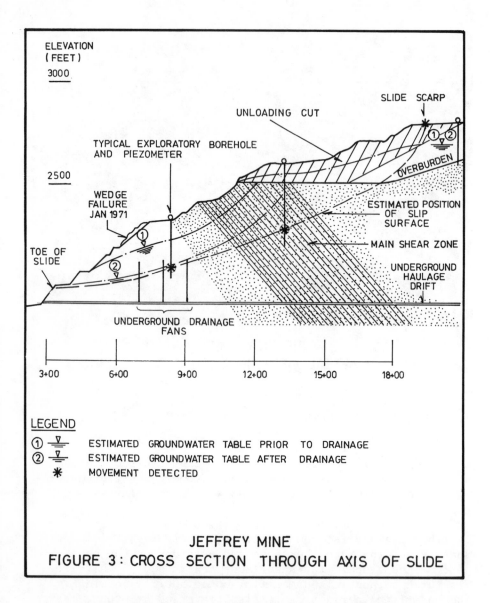

ELEVATION
(FEET)
3000

SLIDE SCARP

UNLOADING CUT

TYPICAL EXPLORATORY BOREHOLE
AND PIEZOMETER

2500

WEDGE
FAILURE
JAN 1971

OVERBURDEN

ESTIMATED POSITION
OF SLIP
SURFACE

MAIN SHEAR ZONE

TOE OF
SLIDE

UNDERGROUND
HAULAGE
DRIFT

UNDERGROUND DRAINAGE
FANS

3+00   6+00   9+00   12+00   15+00   18+00

LEGEND

① ▽ ESTIMATED GROUNDWATER TABLE PRIOR TO DRAINAGE
② ▽ ESTIMATED GROUNDWATER TABLE AFTER DRAINAGE
✳ MOVEMENT DETECTED

JEFFREY MINE
FIGURE 3: CROSS SECTION THROUGH AXIS OF SLIDE

permeability, typically in the range 10^{-6} – 10^{-9} cm/sec. The shear zones contain a significant proportion of rock flour and are probably less permeable than the more competent rocks.

The overburden is characterised by relatively permeable gravel and sandy gravel strata within lower permeability sands, silts and tills. The gravels often form an infilling to pre-glacial channels in the bedrock and carry significant quantities of water along such alignments.

4. GROUNDWATER CONDITIONS

A significant gravel layer carries water from the south and discharges from the lower overburden slopes to the east of the skipway (see Figure 1). This water source, along with surface precipitation, appears to form the main source of groundwater for the south east corner rock slopes.

Piezometers installed in the overburden and rock slopes have indicated a general groundwater table some 50 ft. below the slope surface.

The potential benefits of slope drainage (reduction in groundwater pressures) in the rock were evaluated in detail prior to the slide occurrence, to determine whether or not steeper slopes could be developed. Such studies concluded that overall drainage of the rock slopes was not economically feasible owing to the following factors:

(1)   high recharge from overburden strata that could be only partly controlled by surface drainage/diversion measures.

(2)   extremely low permeability of the rock types requiring short drainage paths.

(3)   scale of drainage measures required for a potentially 1,000 ft. high slope section.

The conclusions are borne out by the extremely limited and local influence of the extensive underground workings at the 2,000 ft. level on the south side of the open pit.

5. SUMMARY OF THE SLIDE DEVELOPMENT

Between 1965 and 1970 the benches forming the upper rock slopes had failed due to rock deterioration within the relatively weak shear zone material (see Figures 1, 3).

Prior to 1970 several relatively shallow slides had occurred within the overburden. These were probably caused by adverse groundwater conditions and the undercutting of the slope toe due to ravelling of the upper benches in rock.

During 1970, a gradual extension of the skipway rails was observed (see Figure 1). The skipway rails had been laid on a 45 degree slope partly composed of fill. (The movements were originally attributed to localised creeping of the fill material.)

Because of the critical role of the skipway installation in the mining operation, extensometers were installed from the crest of the slope and from the ore pass bridge level to check the depth of movement (see Figure 1). The instruments became operational at the end of 1970.

During December 1970 and January 1971, a major over-burden slide developed in an adjoining area to the north. The slide involved an area behind the pit crest forming part of the town of Asbestos. Groundwater pressure build-up resulting from the winter freeze-up was shown to be a contributing factor to the initial slope movements. Further movements were influenced by the leakage of service water from the town into existing cracks forming the rear scarp to the slide.

In January 1971, a localised wedge failure between the 2,220 ft and 2,320 ft elevations occurred below the main haul road in relatively competent rock (see Figures 1, 3). The failure was controlled by localised jointing although some extension of fractures may have occurred due to small, overall movements of the slope.

Mining was being carried out near the toe of the slope (approximate elevation 2,100 ft.) at the beginning of 1971. Relatively rapid progress had been made during the latter part of 1970 with mining below the 2,300 ft level.

In February 1971, a massive, overall movement of the south east corner was suspected. A movement monitoring programme was initiated to determine both the overall extent of surface movement and the depth to which movements were occurring. Approximate piezometric conditions within the slope were also determined from the same boreholes. Both monitoring and investigation were difficult due to the significant snow cover that existed.

Measurements on the surface and in boreholes (inclino-meter measurements or casing deformation observations using sondes) indicated movement of the entire slope some 700 ft. in height, 2,000 ft. in width and at depths up to 250 ft. (see Figures 3, 4). Approximately 20 m tons of material were contained within the slide zone. The observations

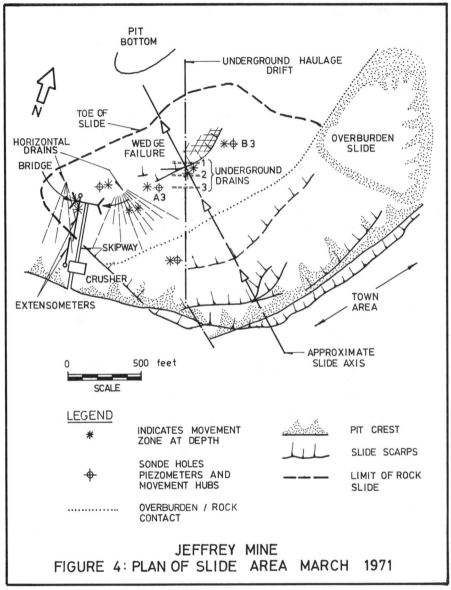

PIT
BOTTOM

UNDERGROUND HAULAGE
DRIFT

TOE OF
SLIDE

OVERBURDEN
SLIDE

HORIZONTAL
DRAINS

WEDGE
FAILURE

B 3

BRIDGE

1
2 } UNDERGROUND
3 } DRAINS

A3

SKIPWAY

CRUSHER

TOWN
AREA

EXTENSOMETERS

APPROXIMATE
SLIDE AXIS

0   500 feet

SCALE

LEGEND

*   INDICATES MOVEMENT
ZONE AT DEPTH

     PIT CREST

     SLIDE SCARPS

⊕   SONDE HOLES
PIEZOMETERS AND
MOVEMENT HUBS

     LIMIT OF ROCK
SLIDE

....   OVERBURDEN / ROCK
CONTACT

JEFFREY MINE
FIGURE 4: PLAN OF SLIDE AREA MARCH 1971

correlated with extensometer data obtained in the vicinity
of the skipway.

Maximum movements were evident at the centre of the
slide area with a gradual decrease in movement rates
towards the lateral slide boundaries. As movements
continued, scarps at the slide crest became evident.
Regular maintenance of the skipway track was required to
counter the overall extension of the rails. The skipway

bridge was subjected to an increasing degree of compression with time, owing to its orientation with respect to the movement axis. Shear displacement of the support columns and jamming of the horizontal ore pass doors were evident.

During April and May 1971, a period during which the main spring run-off occurs, major movements of the slope occurred causing ravelling on the lower rock benches, disruption of the haul road across the upper slope area and extensive damage to the skipway bridge structure.

The primary causes of instability were attributed to the following:

(1)   Mining operations at the toe of the slope. The excavation of material in this area reduced the volume of the competent lower rock buttress (See Figure 3) to a critical state where it was no longer able to support the overlying shear material and overburden. The build-up of shear stress through the buttress probably led to the extension of unfavourable oriented shallow dipping joints to form a continuous shear surface at the base of the buttress. This was accompanied by significant internal shearing along fractures oriented roughly parallel to the main shear zone as well as a general break-up and dilation of the more competent rock.

(2)   Adverse groundwater conditions as detailed below.

In order to control further movements and to protect the crusher installation at the pit crest, stabilisation measures were required.

6.   GROUNDWATER AND ITS INFLUENCE ON THE STABILITY OF THE SLIDE AREA

The investigation of the slide area confirmed the existence of adverse groundwater conditions within the slopes. In addition the break-up of the slope surface and the creation of tension cracks and scarps in the upper slope area led to an increased infiltration of surface water particularly during thaw periods. The overburden area to the north had by early 1971 broken up considerably and was found to contain a large quantity of water within open cracks and fissures much of which was derived from the town area. This water was free to flow southwards into the rock slide.

Later investigations have also shown that a considerable quantity of water probably flowed into the rear scarp of the slide from the buried, gravel-filled channel to the south.

Groundwater sources are illustrated generally in Figure 1. The phreatic surface within the slope profile is shown in Figure 3. The shape of the surface illustrates the high degree of recharge from the overburden slopes as well as the relatively impermeable nature of the major shear zone.

After the geometry of the slide had been defined, preliminary stability analyses using a technique of back analysis were carried out. These analyses demonstrated that the stability of the area could be improved significantly by the adoption of drainage measures that would lead to a reduction in groundwater pressures within the slope at depth.

In addition, unloading of the upper slope area by stripping of the overburden, would further improve stability following drainage.

It had been previously concluded that drainage of the intact rock would be of little benefit in reducing groundwater pressures on a significant scale. However, with the generation of a fairly well defined shear zone at the base of the slide that was likely to be quite permeable (due to dilation of the rock on shearing) it was decided to attempt drainage into the slide base.

7. STABILISATION MEASURES

Drainage measures to reduce groundwater pressures at the base of the slide consisted of:

(1) drainage of the overburden materials to minimise recharge into the underlying rock.

(2) horizontal drains from the skipway bridge area into rock (see Figure 4).

(3) drain holes drilled upwards from the underground haulage drift into the base of the slide (see Figures 3, 4).

The drainage measures were commenced in June 1971.

Drainage of the overburden was carried out using an 'Aardvark' drilling rig used to install perforated PVC casings into the slope. Drilling difficulties occurred when the more permeable gravels were encountered and the programme was only partially successful. Surface water diversion using drainage ditches and sumps was also carried out within the overburden area.

Initial drainage measures within the rock consisted of two fans of horizontal holes drilled from either side of the skipway bridge structure. A heavy duty diamond drilling rig was used to overcome potential difficulties with the highly variable and often sheared rock. Drillholes that did not penetrate the basal zone of the slide yielded little or no water and had only a localised effect on the groundwater pressures.

Most of the drillholes to the east of the bridge penetrated the base of the slide and encountered considerable quantities of water under pressure. The water was contained within a broken, sheared zone at the base of the slide. Dilation resulting from shear movements of several feet had produced an extensive, permeable zone that appeared to be well connected across the base of the slide.

One of the main holes in the east bridge series was temporarily closed off at the outlet after completion. A rapid increase in water pressure to approximately 75 psi was observed indicating high water pressures at a relatively shallow depth. The initial flow magnitudes (of the order of 50 gpm) and the rapid increase in pressure with time indicated the high permeability of the rock at the slide base. After approximately 3 months, the installation was again closed off and pressures were found to have decreased to about 5 psi.

Based on the success of the drillholes from surface, it was decided to rehabilitate the underground haulage drift and drill into the lower central slide area. Twelve drainage holes were drilled from a rail mounted rig so as to intersect the slide zone as illustrated in Figure 5. As expected a highly permeable zone, several feet thick was intersected and water under pressure flowed initially at some 200 gpm. This flow decreased after several months to about 20 gpm after pressures had dissipated across the base of the slide. The relative permeability of the intact and failed material was demonstrated by the lack of influence

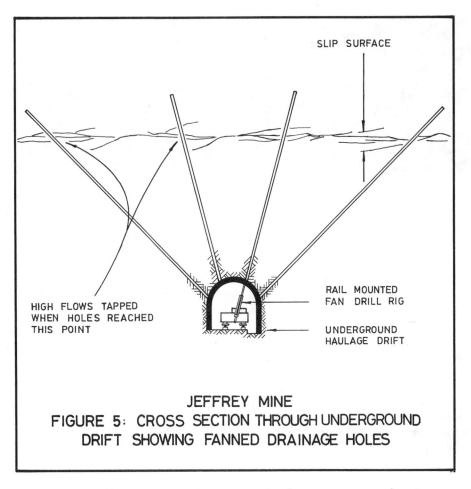

JEFFREY MINE

FIGURE 5: CROSS SECTION THROUGH UNDERGROUND
DRIFT SHOWING FANNED DRAINAGE HOLES

that the adit alone had had on reducing pressures in the
overlying slide.

Details of the drainage arrangements are shown in
Figure 6.

Concurrently with the skipway bridge drainage programme,
some 1.5 m tons of overburden was mined from the upper
slide area.

8.   RESULTS OF THE STABILISATION MEASURES

Surface monitoring of the slide area showed a significant reduction in movement rates following completion of
the initial drainage measures and the overburden stripping
(see Figure 7).

SKIPWAY DRAINAGE RIG   DRAIN OUTLET AND PRESSURE GAUGE

FIGURE 6: DRAINAGE ARRANGEMENTS

Complete stabilisation was achieved after completion of the drainage from underground in August 1971.

A similar movement trend was observed from the lower skipway extensometer as illustrated in Figure 7.

The sensitivity of stability to minor changes in groundwater conditions is indicated by a significant increase in movement rates in early August 1971 following approximately 5 in. of rainfall within 24 hours (see Figure 7).

Since drainage was installed during the summer period when groundwater conditions were more favourable, the success of the measures could not be immediately judged. No re-occurrence of movement was however observed during the winter and spring periods of 1972 and 1973 and ground-water pressures within the slide remained minimal. After 1973 significant changes in the slope geometry occurred and further conclusions on continuing stability trends could not be drawn.

9. CONCLUSIONS

The adoption of drainage measures in an extremely impermeable rock mass to control the movements of a large rock slide proved to be successful owing to the existence of a permeable basal zone that resulted from the overall slope movements.

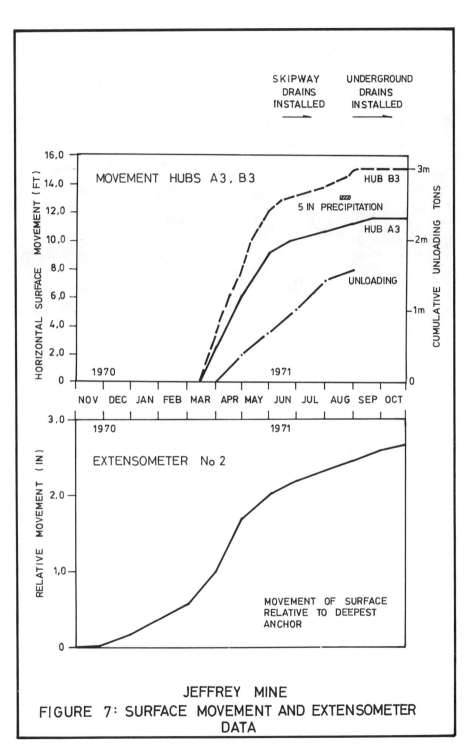

JEFFREY MINE

FIGURE 7: SURFACE MOVEMENT AND EXTENSOMETER
DATA

JEFFREY MINE
FIGURE 8:   SLIDE AREA FROM WEST

The stabilisation measures allowed the operation of critical installations to be maintained. Major break-up of the slope was also prevented thus ensuring access across the slope and safe conditions in the pit bottom below.

Although in low permeability rock masses, drainage may be impracticable (uneconomic) as a means of improving the stability of intact slopes, it can be successfully used as a remedial stabilisation measure.

ACKNOWLEDGEMENTS

The author wishes to thank Johns Manville Canada Inc. for permission to publish this paper and for the material which has been used in its publication.

The contribution of the staff at the Jeffrey Open Pit whose work is reported here is also acknowledged.

20

Dewatering Techniques for Rheinbraun's Open Pit Lignite Mines

by Burkhard Boehm, Senior Hydrologist, and
Dietmar Schneider, Hydrologist,
Rheinische Braunkohlenwerke AG,
Cologne, Federal Republic of Germany,
and Rudolf Voigt, Chief Geologist,
Rheinbraun-Consulting GmbH,
Cologne, Federal Republic of Germany

1. INTRODUCTION

1.1 Geology and Hydrology of the Rhenish Lignite Mining District - an Overview

During the Oligocene and Miocene epochs of the Tertiary period, enormous quantities of organic matter accumulated in the southern part of the Lower Rhine Graben, a major tectonical element to the northwest of the Rhenish Mass. Over an area of 2 500 square kilometers ($\sim$ 965 square miles) between the cities of Aachen, Cologne, and Moenchengladbach, this matter developed into a huge lignite deposit containing some 55×10^9 (metric) tons of lignite (fig. 1). With the present technical means - bucket wheel excavator, conveyor belt, stacker working in a continuous open pit operation - 35 x 10^9 tons out of this total are technically and economically recoverable from pits that may eventually be as deep as 600 meters ($\sim$ 1 950 feet). In recent years, 110 to 120 x 10^6 tons of lignite have been mined annually by Rheinische Braunkohlenwerke AG (abbr. Rheinbraun). The deepest open pit mine is now worked at a depth of 300 meters.

The lignite occurs in three seam formations, two of which are mined by five open pit mines. The nature of the strata top and bottom of the seams reflect the paralic environment between the rising mainland in the south and the then North Sea, where they were deposited. They are made up of very thick sequences of sands which are separated from each other by silt and clay deposits. This kind of stratification fostered the development of three major aquifer units above the seam formations, one within the seams, and two below them. Locally, there may occur even more aquifers (see fig. 2).

To enable a safe mining operation, the topwall aquifers in the pit areas must completely be dewatered, and the footwall aquifers sufficiently depressurized (1).

Some major and numerous minor normal faults with NW-SE strike dissect the mining district and form the characteristic horst and graben structures which are featured in figures 1 and 2. The major faults usually act as barriers to ground water flow.

Sedimentary and tectonical processes thus have created a geologically and hydrologically very complicated deposit which requires intelligent solutions for mining planning and techniques, including dewatering. The aim of this paper is to give a glimpse into the planning and the execution of the dewatering measures.

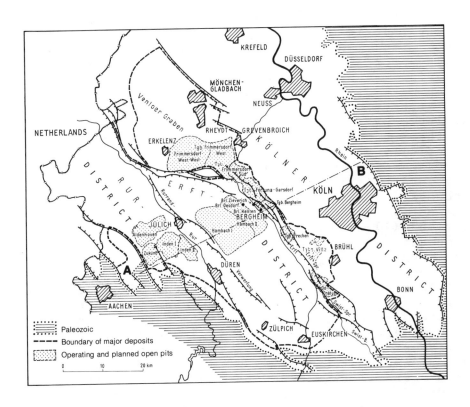

Figure No. 1, Operating and planned open pit mines in the Rhenish Lignite Mining District

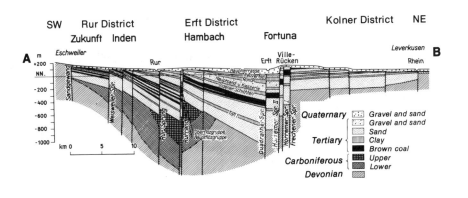

Figure No. 2, Geological section across the mining district

1.2 Hydrological Investigations

The prerequisite for planning the adequate dewatering measures for an open pit lignite mine
which may reach a depth of a few hundred meters,
is information as complete as possible of the hydrologic parameters of the aquifers involved and
of their boundary conditions. The latter may substantially vary in time in the course of maximum
drawdown or even full depletion of an aquifer.
Any investigation of a lignite deposit must be
accompanied therefore by an investigation of the
respective hydrologic properties and boundary conditions (1). The methods to compile and evaluate
such data are standard practice and need not be
mentioned. Special attention is given to maintaining a dense network of observation wells which are
screened in the pumped aquifers. Many investigative
bore holes are turned into such observation wells
or piezometers. Rheinbraun drills approximately
25 000 meters ($\sim$ 82 000 feet) per year for investigative or piezometer bore holes. Across the area
which is affected by the withdrawal of ground water, approximately 3 100 piezometers are monitored
permanently. Up to six of them, sealed against
each other, are arranged in a single bore hole
(fig. 3). State agencies and private users of ground
water observe additional 1 600 piezometers.

2. PLANNING OF DEWATERING MEASURES

2.1 Introductory Remarks

The hydrological planning department of Rheinbraun sees its responsibilities as follows:

- within the longterm planning process, the
dewatering schemes for open pit mines are to be
designed, the cross rates of discharge to be calculated and the effects of ground water withdrawal to be determined

- within the shortterm planning process, the individual wells, galleries of wells and other dewatering means are to be designed, their operation
monitored and their effects continuously checked
against the theoretical calculations.

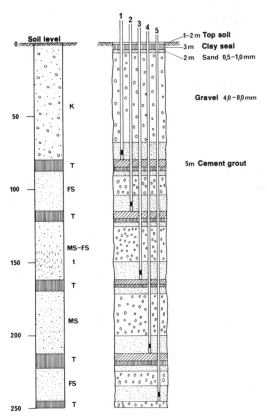

Multiple observation point

Figure No. 3, Piezometer group in a single bore
hole

In doing so, several approaches to solve the
interesting problems are chosen. Based on the
classical well formulas of Dupuit-Thiem and the
semi-empiric investigations of Sichardt (2), diagrams were developed which permit a prompt design
of gravel packed dewatering wells. These take into
account the maximum or Sichardt's capacities at
different phases of drawdown.

Versatile tools are ground water budgets that
quite often enable the hydrologists to assess hydraulic parameters, especially the specific yield,
and certain boundary conditions.

The major tools, however, are methods to model
the dewatering processes by simulation. Traditional-
ly, Rheinbraun's hydrological department has employed one-dimensional approximate methods, originally developed by Siemon (3). For the past years,
however, numerical two-dimensional aquifer models
have come in use (4).

2.2 One-dimensional Approximation of Dewatering Process

Siemon (3), observing the development of the
cones of depression in result of large-scale dewatering for lignite mines, noted typical patterns
during the growth of the cones. He termed them
phases of drawdown.
During the first phase, a gallery of dewatering
wells discharges at maximum capacity. Most of the
withdrawn ground water is taken from storage. The
cone develops as schematically shown in fig. 4-1.

The second phase of drawdown is characterized
by a decrease of the rate of discharge due to decreasing capacities of the wells. A higher percentage of discharged water is now from recharge, the
cone of depression flattens, and withdrawal of water in storage occurs more or less evenly across
the cone (fig. 4-2).

$Q_1 > Q_2 > Q_3$

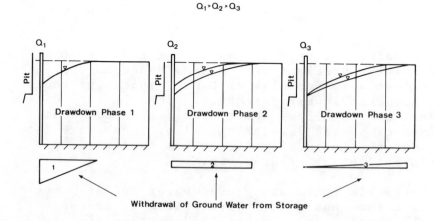

Figure No. 4, Consecutive phases of drawdown in
an aquifer due to mine dewatering, after (3)

To the end of the third phase, the drawdown along the perimeter of the mine has arrived at the required level, and the cone, no more deepening any more, tends to stabilize by adjusting to the rate of recharge (fig. 4-3).

The second phase exists over a long period of the dewatering process. On assuming the even withdrawal of water in storage to be effective and taking account of the boundary conditions the calculation of heads in sections for parallel flow and radial flow becomes possible. This enables the hydrologist to determine for given drawdowns and rates of discharge in the center of the dewatering gallery successive phases of drawdown. Despite inherent errors this method has proven very suitable to model the dewatering process for a mine in more or less good approximation.

2.3 Two-dimensional Numerical Modelling

2.3.1 Mathematical Ground Water Model

The present numerical program GW1 (Ground Water One) was developed for the hydrogeologic conditions of the Rhenish Lignite District. It is based on a mathematical model which utilizes a finite difference method to compute the distribution of head in an aquifer under steady-state or unsteady-state conditions (4, 5).

The continuous aquifer is replaced by a non-uniformly spaced grid of acute triangles, a system which permits a rather accurate image of irregularly shaped aquifer boundaries (6). Thus, Darcy's law is applied to calculate the partial flow rates along the sides of the triangles. The continuity equation becomes an equation that describes for any nodal point the node-to-node water transfer rates, the rate of water released from, or taken into storage, the withdrawal rate and the rates of recharge and/or discharge (e. g. leakage to or from the aquifer). Any nodal point of such a grid is surrounded by o neighbouring nodal points. The mid-verticals of the sides of the triangles form a polygon, the area of which, A_B, is represented by nodal point B (see fig. 5). The area A_B is the surface area of a vertical aquifer prism whose

properties are characterized by the assigned parameters.

The interval r_{Bj} describes the width of the
cross-sectional area between nodal point B and its
j^{th} neighbouring nodal point (fig. 5).

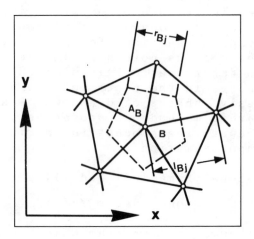

Figure No. 5, Basic element of triangle grid

In analogy to the spatial discretion of the
aquifer, the continuous process of unsteady-state
flow is replaced in the mathematical model by a
discrete series of quasi-steady state flow states.

The continuity equation in nodal point B requires the sum of all node-to-node B water transfer rates plus the sum of all water rates leaving
or entering the system in B to be equal to the
change of storage in the aquifer prism per time
increment.

$$\sum_{j=1}^{o} Y_{Bj} \times (h_{j,u+1} - h_{B,u+1}) + Q_{sonst,u+1}$$

$$= \frac{A_B \times S_B}{\Delta t} (h_{B,u+1} - h_{B,u}) \qquad (1)$$

where

$$Y_{Bj} = \frac{r_{Bj}}{1_{Bj}} \times m_{Bj} \times K_{Bj} \tag{2}$$

$$Q_{sonst} = q_B \times A_B + Q_B \tag{3}$$

and

$\circ$	=	number of neighbouring nodal points
n	=	index of time increment
m_{Bj}	=	saturated thickness
A_B	=	surface area represented by nodal point B
K^B	=	hydraulic conductivity

Under steady state conditions, the right hand side of equation (1) becomes zero.

Calculation is based on the method of successive overrelaxation. By correction of the head calculated for the preceding iteration step, by the change of head, as deduced from the balance quantity Q (bracketed in equation (4)), a new value of head is calculated for a new time increment.

$$h_{B,u+1}^{w+1} = h_{B,u+1}^{w} + \lambda \times \left[\sum_{j<B} Y_{Bj} \times h_{j,u+1}^{w+1} + \right.$$

$$+ \sum_{j>B} Y_{Bj} \times h_{j,u+1}^{w} - (\sum_{j=1}^{\circ} Y_{Bj} + \frac{A_B \times S_B}{\Delta t}) h_{B,u+1}^{w}$$

$$\left. + \frac{A_B \times S_B}{\Delta t} h_{B,u} + Q_{sonst,u+1} \right] \tag{4}$$

with $\lambda = \varphi \times \Omega$ $\tag{5}$

$$\Omega = \frac{1}{\sum\limits_{j=1}^{\circ} Y_{Bj} + \frac{A_B \times S_B}{\Delta t}} \tag{6}$$

where

Ω	=	factor to convert Q to h
φ	=	relaxation coefficient
w	=	iteration index

By utilizing equation (4), all nodal points will successively be calculated again and again

until the balance quantity is less than a given
value.

The water table of an unconfined aquifer is
taken account of by setting the saturated thickness equal to the head that was calculated for the
preceding iteration step.

2.3.2 Modelling the Dewatering Process for an Open Pit Mine

Ground water flow problems that must be solved
by numerical modelling of a dewatering process
for a mine differ somewhat from those usually encountered by hydrologists. Any mine dewatering
aims at completely depleting the aquifer portion
top of the lowermost working level within the mine.
In general, during ground water withdrawal, an initially confined aquifer will successively become
unconfined and finally, in the working area, be
fully depleted. Withdrawal is usually accomplished
by gravel packed tube wells. Here, the special
need arises to simulate discharging wells and to
compute their maximum capacity as function of the
head just outside of the well.

The hydraulically possible rate of discharge
per well and time increment must be computable by
the program to allow for proper selection of the
appropriate pump.

In any nodal point, where the initially confined aquifer becomes unconfined, the storage
coefficient S changes to the specific yield Sy.
Due to the fact, that S and Sy usually differ by
several powers of ten, equation (4) may easily
become unstable. Busch & Luckner (7) recommend a
numerical procedure to compensate for the jump of
S. In GW1, this is done by setting the head h in
any nodal point equal to z_o, the top of the aquifer, as soon h becomes less than z_o. From the next
iterative step on, storativity in this nodal point
is represented by Sy.
Depletion of the aquifer is solved for in a similar
way. As soon as the head h falls short of the base,
z_u, of the aquifer, the respective nodal point is
taken out of computation. The total flux to this
nodal point thus is set to zero. Flow then occurs

around the depleted part of the aquifer.

Single dewatering wells and galleries of wells are simulated by summing up the rates of discharge of all wells that fall into the surface area A_B of the aquifer prism and assigning the sum Q_{sonst} to the respective nodal point B. The head h_B computed this way represents the average head of the prism. As a rule, it will be substantially higher than the water table in a well. To design the dewatering wells and to calculate their maximum capacities, the heads at the effective radii of the wells must be known, however. Since the linearity of Darcy's law does not hold any more in the vicinity of a discharging well in an unconfined aquifer, another approach, that is based on Sichardt's concept, had to be made (2).

The water table for a well under quasi steady-state conditions, that is located in a nodal point, is calculated by utilizing Thiem's formula

$$h_{well} = \bar{h} - \frac{Q}{2\pi K\bar{m}} \ln \frac{\bar{r}}{r_{well}}$$

where

h_{well} = head at effective radius of well

$\bar{h}$ = arithmetical mean of heads of neighboring nodal points

$\bar{m}$ = arithmetical mean of saturated thicknesses between nodal point and neighboring nodal points

$\bar{r}$ = arithmetical mean of horizontal distances to neighboring nodal points

r_{well} = effective radius of well, identical with drill hole radius

For a node representing more than one well, the drawdown must be reduced. Due to the principle of superposition, the resulting cone of depression will be considerably deeper than the individual cones around the wells. To enable determination of the head at each well, a reduction factor, fi, was devised.

From

$$h_{well} = \bar{h} - s_{well} \qquad (7)$$

follows

$$h_{well} = \bar{h} - f_i \times s_{well} \qquad (8)$$

where

f_i = reduction factor.

Its numerical value varies between 1.0 for one well and 0.3 for seven and more wells per nodal point.

The yield of a well discharging from an unconfined aquifer is limited by the so-called Sichardt's maximum capacity (2).

This maximum capacity is the product of wetted area of the well (assumption: wetted area is fully screened) and specific discharge v at the effective radius of the well.

$$Q_{max} = 2\pi \times r_{well} \times \bar{h}_{well} \times K \times I_{max} \qquad (9)$$

and

$$I_{max} = \frac{1}{15\sqrt{K}} \qquad \text{(dimensionally in-correct!)} \qquad (10)$$

where

Q_{max} = Sichardt's maximum capacity

I_{max} = maximum hydraulic gradient

K = hydraulic conductivity

Inserting equation (10) in equation (9) yields

$$Q_{max} = 2\pi \times r_{well} \times h_{well} \times \frac{\sqrt{K}}{15} \qquad (11)$$

After each time increment, the program compares the discharge Q with the maximum capacity Q_{max}. In addition, it controls Reynolds' number if it exceeds the numerical value of 2 (assumed to be the upper limit of laminar flow). As soon as one of both conditions no longer holds, the time increment must be recalculated with a reduced rate of discharge.

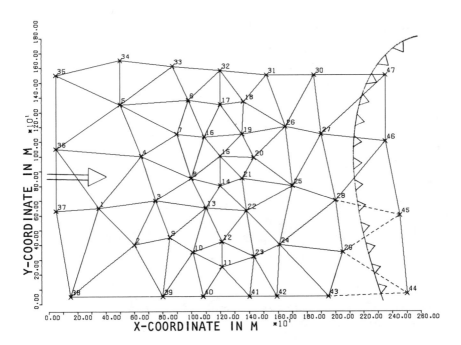

Figure No. 6, Example of plotted model grid.The
flow is directed from West to East. The toothed
line represents the perimeter of the mine.

A few examples of plots of a run of this model
serve to illustrate the results. A cutout of a
plotted model grid is shown in fig. no. 6. The
ground water flow is directed from west to east
towards the open pit. Nodal points 44 through 47
represent the aquifer portion within the boundaries of this pit. Nodal points 11, 12, 14, 16, 17
simulate sites of dewatering wells. In fig. no.
7 a, top and bottom of the aquifer are indicated
by full lines (on the original plots, upper and
lower aquifer boundaries are marked in a different
color). Differently dotted lines represent successive stages of drawdown after 3 months and 20 days,
6 months and so on.

Fig. 7 a and 7 b show drawdown vs distance
graphs for different time steps and drawdown vs
time graphs for nodal point 28 just in front of
the perimeter of the mine.

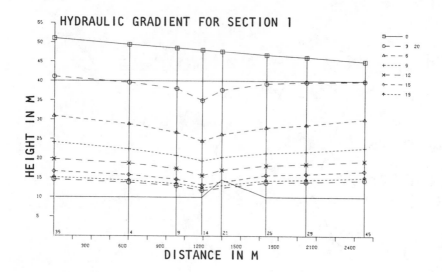

Figure No. 7 a, Drawdown vs. distance plot of successive stages of drawdown.

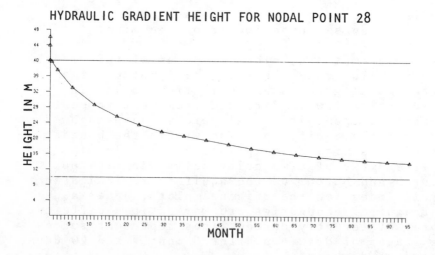

Figure No. 7 b, Drawdown vs. time plot for nodal point 28.

3. EXECUTION OF DEWATERING MEASURES

3.1 Introductory Remarks

The transmissivities of the water-bearing strata top and bottom of the coal reach values as high as $T = 5 \times 10^{-2}$ m^{2}s^{-1} ($\sim 3.5 \times 10^5$ US gallons/day - foot). Such high transmissivities and the large areal extent of these strata render gravity discharge by vertical tube wells the only economical solution to withdraw the large rates of water as necessary.

To lift the water from great depths to the ground surface, high-capacity submersible motor pumps are required which, in turn, demand large drilling diameters and likewise large widths of screens and casings. Today, company-operated drilling rigs regularly sink wells down to depths of more than 500 meters ($\sim 1\ 650$ feet). Standard drilling diameters range between 1 200 and 1 800 mm (about 48 inches and 71 inches) and nominal widths of well screens and inner casings between 300 mm and 800 mm (about 12 inches and 32 inches). All wells are drilled by means of a reverse circulation drilling method (8).

3.2 Reverse Circulation Air Injection Drilling Method

Reverse circulation methods are characterized by the drilling fluid descending within the annulus between drill rods and bore hole wall and ascending loaded with cuttings. Upon discharge into the settling pond, the cuttings settle out and the sediment-free fluid begins its cycle again. The air injection method as applied by Rheinbraun maintains this cycle by injecting pressured air into the drill rods via inlet nozzles above the drill bit or the drill collars. As drilling fluid, untreated water is usually employed.

Fig. 8 shows schematically the operation of such a rig. Generally the bore hole remains stable during drilling only because of the difference in heads of the drill water column and the aquifer. This minimum must not fall short of 3 meters (~ 10 feet), i. e., in case of an artesian aquifer special procedures will become necessary.

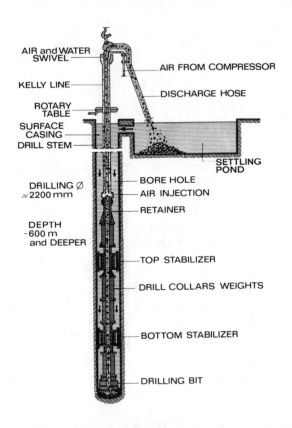

Figure No. 8, Working scheme of a reverse circulation air injection drilling rig (9).

The diagram of figure 9 shows the sequence of
operations for an average 500 m - well (8). Considering preparatory and finishing work, the average
rate of progress of a L 15-rig is 12 meters
(∿ 40 feet) per 8 hour-shift. This figure increases
to 50 meters (∿ 165 feet) per shift if only the
drilling job is considered.

Rheinbraun employs exclusively trailer-mounted
Wirth drilling rigs. Their derricks, draw and feed
works are designed to also handle the strings of
casings and screens during installation. The table
below gives some technical data of Wirth rigs
operated by Rheinbraun.

Type	L 4	L 10	L 15
Drive	230 HP diesel engine	200 HP diesel engine	250 HP diesel engine
Hook load			
a. regular	36 metric tons	100 metric tons	160 metric tons
b. maximum	72 metric tons	120 metric tons	195 metric tons
Compressor	5.7 cubic meters per minute ($\sim$ 1 500 US gallons per minute)	20 cubic meters per minute ($\sim$ 5 280 US gallons per minute) (2 units)	20 cubic meters per minute ($\sim$ 5 280 US gallons per minute) (2 units)
Regular duties with Rheinbraun			
a. drilling diameters	1 200 - 1 700 millimeters ($\sim$ 48 inches - 67 inches)	1 200 - 1 700 millimeters ($\sim$ 48 inches - 67 inches)	1 200 - 1 700 millimeters ($\sim$ 48 inches - 67 inches)
b. drilling depths	400 meters	600 meters	600 meters

Theoretical investigations and field tests revealed that the rate of fluid (water) circulation in 300 mm (12 inches) drill-rods amounts to approximately 12 to 18 cubic meters per minute ($\sim$ 3 170 through 4 755 US gallons per minute). Depending on the depth of injection, between 15 and 30 cubic meters per minute in compressed air at pressures up to 20 bars ($\sim$ 290 pounds per square inch) has to be blown into the drill stem. The total discharge is then 12 cubic meters per minute at a content of solids of approximately 8 per cent. This figure is equivalent to a discharge of 130 through 140 (metric) tons of drill cuttings per hour (9).

The only drill bits still in use are roller bits, i. e. flat head roller bits and multiple-stage bits. To guarantee plumbness, up to eight drill collars, each having a weight of 6 (metric) tons and two stabilizers, are added to the bits. Rheinbraun no longer uses excentric (Züblin) bits. Experience showed that the drilling progress in dewatered, i. e. compacted sediments was unsatisfactory when these bits were employed.

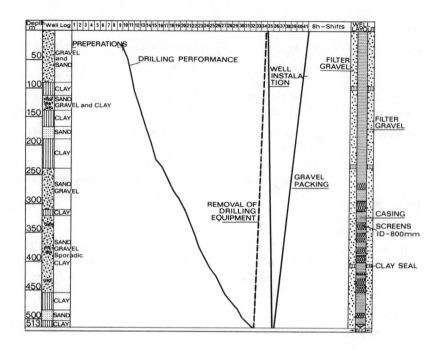

Figure No. 9, Work vs. time diagram for an average 500 meters - dewatering well.

As already mentioned, untreated water serves usually as drilling fluid. Difficulties arise, however, when drilling certain clay formations, because the clays tend to swell by water absorption and to cave in. To overcome these difficulties, natural or synthetic polymeric additives, such as carboxylmethylcellulose (CMC) and Stokopol (a polyacrylamide) are put into the water to increase its viscosity and to hinder the water molecules from entering the crystal lattice of the clay (10).

3.3 Well Design

All dewatering wells are equipped with asbestos-cement inner casings and screens (fig. 10). Special couplings allow for a suspended installation.

Figure No. 10, Asbestos-cement inner casings and gravel wall screens ready for assembly. Some of the couplings are equipped with spacers.

Both casings and screens are distinguished by high tensile strength and sufficient crushing strength. They are corrosion-resistant, i. e. they are hardly affected by aging processes. Below depths of 350 m ($\sim$ 1 150 feet) the casings are wrapped with styrofoam bodies to increase their buoyancy, i. e. to make up for higher tensile stresses. Wells equipped with asbestos-cement tubes can be easily cut portion by portion by the excavators. Even their angular fragments can be transported via the conveyor belts without damaging the rubber. This property renders them very advantageous for continuous open pit mining where the dewatering wells are successively operated on any working level. Screens consist of pierced asbestos-cement pipes of the same widths that are coated with a 30 or 35 mm thick resin-glued gravel walls. The gradations of the gravel used for these walls are 2 - 3 mm, 3 - 5 mm, 4 - 7 mm.

Upon installing the string of casings and

screens and supporting them above ground surface, the annular space is carefully gravel packed (fig. 9). The method applied to ensure proper gradation of filter gravel uses a characteristic grain size of the water-bearing formation. Originally developed in Germany (11), it is also described by (12). It employs the standard relation

Gravel pack standard grain size = Aquifer standard grain size x screening factor

   Aquifer standard grain sizes for any aquifer are taken from charts (11). The screening factor is defined as the increase in grain size necessary to prevent passing of aquifer material through the gravel pack. Usually, its numerical value ranges between 4 and 5.

3.4 Submersible Motor Pumps

   Because of their well-known superiority to other pumps, Rheinbraun uses only submersible motor pumps for regular service. Right now, there are around 1 800 pumps in stock, about half of them are in service, the other in reserve or in repair. Two types may suffice to indicate the lower and upper capacity limits:

Q: 0.035 cubic meters per minute at H: 35 meters
    ($\sim$ 925 US gallons per minute)   ($\sim$ 115 feet)

Q: 32.60 cubic meters per minute at H: 215 meters
    ($\sim$ 8 600 US gallons per minute)   ($\sim$ 705 feet)

   There are numerous other in between types such as pumps with higher delivery heads but lower rates of discharge. All larger pumps are of the double-suction type. To extend their service time, which today may be as high as 32 000 hours, the larger pumps are exclusively powered by slow-moving motors.
Depending on the rate of discharge, standard riser pipes between DN 100 and 400 (corresponding to 4 inches and 16 inches) are used.

   Rheinbraun uses submersible motor pumps manufactured only by two German manufacturers, KSB and Ritz. Both pump producers have developed

several series of pumps, the performance curves
of which link up with each other. Since at least
two, often even six pump changes are necessary
during the lifetime of a single well, selection of
the suitable sequence of pumps is facilitated
(fig. 11).

To power the pumps there are company-owned
110 kV-overhead line systems around the different
mines. Close to the centers of well batteries, the
high voltage is transformed down to local 25 kV-
systems which serve transformers that in turn feed
individually 6.3 kV-transformers and switches in
the vicinity of individual wells and well groups.

3.5 Mine Dewatering - the last Percent

Despite the fact that dewatering procedures as
described above account for perhaps 99 per cent of
Rheinbraun's total discharge of ground water, there
is always the threat of saturated strata just
ahead of the bucket wheel. Typical cases are unde-
tected, narrow strips of sediments between faults
which act as barriers, or strata with low hydraulic conductivities. In both cases, the transmissivities are too low to allow normal gravity flow
dewatering wells to sufficiently operate.

In dealing with such problems two ways to solve
them are possible. The first one is to leave it
the ingenuity of the mining engineers to handle the
semi-liquid flow of material that will occur when
the wheel cuts into the saturated strata. The
other one is to devise emergency-dewatering
schemes that yield satisfactory results in a very
short time.

One of these emergency measure which has proven
very effective is to sink large-diameter bore
holes into the low-transmissivity strata, to design them with small diameter screens and pack
them with very coarse gravel. Because the latter
allows both the water and the sand of the associated formation to pass, it will gradually be
destroyed by such kind of discharge. The well will
last, however, just for the few weeks, the time
required to remove the small volumes of ground
water by intermittent pumping.

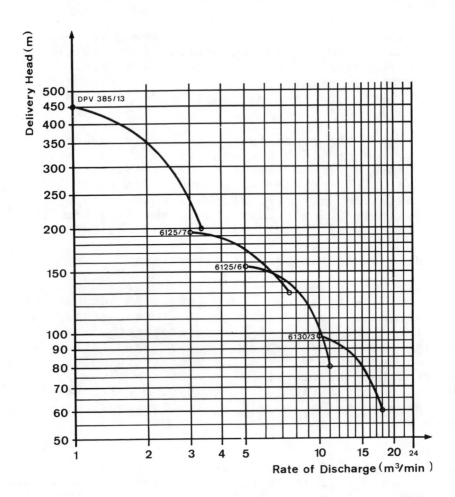

Figure No. 11, Possible sequence of submersible motor pumps in a dewatering well.

Ritz-6130/ 3 stages (865 Volts, 280 kilo Watts, diameter: 600 millimeters ⁓ 24 inches, overall length: 4 260 millimeters ⁓ 168 inches)

Ritz-6125/ 6 stages (865 Volts, 280 kilo Watts, diameter: 500 millimeters ⁓ 20 inches, overall length: 4 615 millimeters ⁓ 182 inches)

A method to enable the excavators to cut slopes in strata with hydraulic conductivities as low as 10^{-6} through 10^{-7} meters per second ($\sim$ 2 through 0.2 US gallons/day - square foot) is to stabilize the latter by vacuum dewatering (13). Figure 12 shows schematically how this method works.

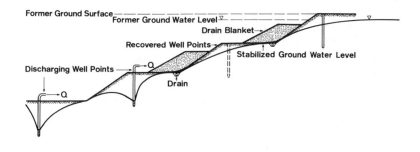

Figure No. 12, Stabilization of ground water level by vacuum dewatering measures.

Two-inch well points, consisting of a slotted screen of one meter length and six meters casing are flush-drilled into the beds at horizontal intervals between one and two meters ($\sim$ 3.3 and 6.5 feet). Upon sealing the annular spaces with clay, all well points are connected to a vacuum pump via a hose pipe. The dump reduces the system pressure to around 0.3 through 0.4 atmosphere, i. e., a vacuum which is equivalent to depths

Ritz-6125/ 7 stages	(865 Volts, 280 kilo Watts, diameter: 500 millimeters $\sim$ 20 inches, overall length: 4 871 millimeters $\sim$ 192 inches)
KSB-DPV 385/13 stages	(865 Volts, 185 kilo Watts, diameter: 315 millimeters $\sim$ 12.4 inches, overall length: 4 875 millimeters $\sim$ 192 inches)

between 7 and 6 meters ($\sim$ 22 feet to 19 feet).
Maintaining such a vacuum results in the withdrawal of ground water that otherwise would not
have flowed to wells in a reasonable time. After
two through four weeks, steady state conditions
prevail.

Under protection of a line of well points, a
6 meters high slope can be cut by a bucket wheel
or a dragline. Along its foot, a drain is designed
to discharge into a pump sump. As an additional
measure of safety, a drain blanket is added as
shown in fig. 12. Eventually, a highwall, consisting of a series of many small slopes, has been
featured. Ground water is still flowing towards
the open hole of the mine but it is intercepted by
the small drains.

4. SUMMARY

In the Tertiary lignite deposits between the
cities of Cologne, Aachen, and Moenchengladbach,
W. Germany, Rheinbraun runs five open pit mines
at depths of today about 300 meters ($\sim$ 990 feet).
The sequence of water bearing and confining strata
above and below the seam formations as well as
numerous faults form a complicated system of
aquifers which, in the pit areas, must be completely or partially depleted.

Specially modelling techniques to simulate the
ground water flow towards dewatering wells have
been applied, both one-dimensionally and two-dimen-
sionally. The latter model is based on a finite
difference method. In addition to "standard"
ground water modelling, it handles specific problems such as full depletion of parts of the aquifer or simulation of the decreasing capacities
of dewatering wells.

More than 100 dewatering wells are drilled annually by Rheinbraun, with maximum depths now
around 500 meters ($\sim$ 1 650 feet). To sink these
wells, the reverse circulation air injection method is employed. The well design is based on the
use of asbestos-cement casings and gravel wall
screens with nominal diameters between 300 and
800 millimeters (12 and 32 inches). The wells are

equipped with submersible motor pumps which discharge between 0.035 and 32.6 cubic meters per minute (∾925 and 8 600 gallons per minute).

Despite all efforts, it is not always possible to remove the water completely from the mines. In such cases, small scale dewatering measures are put into operation that are adapted to the local hydrogeologic conditions.

5. REFERENCES

1. Voigt, R. (1976) "Evaluation of Geologic, Hydrologic, and Geomechanic Properties Controlling Future Lignite Open Pit Mining" - Proc. first Int. Coal Explor. Symp. London, pp. 296 - 323.

2. Sichardt, W. (1928) "Das Fassungsvermögen von Rohrbrunnen und seine Bedeutung für die Grundwasserabsenkung, insbesondere für größere Absenkungstiefen" - Julius Springer Verlag Berlin

3. Siemon, H. (1958) "Berechnung von Grundwasserabsenkungen unter Berücksichtigung des Grundwasserhaushaltes" - Ministerium f. Ernährung, Landwirtschaft und Forsten d. Landes Nordrhein-Westfalen, Düsseldorf, 72 p.

4. Boehm, B. (1975) "Beitrag zur indirekten Ermittlung von Parametern für Grundwasserströmungsmodelle" - Mitt. Institut f. Wasserwirtschaft, Hydrologie u. landwirtschaftl. Wasserbau d. Techn. Univ. Hannover, vol. 32, pp. 3 - 130.

5. Tyson, N. H. & Weber, E. M. (1964) "Groundwater Management for the Nation's Future - Computer Simulation of Groundwater Basins" - J. Hyd. Div. ASCE, No. HY 4, pp. 59 - 77.

6. McNeal, R. H. (1953) "An Asymmetrical Finite Difference Network" - Quarterly of Appl. Mathem., vol. 11 (3), pp. 295 - 310.

7. Busch, K.-F. & Luckner, L. (1973) "Geohydraulik" - VEB Verl. f. Grundstoffindustrie, Leipzig.

8. Blank, R. (1976) "Tagebauentwässerung im Rheinischen Braunkohlenrevier mit großkalibrigen Tiefbrunnenbohrungen und entsprechenden Tauchmotorpumpen" - bbr vol. 27 (3), pp. 87 - 92.

9. Emrich, D. (1979) "Entwässerung der Tagebaue im Rheinischen Braunkohlenrevier" - Bergbau, vol. 30 (3), pp. 126 - 132.

10. Häge, K. (1977) "Die Verwendung künstlicher Polymere als Schutzkolloid in Bohrspülungen" - Braunkohle, vol. 29 (5), pp. 197 - 202.

11. Bieske, E. (1961) "Zur Schüttkornbestimmung bei Kiesschüttungsbrunnen" - bbr, vol. 12 (9), pp. 407 - 411.

12. Blair, A. H. (1970) "Well Screens and Gravel Packs" - Ground Water, vol. 8 (1), pp. 10 - 21.

13. Proff, H.-J. (1975) "Erfahrungen bei der Böschungsherstellung in Altkippen, dargestellt am Beispiel des Tagebaues Alversdorf" - Braunkohle, vol. 27 (6), pp. 168 - 175.

21

Drainage Control at a Central Florida Open Pit Phosphate Mine

by John H. Paugh, Geologist,
Swift Agricultural Chemical Corporation,
Bartow, Florida, USA

INTRODUCTION

The application of gravity connector wells as a method of mine drainage control has been effective in improving the efficiency of ore yardage recovery and productivity at Watson Mine in Polk County, Florida. Open pit mining to depths greater than 50 feet deep without prior dewatering resulted in ore recovery from 40 to 60 percent. The affect of dewatering deep pit areas improved recovery to a range of 70 to 80 percent and increased production tonnage 20 percent.

GEOLOGY

The Bone Valley deposit lies east of Tampa Bay and underlies some 2,000 square miles of the coastal plain. Phosphate rock production from 11 companies in the field is approximately 35 million short tons annually.

The deposit is a deltaic shaped, shallow marine and estuarine sediment of pebble, sand and clay called matrix. It lies on the southwest flank of the Ocala Arch, which was significant to the occurrence and structural control of phosphate deposition during Miocene and Pliocene ages. (1) The ridge areas from Lakeland and Bartow to the eastern boundary are linear uplifts of the Central Highlands Flexure. (2) This region has a typical karst topography with chains of sinkhole lakes along the alignment of the ridges. Jointing and fault systems developed concurrently with the post-Miocene uplift activity. The surface features of sinkhole depressions and lakes are associated with subsurface patterns of structural adjustments on the Flexure. Swift Agricultural Chemicals Corporation operates two mines south of Bartow. Silver City Mine lies west of the karst region, but some of the Watson Mine property lies within the influences of the ridge-sinkhole region, see Figure No. 1.

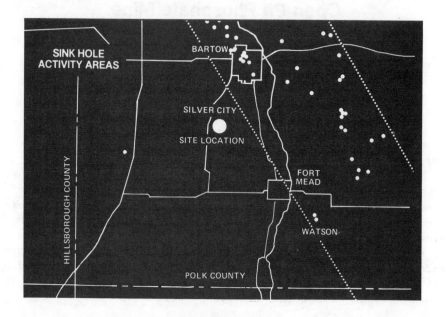

Figure No. 1
Sinkhole Activity

Mining Methods

Conventional mining practice in the phosphate field utilizes electric powered walking draglines with various boom lengths and bucket capacities to simultaneously strip overburden and mine matrix. The mining cut widths vary from 150 to 350 feet and range up to three quarters of a mile in length. In usual pit depths of 30 feet, dewatering is accomplished by waterjacks. The overburden is cast as a spoil into the adjacent mined out cut, see Figure No. 2. The matrix

is stacked in a sump on the highwall where hydraulic monitors produce a slurry of 20 to 40 percent solids. The slurry is pumped to a processing plant where the gangue of sand
and clay is separated from the phosphate particles. Mine
planning for pit conditions in the karst terrain with thick
overburden and deep pits is more complicated than planning
layout in the shallow mining areas. The main concerns affecting productivity are pit slope stability, groundwater
control and the influence of spoil volume on matrix recovery, see Figure No. 3.

Figure No. 2
Shallow Pit

Pit Slope Stability

The most important factor in the stability of the pit
wall is the shear strength of the soil strata beneath
the slopes. Soft clay layers, especially when inclined
toward the pit face, are usually critical. Groundwater
is also a very important factor. It not only reduces
the weight of the soil through bouyancy, thus decreasing the frictional resistance of the soil, but seepage
forces add to the gravity forces increasing the potential

Figure No. 3
Deep Pit

Figure No. 4
Slope Failure

for sliding. In cohesionless soil, below the groundwater level, the slopes tend to "flow" into the pit. In Figure No. 4, a series of circular slope failures, occurring as incremental slices into the pit wall, are a clear danger to the dragline operating near the edge of the pit.

Groundwater Control

Groundwater control is essential for the dragline operator to see the matrix and effectively recover all the matrix yardage in the cut. When water levels are high enough to cover the matrix, spotting the bucket for efficient matrix recovery is impossible. Also, the effective loading in the bucket is difficult as wet matrix falls from the bucket during hoisting from the pit.

Spoil Volume

When wet overburden is cast as a spoil in the adjacent mined out cut, the volume swells. In deep overburden areas the cut widths are changed from 350 down to 250 feet to reduce the spoil volume. This adjustment considers; 1) the effective reach of the dragline, 2) overburden and matrix slope ratios from engineering studies, and 3) an estimate of spoil slope. The amount of matrix yardage lost due to the respective slopes is calculated.

WATSON MINE STATISTICS

Table I relates the variable nature of overburden and matrix thickness, total depth, and the response of mining efficency as a percentage of tonnage recovery over a period of time. Shallow pit areas with 15 feet or less overburden and pit depths of 30 feet or less have the best mining recovery. The fiscal year 1973 illustrates the influence of deeper overburden and pits on recovery efficiency and production. Details are lost in year average data presented in this fashion. During 1973, a small dragline with a 14 cubic yard bucket mined the initial 5 months in a shallow pit deposit with 10 feet of overburden and 9 feet of matrix with a tonnage recovery of 89 percent. The large dragline with a 30 cubic yard bucket commenced mining during April, 1973 in a karst area that averaged 27 feet of overburden and 10 feet of matrix. However, as it included a few small sinkholes to 90 feet deep, the resulting average recovery was 53 percent.

Table No. I

Mining Statistics

Watson Mine, Swift Agricultural Chemicals Corporation

Fiscal Year	Over-Burden	Matrix	Total	% Tonnage Recovery
1970	15	15	30	75
1971	19	14	33	69
1972	14	13	27	78
1973	19	11	30	64
1974	26	15	41	58
1975	18	11	29	71
1976	21	14	35	64
1977	17	12	29	69
1978	22	11	33	65
1979	25	11	36	71

HYDROLOGY

Vertical turbine and submersible pump waterjacks are conventional methods of controlling groundwater seepage in the
mine pits. However, at Watson Mine, the draglines have advanced into the karst terrain. In this locale, the pit bottom limestone, Hawthorne Formation, is the artesian Upper
Floridan aquifer. Transmissivity through the aquifer averages some 2,200 square feet per day, but solution cavity development in the limestone causes wide fluctuations from that
value. The altitude of the potentiometric surface from the
limestone is sufficient to influence the surficial aquifer
level in the overburden, particularily in the surface depressions underlain by sinkholes. Productivity is adversely
affected as mining proceeds into sinkholes filled with thick,
wet overburden and subject to the influx of artesian groundwater from the pit bottom limestone.

Through the efforts of the Swift operating personnel, the
potentiometric surface of the Upper Floridan aquifer is being
reduced in selected mining areas by gravity connector wells.
The result has been dewatering of the surficial aquifer in
the overburden and partial dewatering of the pit bottom limestone. In this case, the dewatered overburden was prestripped by scraper pans to a designed depth in preparation for
mining.

KARST MINING TERRAIN

An aerial view of the mining area in the karst terrain of
Sections 31 and 32, T31S, R26E is shown in Figure No. 5. Route
U.S. 98 Highway is the east/west line along the north section
line. The road turns south along the east section line of
Section 32. Mining cut layout lines are superimposed as over-
lays on the aerial for mine planning purposes.

Mining in Section 32 commenced with the 30 cubic yard bucket dragline in April, 1973, but terminated in March, 1974 as
the result of poor pit conditions and declining productivity.
The dragline moved to a shallow pit area in Section 31. This
photograph was made in 1976, the dragline is located in the
left middle ground.

Connector Well Construction

Gravity connector dewatering wells are identified as dots
on the aerial view. The three wells are located in Section

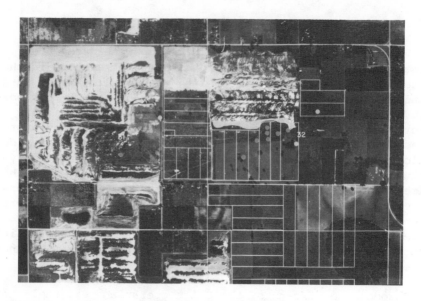

Figure No. 5
Aerial View Karst Terrain

31 in a line of sinkholes dewatered during the first experimental phase. The well in the center of the three was the initial test well, December, 1975, identified as Site 93 in the hydrologic studies by Hutchinson. (3) The construction of all the wells is by cable tool drilling. Casing used was standard black steel pipe, Api-5L, threaded, coupled and welded. As an example, at Site 93 an 8 inch hole is drilled and cased from the surface to 86 feet through the overburden and matrix, then seated in limestone. The 8 inch hole continued as an uncased hole through 30 feet of Hawthorne limestone intersecting several solution cavities. Underlying the Hawthorne is the Tampa Formation, a blue-green clay aquiclude 105 feet thick, which is cased off with a 6 inch pipe. The hole is continued as a 6 inch, uncased hole through the Suwannee and Ocala Group limestones into the dolomitic, caverous Avon Park limestone. The hole bottomed at 855 feet. In January, 1976 the artesian water level in the Hawthorne stood at 33 feet below the surface, the artesian level of the Avon Park Limestone was 66 feet. Therefore, the artesian water of the Hawthorne limestone adjusts to the differential of 33 feet and flows by gravity into the Avon Park Limestone. By February 11, 1976, a monitor well into Hawthorne limestone

located 700 feet west of the connector well had dewatered 8 feet in 14 days.

Hydraulic Data

Before the initial well was drilled through the base of the Hawthorne, a pump test was conducted. Hydraulic data on a 200 gallon per minute test is as follows: Transmissivity at 8,800 square feet per day, hydraulic conductivity of 83 feet per day with a storage factor of 0.18×10^3. (3) A geophysics logging survey on the well in March, 1977 reported a gravity flow rate of 528 gallons per minute into the solution cavities of the Avon Park limestone.

FIELD PROBLEM

Based on the success of the principle of gravity dewatering in Section 31, a second site in Section 32 was selected. It is a sinkhole area of 28 acres located in the center of the section and the point where the large dragline terminated production in March, 1974.

On the surface, a depression of some 20 feet drop in elevation from the surrounding terrain is underlain by the sinkhole. It is of sufficiently low relief to have contained a 5 acre lake as recent as 1957. Underlying the depression was an average overburden of 33 feet and matrix thickness of 15 feet. Due to changes in pit bottom elevation in sinks, the overburden actually varied from 24 to 68 feet and matrix varied from 9 to 23 feet thick. Prospect tonnage and grade evalution identified 300,000 short tons of 73 percent BPL, calcium phosphate content. On Figure No. 5, the area is identified by the cluster of connector wells in the center of the section.

Surface Water Problem

The mined out cuts were flooded with rainfall and groundwater seepage since March, 1974. The water depth was estimated at 20 to 25 feet deep and high enough to cause a recharge into the overburden sands and matrix exposed along the highwall of the old pit.

Soil Engineering Test and Mine Cut Geometry

An engineering test conducted by Ardaman and Associates, Orlando Florida, of the soil in the overburden and matrix indicated a pit slope failure could occur due to the high

watertable near the ground surface. The failure would occur
behind the dragline as it stripped 68 feet of overburden and
mined to an estimated depth of 100 feet.

Matrix Recovery

A graphic pit design shown in Figure No. 6, Exhibit I,
indicated matrix yardage recovery would decline to 65 percent
as slope angles would require 130 feet of horizontal distance
under the highwall. Spoil stacking volume from excessive
overburden depth would fill the mining cut and cause matrix
loss along the base of the highwall. In Figure No. 6, Exhibit
II, the above situation could be improved by dewatering and
removing 20 feet of overburden which would reduce spoil volume and the horizontal distance of the pit slope. Prestripping was then planned by the use of scraper pans which would
be available between dam building assignments.

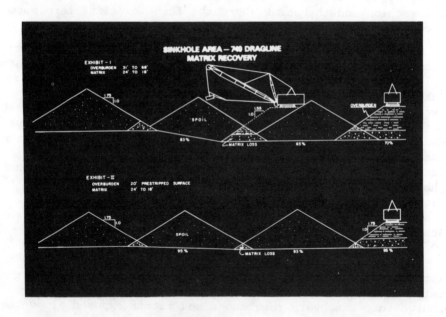

Figure No. 6
Graphic Pit Design

OPERATING PLAN

The surface water problem was the first to be eliminated.
A 22 B Dragline was placed on a bench along the north side of

the highwall. A ditch was dug combining the stored water of the east and west 1974 pits, which was pumped away with water-jacks.

Subsurface dewatering commenced in July, 1976 and by April, 1977, 8 connector wells had been drilled on the flanks and within the sinkhole. A 4 inch monitor well into the pit bottom limestone recorded a change in artesian head of the Hawthorne limestone from 34.4 feet in September, 1976 to 58.7 feet by May, 1977. Some 24 feet of water had been removed from the limestone under 14 acres in the center of the surface depression.

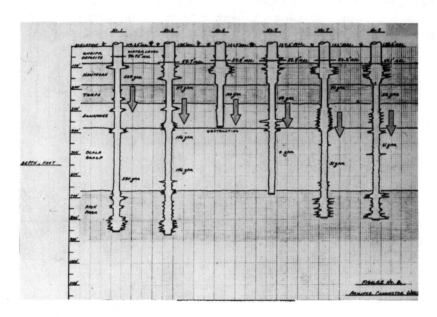

Figure No. 7
Geophysics Profile

Geophysics

The geophysics well surveys were conducted by CH2M Hill Inc. The well logs were run on 5 of the connector wells during the drilling project. The survey included electric, gamma ray, caliper, temperature, fluid conductance, and fluid velocity by the spinner flow meter. Water samples were collected at selected depths using a motorized depth sampler. The survey was designed to determine the hydrologic units penetrated by the wells, identify the dewatering and recharged zones, and determine the quantity and quality of the water flowing down the connector well from the Hawthorne limestone. Figure No. 7 shows the solution cavities in the Hawthorne limestone, a minor solution cavity development in the Suwannee limestone, and the solution cavities in the Avon Park limestone. The dewatering rates in this sinkhole ranged from 40 to 117 gallons per minute. Well No. 1, the initial well, was drilled in December, 1975.

Plugging Procedures

The connector wells were plugged within a week prior to the dragline advance through the well location. For example, the plugging record of well No. 6 as shown on Figure No. 7 is as follows: 20 feet of neat cement plugs were placed at intervals from 80 to 100 feet, at the contact of the matrix and pit bottom limestone, from 140 to 160 feet at the base of the Hawthorne, from 280 to 300 feet at the top of the Suwannee limestone, and 810 to 830 feet in the upper part of the Avon Park limestone. A clean limestone gravel backfill is placed between the cement plug sections and from 830 to 872 at the bottom of the hole.

Table II
Water Analysis (in ppm.)

pH	5.9	–	8.3
P	1.8	–	0.25
F	0.8	–	0.40
SO_4	14.0	–	4.0
NH_3	4.3	–	0.03
Fe	0.06	–	2.0 (unfiltered)
Mg	8.6	–	6.5
Ca	10.4	–	13.5
K	0.9	–	0.2
Na	2.3	–	2.5
Cl	5.6	–	14.3
Alkalinity as $CaCO_3$	20.0	–	70.0

Water Quality

Table II represents the range of water quality analyses
during the period March, 1976 to April, 1979 in 23 wells drilled to date.

These chemical analyses are reported monthly to the Southwest Florida Water Management District which permits the drilling, recording, and plugging of connector wells in the district.

Influence of Dewatering

The results of dewatering is shown in the profile on Figure No. 8. The change in artesian head from the Hawthorne
limestone between October, 1976 to June, 1977 with respect
to the elevation of the overburden, matrix and pit bottom
limestone. Figure No. 9 is the sinkhole profile showing the
change in the elevation of the watertable in the overburden.
In order to speed up this natural dewatering rate, screened
wells were installed in the overburden. Their influence is
shown as cusps on the watertable surface. The screen sections were set at 35 to 55 feet below the surface specifically
to dewater the overburden sands. Screen openings were in the
range of 10 to 24 thousandths of an inch and reinforced with
perforated PVC to permit cable tool drilling through the section into the Avon Park Limestone.

By March, 1977, the watertable had declined sufficiently
to commence overburden stripping by scraper pans. In six
weeks, 340,000 yards of dewatered overburden had been removed
to an average depth of 15 feet.

MINING EXPERIENCE

When the dragline entered the west flank of the sinkhole
in July, 1977, it walked and operated on the prestripped surface as easily as a natural ground surface. The watertable
in the overburden had declined 38 feet below the original
ground surface which was 23 feet below the prestripped surface.

Mining progressed through the sinkhole on plan as shown
in Figure No. 5 from July through November, 1977. The matrix
yardage recovered was 570,000 cubic yards at an 82 percent
recovery. Directly over the deepest portion of the sinkhole,

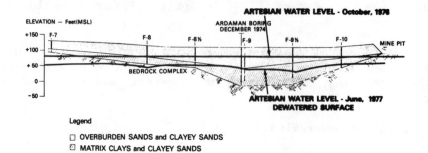

GEOLOGIC CROSS SECTION OF AREA TO BE MINED

Section 32, Township 31 South, Range 26 East

Figure No. 8
Reduction of Artesian Head

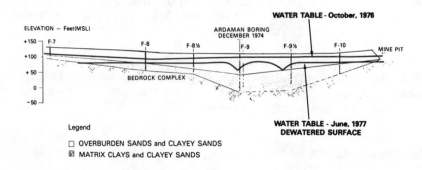

GEOLOGIC CROSS SECTION OF AREA TO BE MINED

Section 32, Township 31 South, Range 26 East

Figure No. 9
Reduction of Watertable

a 14 acre area, overburden after prestripping averaged 28
feet and matrix averaged 20 feet. In this specific area,
matrix yardage recovered was 300,000 cubic yards at a 71 percent recovery.

During March, 1974, the pit condition entering the sinkhole caused mine production to decline from 17,000 to 10,000
short tons per week as tonnage recovery reduced from 48 percent to 32 percent. In July, 1977 at approximately the same
location in the sinkhole, mine production was 19,500 short
tons per week as tonnage recovery averaged 65 percent. The
pit condition had improved significantly, note Figure No. 10.
During the month the dragline operated on the prestripped
surface, it stripped an additional 28 feet of overburden and
mined 20 feet of matrix. Water in the pit was minimal from
overburden groundwater seepage. Artesian springs did not
occur from the pit when the Hawthorne limestone was exposed
after matrix extraction. The spoil stacks were dry, but some
excessive volume covered 10 to 15 percent of the matrix yardage in the pit.

In order to achieve ground stability for scraper pan work
and mining, 8 gravity connector wells were drilled over 800
feet into the Avon Park limestone. Dewatering rates ranged
from 40 to 117 gallons per minute. The wells operated an
average of 192 days for a total time of 1,540 days to remove
185 million gallons of groundwater. The groundwater level
within the sediments overlying the pit bottom limestone declined 42 feet below the original ground surface which in
turn was lowered to greater than 50 feet by pit waterjack.

The effects of dewatering on pit geometry and matrix yardage recovery are shown on Figure No. 11. During 1974, the
high watertable in the overburden caused a 3:1 pit slope and
precludes efficient mining recovery. A dashed line shows the
actual pit geometry after dewatering effort in July of 1977.

Pit Wall Failure

Mining in deep pit areas is a constant hazard. Early in
the morning of September 13, 1977, a pit wall failure occurred
up to the tub of the dragline. It appeared that pit wall failure occurred when the weak layers of matrix were mined as found
in the test hole drilling of 1974 at depths of 88 to 94 feet.
This test found varied types of loose to dense clayey sands
in 70 feet of overburden and two weak zones within the 54 feet
of matrix at the 88 to 94 foot and the 118 to 122 foot

Figure No. 10
Improved Deep Pit Condition

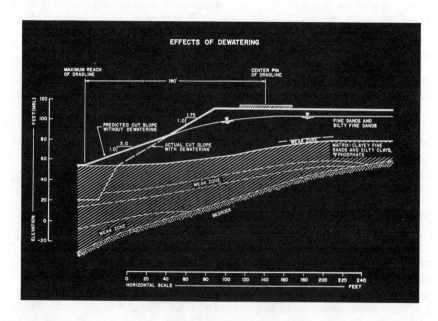

Figure No. 11
Effects of Dewatering

intervals. A dewatering well drilled 100 feet west of this test location, designed to relieve the artesian groundwater pressure in the bedrock limestone, found 80 feet of overburden and 115 feet of matrix to the top of the Tampa Clay Formation. The Hawthorne limestone bedrock was not found in 195 feet of drilling from the surface. The soils test of 9/15/77 was drilled two days after the pit slope failure. The overburden was 40 feet deep with a matrix thickness of 30 feet. Two weak zones were located at 30 to 40 feet and at 55 to 60 feet, see Figure No. 12.

The weak layers of 88 to 94 foot interval of test 12/74 and 55 to 60 foot interval of the test 9/77 are considered continuous and sloping parallel to the. bedrock. The predicted failure by sliding wedge and bishop circular analysis resemble the failure surface. As mining removed the overburden and matrix to the depths of 80-85 feet, the soil mass above this weak zone slid down slope along the plane of failure.

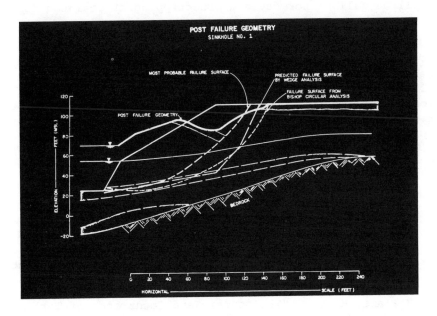

Figure No. 12
Pit Wall Failure

Immediately following the pit wall failure, the dragline retreated about 100 feet to firm ground along the cut line. Mining continued after the engineering test drilling to a depth of 70 feet. This incident confirmed earlier test results that dewatering and prestripping would prevent ground failure from occurring behind the dragline causing it to slide into the pit.

SUMMARY

   In summary, the application of subsurface and surface dewatering is essential to .open   pit mine drainage control in the deep sinkhole areas at Watson Mine. Gravity connector wells have dewatered the surficial aquifer in the overburden and reduced the artesian head in the pit bottom limestone. The effect has been improved matrix yardage recovery, productivity, and dragline safety.

   Prior to the dewatering and prestripping application in mine planning, the production rate in the sinkhole mining area was 1,700 short tons per acre mined, after preparation in 1977, the production rate was 4,700 short tons per acre mined. Based on the success of two field experiments, current mining areas are being dewatered with connector wells at a rate of 3 million gallons per day and prestripping at designed depths in the overburden is a continuous operation.

ACKNOWLEDGEMENTS

   The author wishes to thank the management of Swift Agricultural Chemicals Corporation for their support and permission to publish this paper. A special thanks is extended to Mr. David H. Barnett, Mining Manager, for support and supervision during the project. The author gratefully acknowledges Mr. David R. Spedden, metallurgist, for his many suggestions and critical review of this paper.

REFERENCES

1. Altschuler, Z. S., Cathcart, J. B. and Young, E. J., "Geology and Geochemistry of the Bone Valley Formation and Its Phosphate Deposits, West Central Florida", A Guide Book for Field Trip No. 6, Geological Society of America, November, 1964, pp 18-19

2. Zellars, M. E. , "The Genesis and Occurrence of Tertiary Phosphorites in the Southeastern United States". Mining Engineering Issn 0026-5187, December, 1978, pp 1655-1656.

3. Hutchinson, C. B., "Appraisal of Shallow Groundwater Resources and Management Alternatives in the Upper Peace and Eastern Alafia River Basins, Florida", February 1978 Water Resources Investigations 77-124 pp 22-25.

22

Some Technical Aspects of Open Pit Mine Dewatering

by V. Straskraba, Senior Mining Hydrogeologist,
Dames & Moore,
Denver, Colorado, USA

INTRODUCTION

In recent years the increase in development of new open pit mines, especially in the Western U.S., is evident. Most of the mining activity is concentrated on open pit mines for coal and uranium. Practically all of these mines have to deal with ground water problems either before, during or after mining. The presence of water in a mine has adverse effects on mine production, slope stability, safety, pollution control and therefore mining cost.

The efficiency of well designed and implemented dewatering of mines before and during mining, has been proven in many open pit mines worldwide (1)(2)(3)(4). The cost savings on the mining operations in these cases were substantial. Surprisingly, there are few published papers or textbooks dealing with the designed implementation of mine dewatering.

MINE DEWATERING METHODS

Because of the title and scope of this paper, the more feasible methods of open pit mine dewatering in typical geological conditions of the Western U.S. will be discussed. Following is a listing of these basic dewatering methods:

- Drainage ditches at the surface of the mine
- Drainage ditches at the bottom of the mine
- Horizontal drains
- Vertical wells drilled from the surface
- Vertical wells drilled from benches or pit bottom
- Dewatering shafts and galleries
- Combination of above listed methods

Selection of the proper method of dewatering is crucial to the success of the operation and depends on several factors discussed in the following section.

DEWATERING METHOD SELECTION

The proper and most feasible dewatering method depends upon the following factors:

- geology and hydrogeology of the mine site
- scope of dewatering
- mining method
- cost study

The hydrogeologic investigation of the mine site should be the basis for every dewatering design. Without knowledge of aquifer characteristics like recharge area, general flow direction, thickness and hydraulic conductivity, an efficient dewatering system is difficult to design and implement. The character of primary or secondary aquifer permeability, (intergranular or fractures) is important. Orientation of fracture system in an aquifer with secondary vertical or horizontal permeability can cause success or failure of a dewatering system.

There is a substantial difference in dewatering of confined and unconfined aquifers, especially regarding slope stability. Before the design of an open pit mine dewatering system, an estimate of water inflow into the pit should be performed.

Part of the hydrogeologic study should be the installation of a proper groundwater monitoring system capable of observing the oscillation of water levels; this monitoring system should be installed before the dewatering system is implemented and maintained during the entire mining operation. The fact that water is flowing from horizontal drains which have been installed for stability reasons does not mean that the pore pressure has been sufficiently relieved in strata which is detrimental to slope stability.

The scope of open pit mine dewatering may vary in individual projects. In cases where the ground water inflow into the pit is not high enough to impede the mining activity but high pore pressure in the water bearing strata affects slope stability or slope design, dewatering is oriented toward lowering the potentiometric surface within the zone of potential failures. This may be achieved without draining a great amount of water. Another reason for mine dewatering may be groundwater quality protection. By pumping water from vertical wells, the pollution of water that would otherwise seep into the pit and be pumped out from the sump, can be prevented.

In most cases, and typically in the Western U.S., the reason for mine dewatering would be a combination of the following (with decreasing emphasis as listed):

- improved slope stability
- improved mining conditions
- groundwater quality protection

The mining method to be employed in a new mine or as practiced in an existing mine is also a factor to be considered in a mining dewatering design. Drainage of temporary walls should be different from that of final pit walls. The degree of desired "drying" of the pit bottom depends on the type of equipment used for excavation.

The last, but not the least important, of the factors to be considered for selection of the dewatering method is the cost. Dewatering should be economically advantageous, resulting in steeper and safe pit slopes, higher production of rubber-tired equipment and better working conditions in the pit. The cost of design and implementation of dewatering should always be the dominant factor. There are known cases in the western U.S. where mine operators spent considerable amounts of money to deal with frequent slope failures rather than to spend a lesser amount on mine dewatering. I visited two underground coal

mines in Wyoming and New Mexico where mine superintendents admitted loss of production from 30 to 35 percent of
total production due to water inflow into the mine.
In both cases the drainage of the mines would have been
relatively simple and certainly cost effective.

SOME TECHNICAL ASPECTS OF DEWATERING METHODS

Following is a detailed discussion of some practical
aspects of the dewatering methods that appear to be
feasible in typical hydrogeological conditions of the
Western U.S.

Drainage Ditches at Surface

This relatively inexpensive method is applicable,
mostly together with surface water drainage, when the
aquifer to be dewatered is shallow. In this system, water
from the ditches around the perimeter of the mine is
typically collected at the lowest point in a sump and
pumped out. From European experience (4) this method is
most effective with aquifers 6 to 10 feet thick at a depth
to 60 feet and with hydraulic conductivity of 6-20 feet
per day.

An alternative to this method is to fill a drainage
ditch, which completely penetrates an aquifer, with
bentonite slurry to eliminate the flow toward the mine.
This method has not yet been used in the Western U.S., to
my knowledge, but could be considered applicable in highly
permeable aquifers such as alluvial deposits.

A typical schematic example of a surface drainage ditch
is shown in Figure No. 1.

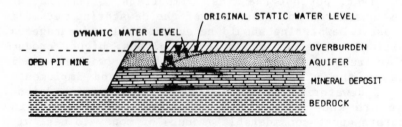

FIGURE 1. DEWATERING BY THE MEANS OF SURFACE DITCHES

DRAINAGE DITCHES AT THE BOTTOM OF THE PIT

A technique similar to that used for ditches at the surface of the pit can be used at the pit bottom. The difference is mostly in the type of aquifer to be dewatered. While surface ditches are mostly applied to drain unconfined aquifers, bottom ditches are used to drain confined aquifers. Maintenance of this type of ditch is more difficult than for surface ditches. The purpose of the ditches, as shown in Figure No. 2, is not only to accomplish drawdown of the potentiometric surface in the pit walls but also below the pit floor. Maximum efficiency is achieved when the ditches can fully penetrate the thickness of the aquifer; but this is often difficult to accomplish. In many practical cases it is difficult to draw down the potentiometric surface beneath the pit bottom in the central part of the pit (as shown in Figure 2).

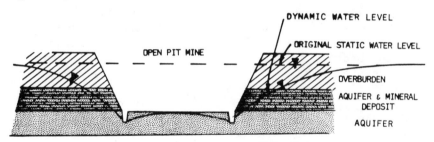

FIGURE 2. DEWATERING BY THE MEANS OF BOTTOM PIT DITCHES

HORIZONTAL DRAINS

Installation of horizontal drains (See Figure No. 3) in an aquifer affecting the stability of a slope in an open pit mine is a very efficient means of dewatering. The main advantage is a relatively low installation cost, no energy consumption for water discharge and low maintenance cost.

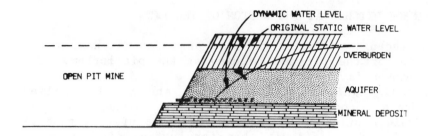

FIGURE 3. DEWATERING BY THE MEANS OF HORIZONTAL DRAINS

The principal limitation in the use of horizontal drains is the fact that it can be economically installed only after the completion of an excavation rather ahead of excavation. In many cases the time necessary for installation of an effective horizontal drainage system is sufficient for the occurrence of a slope failure.

Horizontal drains can be installed in most types of aquifers and are highly efficient in confined aquifers with high pore pressures. They are also the best means of dewatering bedrock aquifers with a well developed vertical fracture system.

Typically, horizontal drains consist of 1 1/2 to 2 inch PVC slotted pipe installed inside the drill rods. In most cases, for slope stability protection, drains 250 to 500 feet deep are sufficient. Hydraulic and economic efficiency sharply decrease with drains deeper than 400 to 500 feet; therefore, deeper drains should be installed only in special cases. The deepest horizontal drains ever installed by the author were over 800 feet deep in relatively difficult geological conditions.

The size of slots in the PVC pipe should be designed according to the drained material. From practical experience, a maximum slot size which would allow discharge of a reasonable amount of sand particles, should be used, especially in cases where chemical incrustation in the pipe can occur.

The drains can be drilled from the bottom of the pit or from a bench, but always from the lowest part of the aquifer to be drained. The drains should be installed at a gentle upslope angle (1 - 5 degree) for the following reasons:

- minimal hydraulic losses
- water does not freeze at the drain mouth so easily
- elimination of drill rod bending effect as per following discussion

During the drilling of horizontal drains the hole is bent down by the weight of drill pipes. Zaruba (5) states that a drain at a depth of approximately 200 feet, can deflect 7 to 10 feet. The opposite effect can also occur. From my personal experience, the drain can be bent drastically up by application of excessive pressure during drilling by a driller who is paid by the foot. During one installation of a 600-foot deep drain at a 3 degree upslope angle in coal waste materials, the drill pipe and bit bent to a 90 degree angle and broke the ground surface about 250 feet above the elevation of the drilling. Similar circumstances can explain why many drains installed without the supervision of an experienced engineer are discharging much less water than calculated. The cost of an experienced supervisor is, in my opinion, well justified. In an average installation of 600 feet of drains per day, the cost of supervision is only about $0.8 per foot. The actual average cost for installing 1 1/2 inch PVC horizontal drain is between $8 and $10 per linear foot.

Drilling of downslope drains downslope is also used (7)(9), but for the above mentioned reasons is recommended only in cases where there is high incrustation potential of drained water.

From a practical point of view, drains are usually installed in a fan-shaped layout, typically four to six drains fanning from one location. This setup is advantageous because of easier preparation of the drilling pad, less time for drill rig movement and also because it means a simpler water discharge collection system.

Proper design of a dewatering system by means of horizontal drains is necessary. The calculation of distances between drains, depth of drains and average discharge from drains should be based on a good knowledge of hydrogeologic characteristics of the site.

Vertical Wells Drilled from the Surface

Dewatering by means of vertical wells (See Figure No. 4) drilled from the surface is a common mine drainage practice (1)(4)(6). The water from the wells can be discharged by pumping, gravity flow or artesian flow. In most case, submersible type pumps are utilized in vertical perimeter wells.

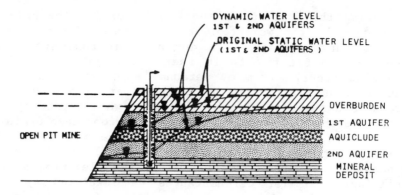

FIGURE 4a DEWATERING BY THE MEANS OF VERTICAL WELLS FROM SURFACE

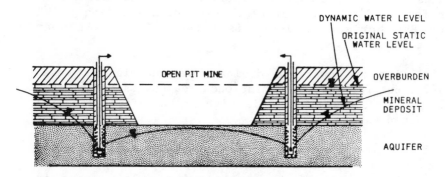

FIGURE 4b DEWATERING BY THE MEANS OF VERTICAL WELLS FROM SURFACE

The major advantages of such systems are the possibility of dewatering ahead of pit excavation, prevention of water pollution and practically no interference with the mining operation. Also, the possibility of draining several aquifers with a single well is not readily achieved with the other methods discussed.

Disadvantages of this method are the cost of energy limitations in drawdown achieved and cost effectiveness in dewatering more impervious aquifers. From experience in dewatering unconfined aquifers in unconsolidated materials in open pit coal mines (6) it is possible to accomplish drawdown of only about 65 to 85 percent of the saturated thickness of the water bearing strata. Other experience (4) shows that cost effective dewatering by pumping the water from vertical wells is feasible when the hydraulic conductivity of the drained strata is not less than about 10 feet/day for unconfined aquifers and not less than about 1.0 to 1.6 feet/day for confined aquifers. Attempts to use vertical wells to dewater a bedrock aquifer with predominantly secondary permeability caused by vertical fractures usually result in failure.

The scope of dewatering wells is different from a water supply well because the well yield is not as important as the drawdown achieved. The spacing of dewatering wells is therefore different from that of water supply wells. The optimum distance between dewatering wells is calculated from the results of aquifer tests usually performed during the hydrogeologic investigation. The second well should be placed within the steep part of the cone of depression developed by pumping the first well. As a rule (6), the effective radius of dewatering of a well is usually equal to one-third of the radius of influence of the pumped well.

For most vertical dewatering wells, the water supply well technology is applied. Five- to six-inch PVC casing with slots or PVC screen and proper gravel pack in drained materials are usually used. The cost to drill, install and properly develop a dewatering well to a depth of about 600 feet is in the range of $15 to 18 per foot, including the cost of supervision, which amounts to approximately $2 per foot.

Vertical Wells Drilled from Benches or Pit Bottom

Most of the technical aspects discussed in previous sections are valid for wells drilled from pit benches or pit bottom. The advantage of locating dewatering wells at a lower elevation is reduction of pumping head, and therefore lower energy costs. Limitations are more difficult access to the drilling locations and inter- ference with mining operations.

In cases of water seepage from an aquifer located beneath the pit floor (8), pressure relief wells can be drilled at the pit bottom. Such wells relieve excessive hydraulic pressure without the necessity of pumping.

Dewatering Shafts and Galleries

Because of the high cost of dewatering shafts and galleries, this method is usually applied only in complicated hydrogeologic conditions where other dewatering means are not effective. In the sedimentary coal and uranium deposits of the Western U.S., dewatering shafts and galleries are not used in open pit mine dewatering. A conservative estimate is that dewatering galleries are at least five times more expensive than drainage borings (5).

Combination of Various Dewatering Methods

In many dewatering projects, a combination of two or more previously discussed dewatering methods have been used. In this way, the advantages of various dewatering methods may be combined. For example, with initial dewatering by means of vertical wells before mining activities begin, safe and effective excavation can be achieved. In a later phase of mining, a series of horizontal drains may be installed on the final pit walls to eliminate the necessity of energy consuming pumping.

In every case the mine dewatering design must be based on the knowledge of site hydrogeology and on an overall cost study.

REFERENCES

1. Loofbourow, R.L., and Brittain, R.L., "Dewatering Through Wells before Mine Development." Mining Congress Tour., July, 1964, pp. 43 - 50.

2. Brealey, S.C., "Ground Water Control in Opencast Mining", Proceedings of Symp. on Opencast Mining, Inst. of Mining and Met., November, 1964, pp. 390 - 415.

3. Stubbins, J.B., and Munro, P., "Open Pit Mine Dewatering Knob Lake", Canadian Ins. of Mining and Met. Bully, August, 1965, pp. 229 - 237.

4. Abramov, S.K., and Skirgello, O.B., "Methods, Systems and Calculations of Underground and Open Pit Mines

Dewatering", Nedra Publishing Co., Moscow, 1968, p. 254. (Original in Russian).

5. Zaruba, Q., and Mencl, V., "Landslides and Their Control", Elsevier Pub. Co., Prague, 1969, p. 193.

6. Kamenskij, G.N., Klimentov, R.R., and Ovcinikov, A.M., "Hydrogeology of Mineral Deposits", SMTL, Prague, 1957, p. 298. (Translated from Russian).

7. Abrao, P.C., "Open Pit Mine Slopes-Drainage Through Horizontal Boreholes", Proceedings, Water in Mining and Underground Works, Granada, Spain, 1978, Volume 1, pp. 573 - 583.

8. Brawner, C.O., "Rock Mechanics in Open Pit Mining", Presented at Geotechnical Factors in Mining, Berkeley, California, March, 1976, Volume 2.

23

Drainage of Coal and Lignite Mines

by Rafael Fernández-Rubio,
Professor of Hydrogeology,
University of Granada,
Granada, Spain

INTRODUCTION

The presence of water in mines, and the complications it causes, is a problem that has taxed all concerned since mining began. In early years the miner had to use his ingenuity, since he suffered from a lack of technology and of equipment. Today, the decisive factor in drainage is often economic, especially when the maximum production of coal compatible with minimum water risk is required.

On the other hand, the demand for coal has increased greatly in recent years, primarily as a result of the oil crisis. Furthermore, this increased demand occurred precisely at a moment when, in many countries, coal mining was going into a recession.

This increase in the demand for coal caused further hydrological problems, brought about by a number of factors including the need: to exploit new mines in a short space of time; to reopen others long-since abandoned and in many cases flooded; to deepen existing workings, or to open up more complex areas of coal deposits, below the natural water table.

At the same time, however, the need to combat inflow of water became pressing just at the moment when the importance of the preservation of the environment became a vital public issue. Any drainage process in mines inevitably affects the environment, since it reduces the yield of existing springs and produces waste water that is often polluted.

Thus the influence of mining on existing groundwater systems, the immense amount of water needed to operate the installations used to treat the coal, and the large quantities of residual water that such treatment produces--all are factors intrinsic to coal exploitation and so such mining plays a special part in questions of water economy.

Therefore, there are great risks involved in dealing with a broad and at the same time complex subject such as drainage in coal and lignite mines. I am fully aware of these dangers and I know that this is a task, not for one specialist, but for a full team of highly qualified experts. I would therefore like to point out that this chapter aims merely to present a general survey of the problem--including a presentation of the methodology of the most commonly used drainage systems--based on direct personal knowledge or on evidence gained from the bibliography I have consulted.

It should be made quite clear from the start that, despite frequent claims to the contrary, there is an extremely wide-ranging body of written work on the problem of water in mining, and within this bibliography by far the largest section is that dealing with coal mining (1). The difficulty is to cope adequately with the great dispersion of the worldwide bibliography which, until the SIAMOS Congress (2), had never been collected in one monograph.

The reader interested in these subjects will find further information in the bibliography provided at the end of this chapter. It will enable him to study in greater detail certain aspects of the problem that cannot be treated adequately in a general discussion.

FACTORS DETERMINING DRAINAGE

Lithological Factors

The problems caused by water in coal mines are extremely diverse, depending on such factors as the nature of the surrounding rocks, the existence or absence of waterproofing in the hanging wall, the degree of fracturing in the enclosing rocks, and certainly the anisotropy caused by mining (3).

We can roughly distinguish three main types of mining, arranging them according to the hydrogeological problems they originate:

1) Mining carried out in areas of nonconsolidated detritic materials with the associated problems of a possible inrush of water carrying mud and sand, or of subsidence and interconnection of the aquifers.

2) Mining in consolidated and fractured materials, where the water finds its own channels according to these structural discontinuities, and particularly in the tension fractures, which can form a connection between aquifers in the same system.

3) Mining in karstic areas where the water channels are closely related to solution processes, which in turn can determine the direction of flow (4,5).

We should add the following to these three groups, since they cause similar problems:

4) Mining in nonconsolidated materials, of whatever origin, insofar as water affects geotechnical behavior.

5) Mining in cemented detritic formations that can initiate aquifers through porosity, which in general behave isotropically.

I should point out here, however, that though we have differentiated five basic types of hydrogeological systems, according to lithology, we can of course find complex systems--a mixture of two or more of the above--and especially multilayer systems, where the aquifers are to be found between semipermeable materials.

Structural Factors

In all cases structural features play a vital role as far as water flow is concerned, since we have seen in a great number of cases that water inflow takes place primarily along structural discontinuities, such as faults and the fractures related to them (6), and especially in tension fractures. For example, the studies carried out in Dorog Mine (Hungary) demonstrated that 80% of the water inflow took place at faults; 16% in areas of fractures; and in only

4% was it impossible to establish the role played by tectonic factors (7). Thus we can see that a structural geological study is always necessary.

The flow of water toward mining works can take place downward from higher aquifers, or upward from captive underlying aquifers (8), or it can take place sideways in structural discontinuities. It is obvious that drainage systems are determined by the characteristics of this water flow.

Hydrological Factors

The waters that flow into a mine, and must therefore be drained off, are generally fed from the rainfall, or from rivers; and in these cases a "delay" may be observed, which may be for a greater or smaller period according to the hydrodynamic characteristics of the hanging wall and surface. This means that it may be necessary at times to drain very high water inflows, far above the average yield.

Hydrogeological Factors

The obvious need for adequate protection against, and subsequent drainage of, water inrushes necessitates in turn a close examination of the characteristics of the aquifer systems; especially of: the speed and direction of the water flow; the connection between the source area and the discharge area; the placing of any depressions or hollows; the barrier in the system that forms obstacles to the water flow, and so on.

Anthropic Factors

Finally, it is important to emphasize the significance of the human element, since a mine in itself forms an obvious conduit for the transference and flow of water; and to this must be added the question of the overall capacity of the working. This is particularly important when there are abandoned flooded mines near the mines still being worked and also in the rainy season, especially when the workings are relatively shallow (9).

In this respect, the systems of mine working, which are of many types, certainly determine the importance and effect of water, as well as the drainage possibilities.

On the other hand, when a mine is no longer worked it can pose a threat to active workings which will then have to bear the increased cost of drainage (10). The problems due to the closeness of old underground or open workings, or to the existence of underground aquifers (11), also occur when mines are closed down and subsequently used for storing water underground (12). Sudden inflow of water to underground workings can produce extremely dangerous situations, especially since such inrushes are sometimes accompanied by quantities of mud and sand, which can rapidly erode the rocks enclosing the working and can bring about collapse (13,14).

This influx of mud can originate in nonconsolidated materials or in the fillings of old mines, or in settling basins on the surface (15).

The drillholes, and sometimes abandoned gas or oil boreholes, which cross coal deposits are also a potential menace, because of the possible inflow of water into the mine workings.

Given all these factors, then, it is frequently necessary to take water out of mine workings in quantities even greater than those of the coal that is mined (16), and we find workings with a very high flooding coefficient (17).

As examples of what we have stated above, we can consider the following: for instance, the drainage in the coal mines of Upper Silesia (Poland), where more than 10 cubic meters per second of water is pumped; or the inrush of water in the Julia Mine in Czechoslovakia, together with 250 grams per liter of very fine sand, which took more than a month to bring under control (18). A series of accidents in collieries in England, which had a significant effect on the laws governing the measures necessary to prevent such accidents, have been described (11,19). In Great Britain the nationalization of the coal mines has led to a detailed government-financed study of the drainage systems of old mine workings.

Very detailed studies have also been carried out in the Sokolov Basin in Czechoslovakia, where the lignite workings of the Antonin Coal Field have affected the famous hot springs of Karlovy Vary, producing a drop in the water flow at the same time as the inflow of water into the mines. Again, the drainage of the Joseph Seam caused a gradual reduction in the flow of the springs. These were later restored to their full yield after the mines were flooded (20).

In this case, the water inrushes took place along fault lines and the effect could have been the result of a loss of gas (CO_2) in the water, or of a drop in the level due to long-term pumping.

In view of this, it seems that there is a clear need to carry out more detailed studies, especially in those deposits where we can foresee flooding problems. These studies should allow us to collect the maximum amount of information on technical and practical aspects of possible protective measures, within the context of the relevant geological processes and of the action of the miner himself; all of these factors determine the movement of the water.

DRAINAGE PLANNING

Basic Considerations

In general, it is impossible to work below the piezometric level unless there is a protective layer, or unless suitable techniques are used to prevent water from entering the mine workings.

Therefore, the most important task of the hydrogeologist with regard to mining is to calculate, if at all possible, the probabilities of water inflow and to draw up preventive measures, based on a detailed study of the situation, using all the technology available to applied hydrogeology. The purpose of this study is to set up the appropriate drainage system, according to the local hydrodynamic characteristics and geometry.

The fight against water is as old as mining itself; therefore, to combat possible water inrushes, coal mining has developed an advanced technology, which is adjusted to the particular circumstances of every specific case. This technology has been recorded in detail by several specialists (21). The aim of this highly developed technology is to foresee inrushes of water and to take protective measures, especially in cases of violent inflow which can have catastrophic consequences.

The methods to be employed are generally closely related to local conditions and can be classified according to the effects they have on the environment and on the length of time needed for their implementation. However, it is more usual to classify them according to whether they are defensive or offensive, that is, whether they are restricted to control or elimination of water inflow once it has occurred, reducing the damage to a minimum, or whether, on the other hand, they lead to a systematic protective action against water.

In general we distinguish between prevention and passive and active protection. We should also add the aspect defined as instantaneous protection (22).

Prevention

Preventive methods aim to prevent or delay water inflows; or to reduce their intensity. For these preventive measures to be effective, the following conditions must be fulfilled: nontectonic formations must be present, together with an impervious layer of adequate specific thickness.

In important structural discontinuities, it is necessary to leave isolating protective pillars.

Passive Protection

The oldest method of protection is the so-called passive method. This is the attempt to evacuate the water that has infiltrated the mine by means of pumping (generally progressively increasing in volume), or by closing off the flooded area, or again by sealing off the fractures through which the water has entered. The fact that this method is old does not mean that it is not used at present.

On the basis of this passive protection, it is possible to plan mining works with a predetermined safety level, which directly affects the preparation costs. We must nevertheless bear in mind that, in the event of a water inrush, these technical points of view must take second place to the risk of danger to human lives--naturally, an aspect that cannot be taken into account in economic or mathematical calculations.

The hydrogeological survey of the coalfield and its environment should provide concrete information, allowing us to judge the degree of danger from possible inflows. The aim is to prevent those inflows that can have catastrophic results, and to do this by means of an adequately planned protective system.

Active Protection

The active protection system is based on an attempt to influence the piezometric level in the surroundings of the mine in such a way that the workings are not threatened by any water inflow.

In general, the technique is to reduce the water pressure by means of pumping from wells. This technique is especially effective in tectonic or karstified zones, or in deposits with no protective layer or one that has limited influence.

Owing to the fact that the volume of water to be drained is considerable, it is necessary to prepare active protection systems some time ahead; they should also be continued while the mine is being worked, which means that they are particularly costly, especially if we take into account the extent of the area that has to be protected and the costs of maintaining the system.

The active protection system also has a considerable and quite long-lasting effect on the hydrological balance. Thus there comes about a regional influence on the hydrological surroundings that can cause environmental disturbances—which at the present time are of great public concern. For this reason the use of this method of protection must be very carefully planned.

Instantaneous Protection

There is a constant drive to implement new protective methods that will incorporate the advantages of the methods previously described while avoiding their disadvantages. Kapolyi, for example, has described a method that he calls "instantaneous" (22). This method does not attempt to eliminate the water by means of regional drainage, but rather by means of a partial reduction in pressure, effected by local drainage works in the area immediately surrounding the mine works. In this case, the volume of water to be drained is considerably less than that involved in the active protection method; at the same time, the water inflows are not so intense as those that can occur in a system of passive protection. The volume of water drained and the changes that have to be made in the aquifers are also less significant. According to this method, the preventive work needed to raise the water, and to reduce water pressure, is carried out in the area of the mine, with no delay.

Instantaneous protection offers the possibility of using the changes in the state of the lithological materials as a factor that can impede the transport of liquids, since the size of interstices in the rock and the corresponding possibilities of water flow clearly depend on the mechanical state of the rock. It is well known that as regards the state of pressure of liquids in situ some strata are porous, but as the water pressure is reduced, so is the porosity. It is even more obvious that impervious rocks become pervious and water-carrying as a result of fracturing. So we have to take into account the correlation existing between these two means, as regards the state of the rock as well as that of the water, since the degree of porosity and water conductivity govern the existence and movement of fluids. As these factors vary with time, we should consider them as stochastic processes.

Comparison of the Various Methods

In order to make a comparison between the various methods as to their effectiveness in affording protection against water, Kapolyi undertakes a theoretical study, though with a practical slant, of all the essential factors that can be involved in the problem. He does this in such a way that his method of calculation can be applied to a specific model.

Starting from the establishment of a mathematical model, he develops a numerical analysis that allows him to study the volume of water that enters mining works protected by:

a) the passive protection method;

b) the active method with a lowering in the piezometric level;

c) the instantaneous protection method.

He reaches the conclusion that the costs of the various protection methods depend on the infiltration factor; this presumably means that there is an optimum situation for the application of each of the three systems respectively.

The planning of work by the instantaneous method, and its implementation, clearly gives rise to problems that are much more complex than those posed by the active or passive methods. For the passive method, it is necessary to know only the immediate surroundings; and for the active method we need to take into consideration the behavior of the whole water layer. For the instantaneous method, however, we have to take into account both the above factors, and give equal importance to each.

Practical Considerations

We must always remember that any mining activity changes the characteristics of the rock formations where it takes place. So, even if there is a protective layer, any fracturing of the rocks, and especially due to tension, will favor the movement of water; the presence of water will in turn produce changes in the pressures of the strata, having a direct effect on its geotechnical behavior (23).

One complex problem that generally occurs in any preventive treatment is to determine the proper thickness of the hanging wall protective layer placed between the mine workings and the aquifers (24). Experience has shown that a specific thickness of at least 1.5 meters per atmosphere is needed to achieve an efficient protection (17), providing there are no faults that may be particularly suitable for the flow of water.

In the working of new coal resources under the sea, in the deposit found to the east of Durham (England) with a roof formation of Permian dolomites, a protective layer of 100 meters has been left; this gives an adequate safety margin. As a matter of course, the position of the Permian and of the adjacent aquifers is determined by means of core drilling (25).

The size of crown pillar has led on occasion to economic difficulties that have proved insoluble (26).

As regards room and pillar mining under the sea, special precautions are needed as far as the dimensions of the pillars, the thickness of the protective layer, the length of the working faces, and so on, are concerned (28).

Furthermore, when there are boreholes that can connect the deposit with aquifers, a protective pillar is needed around these holes, and this may mean the loss of an important amount of coal. So it is most desirable to seal off these abandoned boreholes. Gas is occasionally used as a tracer to check the effectiveness of this sealing (28).

If older workings with voids are found above the new working, coal washing plant slimes can be injected, from boreholes, to form a sealing screen.

The methods used to combat water when an inflow has occurred are very wide-ranging, particularly in underground mining. They include: the construction of filtering dams; the drilling of boreholes for injection; the establishment of a drainage station; the cleaning of the area and extraction of sand, and so on (13, 14).

Underground dams can also be used to create a series of water storage containments when we are dealing with an operating mine that has large mined out areas with many water inflow sources. A detailed knowledge of fissure systems is needed for the correct design of these dams; and this knowledge should include not only the degree of porosity but also the mechanical properties of the rock in question (29).

Dams to seal off water inflow can be built in underground workings, and they have been used in different situations with varying degrees of success. Filtering dams have been used when dealing with water inflows containing a considerable volume of solids in suspension. In general the problem is to establish adequate stability conditions to resist the water pressure. This is one aspect of the careful selection of an appropriate site for the dam emplacement and of a well-adjusted relation to the water pressure, the tensions of the surrounding rocks, and the geomechanical characteristics of the rocks, apart from injections that seal the retraction fissures with cement. The bibliography on this subject is extensive (30, 31, 32, 33, 34, 35, 36).

In the case of shaft excavation with water problems, we often use preliminary sealing injections, through boreholes, and sometimes high pressure injections of chemical products in liquid state that form a solid and sealing barrier by means of catalysis in the surrounding formations. This system has been successfully used in flooded pits in Australian coal mines, worked at a depth of 180 meters under Lake Macquaire (37), and in other mines. The necessary complement to this method is still the installation of appropriate pumping systems (38).

In any case exploratory boreholes should always be drilled, sometimes from a concrete dam at the front of a gallery (39). This is particularly advisable in workings that are rendered especially difficult by the presence of water.

The recovery of flooded workings and the rescue of trapped miners gives rise to extremely complex working conditions (40). For this reason, the experience that has been gained by specialists should serve as a guideline in the adoption of adequate precautionary measures, designed to reduce such risks.

Despite the obvious technological complexity of drainage, the economic outlay needed for establishing an adequate protection system is very profitable, if we take into account the economic advantages that arise from efficient drainage. This is particularly true if one considers the fact that any inflow of water not only represents an immediate expense, but also brings with it a drop in production and, occasionally, the forced abandonment of the working.

We should not forget, however, that it is not only financial resources that we need in order to solve these drainage problems: an adequate intellectual investment is also vital. So we should really take to heart Niels Bohr's well-known phrase: "Gentlemen, we are poor; so we must think."

REFERENCES

1. Fernández-Rubio, R. "Investigaciones hidrogeológicas aplicadas a la minería y trabajos subterráneos." Water in Mining and Underground Works. SIAMOS Proceedings. Granada, 1979. 3: 1,435-1,452.

2. "Water in mining and underground works." Asociación Nacional de Ingenieros de Minas. SIAMOS Proceedings. Granada, 1978-79. 3 volumes. 1,550 pp.

3. Saul, J. "Current mine drainage problems." The Mining Engineer. August 1970. 643-657.

4. Willems, T., and Dallos, I. "Investigations of water flow in the matrix of Dorog Coal Field by means of chemical tracers." Publications Hungarian Research Institute for Mining. 1962. 6:115-123.

5. Fernández-Rubio, R. "Introduction a l'hydrogéologie de mines dans des formations karstiques." Le Karst, son originalité physique, son importance économique. Association de Géologues du Sud-Ouest. France (in press).

6. Tettamanti, T. "Hydrological and hydraulic characteristics of water flowing from fissured carbonate rocks into mines." Hydrology of Fractured Rocks. Proceedings of the Dubrovnik Symposium. AIHS. October 1965. 73: 105-118.

7. Schmieder, A. "Développment et résultats de la protection contre l'eau karstique et les nappes captives." Publications Hungarian Mining Research Institute. Budapest, 1969. 12: 33-43.

8. Fernández-Rubio, R., and Pulido-Bosch, A. "Problemas hidrogeológicos que afectan a la explotación de la turbera de Padul (Granada, España)." Water in Mining and Underground Works. SIAMOS Proceedings. Granada, 1978. 1: 125-132.

9. Snel, M. J. "Infiltration des eaux dans les mines du bassin de Charleroi-Est." Annales des Mines de Belgique. September 1963. 997-1,007.

10. Knufinke, P. "Entwicklung der Wasserhaltung in Ruhrbergbau." Bergfreiheit. July-August 1968. 140-143.

11. Davies, A. W., and Baird, W. K. "Water dangers." The Mining Engineers. December 1976 - January 1977. 175-184.

12. Smeard, R. L., and Hust, K. G. "A history of water problems in the South Lancashire coalfields." The Mining Engineers. August-September 1973. 557-573.

13. Sommer, H. "Die Überwindung eines Schwimmsandeinbruchs auf der Grube Sophia-Jacoba." Glückauf. June 1977. 553-539.

14. Kutz, W.; Schmidt, R.; and others. "Wasserabschlussdamm aus Fertigbeton in einer Flözstrecke auf der Zeche Sophia-Jacoba." Glückauf. July 1975. 613-618.

15. Anonymous. "Accident de la mine de Léhota (Tchécoslovaquie). 15 aout 1963." Annales des Mines. November 1965. 90-91.

16. McGree, E. "Mine drainage." Mining Congress Journal. August 1953. 42-45.

17. Fernández-Rubio, R. "Hidrogeología aplicada a la minería." Industria Minera. Madrid 1977. 170: 15 pp.

18. Groot, H. de. "Een water en zanddoorbraak van het Dekterrein vit in de Mijn Julia te Eygelshoven." Geologie en Mihnbouw. December 1958. 421-429

19. Sheard, R. L., and Hurst, K. G. "A history of water problems in the South Lancashire Coalfield." The Mining Engineer. August-September 1973. 557-571.

20. Klir, S. "Brown coal opencast mining near Sokolov and protection at the Spa Karlovy Vary. Introduction." Hydrogeological Selected Papers. Geoindustria. Praha. 1972. 5: 8 pp.

21. Babcok, C. O., and Kooker, V. E. "Results of research to develop guidelines for mining near surface and underground bodies of water." U.S. Bureau of Mines. Information Circular 8741. 17 pp.

22. Kapolyi, L. "New trends of research protection against mine water." 7 Bányavízvédelmi Konferencia Budapest. 1976. 1: 24-49.

23. Labasse, H. "Les pressions de terrains dans les mines de houille. L'eau dans la mine." Annales des Mines de Belgique. May 1967. 531-540.

24. Hrastnik, J. "Problems of determining the safe thickness of impermeable clay layer between coal seam and water-bearing sand layer in the hanging wall." Mining and Metallurgy Quarterly. Ljubljana. 1971. 1: 47-59.

25. Anonymous. "Cement grouting extends mine productivity." Colliery Guardian. January 1974. 29-31.

26. Semmler, W. "Der Abbau von Steinkohle unter Berücksichtigung der zusitzenden Wässer in Ruhrbergbau." Berfreiheit. May 1960. 143-149.

27. Saul, H. "Water problems in the coalfields of Great Britain." Colliery Guardian. October 1959. 229-234.

28. Passini, J.; Renninck, G. E.; Armstrong, F. E.; and Abrams, J. R. "Plugging abandoned gas and oil wells." Mining Congress Journal. December 1972, 37-42.

29. Wittke, W. "Anwendung der Finite-Element Methode auf den Entwurf von untertägigen Dämmen." Erzmetall. 1973. 2: 66-74.

30. Schmidt, R. "Sicherung von Grubenbauen durch Wasserdämme." Schlägel und Eisen. October 1964. 654-664.

31. Dussart, L. "Construction d'un serrement au siège Ledoux des Houillères du Bassin du Nord et Pas-de-Calais." Industrie Minérale. Mines. 1973. 5: 327-340.

32. Förster, W., and Sitz, P. "Zum Beanspruchungszustand von Kalotten und Propfen als untertägige Abdämmungen bei unterschiedlichen Balastungs-und Lagerungsbedingungen." Neue Bergbautechnik. 1973. 11: 835-849.

33. Foster, W., and Walde, M. "Geomechanische probleme der Bemessung von Dämmen für die Abriegelung wasserführender Strecken im Braunkohlentagebau." Berbautechnik. 1973. 3: 177-183.

34. Langer, G. "Abschlussdämme unter Tage." Glückauf Betriebsbücher. 1973. 14: 70 pp.

35. Markgraf, H.; Heise, W.; and Klose, D. "Abdichtung von Talsperren im Lockergebirge mit hilfe von unterirdischen Dichtungswänden in der Deutschen Demokratischen Republik." Neue Bergbautechnik. 1973. 4: 307-312.

36. Kutz, W.; Schmidt, R.; and others. "Wasserabschlussdam aus Fertigbeton in einer Flözstrecke auf der Zeche Sophia-Jacoba." Glückauf. July 1975. 613-618.

37. Anonymous. "Chemical grout saves flood shafts." Colliery Guardian. May 1963. 616.

38. Baechstroem, H. "Die Wasserabdichtung von Schächten mit Asphalt-Latex." Glückauf. January 1964. 47-48.

39. Sanyas, M. "Cementation in roads in Merlebach Colliery." Colliery Guardian. January 1964. 81.

40. Cox, D. A. S. "Exploration and recovery in flooded workings." The Mining Engineer. February 1976. 265-274.

24

Controlling Mine Water

by R. L. Loofbourow, Consulting Engineer,
Minneapolis, Minnesota, USA

ABSTRACT

As mines go deeper there's the prospect of
pumping more water from greater depth at higher
unit costs. For efficient pumping, direct costs
are now likely to be $0.20 to $0.30 per million
foot gallons. But water inflow can increase total
costs and decrease production in many important
indirect ways.

This paper lists eight groups of ways which
could be used to reduce pumping. Most would reduce
inflow. Most could be used in both open pit and
underground mines. All but three of the 29 items
have been demonstrated in mining. Current and
foreseen conditions urge operators to reconsider
these and add to the list. The new methods suggested
are mining from the bottom up and reducing mass
permeability with chemical or bacteriological
precipitates.

INTRODUCTION

For those who work wet mines or plan to, the carrot of potential savings and the stick of increasing costs point to the prudence of reducing pumping energy. If water is needed and used, the objective should be to produce it at least cost, which generally means least pumping.

Groundwater resources are increasingly valued and protected. To mine without affecting groundwater in any way would be ideal. Plans which are feasible to reduce inflow may help obtain permission to mine and to maintain good local relations.

Manufacturers strive to make more efficient pumps. Here we review ways intended to control water more efficiently. Only the mine operator can do that.

GENERALIZED COST APPROXIMATION

Power alone, at $0.04 per kilowatt hour, contributes about $0.17 per million foot gallons to pumping costs, with reasonable allowance for electrical and mechanical losses in an efficient plant. Other direct costs, including recovery of capital cost of the system may increase that by 50 per cent. So we may expect direct costs of 20 to 30 cents per million foot gallons pumped by well designed, sizable plants, without special problems such as gritty or acid water. Many pumping plants, to be sure aren't so well planned and others handle water of poorer quality.

The direct costs of pumping can be bad enough, especially when we realize that inflow continues whether the mine produces or not. To emphasize we might say inflow continues at least 525 600 minutes of each year.

So far we have talked about cost of pumping per unit of water handled. Now let's turn attention to the total cost of water inflow per unit of mine product. This can be very different and the total cost of production is next to the bottom line.

Actual costs were reported seven years ago by a company working two mines near Grants, New Mexico. The two mines were comparable except that one was wet and the other dry. Each ton of ore hoisted from the wet mine cost more than twice as much as one from the dry mine. The more efficient methods and equipment used in the dry mine could not be used in the wet. Even where rock is strong, indirect costs of inflow can be high. Table 26.2.2 of Chapter 26, Mining Engineers Handbook AIME, NY, 1973, shows 17 indirect ways in which inflow can increase mine costs and there is no reason to feel that this enumeration is complete. At many wet mines the evaluation of these indirect costs should be both enlightening and stimulating.

DEMONSTRATED METHODS OF WATER CONTROL

Table 1 is based on correspondence and conversation with others, literature study and the author's observations over a period of several decades.

METHODS JUDGED TO MERIT APPLICATION

1. No mining from the bottom up as indicated in Figure 1 is known to have been undertaken primarily to minimize inflow.* Two requirements and two possible disadvantages are foreseen:

* Unusually thorough planning is required. At least a large part of the mineral deposit must be explored adequately with special attention given to water occurrence. Decision should then be based on a comparison of advantages and disadvantages.

---

* When water broke into the West Driefontein Mine in South Africa October, 1968, the open space in the lower mine and a heroic pumping effort provided 23 days of grace during which 4 concrete plugs, to withstand high pressure, were built to prevent flooding the entire mine.

The Frood Mine near Sudbury, Ontario, was mined from the bottom up. The lower part of the mine was virtually dry. However, the author doubts that this was an important planning consideration.

* To get the mine into production without taking water from nearby wells, shafts would have to be sunk without substantial effect on the water table. That might or might not be the least costly way.

* First expenses for shaft plant will be greater but total pre-production cost may be less because it is not necessary to pump at high rate for a long time to lower the water table before mining can be begun. Shaft plant would be completed in a single step rather than piecemeal, as is usual at deeper mines.

* Mining from the bottom up would make it more difficult to go back to the deeper part of the mine to recover any low grade fringes not extracted originally.

Where the conditions are really favorable for it, the advantage of mining from the bottom up could be substantial. Bottom-up mining is likely to merit careful consideration where several of the following conditions exist:

* Rate of water inflow to the upper levels would be very large. Inrushes may increase it to rates which could hardly be pumped.

* As is common, ground becomes tighter with depth so that potential flow into deeper parts of the mine is less and can be estimated with more confidence.

* Good ore can be produced from the lower part of the mine, thus helping to recover investment.

* The conventional alternative would dry up many wells for a long time.

Expectable advantages include:

* The total pumping energy and total volume of water should be reduced considerably because:

   1. Maximum pumping rate would last only through the latter part of the mine life rather than throughout it.

2. While pumping is at its maximum rate the head could be reduced instead of increasing as is usually the case as the mine is deepened. Where a large part of the inflow is caught near the surface, this advantage is reduced. See Figure 10.

3. Depression of the local water table would be postponed and would not last as long as normally. Depression may not be as deep nor affect as large an area.

* Until heavy pumping is begun, the operator has more flexibility. He is more likely to survive an interruption of production.

* Any lower space which can be kept open provides more time to get crew out of danger, perhaps to stop an inrush or if not, to retreat in better order.

* The lower part of the mine will become an ideal settling basin to clarify water when the pumping rate increases. Thus high pump maintenance, construction of large underground settling basins or installation of filters is avoided. Settling basins on the surface might be reduced or eliminated.

METHODS WHICH HAVE BEEN DEMONSTRATED BUT LITTLE USED IN MINING

Clay grouts are used effectively to reduce the permeability of alluvium and some stronger rock. Their special advantages include:

1. Properly mixed clay grouts do not "bleed" or give up water to adjacent shale or clay. They are useful in plugging pores and fractures in those rocks and clay-coated fractures in harder rock.

2. Masses of clay-grouted ground can be deformed without fractures being opened.

3. Because clay is not granular it can be used effectively in medium sand.

4. Where suitable local clay or material which can be made suitable with minor additions, is available, large quantities of grout can be provided at moderate cost.

Probably the most spectacular application was to reduce flow below the Aswan High Dam, which is built on a deep, wide valley fill of silt, sand, and gravel. Clay grouting is probably used by civil engineers more commonly in Europe than in America.

On a first attempt to mine on a 300-acre tract near Leadwood, Missouri, St. Joseph Lead Co., now St. Joe Minerals Corporation, was repeatedly flooded with water and mud from fractures enlarged by solution and partly clay filled. Repeated cement grouting did not solve the problem. In the early 1940's, 450,000 tons of desanded mill tailings were injected from the surface through 763 existing diamond drill holes. Thereafter the ore was mined with minor grouting from underground as work advanced.

Pregrouting has been developed and used with excellent results by the South Africans in preparation for sinking many of their recent large, deep shafts. In comparison with shaft sinking, the pregrouting is inexpensive. Pregrouting can begin even before details of shaft planning are altogether complete and be continued while the surface plant is being built. This minimizes delays for grouting from the shaft bottom. See Figure 2.

PLUGGING CONDUITS THROUGH WHICH MINES HAVE BEEN FLOODED

On at least five occasions, conduits through which mines have been flooded have been plugged under water. In each case the source and the conduit were too large for any pumps which it was practical to install. If sufficient pumps had been put to work, the rapid inrush of water would have been expected to erode and enlarge the conduits. Under these circumstances there is the opportunity to introduce a mass of concrete or grout into the conduit when water in it is virtually still. To avoid dilution, grout can generally be placed by tremie.

The first of these known recoveries was at a mine in Belgian Congo probably in the 40's. An account of this accomplishment from the Belgian mine manager contributed to the recovery of the Friedensville shaft in 1952, and that method in turn was improved and modified for use in Indiana in 1960. See Figures 3 to 9.

The recovery of the Levant tin mine in Cornwall with the placement of a concrete plug on the sea floor in 1965 was a spectacular undertaking. Most of the work was done by divers from small work boats.

The stopping of the conduit through which water from the Cumberland River entered the Moodie Mine, a small fluorspar mine in Kentucky, was similar to the Levant plugging but apparently quite independent of it.

METHODS NOT KNOWN TO HAVE BEEN APPLIED IN MINING

Some time ago the author began looking for ways of reducing rock permeability for use in mining and some types of underground construction. The following were considered desirable features:

* Treatment should affect substantial masses of rock or broad areas of rock surface. Ideally the treatment should go to all points where fluid movement is troublesome. It should be at some depth within the rock mass, not only at the surface.

* There should be some control over the time and place of the action.

* Treatment should not be hazardous to those applying it or others. It should protect rather than harm water supply.

* Treatment should be useful under mine conditions, including temperature and dilution by still or running water in large or minute conduits, some with clay, etc.

* Useful treatment must be an improvement over methods we have, generally based on cost or effectiveness.

Dr. John B. Patton, Director of the Indiana Geological Survey called attention to the chemical and bacteriological treatment given water before it is injected for the secondary recovery of oil. The purpose of treatment is to prevent rock pores and fractures from being plugged. This was studied with the help of Professor W.D. Lacabanne, Petroleum Engineering, University of Minnesota. Several years later practice developed by the Chowchilla Irrigation District in California to seal leaky concrete mains, was studied. They found that a simple chemical precipitate tends to attach itself firmly to surfaces over which water movement is rapid. In a surprisingly short time, leakage was stopped. In some ways this is like the formation of scale in pipe, which is sometimes caused and to a degree controlled, to reduce corrosion.

Further investigation in a series of tests at increasing scale is suggested.

Surely any competent effort should add to the items shown in Table I.

Table I

METHODS FOR WATER CONTROL

METHODS	EXAMPLES (for bibliography see SME (AIME), 1973, Mining Engineers Handbook for references)
1. Reduce, postpone or avoid inflow.	
a) Locate shafts or excavations in least permeable ground.	Naica, Kimballton, San Antonio
b) Mine from bottom up.	As at West Driefontein
c) Work under water by dredging, mining with draglines, leaching in place, Slurry Trench.	Alluvial gold, tin, sand, gravel, phosphate, Shirley Basin uranium, foundations in ground difficult to dewater and to support.
2. Protect workings from inflow.	
a) Leave enough solid ground between the mine and water.	Wabana (Newfoundland), Submarine coal in Durham (England) and Nova Scotia, metal mines in Ontario, Quebec.
b) Leave pillars on fissures to prevent or minimize movement.	South Africa gold mines

METHODS	EXAMPLES
c) Plug or case test holes or survey and don't mine near them.	Plugging is required in many localities. Most salt mines are especially careful.
3. Divert, drain or intercept water near surface.	
a) Divert rivers, drain lakes.	Griffiths, Black Lake, Caland, Bancroft, Steep Rock Lake, Biwabik
b) Cover intakes with concrete or ponded slime, with great care.	Leadwood, Bancroft
c) Clear slopes, build drains, plant trees in low, flat areas to increase evapo-transpiration.	Bancroft
d) Catch water in shafts or on an upper level to prevent it going deeper in the mine.	Most wet shafts; Champion Mine, Michigan
e) Intercept water in shallow wells.	Homer Wauseca (See Figure 10)
4. Keep water from shafts with impervious linings.	
a) Pregrout from the surface, then test and grout from the shaft bottom.	Many recent South African shafts, e.g. Kinross (See Figure 2)

METHODS	EXAMPLES
b) Sink with grouting from the shaft bottom only.	Venterspost, Friedensville, Deep Ruth, Meremec.
c) Freeze, sink and set lining.	European coal mines, Saskatchewan potash, some Carlsbad potash shafts.
d) Bore, usually with mud, and place casing.	Beatrix Shafts(Netherlands), Grants, Carlsbad.
e) Drop shafts, stationary slip forming.	Chicago Metropolitan Sanitary Commission.
5. Reduce Permeability of the Rock Mass	
a) Grout with cement slurry.	Port Radium, Deep Creek.
b) Plug solution channels with desanded tailings and grouting.	Leadwood
c) Plug pores or fractures with clay.	Aswan Dam and others especially in Europe.
d) Plug with chemical or bacteriological precipitate.	No trial known in mining.
6. Drain water through an adit.	Many wet mines in hilly places.

METHODS

EXAMPLES

7. Use Special Practices to Aid Control, to Reduce or Prepare for Surprises.

a) Compartment the mine to confine inrushes and minimize damage.

Leadwood, Nova Scotia coal mines

b) Mine from bottom up to provide space for water and time to build protection.

As at West Driefontein

c) Regularly get informed outside opinion.

d) Regularly drill test holes in advance of work.

e) Regularly plot, record pertinent data on water occurrence and protection, plan and test procedures.

f) Maintain material, tools and trained crew, ready to carry out protectice procedures.

METHODS	EXAMPLES
8. Procedures Which Have Been Used in Emergencies.	
a) Working from the surface, plug a large conduit under water.	Levant (Cornwall), Moodie (Kentucky)
b) Working from the surface through pipe or drill holes, plug a large conduit in the mine.	Belgian Congo, Friedensville, Figs. 3 to 8. Indiana Gypsum mine, See Figure 9
9. Dispose of water more conveniently as by dropping it into a conduit, dropping or pumping it into an aquifer against lower pressure.	Chief Consolidated

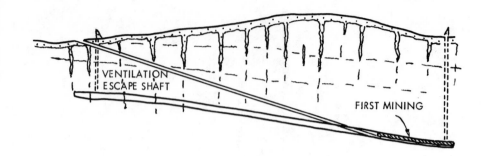

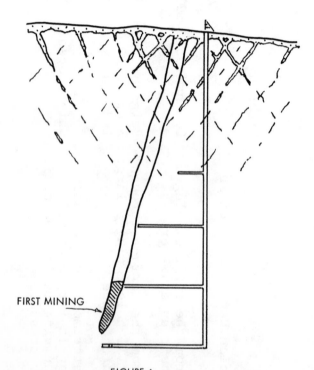

FIGURE 1

FIRST MINING IN TIGHTEST GROUND TO MINIMIZE INFLOW,
DRAWDOWN AND TOTAL PUMPING

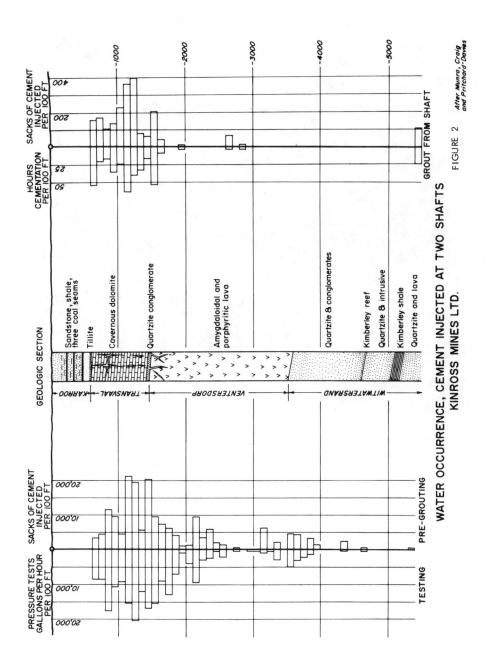

WATER OCCURRENCE, CEMENT INJECTED AT TWO SHAFTS
KINROSS MINES LTD.

FIGURE 2

After Munro, Craig
and Pritchard-Davies

FIGURE 3

FACE OF 700 CROSSCUT, 100 FEET NORTH OF FRIEDENSVILLE SHAFT
SHOWING SOME 50 TEST-GROUT HOLES

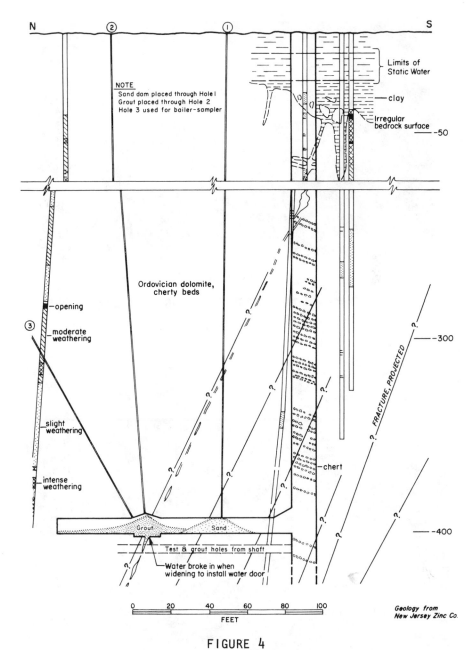

N   ②   ①   S

Limits of
Static Water

NOTE
Sand dam placed through Hole 1
Grout placed through Hole 2
Hole 3 used for bailer-sampler

clay

Irregular
bedrock surface

—-50

Ordovician dolomite,
cherty beds

—opening

③ —moderate
weathering

—slight
weathering

—300

—intense
weathering

chert

FRACTURE, PROJECTED

—400

Grout   Sand

Test & grout holes from shaft

Water broke in when
widening to install water door

0   20   40   60   80   100

FEET

Geology from
New Jersey Zinc Co.

FIGURE 4

SECTION ACROSS FRIEDENSVILLE SHAFT
SHOWING PROCEDURE FOR PLUGGING 400' LEVEL BREAKOUT

FIGURE 5

PLEXIGLASS MODEL FOR PLANNING RECOVERY
OF FRIEDENSVILLE SHAFT

FIGURE 6

AGITATOR AND GROUT PUMP FOR PLUGGING FLOOR
OF 400 LEVEL, FRIEDENSVILLE SHAFT

FIGURE 7

GROUT PLUG IN FLOOR OF CROSSCUT, LOOKING TOWARD SHAFT
NOTE HALF DOZEN TEST-GROUT HOLES POINTED TO BASE OF PLUG

FIGURE 8

CONE OF LOW STRENGTH GROUT PLACED ABOVE PLUG
FRIEDENSVILLE SHAFT

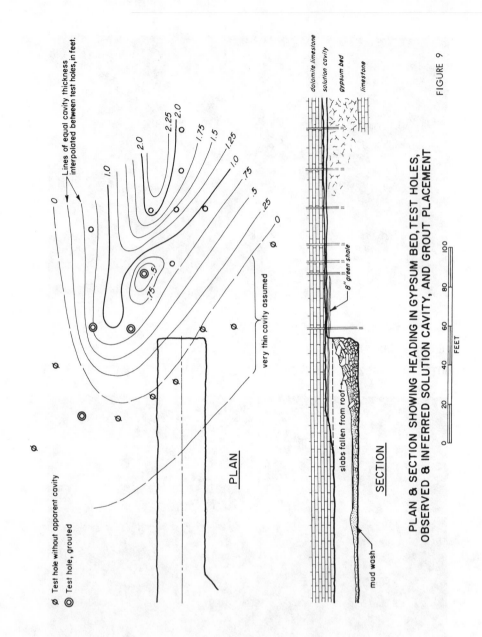

∅ Test hole without apparent cavity
◎ Test hole, grouted

Lines of equal cavity thickness,
interpolated between test holes, in feet.

0

2.25
2.0

2.0

1.75
1.5

1.0

1.25

.75

1.0

.5

.75
.5

.25

0

very thin cavity assumed

PLAN

dolomite limestone
solution cavity
gypsum bed
limestone

8" green shale

slabs fallen from roof

SECTION

mud wash

0   20   40   60   80   100
FEET

PLAN & SECTION SHOWING HEADING IN GYPSUM BED, TEST HOLES,
OBSERVED & INFERRED SOLUTION CAVITY, AND GROUT PLACEMENT

FIGURE 9

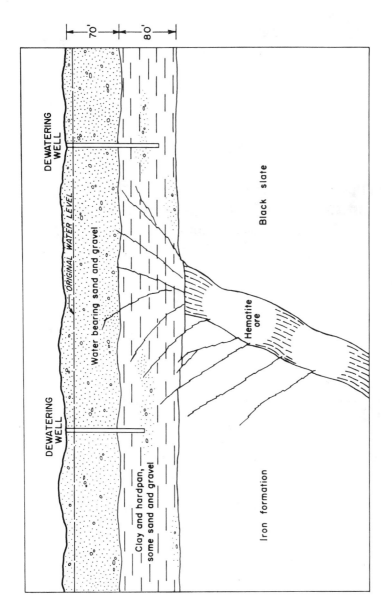

SKETCH OF DEWATERING WELLS
OF
HOMER WAUSECA MINES, IRON RIVER, MICHIGAN

Not to scale

FIGURE 10

25

Simple Mine Inflow Evaluation for Underground Oil Shale Mines

by Adrian Brown, Associate,
Golder Associates Inc.,
Denver, Colorado, USA

INTRODUCTION

Developers of major oil shale mines in the Piceance Basin have already had some unpleasant surprises from ground water despite the early stage of these developments. These surprises include:

- C-a tract shaft sinking had to be halted to allow dewatering of near surface materials.

- C-b tract shaft sinking encountered considerably more water than was expected.

- The Colony mine, despite being on the edge of the Parachute Creek canyon, encountered measurable water inflow from the supposedly unsaturated roof strata.

- The U.S.B.M. Horse Draw Shaft encountered high pressure, methane-laden water when the proposed development level was opened, despite expectations that the target strata were impermeable.

This paper presents a simple approach to the evaluation of the geohydrology problems associated with underground oil shale mines. The basic analytical tools are presented, followed by a typical geohydrology model for an oil shale mining area. These are used to illustrate simple methods of computation of shaft inflows, shaft dewatering, mine inflows and ground water impacts of mining. After looking at the uncertainties associated with the results, some conclusions are drawn about mine geohydrology evaluations in this type of geological system.

ANALYTICAL TOOLS

There are a vast number of ways which geohydrology analyses can be performed. They can in general be characterized as:

i. Simple and Cheap, or
ii. Complex and Expensive

As a general rule, mining hydrology should be performed with the first type of approach, for two reasons. First the required accuracy of analyses of mining hydrological systems is usually not high; an order of magnitude estimate is often all that is needed for inflows or impacts. Second, the available accuracy of information – geology and parameters is usually not high, and thus it is inappropriate to use highly accurate analytical methods to compute results.

There are three main analytical tools which I use for mine hydrology analyses.

Darcy's Law

Darcy (1) had the great insight that the volumetric rate of flow of a fluid through a porous medium was proportional to the head gradient in the medium (i) and the area through which flow is taking place, (A), or

(1) $Q = kiA$

where the constant of proportionality (k) is defined as the hydraulic conductivity. This is the fundamental relationship for mine geohydrologists. It is not always true (the relation is not always linear) but it always produces an upper bound to mine inflow and environmental impacts.

The Well Equation

Theis (2) performed an analysis of flow to a well in an infinite, homogeneous, compressible confined aquifer, and produced the classic well equation solution

$$(2a) \quad D = \frac{Q}{4\pi Lk} W(u)$$

where D   = drawdown

Q   = flow to the well

L   = thickness of the formation being dewatered

k   = hydraulic conductivity

$W(u)$ = well function

$$u \quad = \frac{r^2 S_s}{4kt}$$

r   = radius at which drawdown is desired

S_s = specific storage

k   = hydraulic conductivity

t   = elapsed time

Values of $W(u)$ are given as a function of u in Table I. This equation is very usable in this form, but it is also convenient when quoted in an approximate steady state form (3):

$$(2b) \quad D = \frac{Q \ln(R/r)}{2\pi Lk}$$

where $R \div r_w \sqrt{\dfrac{4kt}{r_w^2 S_s} + 1}$ = effective radius of influence

r_w = radius of the well (or mine) and other symbols are as above.

This has the great attraction that it is readily computable using a programmable calculator, and the involvement of

TABLE I

VALUES OF $W(u)$

u or u_{xy} / N	$N \times 10^{-10}$	$N \times 10^{-9}$	$N \times 10^{-8}$	$N \times 10^{-7}$	$N \times 10^{-6}$	$N \times 10^{-5}$	$N \times 10^{-4}$	$N \times 10^{-3}$	$N \times 10^{-2}$	$N \times 10^{-1}$	N
1.0	22.4486	20.1460	17.8435	15.5409	13.2383	10.9357	8.6332	6.3315	4.0379	1.8229	0.2194
1.5	22.0432	19.7406	17.4380	15.1354	12.8328	10.5303	8.2278	5.9266	3.6374	1.4645	0.1000
2.0	21.7555	19.4529	17.1503	14.8477	12.5451	10.2426	7.9402	5.6394	3.3547	1.2227	0.04890
2.5	21.5323	19.2298	16.9272	14.6246	12.3220	10.0194	7.7172	5.4167	3.1365	1.0443	0.02491
3.0	21.3500	19.0474	16.7449	14.4423	12.1397	9.8371	7.5348	5.2349	2.9591	0.9057	0.01305
3.5	21.1959	18.8933	16.5907	14.2881	11.9855	9.6830	7.3807	5.0813	2.8099	0.7942	0.006970
4.0	21.0623	18.7598	16.4572	14.1546	11.8520	9.5495	7.2472	4.9482	2.6813	0.7024	0.003779
4.5	20.9446	18.6420	16.3394	14.0368	11.7342	9.4317	7.1295	4.8310	2.5684	0.6253	0.002073
5.0	20.8392	18.5366	16.2340	13.9314	11.6280	9.3263	7.0242	4.7261	2.4679	0.5598	0.001148
5.5	20.7439	18.4413	16.1387	13.8361	11.5330	9.2310	6.9289	4.6313	2.3775	0.5034	0.0006409
6.0	20.6569	18.3543	16.0517	13.7491	11.4465	9.1440	6.8420	4.5448	2.2953	0.4544	0.0003601
6.5	20.5768	18.2742	15.9717	13.6691	11.3665	9.0640	6.7620	4.4652	2.2201	0.4115	0.0002034
7.0	20.5027	18.2001	15.8976	13.5950	11.2924	8.9899	6.6879	4.3916	2.1508	0.3738	0.0001155
7.5	20.4337	18.1311	15.8280	13.5260	11.2234	8.9209	6.6190	4.3231	2.0867	0.3403	0.0000658
8.0	20.3692	18.0666	15.7640	13.4614	11.1589	8.8563	6.5545	4.2591	2.0269	0.3106	0.0000376
8.5	20.3086	18.0060	15.7034	13.4008	11.0982	8.7957	6.4939	4.1990	1.9711	0.2840	0.0000216
9.0	20.2514	17.9488	15.6462	13.3437	11.0411	8.7386	6.4368	4.1423	1.9187	0.2602	0.0000124
9.5	20.1973	17.8948	15.5922	13.2896	10.9870	8.6845	6.3828	4.0887	1.8695	0.2387	0.0000071

TABLE II

VALUES OF $K_0(r/B)$.

N	$r/B = N \times 10^{-3}$	$N \times 10^{-2}$	$N \times 10^{-1}$	N
1.0	7.0237	4.7212	2.4271	0.4210
1.5	6.6182	4.3159	2.0300	0.2138
2.0	6.3305	4.0285	1.7527	0.1139
2.5	6.1074	3.8056	1.5415	0.0623
3.0	5.9251	3.6235	1.3725	0.0347
3.5	5.7709	3.4697	1.2327	0.0196
4.0	5.6374	3.3365	1.1145	0.0112
4.5	5.5196	3.2192	1.0129	0.0064
5.0	5.4143	3.1142	0.9244	0.0037
5.5	5.3190	3.0195	0.8466	
6.0	5.2320	2.9329	0.7775	0.0012
6.5	5.1520	2.8534	0.7159	
7.0	5.0779	2.7798	0.6605	0.0004
7.5	5.0089	2.7114	0.6106	
8.0	4.9443	2.6475	0.5653	
8.5	4.8837	2.5875	0.5242	
9.0	4.8266	2.5310	0.4867	
9.5	4.7725	2.4776	0.4524	

each parameter is clear. The degree of approximation is small. Unlike the Theis form, it is valid for finite sized wells (or mines).

Steady State Leaky Aquifer Equation

Hantush and Jacob (4) presented the solution to the problem of flow to a well and its associated drawdown when the aquifer being pumped is overlain by a leaky layer. The leakage reduces the spread-out of the drawdown effect, and increases the flow to the well slightly. Unlike the non-leaky case, it also reaches steady state, when all water influent to the well is provided by leakage through the leaky layer. At steady state, the equation is given by:

$$(3a) \quad D = \frac{Q}{2\pi Lk} K_o(r/B)$$

where D = drawdown

Q = flow

L = thickness of aquifer

k = horizontal hydraulic conductivity

K_o = Modified Bessel Function

r = radius

B = $\sqrt{k\ L\ L'/k'}$

k' = vertical hydraulic conductivity of leaky layer

L' = thickness of leaky layer

The relationship between $K_o(r/B)$ and r/B is given in Table II. An approximate steady state form is possible (5) which is comparable with equation 2(b).

$$(3b) \quad D = \frac{Q\ \ln(R/r)}{2\pi Lk}$$

where R = effective radius of influence of drawdown and other symbols are the same. The relation for R as a function of r_w and B is given in Figure 1. This equation is especially useful for computing environmental impacts. Note that it is an upper bound for flows, but a lower bound for impacts.

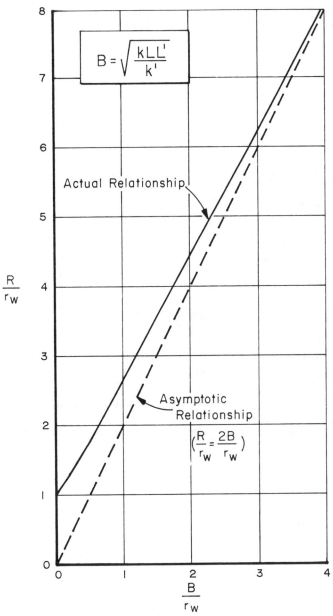

$$B = \sqrt{\frac{kLL'}{k'}}$$

Actual Relationship

Asymptotic
Relationship

$$\left(\frac{R}{r_w} = \frac{2B}{r_w}\right)$$

See reference (5) for derivation.

Figure 1 – Radius of Influence For A
Leaky Aquifer (Approx.)

These then are the three fundamental tools. There are a vast array of other useful relationships and methods of analysis, but it is possible to perform most oil shale mining hydrology work with these.

THE GEOHYDROLOGY MODEL

Geology

The site chosen for presentation in this paper is in the Piceance Creek Basin of Northwest Colorado, just to the South of Piceance Creek (Figure 2). The typical geological column in the area is given in Figure 3. This comprises, from the surface,

i.   The Uinta Sandstone. This is a fine to medium sandstone, extensively fractured, of late Eocene age. It was deposited in lacustrine to fluviatile environments.

ii. The Parachute Creek Member of the Green River Formation. This is a white to grey varved dolomintic limestone with varying amounts of kerogen intimately mixed with the matrix. The kerogen is a wax-like organic compound which decomposes to an oil like substance when heated. Sodium anhydrite minerals also occur in varying amounts.

iii. The Garden Gulch Member of the Green River Formation. This is a dark, finely laminated shale and dolomintic limestone, generally barren of kerogen.

All strata are flat bedded, except in the extreme north of the basin. Fracturing is in general slight, but bedding fractures are common. There is little evidence of deep seated fault activity in the basin. The Mahogany Zone is a particularly rich oil shale layer, and is shown shaded in Figure 3. It is considered to be the target of mining for the present paper, and it is also assumed that mining will be by room-and-pillar methods. (Note that other methods of mining can be, and are being, considered.)

Geohydrology

Once the geology has been determined it is necessary to assign the needed geohydrologic parameters to the various

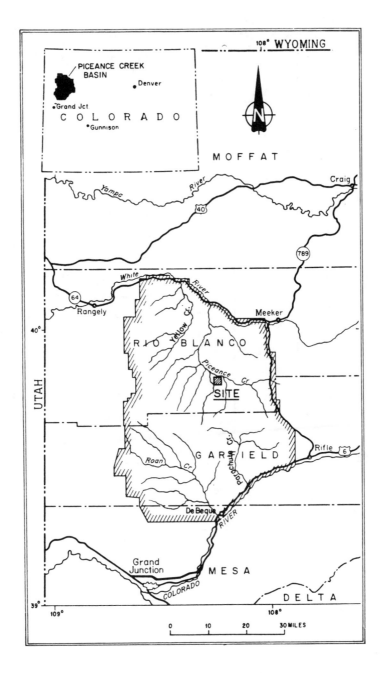

Figure 2 - Location Plan

GEOLOGIC UNIT	MATERIAL TYPE	FEATURE DESCRIPTION	ELEVATION (feet above Mean Sea Level)	DEPTH (feet)
		Ground Surface	6740	0
UINTA FORMATION	Sandstone	Water Table Uinta Sandstone	6410	330
			5820	920
GREEN RIVER FORMATION / PARACHUTE CREEK MEMBER	Kerogenous Marlstone (Oil shale)	A Groove	5490	1250
		Mahogany Zone	5460	1280
			5410	1330
		B Groove	5310	1430
			4630	2110
		R-4 Zone	4500	2240
GARDEN GULCH MEMBER		Blue Marker	4200	2540

Source: Brown et al, Ref.(6)

Figure 3 – Geology Model

geological units. Four fundamental parameters are of relevance in this case, as follows:

i. Horizontal Hydraulic Conductivity

This parameter relates primarily to the ability of the unit to transmit water along the bedding direction. In this particular model horizontal hydraulic conductivity is assumed to be isotropic.

ii. Vertical Hydraulic Conductivity

This parameter relates to the ability of the unit to transmit water across the bedding plane direction - i.e. roughly vertically.

iii. Drainable Porosity

This parameter indicates how much water is available if a section of the unit de-saturates.

iv. Specific Storage

This parameter determines the amount of water which is released from a unit volume of rock when the water pressure is lowered by a unit of head. It is related to the compressibility of the rock.

Figure 4 shows the best estimates of each of the parameters for the geological units shown in Figure 3. The data is taken from a report by the Author and others (6). It should be noted in passing that a consistent set of units is used. I happen to have chosen the following set:

Length - Feet
Time   - Days
Mass   - Pounds

Using this set of units, flows come out as cubic feet per day, which can be converted as required. The important factor is that the units be consistent, as all the formulae presented in this paper are for consistent units. For the reader more used to oil field units, 1 foot per day is equal to 350 millidarcy (approximately). The testing with which the values in Figure 4 have been obtained is described in detail elsewhere. I have chosen to concentrate in this paper on the use of the data.

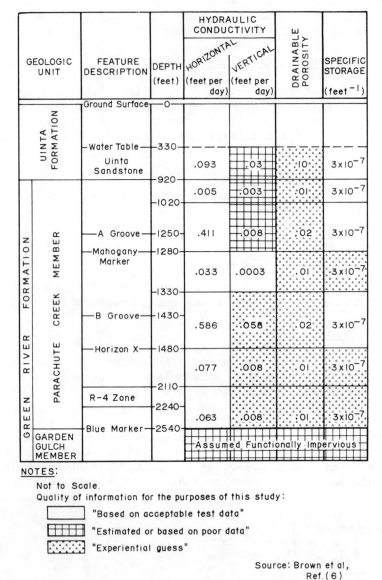

Figure 4 – Geohydrology Model

ANALYSES

We have the geohydrology model, and some analytical tools, so it is now possible to compute some typical inflows and other results. The examples will be taken in order of the development of a mine in the Mahogany Zone, which is about 1,300 feet deep (Figure 3).

Shaft Inflow and Effect

Assume that a 24 foot diameter shaft is to be conventionally sunk without any prior dewatering. A maximum of fifty feet of the shaft is open to the formation at one time, and the shaft lining is fully sealed. What is the inflow likely to be? Shaft advance is assumed to be 5 feet/day.

The shaft constitutes a large diameter well. When the shaft is (say) at the 'B Groove' (Figure 4) the parameters are:

L = thickness open = 50 feet
D = drawdown = 1430-330 = 1,100 feet
k = hydraulic conductivity = 0.586 feet/day
r = "well" radius = 12 feet
S_S = specific storage = 3×10^{-7} feet^{-1}
t = time that shaft section is open = 5 days (average)

Applying equation 2(b) gives

Q = 32,500 feet^3/day = 170 gallons per minute

Performing this analysis for the entire shaft gives the result in Figure 5. Inrushes to the shaft might be ten times this amount for short periods.

Shaft Dewatering

The result in Figure 5 suggests that some flow control will be necessary for the shaft. Perhaps more important, pressure control would be advantageous in the vicinity of the shaft, to prevent failure of the floor materials, and to reduce the risk of very large, sudden inrushes. If a reduction of 90 per cent of the original pressure is considered necessary, how many wells will be needed, and what flows will they produce?

NOTE: Inflow to a 50 foot open section only.

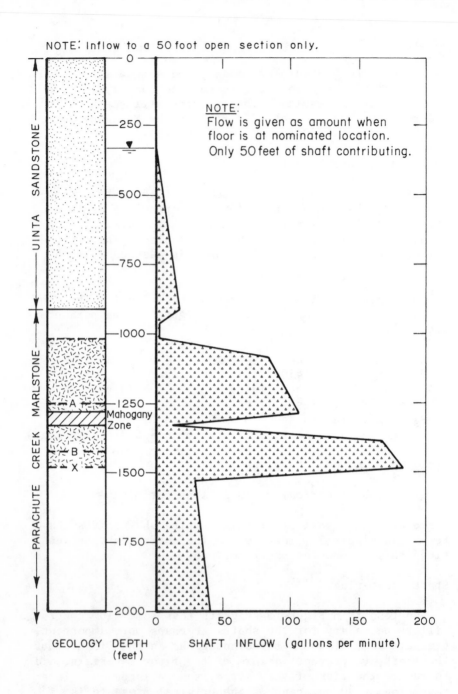

Figure 5 — Average Flow To Shaft Without Dewatering

By way of example, consider one fully drained well. The distance drawdown characteristic near the 'B' Groove is shown on Figure 6A. Applying this curve to drawdown at the shaft center, with dewatering wells located at 100 feet from the centerline (for blast protection) shows that a single well reduces the head about 52 per cent. A second well can be shown by superposition to reduce the head at the shaft by a further 20 per cent to 72 per cent, and so on as shown in Figure 6B. For 90 per cent reduction in head (the design requirement), about 6 wells are needed. Flow from each of these wells can be found by integrating the flow to a single well over its full depth, and taking 10 per cent of it, giving 70 gallons per minute per well (after 30 days). The wells would reduce the maximum steady flow to the shaft to about 20 gallons per minute. After dewatering, inrushes might be ten times that amount for short periods.

Underground Mine Inflow

Inflow to an unsubsided underground mine comes in this environment from two sources; horizontal flow along the strata disturbed by mining, and vertical flow from the roof. The general scheme of flow is shown in Figure 7. Each component can be relatively easily computed as follows.

Horizontal Flow. For inflow purposes the mine can be considered as a large well. Consider a two mile diameter mine extracting the Mahogany Zone, and with roof drains dewatering up to the 'A' Groove (Figure 3). In addition, it seems reasonable to assume that the stress relief in the floor will influence a thickness of the floor material equal to about half the roof span, or about 50 feet.

Flow could be computed asuming confined conditions, giving about 450 gallons per minute. However the significant vertical permeability of the model creates a situation where leakage is coming from the Uinta Sandstone. Accordingly, the conditions are leaky, with the following parameters:

k = average horizontal hydraulic conductivity of aquifer = .333 feet/day (average)
k' = vertical hydraulic conductivity of roof material = 0.01 feet/day (average)
L = aquifer thickness = 130 feet

NOTE: These curves are valid only for parameters given in Figure 4.

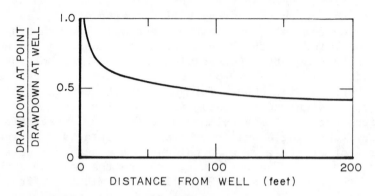

A) DRAWDOWN AROUND A WELL AFTER 30 DAYS PUMPING.

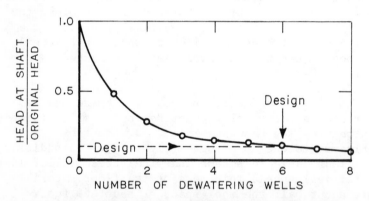

B) HEAD AT SHAFT IN LOWER AQUIFER VERSUS NUMBER OF DEWATERING WELLS.

Figure 6 – Shaft Dewatering Design

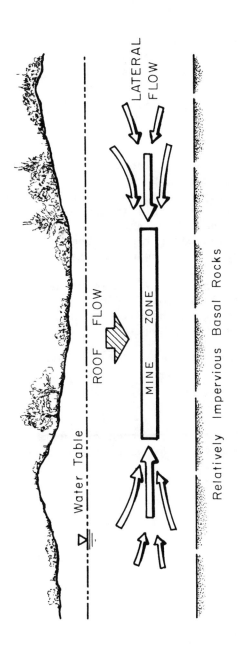

Figure 7 – Scheme Of Flow To A Mine

```
L'  = aquitard thickness = 920 feet
r_w = mine radius = 5,280 feet
D   = drawdown at mine = 975 feet (average)
```

Using Equation 3(b) and Figure 1, for B = 1,995 feet,

$$Q = 575,000 \text{ feet}^3/\text{day} = 3,000 \text{ gallons per minute}$$

Flow From Roof. The flow from the roof occurs under conditions of gravity drainage. Vertical hydraulic gradients are about equal to unity, and the water pressure above the mine approaches zero. While this is approximate, it becomes more true for mines whose extent is large compared with the depth below the water table. The vertical inflow can be computed using the following parameters:

```
k'  = average vertical hydraulic conductivity to
      water table = 0.01 feet/day
i   = hydraulic gradient = 1 approximately
A   = mine area = 3.14 square miles
```

Thus, using equation 1,

$$Q = 963,000 \text{ feet}^3/\text{day} = 5,000 \text{ gallons per minute}$$

This flow is proportional to the area of the mine, and originates from movement of the water table as a result of drainage.

Total Flow to the Mine. The total flow to the mine is therefore made up as follows:

i.	Horizontal flow	3,000	gallons per minute
ii.	Roof flow	5,000	gallons per minute
	Total	8,000	gallons per minute

This is a modest flow by comparison with similarly sized mines in pervious media.

Impact of Drawdown

The simple equations and the model can be used to make a first cut at environmental impact of the mine. In the case under study the impact of drawdown is primarily as a result of vertical seepage to the mine. The maximum rate of movement of the water table is found by evaluating the real rate of vertical seepage, which is given by:

$$V_{real} = V_{Darcy} /n$$

$$= k'i /n$$

As in the section on flow to the roof, we have

k' = vertical hydraulic conductivity = 0.01 feet/day (average)
i = vertical hydraulic gradient = 1 (average)
n = drainable porosity of Uinta Sandstone = 0.1 (Figure 4).

These parameters give

$$V_{real} = 40 \text{ feet/year}$$

and at that rate it would take a minimum of fifteen years for the Uinta Sandstone to de-saturate over the mine itself.

The impact would spread out from the mine as the drainage took place. Perhaps the easiest way to get a feel for the maximum extent of this effect is to analyze the entire system as a two mile diameter well in an unconfined aquifer. Parameters are:

Q = flow = 8,000 gallons per minute = 1,500,000 feet^3/day
k = average horizontal hydraulic conductivity = 0.164 feet/day
L = total thickness = 1,000 feet
n = drainable porosity = 0.1
S_s = effective specific storage = n/L = 10^{-4} feet^{-1}
r_w = radius of mine = 5,280 feet
t = time elapsed = 20 years = 7,300 days

Using equation 2(b) gives that the 8,000 gallons per minute flow would cause a drawdown after 20 years of 700 feet at the edge of the mine, and that the cone of depression would not extend much beyond 2 miles from the edge of the mine. This result fits well with the vertical seepage result above. The impact of mine seepage on ground water levels would be substantial over the mine, but would rapidly diminish away from the mine.

It goes without saying that much better analyses of ground water depletion impact, both local and regional, are needed for full mine design. The above approach does, however, indicate the likely flavor of the end result. (For examples of basin-wide analyses see, Weeks et al (7) and Brown et al (6)).

ACCURACY AND UNCERTAINTY IN THE RESULTS

How accurate are the above results? Or put another way; how much variability could there be in the answers? Uncertainty as to the results can arise from a number of sources:

i.   Inaccuracies introduced by the use of an idealized geohydrology model.

ii.   Inaccuracies introduced by the analytical evaluations performed with the model.

iii. Uncertainties associated with the measurement of parameters for the model.

While the model and the analytical methods used in this paper are deliberately crude, most of the uncertainty in the final result derives from the parameters. This section briefly reviews the accuracy of some of the above evaluations.

Shaft Inflow Accuracy

Review of the analysis presented above shows that the variability of shaft inflow is mainly dependent upon the variability of the horizontal hydraulic conductivity.

There are three forms of variability of this parameter:

i.   It is variable on a macroscopic scale in the vertical direction, due to gross lithological changes. This variability is reasonably quantifiable and is presented on Figure 4.

ii.   It is variable laterally in the same lithologic unit. As an example, consider the results

presented in Figure 8, of tests of a highly permeable, confined unit at C-a Tract at 22 different
locations. Depending on where a shaft happened to
be located in this unit, there is a reasonable
probability that the flow might be as little as 1/3
or as much as 3 times that expected at the median
hydraulic conductivity.

iii. It is variable locally in the same lithologic unit.
Due to the fractured nature of the medium, it would
be reasonable to expect to find differences in
inflow of perhaps an order of magnitude on a 50
foot sampling basis due to random intersection of
major joint or fracture systems.

Thus the average flow to the shaft may vary, by perhaps
a factor of five either way from the flows shown in Figure
5 and the flow at any given time may vary a factor of
perhaps ten either side of this average, at least for short
periods. For design purposes a carefully tested pilot hole
on the centerline of the shaft can evaluate the expected
average flow to good precision, but an allowance of a
factor of something like five for inrushes should be made
in these materials.

Mine Inflow

As is clear from the analysis, the mine inflow is an
almost total function of vertical hydraulic conductivity.
Figure 9 shows this dependence. Only three meaningful
tests of this parameter are known to have been conducted in
the Basin (Ref. 6, p. 114), all of them on the Mahogany
Zone, which for this evaluation is not particularly useful.
Thus the estimates given in Figure 4 are only order of
magnitude estimates. We believe that they are close to the
upper bound; the lower bound may be up to two orders of
magnitude lower. Accordingly it might be reasonable to
expect inflows in the range 1,000 gallons per minute to
10,000 gallons per minute. While this sounds like a huge
range, it is probably about as good a prediction as can be
obtained with anything but the most extensive (and
expensive) testing program.

CONCLUSIONS

The conclusions of this paper are, I believe, straightforward:

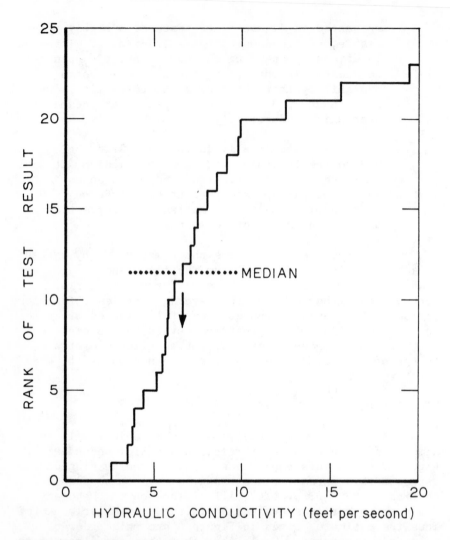

Data from Reference (8)

Figure 8 – Horizontal Hydraulic Conductivity Results –
Lower Aquifer, C-a Tract

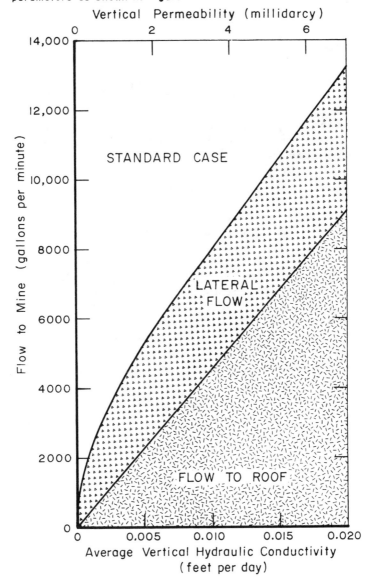

NOTE:
For a 2 mile diameter mine in the Mahogany Zone with other parameters as shown in Figure 4.

Figure 9 – Relationship Between Inflow and Vertical
Hydraulic Conductivity

i.   For oil shale geohydrology analysis, the use of simple models and simple analytical relationships produces results which are of a degree of accuracy which is appropriate to the accuracy of the parameters, and in general to the needs of mine planners.

ii. Use of these simple model forces the analyst to recognize the major parameters influencing the results. This is of great value when an investigation program is being planned, as much money can be, and often has been wasted refining non-critical parameters.

iii. An analysis of uncertainty is essential to this (or any) mining geohydrology study. The responsible engineer must not only produce a best estimate, but also an indication of the spread of possible results of actual mining.

The methods used in this paper are applicable to a wide range of mining geohydrology studies in sedimentary systems. I trust that the methods are of use to those whose responsibility it is to plan mining evaluations, as well as those whose profession is geohydrology.

REFERENCES

1. Darcy, Henri, Les Fontaines publiques de la Ville de Dijon, Dalmont, Paris, 1856.

2. Theis, C.V., The Relation between the Lowering of Piezometric Surface and the Rate and Duration of Discharge of a Well using Ground Water Storage, Trans. Am. Geophysical Union, 16th Annual Meeting, Part 2, 1935.

3. Brown, A. A Simple Approximate Formulation for the Confined Well Equation, (Unpublished note available from the Author), 1979.

4. Hantush, M.S. and C.E. Jacob, Non-steady Radial Flow in an Infinite Leaky Aquifer, Trans. Am. Geophysical Union, Vol. 36, No. 1, 1955.

5. Brown, A. A Simple Approximate Formulation for the Steady State Leaky Aquifer Well Equation, (Unpublished note available from the Author), 1979.

6. Brown, A. M.I. Schauer, J.W. Rowe and W. Heley, Water Management in Oil Shale Mining, Golder Associates, 1977 (U.S.B.M. Contract J0265019, report of investigation).

7. Weeks, J.B.: G.H. Leavesley; F.A. Welder, and G.J. Saulnier, Simulated Effects of Oil Shale Development on the Hydrology of Piceance Basin, Colorado, U.S. Geological Survey Professional Paper 908, 1974.

8. Rio Blanco Oil Shale Project, Progress Report #1, Gulf Oil Corporation and Standard Oil Corporation, 1974.

26

Hydrogeology of a Lead-Zinc Mine

by B. D. Trexler, Jr.,
Hydrogeologist, Metal Mines Division,
Kennecott Copper Corporation,
Salt Lake City, Utah, USA

INTRODUCTION

The Bunker Hill Mine consists of lead-zinc mining properties located along the Coeur d'Alene River near Kellogg,
Idaho (Figure 1). Mining began in 1885 in the form of many
shallow, small drifts and stopes around the original discovery site. The mine now includes more than 150 miles of workings to a depth of almost one mile below land surface. The
volume of ground disturbed by mining is approximately five
cubic miles. Development averages about four miles per year
drifting and about 60,000 feet per year of diamond drill
holes. (1)

Acid mine drainage from the Bunker Hill Mine is discharged into the Bunker Hill tailings pond and constitutes
a major portion water treatment cost. The mine drainage
averages about 2,000 to 2,500 gallons per minute with a pH
of about 4 to 4.7. The pH occasionally drops to 3.3. The
mine discharge is a major contributor of acid, heavy metals
and suspended solids.

Acid production from the mine workings is controlled by:
1) oxygen, 2) availability of pyrite, 3) moisture in the mine
atmosphere, 4) availability of other metal minerals, 5) availability of water to flush oxidized products throughout the

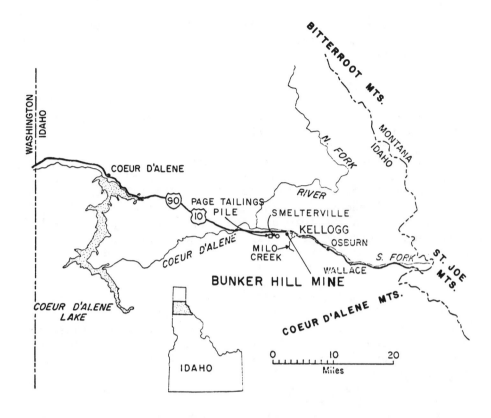

FIG. I MAP OF PART OF NORTHERN
IDAHO AND ADJACENT AREAS
SHOWING THE LOCATION OF
THE BUNKER HILL MINE AND
THE PAGE TAILINGS PILE

mine, and 6) mine characteristics (2). The availability of water in the mine to flush the oxidized minerals is the major factor in the production of the acid discharge.

PREMINING HYDROGEOLOGY

Milo Creek and Deadwood Creek are perennial streams which drain the majority of the surface area over the mine. All of the initial workings are located in the two drainages. Land use in the two drainages is limited primarily to mining activities. The Silverhorn Ski Area is located in the upper part of the Milo Creek drainage basin. The tall peaks (+6,100 feet) and surrounding slopes receive most of their precipitation in the form of snowfall. The average snow-water equivalent on April 1 is 33.5 inches as measured by the U. S. Department of Agriculture, Snow Survey Section (1958-1977 period of records).

The vegetation in the drainage is mostly conifers with strands of fir, pine, and larch in the higher elevations. Some deciduous trees are present in the lower elevations along the creeks. Much of the forest in the lower elevations was cut for mine timbers, lost in forest fires, or the new growth retarded by smelter fumes. The lack of vegetation and the steep slopes create quick runoff responses to rainfall and snowmelt.

The basins are underlain by crystalline rock of the Belt Series which have extremely low primary hydraulic conductivity. Ground water is limited to alluvium in the stream channels, the thin soil and rock cover of the slopes, and the fractures in the basement material. The stream channels are narrow, and alluvium is generally less than ten feet thick.

MINE HYDROGEOLOGY

Available Water in the Mine

The occurrence and movement of water in the Bunker Hill mine are controlled by five mechanisms. These mechanisms are: 1) natural ground-water flow and seepage, 2) faults and shear zones, 3) diamond drill holes, 4) mam-made openings (drifts, stopes, shafts, raises), and 5) water injected into the mine as potable water and sand-fill water. The average yearly total flow discharged from these mechanisms is 3,600 acre-feet.

Natural Ground-Water Flow

One source of available water is from ground-water seepage through country rocks and from natural fracture systems. The county rock is relatively impermeable quartzites and siltite-argillites having extremely low primary hydraulic conductivity except where faulted or fractured.

The primary source of ground water is from the natural fracture systems intersected by drill holes and workings. A survey of approximately 2,340 drill holes and accessible drifts showed 115 drill holes and two drifts flowing 400-500 gallons per minute. Many other drill holes were capped and valved for use in drilling. A crude estimate of the volume of ground water from these valved holes actually used in drilling was calculated. Approximately seven diamond drill rigs using 15 gallons per minute and 55 production drills using 2 gallons per minute are in use during any given year (actual drilling time approximately five hours per day for 220 days per year).

Combining both the free flowing drill holes and the drill water used gives a volume of about 690 acre-feet per year. These values should be considered minimum potential ground-water flow values.

Sand-Fill Water

The sand fill is another mine activity that furnishes water to the mine. Approximately 6.9 acre-feet of water per week is used to transport the sand fill from the mill to the sand tanks. Approximately 1.3 acre-feet of water per week is used in transporting the sand from the sand tanks to the stopes. Estimates of actual sand fill placed and transport water used from 1961 to 1977 are presented in Table I. It can be seen that sand fill is increasing yearly with a resulting increase in transport water.

TABLE I

Sand and Transport Water Used in the Bunker
Hill Mine Sand Backfilling

Year	Sand (tons/year)	Transport Water (acre-feet/year)
1961-1962	100,000	160
1969	188,000	300
1970	179,000	290
1971	188,000	300
1972	214,000	340
1973	223,000	360
1974	272,000	390
1977	296,000	430

Other Mechanisms of Water

The sand-fill water volume (430 acre-feet) and the drill
water volume (690 acre-feet) add to approximately 1120 acre-
feet and account for approximately 30 percent of the total
mine drainage discharged through the Kellogg tunnel. This volume of water represents water needed in the mining (sand fill
and drilling water) and ground-water flow. Said volume of
water is not available for reduction until active mining
ceases. The other 70 percent of the Kellogg tunnel discharge
can be reduced or eliminated during active mining by eliminating surface recharge.

MINING FEATURES RELATED TO WATER MOVEMENT

Proximity of Mining to the Surface

After the mining began in 1885, the equilibrium of the
ground-water system in the mine area was disturbed. Often
the stopes were worked to the surface, some even into creek
beds. This caused increased recharge through stopes and increased discharge from the portals. The Milo Creek area and
the Deadwood Creek area are examples of such a disturbance
(Figure 2).

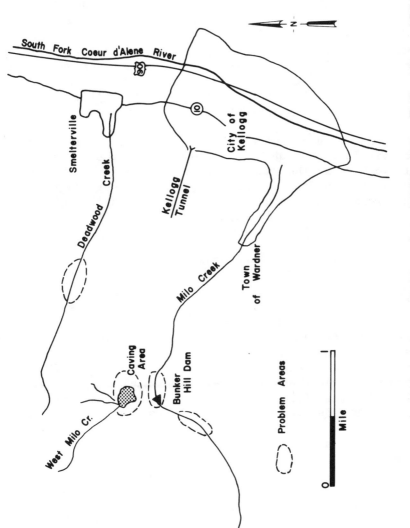

Figure 2.   LOCATION OF BUNKER HILL MINE AND THE MILO CREEK
AND DEADWOOD CREEK PROBLEM AREAS.

As the mining activity extended downward from the upper levels, a vertical zone of high permeability was developed. The porosity is secondary, formed from multi-level stopes and other interconnections. As the water drains down the man-made openings, some of it moves through stopes containing ore and waste fill rich in pyrite. The water becomes acidic as it passes over the waste. The upper levels of the Bunker Hill Mine shown in Figure 3 constitutes a typical example of this vertical zone of high permeability.

Block caving, used in the upper levels of the mine, forms another vertical zone of high permeability. The surface depression caused by the subsidence brought about by the caving creates a major surface recharge site. This surface feature channels three small intermittent tributary valleys of Milo Creek directly into the caved area where the water freely moves on down through the old workings.

Hydrograph Similarity Between Mine and Surface Flows

It was noted that certain areas in the mine discharge water only during periods which correspond to high surface flows. Hydrographs from the Kellogg Tunnel (the main drainage path from the mine), the Cherry Ditch (drainage into the Kellogg Tunnel from the levels of the mine above level 9), and a surface stream are presented in Figure 4. The hydrograph of Milo Creek is shown in Figure 4 for the water year from October 1972, to September 1973. The difference of water volume between the Kellogg Tunnel and Cherry Ditch hydrographs is the water pumped from levels 10 and below and the sand-fill tank overflow.

A similarity exists between the hydrographs from the Kellogg Tunnel, Cherry Ditch and Milo Creek. The high flows in the mine correspond to high flows in the surface streams resulting from snowmelt; little lag time is noted. Daily discharge measurements show a lag time between 12 to 24 hours. The similiarity of the hydrographs implies a rather direct connection of the mine to the surface.

A similar pattern exists between the hydrographs of the pumping levels of the mine when compared to Milo Creek (Figure 5). Sharp distinctive peaks are seen on each pumping level. The lower the pumping level from the 20 level, the less sharp the similarities between surface and mine flows. This implies less direct interconnection of the lower levels to the surface. However, there is sufficient

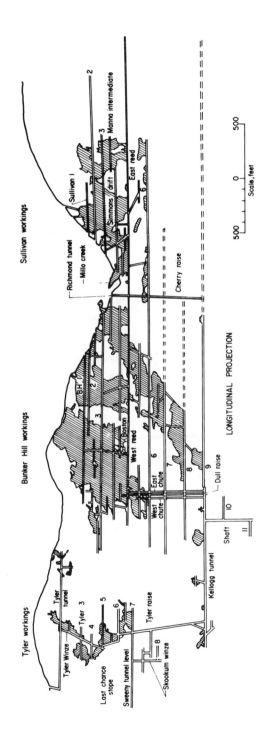

Figure 3. CROSS SECTION OF UPPER COUNTRY OF BUNKER HILL MINE SHOWING STOPED AREAS.

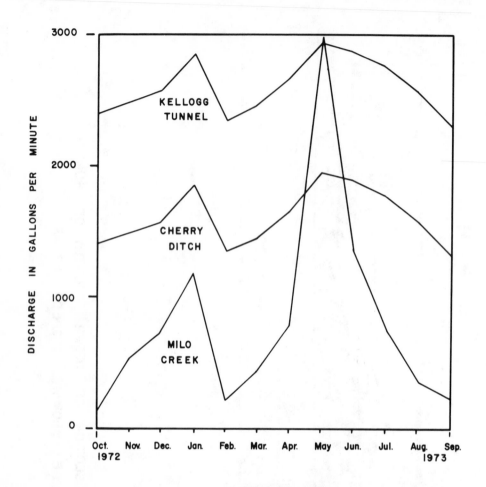

Figure 4.   MEAN MONTHLY DISCHARGE OF MILO
CREEK AND MINE DRAINAGE.

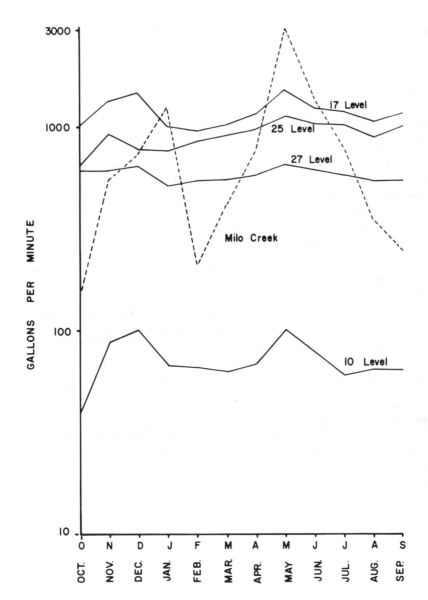

Figure 5. HYDROGRAPHS OF MEAN MONTHLY PUMP FLOWS FOR THE PERIOD 1972-73 FOR THE BUNKER HILL MINE, PUMP FLOW VALUES DERIVED FROM POWER CONSUMPTION VALUES. (27 AND 25 LEVEL PUMPS ARE INTERMEDIATE LIFT STATIONS)

interconnection to warrant an investigation to stop or direct this water higher in the mine to save on pumping cost.

Recharge Potential in the Milo Creek Basin

Many of the old workings on the upper levels of the Bunker Hill Mine are located in the Milo Creek drainage. Much of the recharge to the mine occurs in this area. Most of the precipitation in the upper parts of the drainage is in the form of snow which generally remains well into the spring. The average snowwater equivalent on April 1 is 33.5 inches. The surface area above the potential recharge areas consists of 2,200 acres. This gives a potential runoff (assuming that runoff is 50 percent of total water) of 3,070 acre-feet.

Small Hopes Drift Dye tracer tests were conducted to determine any potential hydrologic interconnection of surface water with underground workings. The procedure was to collect background samples from selected sites, the Reed Tunnel and the Small Hopes drift. The Reed Tunnel is the major drainage path of water from the 5 level, especially the east 5 level and stopes paralleling Milo Creek. The Small Hopes drift is on the 4 level of the mine and drains into the east 5 level. Rhodamine WT dye was injected in Milo Creek for two 5-minute intervals. Samples were periodically collected from the Reed Tunnel and the Small Hopes drift. The results of the trials, shown in Table II, show that seepage loss does occur from Milo Creek from the reach investigated and that recharge does occur to the mine workings. The lag time was less than one hour. The interconnection is thus very direct. Hydrograph records from the Small Hopes drift show a pattern similar to the Milo Creek hydrograph at the Bunker Hill dam.

TABLE II

Fluorescent Tracer Analysis for the Recharge Potential
of Milo Creek to the Underground Workings

Time	Small Hopes	Reed Tunnel
Background count	0.0096	0.044
8:25 a.m.	Dye injected into Milo Creek	
8:25 a.m.	0.0096	0.044
8:40 a.m.	0.0220	0.110
9:10 a.m.	0.0132	0.175
9:25 a.m.	Dye injected into Milo Creek	
9:25 a.m.	0.0096	0.044
9:45 a.m.	0.0230	0.078
10:10 a.m.	0.0106	0.230

Milo Creek Dye dilution measurements of the streamflow were
conducted upstream from the Bunker Hill dam. The purpose of
the dye dilution measurements of the stream was to detect
stream losses that could be correlated with recharge to the
mine.

Milo Creek was then divided into sections for a distance
of a few thousand feet above the Bunker Hill dam for the investigation of stream loss. This reach of the creek was
selected because the Cate Fault is known to strike approximately parallel to Milo Creek in this area. The Cate Fault
is associated with most of the water being discharged from
the natural fracture system underground.

The first trial was to determine the amount of seepage
through the Bunker Hill reservoir. The difference between
upstream and downstream measured rates show a loss of about
60 gallons per minute. The seepage loss was caused by the
removal of a fine silt-sediment cover by the mining company
in an attempt to gain more storage behind the dam. The removal of the fine sediments allowed water movement through
the reservoir bottom and down through the Small Hopes drift
and the Reed Tunnel. As the fine sediment cover is being
redeposited, the seepage volumes into the workings have
slowly declined.

Other discharge measurements were made in Milo Creek above
the dam for several thousand feet. A reach of stream beginning approximately 1,000 feet from the reservoir and continuing for about 1,000 feet showed statistically significant
losses. The losses are shown in Table III along with the
volume of water flowing in the stream at the time of measurement. The higher losses are due to greater mean flow in the
stream. At high flow, the creek spreads out five to ten
times the normal width. The recharge potential may be increased because of the larger surface area of the stream and
the greater head. The low loss occurred when the stream was
confined to its smallest stream bottom areas.

TABLE III

Losses from Milo Creek Above the Bunker Hill Dam

Time Period	Loss, in gpm	Stream Flow, in gpm
10-5-73	450	1530
17-5-73	1470	4810
11-7-73	1390	2150
23-7-73	560	740

The significant aspect of the recharge from the Milo Creek
area is the volume of water entering the mine. This water is
not believed to recharge any major acid-producing areas in
the mine. The recharge water dilutes the poorer quality
water in the underground workings. The additional water from
Milo Creek water contributes to several problems. These problems are: 1) additional water to pump or drain, 2) additional
water volume to treat, 3) "wet" working environment, and 4)
potential water to flush any acid-producing area that might
become exposed in the future.

Guy Caving Area A second area of recharge to the mine is
located in the West Milo Creek drainage (Figure 2). Recharge occurs through a surface depression formed from block
caving. Caving mining methods were initiated on the 4, 5,
and 6 levels of the mine in the late 1940's. Once caving is
started, it continues until it reaches a stable condition.
In the West Milo Creek basin, the caving has extended to land

surface leaving a crater about 200–300 feet across and 40 feet deep. The movement initated by caving is continuing in the area. The caving feature is very important with respect to recharge to the mine as it provides a highly permeable vertical connection between 4, 5, and 6 levels of the mine and the surface. Warm moist air rises as a vapor cloud from the caving area through portions of this highly permeable, vertical zone during the winter. The source of the vapor cloud is the exhaust ventilation from the deeper mine areas. The presence of the vapor cloud confirms that this highly permeable zone is connected with the lower mine workings.

The caving area is located at the intersection of three small valleys, all tributaries of Milo Creek. Much of the runoff from this area is funneled into the depression formed by caving. No signs of surface outflow from the depression are present. The potential surface runoff to this area is significant. The average water content of the snowpack at the head of the valley is 33.5 inches as measured on April 1. The snowpack covers approximately 230 acres in the drainage. A total of about 300 acre–feet of potential runoff (using runoff as 50 percent total water) is thus available for recharge to the caving area.

The mining company attempted to divert surface flows from the caving area through use of several dams and raises connected to the Phil Sheridan adit (Figure 6). The Phil Sheridan adit is located about 300 feet north of the caving area. The elevation of this level is approximately the same as the upper part of the caving area. There are two drifts which join near the portal. The left drift follows a path around the caving area and connects with two raises which were driven to the surface to collect and divert surface water from the caving area. These raises are located in the bottom of small draws to intercept surface runoff above the caving area.

A sharp-crested, V-notch weir and a continuous recorder were installed in the West Milo Creek drainage to obtain an estimate of the potential flow into the caving area. The weir becomes operational at about the same time that snowmelt begins in the upper part of the drainage. The hydrographs show a steady rise in flow because of increased snowmelt during the period. The water discharging over the West Milo weir is lost to ground water about 3,000 feet downstream from the weir.

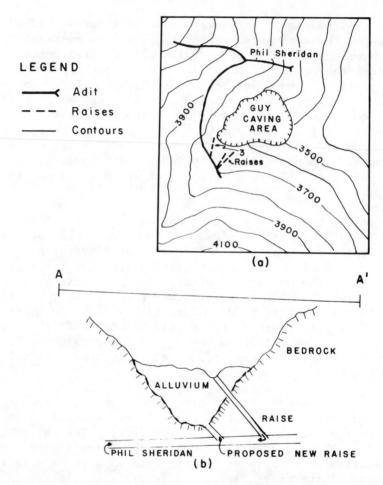

Phil Sheridan

GUY
CAVING
AREA

3900

3500

3700

3900

4100

3
Raises

(a)

A   A'

BEDROCK

ALLUVIUM

RAISE

PHIL SHERIDAN   PROPOSED NEW RAISE

(b)

FIG. 6. (a) MAP VIEW OF GUY CAVING AREA AND
PHIL SHERIDAN ADIT. (b) CROSS-SECTION
SHOWING PROPOSED NEW RAISE.

One of the raises that connects to the Phil Sheridan adit is located a few hundred feet down drainage from the recharge point. Some of this runoff is collected by the two raises and is diverted through the Phil Sheridan around the caving area (Figure 6). The two raises are located near the two largest drainages and have cobble dikes to divert the water into the raises.

The dikes which were constructed to divert water into the raises are only partially effective. The dikes are high enough (about 4 feet) and the raises large enough (about 5-feet diameter) to capture much of the high flow runoff. These dikes do not capture the ground water flowing in the shallow alluvium. Leakage through the dikes probably occurs because of the cobble material making up the embankments. Water passing the dikes recharges the underground workings through the caving area. Some evapo-transpiration occurs in the area, but the loss is believed to be small. Ground-water outflow from the west drainage to the lower drainage is considered negligible. Much of the area consists of exposed bedrock, and any ground water in fractures would most likely be intercepted by mine workings before it could reach the lower drainage.

An unknown quantity of water seeps from the drifts of the Phil Sheridan adit. The water must pond and fill up the tunnel to a depth of several feet in some areas before it will flow out the adit. This ponding disappears after flow occurs indicating downward seepage. Evaporation from ponds in the drift would probably be small because the air is nearly saturated from the exhaust from the lower sections of the mine.

An attempt was made to determine the effectiveness of the diversion system around the caving area by measuring the discharge from the Phil Seridan adit. A sharp-crested, V-notch weir and a recorder were installed at the portal of the Phil Sheridan to record the amount of runoff diverted by this system. The volume of water discharged through the Phil Sheridan weir during the 1973 flow period totaled 0.13 acre-feet. Some seepage probably occurs out of the drift leading to the raises because of its proximity to the caving area. The recorded discharge is thus only a minimum estimate of the water entering the raises.

The area of surface caving consists of about 1.3 acres. This area receives the runoff that is not intercepted by the diversion raises plus direct precipitation. There is no apparent surface water discharge from the caving area. Water entering the depression must either evaporate or move downward into the underground workings. Evaporation is believed to be nil from the caving area. No signs of ponding are evident in the depressions.

A water loss of at least 18.6 acre-feet was noted from a comparison of the hydrographs of the Phil Sheridan and West Milo weirs during the 1973 flow period. Most, if not all, of this water loss is to the mine. This is a minimum estimate of water loss to the mine workings in the caving area because the records from the upper weir include flow from only the upper one-third of the west drainage area. The total runoff cannot be accurately calculated by comparing the drainage areas because the snowfall is greater in the area above the West Milo weir than below. The total runoff above the caving area during this period is estimated to have been about 50 acre-feet.

If the runoff occurs during short periods of high flows when the ground surface is frozen, then the diversion system through the Phil Sheridan adit keeps most of the water out of the mine. However, if runoff occurs at a more moderate rate over a long period of time, the diversion system does not capture much of the water.

Recharge to the mine from the Guy Caving area is important, not only because of the quantity of water but because of the path the water recharge follows in the mined area. The recharge is directed over and through stopes containing pyrite-rich ore. With the addition of large quantities of water to these stopes, acid solutions are washed downward where they leach out heavy metals. This particular recharge area is a major concern for the production of low pH water.

Deadwood Creek The Deadwood Creek area is the third area of recharge. Recharge occurs where older workings have intersected the creek channel. Precipitation is mainly in the form of snow with an average snow water equivalent of 33.5 inches as measured on April 1. Deadwood Creek during late summer and early fall has no low flow component. The surface area above the potential recharge zone includes 1,005 acres. This gives a potential runoff (using runoff as 50 percent total available water) of 1,400 acre-feet per year.

Dye tracer tests were used to determine the extent of hydrologic interconnection between surface waters and underground

workings. Sample points established on the 9 level nearly
2,000 feet horizontally and 1,200 feet vertically from the dye
injected area. Samples could not be obtained underground at
any point closer to the suspected recharge area because of
caving of the old workings. The tracer data show a definite
interconnection between Deadwood Creek and water discharged
on level 9 (Table IV). The differences in lag times are believed to be due to the variation in streamflow rates. These
data show the interconnection of surface to underground
through the Arizona-Oakland-Inez workings. These workings
are located at the extreme west area of the mine and are approximately at the same position as level 4 and level 5 in
the Milo Creek area.

TABLE IV

Appearance Time of Injected Dyes on Level 9

Run Number	Concentration (ppm)	Peak Appearance time hours)	Visual Estimate of Surface Flow
1	5,600	20	200 gpm
2	54,000	36	120 gpm
3	200,000	12	200 gpm

CONCLUSIONS

The Bunker Hill Mine discharges approximately 3,600 acre-
feet of water yearly. The sources comprising the flow are:
1) ground-water flow (approximately 690 acre-feet yearly), 2)
sand-fill water (approximately 430 acre-feet yearly, and 3)
surface water recharged to the mine (approximately 2,500
acre-feet yearly). The surface water recharge to the mine
is a major factor in the movement of poor quality water in
the mine.

Four areas recharging the mine were identified. The potential
recharge from these four areas is 4,800 acre-feet yearly. Reduction or elimination or recharge from the four identified
areas should reduce the Kellogg Tunnel discharge by about 30 to
50 percent. Reduction measures include:

1. Relocation of raises and construction of cutoff walls above the Guy Caving area.

2. Pipes or flumes with collector inlets to bypass areas of faults and fractures in Milo Creek and areas of mine workings in Deadwood Creek.

3. Elimination of water flowing from diamond drill holes by capping and valving.

4. Reduction in water used in the sand-fill process by increasing slurry density.

ACKNOWLEDGEMENTS

The author wishes to thank the U. S. Bureau of Mines, the Bunker Hill Company, and the University of Idaho for funding this study from which this paper is generated. The opinions expressed are those of the author and not necessarily those of the U. S. Bureau of Mines or the Bunker Hill Company.

REFERENCES

(1) Farmer, J, 1974, Bunker Hill Mine Technical Services, personal communication.

(2) Trexler, B. D., Jr., Ralston, D. R., Reece, D. R., and Williams, R. E., 1975, Sources and Causes of Acid Mine Drainage: Idaho Bureau of Mines and Geology Pamphlet No. 165, Moscow, Idaho, 129 p.

27

Depressurization for Shaft Sinking

by William M. Greenslade, Partner,
Dames & Moore,
Phoenix, Arizona, USA

INTRODUCTION

As the search for minerals leads to deeper mines the need to control water inflow into mine shafts and mine workings will grow. As shallower more readily available minerals are exploited, ore bodies which were previously uneconomic because of their depth will now become attractive targets. In known mining districts new ore bodies are being discovered down dip of existing ones. In the west many metal deposits are being developed in rocks of the mountain front pediments, frequently covered by several hundred feet of saturated alluvium. Greater depth often means that workings are developed well below existing water tables, creating high hydrostatic heads adjacent to mine workings.

The purpose of this paper is to review some of the methods available for determining if water control will be necessary and to present some of the techniques for locating water bearing zones and the amount of water to be expected. The paper will concentrate on problems associated with water control in mine shaft development, although many of the exploratory techniques are similar to those needed for assessing overall mine water inflow problems. A brief case history on water control problems in mine

shafts in the Grants mineral belt of northwestern New
Mexico is presented.

Water control during shaft sinking presents some unique
features. First, the problem is a relatively short term
one, since water control is often necessary only while the
shaft is being sunk. Control measures may be necessary
only while the shaft is open into the water bearing zone
and the lining installed and cemented. Secondly, limited
working space within the shaft area presents difficulties
in handling large amounts of water inflow. The presence
of water in the shaft working area increases sinking time
and the potential hazard to miners. Finally, there is the
economics of shaft sinking. While the shaft is being sunk
no ore is being produced and there is every incentive to
minimize costs.

IMPORTANCE OF WATER CONTROL

The importance of controlling water inflow during shaft
development has been well known to those faced with the
problem. Depending on the amount, temperature, and quality
of the water, the extra costs of working in wet conditions
can easily be several times that for the same work under
dry conditions. I have heard estimates of cost increases
from 25 percent to 300 percent. The actual cost increase
can be controlled if the water inflow is expected and if
adequate control measures are employed prior to encountering the water.

Table 1 lists some of the problems that can be associated with working under wet conditions. The more obvious
of these effects are considered direct, that is directly
associated with pumping or controlling water inflow.
Usually most mining projects will have taken these into
account at feasibility stage. However, there are also
indirect effects which are not always fully accounted for
during the early feasibility stages. These include such
items as muddy conditions, freezing of water in the
shafts, added equipment maintenance, reduction in ground
stability and washed ground, problems with explosives and
scaling of pipes. These are indirect effects which occur
within the shaft itself. Others may occur outside the
shaft area including the effect on surrounding water users
of drawing down local water tables during pumping from the
shaft and the discharge of potentially poor quality water
to surface drainages.

Table No. I

EFFECTS OF WET CONDITIONS
(After Loofbourow, SME Mining Engineering Handbook)

1. Direct Effects

 - Costs of pumping.
 - Failure to handle inflow may interrupt sinking and could damage the shaft, perhaps beyond recovery, perhaps with loss of life.

2. Indirect Effects in Shaft

 - Freezing water in cold areas.
 - Reduced efficiency of crews and equipment.
 - Added equipment maintenance.
 - Reduced stability of walls and potential for washed ground.
 - In areas of hot water, increased heat and humidity.
 - Interferes with certain explosives.
 - Scale in pipes and pumps.

3. Indirect Effects outside Shaft

 - Drawdown may effect surrounding water wells.
 - Poor quality water may pollute surface waters.

DETERMINING THE NEED FOR WATER CONTROL

The first question to be answered is whether or not water control during shaft sinking will be necessary. Ground water occurs to some degree or another in nearly all rocks below a few tens of feet below the ground surface. Whether or not water is present in sufficient quantity or is of such poor quality as to warrant control measures must be determined prior to selection of the shaft sinking method.

One of the best indicators is previous experience. If the mine is located in an area of previous or existing mining activity, it is relatively simple matter to evaluate whether water will be a problem or not. Even in this case, however, care should be taken to determine if the new shaft will be in a hydrogeologic setting that is the same as the surrounding existing shafts. It is best to carefully review what is known of the existing geology of the area in order to evaluate known or suspected aquifers or water-bearing zones in the new shaft area.

Whether the shaft is located in an existing mining district or not, data from exploration borings can be very valuable, especially if at least some are designed to evaluate hydrogeologic conditions. Usually borings are drilled without regard to hydrogeologic parameters. Detailed logs are often only kept on the portion of the hole that penetrates the suspected ore horizon. No attempt is made to locate or measure water levels in borings. This is unfortunate because it is usually possible, at very little additional cost, to add hydrologic parameters to the geologic parameters normally considered during an exploration program. It is an investment which can produce a very high rate of return in terms of early identification of potential water problems and can reduce the need to essentially re-drill footage once a water problem is identified.

ASSESSING THE LOCATION AND AMOUNT OF WATER

Once it is determined that the potential for significant water inflow into the shaft exists, detailed knowledge of the subsurface conditions must be obtained. The exact level of detail required is dependent upon the specific geohydrologic conditions in the shaft area. In areas where the geology is relatively uniform and water movement is not controlled by fractures and faulting, much useful information can be obtained from other mines, exploration boreholes, and a general knowledge of the site hydrogeology. However, when water movement is thought to be predominately fracture controlled, detailed knowledge of the specific shaft site is needed, as water inflows can vary by several orders of magnitude if a significant fracture or other zone of high permeability is encountered in the shaft. The following paragraphs discuss some of the available field techniques to assess the hydrogeologic character of subsurface materials.

Field Methods

A number of field methods are employed to locate potential water bearing zones and to estimate their water yield to the shaft. As in all engineering studies, a balance between costs and expected results must be maintained. Field methods can be divided into two broad categories, direct and indirect. Direct methods involve coring, in-

hole testing, and laboratory testing. Indirect methods
include geologic mapping, preparation of cross sections,
and geophysical logging. Direct methods generally produce
more accurate and reliable results but also cost more.
Table 2 compares some of the advantages and disadvantages
of the various field methods in general use.

The results of the field program must allow a reasonable
estimate of the parameters necessary to calculate: 1) the
hydrostatic head in the shaft area, 2) anticipated inflow
rates with time, and 3) the ground water velocity across
the shaft area. Specifically, the following data must be
known:

1. Location, depth, thickness and extent of known
    aquifers and confining beds.

2. Tranmsmissivity and storage coefficient of aquifers
    and confining beds.

3. Whether aquifers are under water table or artesian
    conditions.

4. Head relationships.

5. Location and attitude of faults.

6. Nature of fault zones (impermeabile barriers or con-
    duits for water movement).

7. Position of proposed shaft within the areal hydrologic
    system (recharge, discharge, or horizontal flow area).

8. Water quality.

Predicting Water Inflow

Relative to the larger problem of mine dewatering, estimates of probable water inflow to a shaft are simplified by
the fact that a shaft is essentially a large diameter well
and there is an extensive body of theory governing flow to
wells. Once the above design parameters for each potential
water-bearing horizon are known, the approximate water
inflow at any given time can be estimated with the following equation:

Table No. II

FIELD TECHNIQUES

	Advantages	Limitations
Coring	- Excellent Stratigraphic Control - Visual Log of Subsurface - Samples for Testing - Record for Use During Sinking	- High Cost - Time to Drill - Small Area Examined
Geophysical Logging	- Good Stratigraphic Control - Low/Moderate Cost - Rapid - Continuous Record - In-situ Properties	- No Samples - Affected by Borehole Fluid - Results Relative - Required Skill Interpreter

Table No. II (cont'd)

Drill Stem Tests	– Rapid – Moderate Cost – Evaluate Borehole Effects – Samples – In-situ Properties	– Low/Moderate Premeabilities – Possible Leakage Around Packers – Limited Area Investigated
Injection Tests	– Rapid – Moderate Cost – Good Grouting Data – In-situ Properties	– Low/Moderate Permeabilities – Possible Leakage Around Packers – Usually Underestimate Permeability – No Samples – Affected by Borehole Condition
Pumping Tests	– Large Area Investigated – Assess Boundary – Water Samples – Simulate Actual Dewatering – Experimental Design Data	– High Cost – Control Water Discharge – Temporary Effect on Surrounding Wells – Time to Drill and Test

$$Q/s = \frac{T}{264 \log \left[\dfrac{Tt}{1.87 \, r_w^2 \, S}\right]} - 65.5$$

where r_w is the radius of the shaft, in feet, S is the storage coefficient, T is the transmissivity, in GPD/FT, t is the time after pumping started, in days. This equation yields the theoretical full-penetration specific capacity (Q/s) of the shaft in gallons per minute per foot of drawdown (GPM/FT). The inflow rate is found by multiplying the available drawdown (s) by the specific capacity.

Depending upon the type of shaft construction and the aquifer thickness, a given water-bearing horizon may not be exposed throughout its entire thickness at any given time. Such would be the case for a thick aquifer where the shaft is excavated 10 to 20 feet ahead of the lining. In this case, the theoretical full penetration specific capacity would overestimate the actual quantity of water that will flow into the shaft. If the amount of partial penetration at any given time is known, the reduced specific capacity can be calculated from the following equation:

$$Q'/s' = Q/s \left[\frac{L}{M} \left(1 + 7\sqrt{\frac{r_w}{2L}} \cos \frac{\pi L}{2M}\right)\right]$$

where Q'/s' is the specific capcity of the partially penetrating shaft, L is the length of the open hole, and M is the aquifer thickness. The adjusted specific capacity (Q'/s') is then multiplied by the total available head to estimate water inflow. This equation is valid only under near steady state conditions.

SELECTION OF WATER CONTROL METHOD

Once a determination is made that water control techniques will be required, it remains to select the optimum control system. Common systems include installation of water rings, sump pumping, grouting, freezing, and pumping from deep wells outside the shaft perimeter. It is not the purpose of this paper to compare advantages and disadvantages of various water control methods. However, a few general observations can be made.

Collecting water that flows into the shaft and pumping it to the surface is the most time honored method of water control. Water rings can be installed as the shaft liner advances allowing for better control of the inflowing water. This is probably the least cost method, however, it is not effective where large water inflows, especially in poor ground, are encountered.

Grouting is probably the second most popular method. Water-bearing zones can be grouted from the surface or from various levels within the shaft as it advances. In addition to reducing rock permeability, grouting can also increase strength in weak ground. Grouting is not without its difficulties, however. It is as much an art as a science and works best when there are well defined isolated fracture systems that contribute most of the water. Grouting may be less effective in fine-grained materials or in fractured areas where clay may be present along openings.

Freezing is a technique that has gained popularity in soft ground areas. Unlike grouting, freezing is undertaken from the surface and may require relatively deep, very closely spaced holes ringing the perimeter of the shaft. In some cases, the time to freeze the ground may be a factor in considering this technique. It is generally recognized as one of the most expensive methods of water control.

Deep dewatering wells can be used to reduce hydrostatic pressures and water inflow rates. Wells are often used in conjunction with sump pumps and grouting. In many cases, dewatering wells will only reduce water inflow into the shaft, not completely stop it. Wells are only effective when there is a continuous, sufficient flow of water to allow continuous pumping.

The remainder of this paper presents a typical case history of a water control method that is gaining acceptance in the deep uranium mine shafts in northwestern New Mexico.

CASE HISTORY

Introduction

Uranium mining in northwestern New Mexico began in the 1950's. Early mines were generally less than 800 feet in depth and water was removed from shafts and workings with sump pumps. New ore discoveries at depths of 2,000 to

4,000 feet and the presence of aquifers with water under 1,000 feet or more of hydrostatic head have necessitated new methods of water control.

Hydrogeology

The Grants Mineral Belt is located in the San Juan Basin, a structural depression that occupies a 25,000 square mile area in northwestern New Mexico and adjacent parts of Colorado, Arizona and Utah. Approximately 15,000 feet of sedimentary rock are present in the deepest part of the basin.

Geology of the southern and western parts of the basin, in which the Grants mineral belt is located, is characterized by a thick sequence of sandstones and shales generally dipping to the northeast. The basin was formed during late Cretaceous to Eocene time. A typical geologic column is shown on Figure 1.

The area is relatively free of major structural activity. Locally some faulting and folding has been detected but displacements are relatively small. In general, permeability is primary, or through the rock interstices.

The ore is located in the Westwater Canyon Member of the Morrison Formation (Late Jurrasic). Depending on the precise location within the basin, overlying units consist of interbedded sandstones and shales of Cretaceous age and unconsolidated alluvium. Existing mines in updip portions of the Westwater Canyon formation are known to produce significant quantities of water. Some overlying sandstones are also known to be waterbearing. In some of the deeper mine areas, exploration boreholes exhibit artesian conditions with water flowing at the surface.

The following case history is a composite of several studies performed by the author over the past few years. The data presented do not apply to any particular site, but is representative of the general area.

Determination of Water Producing Zones

Usually shaft investigations are concerned not only with water control but also rock conditions which could effect shaft sinking. Therefore, the field program is designed to develop pertinent data for both the hydrologic and geotechnical studies. All studies have included a bore hole

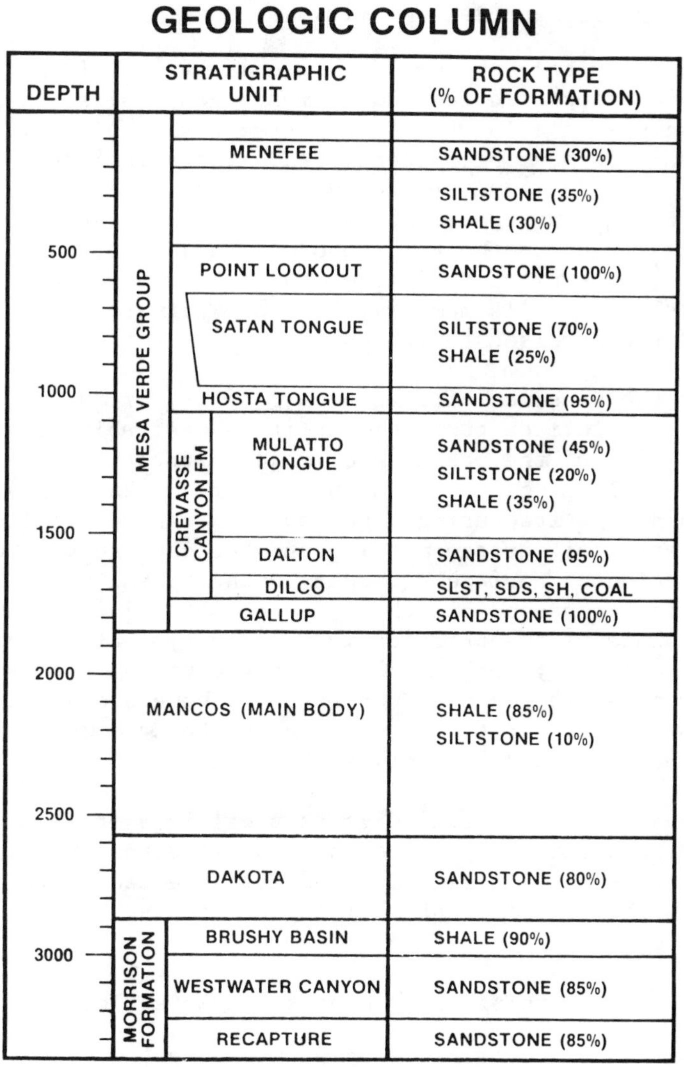

GEOLOGIC COLUMN

DEPTH	STRATIGRAPHIC UNIT			ROCK TYPE (% OF FORMATION)
	MESA VERDE GROUP		MENEFEE	SANDSTONE (30%)
				SILTSTONE (35%) SHALE (30%)
500			POINT LOOKOUT	SANDSTONE (100%)
			SATAN TONGUE	SILTSTONE (70%) SHALE (25%)
1000			HOSTA TONGUE	SANDSTONE (95%)
		CREVASSE CANYON FM	MULATTO TONGUE	SANDSTONE (45%) SILTSTONE (20%) SHALE (35%)
1500			DALTON	SANDSTONE (95%)
			DILCO	SLST, SDS, SH, COAL
			GALLUP	SANDSTONE (100%)
2000	MANCOS (MAIN BODY)			SHALE (85%) SILTSTONE (10%)
2500				
	DAKOTA			SANDSTONE (80%)
3000	MORRISON FORMATION		BRUSHY BASIN	SHALE (90%)
			WESTWATER CANYON	SANDSTONE (85%)
			RECAPTURE	SANDSTONE (85%)

Figure No. 1

drilled from the surface to below the ore horizon. The core
obtained from this hole is analyzed for rock strength and
engineering characteristics as well as hydrologic properties. The hydrologic properties included stratigraphy,
lithology, fracture intensity, and cementation. Representative samples of the sandstone were tested in the laboratory
for permeability and grain size distribution. A set of geophysical logs are usually obtained from the core hole. These
include caliber, density, temperature, self-potential, resis-

tivity, porosity and 3-D velocity.

Potential water-bearing zones are identified from the hydrologic properties log and from the geophysical logs. Depending upon the location within the basin up to six major aquifers have been identified. These include, in descending order, some of the thicker sandstones in the Menefee Formation, the Point Lookout Sandstone, the Hosta Sandstone Tongue of the Point Lookout Sandstone, the Dalton Sandstone, the Gallup Sandstone, the Dakota Sandstone, (including the Two Wells member), and the Westwater Canyon sandstone of the Morrison Formation.

Since the presence of fractures, joints, or faults can significantly affect permeability it is desirable to obtain an indication of the presence of major discontinuities. In addition to logging fractures in the core, a knowledge of areal jointing, fracturing, and faulting can be obtained by a combination of surface mapping and the construction of cross-sections. Surface outcrops in the vicinity of the shaft site are mapped and the orientation of joints and fractures analyzed statistically. As is typical of thinly bedded sedimentary rock, two prominent dividing plains are commonly noted in the San Juan Basin. These are approximately perpendicular to the bedding and to each other. Both joints sets are predominately subvertical.

Cross-sections, utilizing geophysical logs from nearby exploration boreholes, can be constructed across proposed shaft site areas. These cross-sections are useful in determining whether significant faulting or folding occurs in the vicinity of the proposed shaft.

Estimation of Hydrologic Properties and Water Inflow Rates

Following the identification of the potential water-bearing zones a test program must be designed to determine the major hydrologic parameters. These parameters include transmissivity, storage coefficient, water levels and boundary conditions. An ideal test program would consist of the installation of a pumping well and at least one observation well in each major water producing zone. However, from a practical standpoint it is not always cost effective to drill two or more wells to each zone and some alternative methods have been devised that represent a compromise between cost and information obtained.

One such compromise involves the installation of observation wells in the most prolific of the aquifers, with the remaining zones being tested in a single well that penetrates all aquifers. Typically, observation wells are located in the Point Lookout, Dakota, and Westwater Canyon Sandstones. Where wells flow at the surface hydraulic coefficients can be determined for each observation well by utilizing constant drawdown testing procedures. Where wells do not flow a pump must be installed. In either case, a test well is installed and designed to test all identified aquifers, including those with observation wells. Since the head and expected flow from each aquifer usually varies greatly, the pumping system must be flexible to accomodate these expected variations. A system utilizing compressed air or nitrogen eliminates the cost of purchasing, installing, and removing several different pumps in order to test all the zones. Construction of a typical test well is shown on Figure 2. In this case the well is drilled to the lowermost aquifer and casing installed and cemented to the surface. The well is then pump tested. Overlying formations (starting with the Gallup Sandstone) are tested by installing a wireline bridge plug below each zone and perforating the casing over the entire aquifer thickness. Following pumping of the perforated zone a second wireline packer is set below the next overlying zone and the perforating-pumping sequence repeated for each zone going up the hole.

Field test results, laboratory permeability and grain-size determinations, and visual examination of rock core are used to select design parameters. Transmissivity and permeability values normally vary considerably, reflecting the complex depositional pattern of the deposits. Normally, the results of field pumping tests are given the most weight in parameter selection, as these tests indicate any secondary as well as primary permeability effects and a much greater volume of aquifer is tested. Pump test results are analyzed for evidence of recharge or discharge boundaries, and leakance through the confining beds calculated. Since shaft sinking is a relatively short-term operation, it is not necessary to conduct long-term pumping tests. Typically, tests are run from between 24 and 72 hours on major aquifer zones and as short as four hours on minor zones. The ability to define boundary conditions during tests less than 24 hours is limited, however.

Following the selection of design parameters, estimates of water inflow rates from each aquifer can be made utilizing the formula presented earlier. The results of a typical study in a deeper portion of the San Juan Basin are shown

SCHEMATIC OF TEST WELL CONSTRUCTION

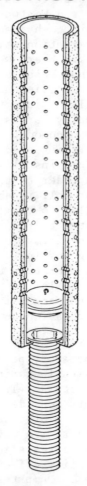

Figure No. 2

on Table 3.

Design of Deep Well Water Control System

Recent deep shafts in the Grants mineral belt have utilized a system of grouting, sump pumping and pumping from deep
wells. Wells are installed and pumped for some time period
prior to the penetration of each aquifer by the shaft.

The sandstone aquifers in the San Juan Basin cannot be
completely dewatered with wells. The aquifers are artesian,

Table No. III

ESTIMATED WATER INFLOW

22-FOOT DIAMETER SHAFT

Aquifer	Transmissivity (Gallson/Day/Foot)	Penetration (Feet)	Average Flow Rate (GPM) (@ 90 Days)
Menefee*	200	40	25
Point Lookout	2000	10	250
		20	400
		30	500
Hosta*	500	86	400
Dalton	100	10	75
		20	100
		30	125
Upper Gallup*	500	40	650
Lower Gallup*	200	80	300

Table No. III (cont'd)

Dakota	600	10	400
		20	600
		30	750
Westwater Canyon	1000	10	450
		20	700
		30	900

*Thin aquifers not analyzed for partial penetration.

deep, relatively thin, and have low tranmissivities. If the water level is drawn down below the top of the aquifer in the pumping well, very little additional drawdown at the shaft (compared to the total available drawdown) is gained and it is readily offset by a decrease in transmissivity at the pumping well due to the reduction of the saturated thickness of the aquifer. The principle benefit to be obtained from pumping from wells is a major reduction in hydrostatic pressure; and while the flow into the shaft is not eliminated it is significantly reduced. Since the wells are not designed to dewater the aquifers they are referred to as "depressurizing" rather than dewatering wells.

If grouting is to be conducted while depressurizing wells are in operation, it is desirable to prevent excessive migration of the grout away from the shaft by minimizing ground water velocities in the shaft area. A ground water velocity less than two feet per day is considered optimum.

Design alternatives for a depressurizing system involve comparison of well construction procedures, number of wells, field geometry, duration of pumping, and ground water velocity across the shaft area. Consideration must be given to the feasibility of completing each depressuring well in more than one aquifer and of deepening wells to lower aquifers when depressurization is no longer required.

Multiple completions (in more than one aquifer) involve pumping larger quantities of water and are more complicated to construct. If the pumping level is drawn below the upper aquifer, cascading water will occur and larger diameter casing may be needed for a pump shroud in order to provide adequate pump cooling. A screen and possibly gravel packing of the upper aquifer may be necessary to elimate sand inflow and caving which could result in the loss of the well or pump. Also, if entrained air in the cascading water is significant a gas separater may be required to prevent the pump from excessive corrosion and cavitation. Multiple aquifer completions where the pumping level is not drawn below the top the upper formation are favored, as these avoid the problems of partially dewatered aquifers and cascading water.

Deepening of wells is feasible if sufficient time is available for deepening between the end of the pumping period required for the upper aquifer and the required start of pumping in the lower aquifer. The time available is dependent upon the grouting and sinking schedule which is, in part, a function of the depth between aquifers. In some cases there is insufficient time to deepen wells from any one aquifer to the next deepest one, however, it is frequently possible to deepen wells from a shallow aquifer to the deeper aquifers.

The selection of pumping duration prior to entering the aquifer with the shafts must allow for sufficient time to work out any problems in the mechanics of the pumping system and provide a reasonable reduction in head of the shaft. The time required to reduce the head can be estimated from aquifer properties determined by the field test program. Typically, in the San Juan Basin, a 60-to 100-day pumping period prior to shaft sinking provides adequate time for both head reduction and resolution of any system problems.

Various symmetrical well arrangements with the number of wells varying from two to eight are usually evaluated. A minimum distance of 100 feet from the center line of the shaft is usually required in order to reduce congestion of the drilling equipment with the head frame and other construction equipment near the shaft collar. Utilizing a computer program to solve the well flow equation; a comparison of the various well systems and their respective pumping rate, head reduction, and associated ground water velocity can be made.

Figure 3 shows a plan view of a depressurizing system for a six aquifer system. Table 4 gives a summary of each system and its predicted results.

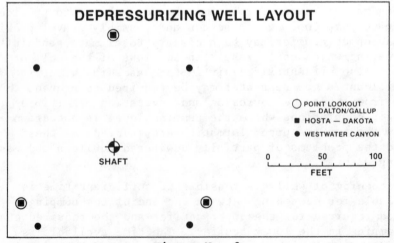

Figure No. 3

TABLE 4

DEPRESSURIZING SYSTEM PERFORMANCE

AQUIFER	NO. WELLS	HEAD REDUCTION @ SHAFT %	SHAFT INFLOW (GPM) WITHOUT	SHAFT INFLOW (GPM) WITH	AVERAGE WELL PUMPING RATES (GPM)
Point Lookout	3	77	780	200	150
Hosta	3	71	425	100	75
Dalton	3	73	160	50	30
Gallup	3	73	780	250	100
Dakota	3	73	1,750	500	320
Westwater Canyon	4	79	2,500	550	400

SUMMARY

This paper has attempted to review some of the techniques available to assess the need for water control, estimate the location and amount of water inflow expected, and briefly outline the techniques commonly in use. The application of these techniques to a practical problem is illustrated by recent work in the uranium mines of northwestern New Mexico.

While the shafts studied by the author are still under development, it appears that a combination of depressurizing wells and grouting is successful in controlling water inflow during sinking. Available data indicate that head reductions in excess of seventy percent are possible. Water inflow rates during shaft sinking are less than one-half that estimated to occur without depressurization.

The use of these techniques does not eliminate the water problem, however, they can make the problem more predictable and consequently manageable. Good planning is possible only if the conditions to be encountered during shaft sinking are known in advance.

28

Mine Dewatering—A Package Approach

by Neil F. Archer, President,
Arch Environmental Equipment, Inc.,
Paducah, Kentucky, USA

This discussion will attempt to cover the general areas and problems encountered in the design and installation of an underground dewatering system. Prior to designing any system, the areas of geology, hydrology, and ecology should be thoroughly investigated.

The geological considerations will dictate the ultimate design of the mine. It will be the controlling factor in the operation of the mine. It will also dictate the basic head conditions, type of discharge piping, flow control system, power requirements, gathering equipment, and the location of the necessary treatment equipment and mine openings.

The hydrological considerations will dictate the capacity of the dewatering system. The capacity of the system should be carefully considered. This information will size all the equipment to be used such as pumps, pipes, fittings and the power supply. This study should include the quality of the water. This will give the parameters for the material selection. Also included should be any seasonal flow patterns if they can be determined.

The ecological considerations must include the quality of the water that will be delivered to the receiving stream. The quantity of water should also be a major consideration. Is the discharge water going into an existing stream or will the discharge create its own stream? If the water has to be treated, can the treatment equipment be feed in surges or must it receive the water in a continuous flow? Once these areas have been covered, the overall design can be completed.

Given this data and knowing that it is accurate, the system can be designed. With the vertical head and flow being known, the discharge system can be selected. This may appear to be starting in the middle of the system and it is. I have started at the bottom and worked my way to the surface many times only to discover that there was not room for the 12 inch or 14 inch discharge pipe. I have been asked if I could get by with two 6 inch lines. Six and six does make twelve. The 1,000 feet of head turned into 1,300 feet and the horsepower requirements went up by 30 percent.

This also increased the size of all electrical equipment. This is why a system design should start with the discharge piping. This item is so critical that we have a routine programmed into our computer to calculate pipe size, friction loss and horsepower just for this reason.

Now we have our two basic numbers: total flow and total dynamic head. This will allow us to select the proper pumping equipment and will give us the horsepower necessary to drive the system. In turn this will allow us to select the proper switch gear, power conductors and standby generators if these are necessary.

The next step in this process is to select the proper pump materials (i.e. cast iron, bronze, stainless steel etc.). This should be done only after evaluating the quality of the water. Is it an aggressive water? Will it carry a high concentration of abrasives? Will dissolved gas be a problem? Hydrogen sulfide for example is very corrosive and is easily removed from the water by slight aeration. It is apparent that the sump design is very important.

The sump should be designed for easy access for cleaning and pump repair. If gas is a problem, a tight fitting top should be a part of the sump design. If sand or other abrasives are carried in the water, the sump should allow for adequate detention time to allow settling or treatment.

To preclude cycling, the sump design should include all necessary gathering equipment and drains. A common power supply should be used as much as possible to preclude power interruptions and line relocations. This also will give a central location to check power consumption and pump performance. If the power consumption is up and the flow down, it is time for maintenance or at least a check. The design should include necessary level controls, alarms and backup control systems.

We now have selected all the equipment and designed the sump. The only consideration left is the redundancy of the system. The average system should have a minimum of 50 percent in spare parts. The spare parts may have to be increased if the wear is above normal or are difficult to obtain.

The system is now designed and ready for installation and startup. What problem areas need to be considered? If all areas were evaluated properly, there should be only a few problems. The problem now becomes one of operator training and maintenance. There is no substitute for good personnel and adequate maintenance. Records should be maintained on all repair work and duration of operation. Repair frequency should be carefully noted. These will help make any modification to the equipment that may be necessary.

In closing, I would like to make one comment. Of all the areas that a package dewatering system covers, the most important is the initial design information. If this information is not accurate, then the design will not be adequate. If the information is accurate, then by all means use it. Many times thousands of dollars in field studies were left in the filing cabinet and the old rule of thumb was used to design a system. Then the system became a bottleneck to the entire mine operation. If you have good information, use it. If not, get it.

29

High Voltage Submersible Mine Dewatering Pumps for Extremely High Lifts

by O.H. Schiele,
Member of the Board, Research & Development,
and H. Kuntz, Chief Engineer,
Klein, Schanzlin & Becker,
Frankenthal, Federal Republic of Germany

1. INTRODUCTION

The submersible motor pump owes its development to the requirement for a pump set capable of operating reliably in the fully submerged state, and consequently totally without maintenance.

An important aspect of submersible motor pumps is the physical fact that the suction lift of a pump operating in open circuit is limited by the barometric pressure. The submersible motor pump, on the other hand, operates totally submerged in most applications, so that the question of an adequate NPSH does not arise, apart from a few exceptional cases.

The main fields of application for the submersible motor

pump are:

- Groundwater winning from deep wells, and water drainage in mines, civil engineering projects and tunnel construction etc.

- Pumping of hydrocarbons from underground storage caverns

- Used as cooling water, ballast and firefighting pumps on drilling and production platforms

The present paper will confine itself to the application of submersible motor pumps in the mining industry, a field of application which has made an outstanding contribution to the present-day stage of development of these pumps, because of the stringent requirements involved.

2. DESCRIPTION OF DESIGN

2.1 Submersible Pump

The main feature of this pump is its slim shape, which facilitates its installation in narrow and deep boreholes. Figure 1 illustrates two s.m.p.'s in cross-section, with the motor shown in shortened form. Because of the relatively small diameter of the pump, a large number of stages (impellers and diffusers) is usually required to achieve the desired total head.

Total heads in excess of 1000 m (3300 ft) are attainable, and if the pumps are fitted with mixed flow impellers (Figure 1, left-hand side), rates of flow (capacities) in excess of 3000 cu.m /hr. (13200 USGPM) can be achieved.

Most submersible pumps are of the single flow or single entry type, on condition that the axial thrust generated

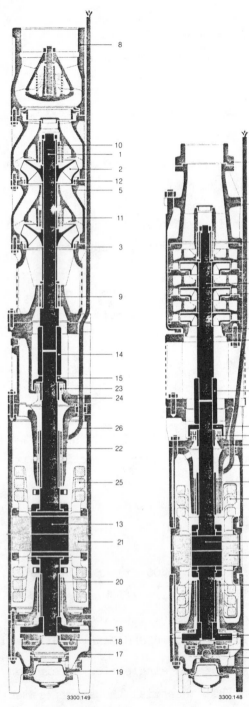

1 Pump shaft
2 Impeller
3 Suction casing
4 Inlet ring
5 Stage casing
6 Discharge casing
7 Adapter piece
8 Non-return valve
9 Bearing bush
10 Bearing bush
11 Bearing bush
12 Casing wear ring
13 Rotor
14 Sleeve coupling
15 Sand guard
16 Thrust bearing disc
17 Thrust bearing housing
18 Thrust bearing
19 Diaphragm
20 Bearing bush
21 Stator
22 Bearing bush
23 Radial seal ring
24 Connecting piece
25 Winding
26 Cable

3300.149   3300.148

Fig. 1: Submersible motor pump

is capable of being absorbed by the thrust bearing arranged in the motor.

Figure 2 illustrates a double entry pump with its associated driving motor. The hydraulic axial thrust in this case is balanced almost completely, and the thrust bearing arranged at the lower end of the motor is only required to absorb the rotor weights of the pump and motor.

The radial forces of the pump are absorbed by plain bearings arranged in the suction casing and discharge casing respectively. Because the liquid pumped acts as lubricant, the bearings are designed in such a way that the solid particles entrained with the liquid are prevented as far as possible from penetrating inside the bearings; this is particularly relevant in the case of mining applications. However the ingress of abrasive solid particles into the bearings cannot be entirely prevented, and abrasion-resistant bearing materials have therefore to be adopted. All the throttling clearance gaps through which the fluid flows contribute to the guidance of the shaft. This results in exceptionally quiet running characteristics even in the case of badly worn pumps, because of the multistage design and relatively small impeller diameters of submersible pumps. In addition, the submersible pump has a longer service life than conventional mine drainage pumps.

2.2 Submersible Motor

The submersible motor is rigidly coupled to the pump. There have been a large number and variety of developments of this type of motor, but only three of these are of

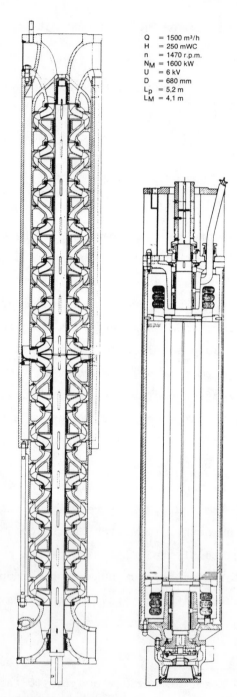

Q = 1500 m³/h
H = 250 mWC
n = 1470 r.p.m.
N_M = 1600 kW
U = 6 kV
D = 680 mm
L_P = 5,2 m
L_M = 4,1 m

Fig. 2: Submersible motor pump

real significance:

a) the oil-filled motor

This type of motor must be fitted with an absolutely
reliable and leak-tight shaft seal. The dissipation
of the heat losses and the thermal expansion require
special attention and a correspondingly high expendi-
ture, because of the lower thermal conductivity of
oil as compared with water. Compared with water, oil
has the disadvantage of a higher fluid friction, but
on the other hand it permits the adoption of antifriction bearings, in so far as the service life
requirements of the bearings allow it. Antifriction
bearings are not generally regarded with great favour
for mining applications.

b) the semi-wet submersible motor (canned motor)

The stator compartment and stator winding of this
type of motor are sealed off from the water-filled
rotor compartment by a can. In order to improve
heat dissipation, the winding space is filled with
casting resin poured into it.

This type of motor has an inferior efficiency and is
usually adopted only for low ratings up to 30 kW
approx.

c) the wet or water-filled motor

Whereas developments in the USA centered mainly
around the oil-filled motor, developments in Europe
were concentrated on the water-filled motor. This
type of motor is completely filled with water, i.e.
the winding is immersed in water, and the plain bearings are water-lubricated (Figures 1 and 2). These

water-lubricated bearings have reached such an advanced
stage of development that they offer complete and absolute operational reliability and a very long service life
even under heavy loadings.

The remarkable increase in output ratings of the water-
filled motor during the past 20 years, and its proven
reliability in service point to this type of motor as
the most likely solution for the future. Motors with
ratings of 1800 kW have now been operating successfully
over a period of several years, motors of 2400 kW have
been built, and ratings of 3000 kW are in the development stage at the present time. One feature of decisive
importance in this development has been the progress
made in the field of waterproof and pressure-tight
plastic insulating materials for the winding wires. The
quality of the plastic materials and the processing
technology have improved continuously, with the result
that present-day winding wire insulations are capable
of withstanding very high electrical, thermal and mechanical loadings.

The normally selected supply voltage for motor ratings
up to 300 kW approx. is low voltage (low tension); for
ratings up to 1000 kW, high tension of 3kV is adopted,
and for even higher ratings, 6kV.

A 10 kV motor has been operating for the last 5 years
without any trouble (see Figure 2).

Basically the design of the water-filled submersible
motor does not differ from that of conventional three
phase squirrel cage rotor motors, i.e. the construction

is simple and sturdy. The salient points of the design
are the slim shape and the fact that the motor is completely filled with water. The following data tabulation
relating to a series of submersible motors proves con-
clusively that high efficiencies are attainable with this
type of motor:

Rated output kW	Voltage V	Length/O.D. mm	At 50 Hz Rot.speed r.p.m.	Efficiency %
1800	6000	4025/680	1450	91
1600	6000	3925/680	1450	91
1200	6000	3425/680	1450	90
1000	3000	3380/614	1450	90
800	3000	2960/614	2900	90
500	3000	2864/450	2900	90
300	500	2470/343	2900	90
150	380	2010/282	2900	88
100	380	1730/361	2900	87
50	380	1490/226	2900	87
10	380	920/180	2900	83
1	220	420/141	2900	70

The motor is filled with conventional drinking water
shortly before final installation.

The advantages of the water fill are:

- Water is an excellent conductor of heat. Heat dissipation can be improved even further by auxiliary devices such as a special paddle wheel to circulate the
  water, making it possible to operate the motor at high
  ambient temperatures if necessary, such as those which

frequently occur in mines.

- There is no need for absolute leak-tightness, only for the prevention of an exchange of fluid; should there be a leak, or should a seal fail, the ingress of fluid pumped will not result in failure of the motor.

In order to achieve a long service life, special attention must be paid to the prevention of an exchange of fluid and to protection against the ingress of dirt in submersible motors for mining applications. The adoption of mechanical seals has proved unsatisfactory for a considerable time already, because these seals are very sensitive to sediments which are frequently present in mine waters. It has needed a long and painstaking series of experiments and trials under conditions simulating practical mining applications to arrive at a final solution which functions satisfactorily even under the most arduous operating conditions.

The rotor is guided in two radial bearings. The thrust bearing plate is mounted at the lower end of the rotor shaft, and it rotates against a ring of tilting pads which are stationary in the peripheral direction, but which are otherwise free to tilt in all directions.

Figure 3 shows how the weight per unit of output has decreased over the years from 1950 to 1978. This graph illustrates very clearly the continuous further development and improvement of the submersible motor over the years.

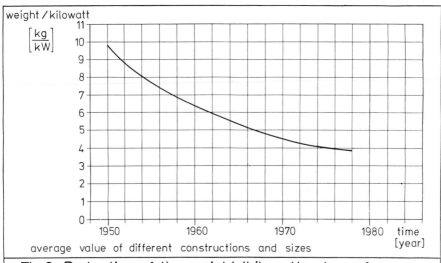

Fig.3. Reduction of the weight/kilowatt value of submersible motors from 1950 until 1978

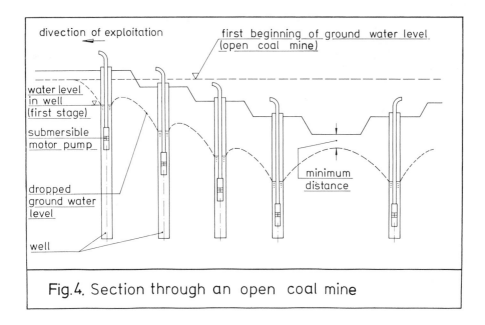

Fig.4. Section through an open coal mine

3. EXAMPLES OF APPLICATIONS IN THE MINING INDUSTRY

Because water-filled electric motors which operate completely submerged do not require any special explosion proofness (firedamp proofness), the entire range of submersible motors (i.e. the complete range of outputs) used for other purposes is equally suitable for the mining industry in its basic form.

It is only necessary to know the operating data and conditions in each specific application, such as the nature and condition of the medium pumped (temperature, chemical properties, solids content), and the mode of installation and operation (mode of starting, switching frequency (number of stops and starts per hour), and length of downtimes (shutdown periods)).

3.1 Opencast Mining, e.g. Brown Coal (Lignite)
Opencast Mining

Submersible motor pumps have been used in opencast mining applications for many years now, in the world's largest opencast coal mining operation, the Rhineland soft coal basin near Cologne. Figure 4 illustrates such an opencast mining operation sectionally. The ground water table is indicated diagrammatically, and the purpose of the submersible motor pumps installed below the deepest bed level is to lower this ground water table. At present, some 2500 submersible motor pumps in all, with a combined capacity of over 700 000 USGPM are installed at the Rhineland Soft Coal Mines. These submersible motor pumps are installed in wells with borehole diameters up to 32" and at depths down to 1700 ft.

Figure 5 illustrates a section through a deep well with a submersible motor pump.

The largest submersible motor pump in this coal field has a rating of 1600 kW. Special attention has been devoted to the problem of abrasive wear, because most deep wells contain sand in the water, to a lesser or greater extent.

Because the hydraulics of a mixed flow pump are characterized by more gradual changes of direction of flow than those of the equivalent radial flow pump, the mixed flow pump will be less prone to abrasive wear and erosion than the equivalent radial flow pump under similar operating conditions.

Figure 6 illustrates the conventional mode of installation in a deep well. As a general rule, a non-return valve is mounted directly above the pump discharge nozzle, to prevent the rising main from running empty every time the pump is switched off. In addition, the reflux of liquid from the rising main would cause the pump to "windmill", i.e. run as a turbine.
Finally the problem of pressure surges (water hammer) which can occur in the rising main when the pump sets are switched on and switched off must be mentioned.
Calculations and experimental measurements point to the fact that these pressure surges can present a serious hazard to the safe operation of the pump sets and installation (1). On condition that the necessary data are made available to us, it is a relatively easy matter to ascertain whether pressure surges will in fact occur, and to take suitable preventive measures.

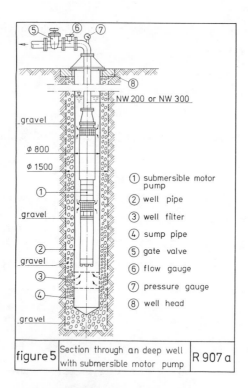

①	submersible motor pump
②	well pipe
③	well filter
④	sump pipe
⑤	gate valve
⑥	flow gauge
⑦	pressure gauge
⑧	well head

gravel

Ø 800

Ø 1500

gravel

gravel

gravel

NW 200 or NW 300

figure 5	Section through an deep well with submersible motor pump	R 907 a

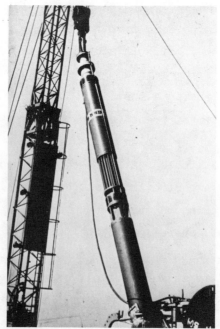

Fig. 6

3.2 Underground Mining (Hard Coal and Ore Mining)

Submersible motor pumps are installed in collieries and ore mines for drainage duties, i.e. to remove the water which collects in the individual bottoms. The water concerned arises from natural affluxes, and in certain cases from hydraulic stowing operations.

Depending on the depth of the bottom on which the submersible motor pumps are installed, they will pump the water either direct above ground, or from a bottom deeper down to the drainage facility of a bottom situated higher up, whence it is pumped above ground. In most cases, the submersible motor pumps are suspended in a sump on the bottom concerned.

A diagrammatic representation of a mine drainage installation of this type is shown in Figure 7; it has been in operation since 1960. Hartmann and Guillaume (2) have described this installation in detail in a paper, and have demonstrated the submersible motor pump is the most suitable and even essential item of equipment for the automation of the complete installation.
The trend during the last ten years has been towards the direct pumping from the deepest bottom to a level above ground by means of a single pump, which is capable of generating the necessary total head. In the hard coal mines of Germany, this requires total heads of up to 3300ft and driver ratings of up to 1800 kW. In mining circles, a conservative approach and considerations of safety are paramount, and consequently two requirements are imposed in the case of machines with higher ratings:

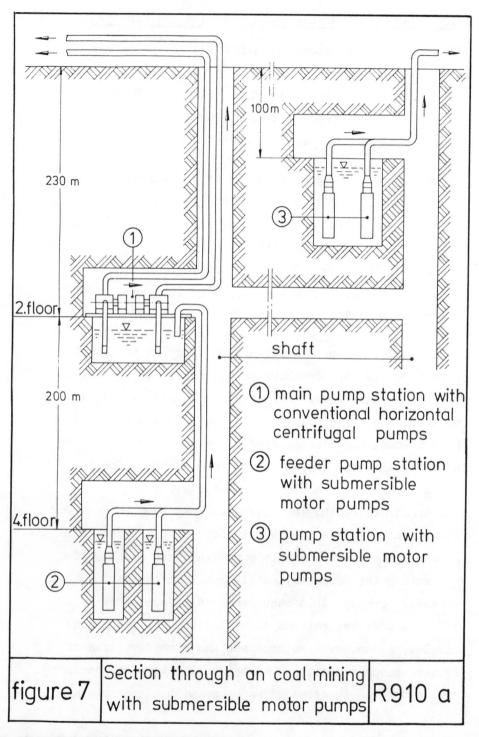

230 m

100 m

1 main pump station with conventional horizontal centrifugal pumps

2 feeder pump station with submersible motor pumps

3 pump station with submersible motor pumps

2.floor

200 m

shaft

4.floor

| figure 7 | Section through an coal mining with submersible motor pumps | R910 a |

1) A 4 pole motor, i.e. a rotational speed of 1450 or
   1700 r.p.m. respectively

2) A pump of double entry type (double suction design)

Whereas the first of these two requirements will only
occasionally meet with any objections from the viewpoint
of the pump manufacturer, there can only be one single
valid argument in favour of the second requirement, viz.:

The balancing of the hydraulic thrust in the eventuality
that the thrust bearing is incapable of absorbing the
thrust of a single entry pump. Other axial thrust balancing devices not only dissipate power but also lose their
effectiveness as a result of abrasive wear, and consequently they can only be adopted in the case of pumped
media which do not contain any solid particles. This
can never be achieved fully in any mining operation.

The double entry pump design is, however, unsatisfactory in the case of very low rates of flow in relation
to the total head. The flow channels become very narrow
and the efficiency of the pump deteriorates as a result.

The decision as to whether a two pole or a four pole
motor is the better solution cannot be made by the pump
manufacturer alone. There is no doubt that a two pole
motor pumping set is the more economic solution for pumping water containing only a very small percentage of
solids (less than 25 ppm). Pumping sets with two pole
driving motors of 600 kW rating have been built and have
proved themselves in service.
These pumps are designed for the following operating
data:

$$Q = 300 \text{ cu.m/hr } (1320 \text{ USGPM})$$
$$H = 450 \text{ m } (1476 \text{ ft})$$

Elevated temperatures of the liquid pumped

Whilst the operating conditions in brown coal open cast
mines usually deal with cold water of less than $25^{\circ}C$
($77^{\circ}F$) handled by the pump, the water pumped out of
underground collieries is warm in most cases (40 to $50^{\circ}C$,
i.e. 105 to $125^{\circ}F$). This makes the dissipation of the
motor heat losses more difficult, and special measures
have to be taken, such as the use of a plastic insulating
material for the winding wires resistant to elevated
temperatures, and the additional incorporation of a cooling jacket. The cooling jacket stretches from the top
edge of the pump inlet body (where it is closed) to the
bottom edge of the motor (where it is open); consequently
the water aspirated by the pump is forced to enter the
pump via the bottom end of the cooling jacket. The water
thus pumped is obliged to flow around the outer surface
of the motor casing at a predetermined velocity, and
carries off the motor heat losses quite satisfactorily.
Here again, motor designs which incorporate an auxiliary
paddle wheel can be adopted if necessary, to circulate
the motor fill water via cooling ducts in countercurrent
to the pumped water, in order to improve the cooling
action still further.

The protection of the winding against excessive overheat-
ing is ensured by means of a so-called thermomonitor
embedded in each of the two winding ends of the motor;
these monitors automatically switch off the motor via a
special control current line (trip line) as soon as a

given pre-set limit temperature has been attained, which is below the temperature which might damage the winding.

The cooling jacket has the added advantage of preventing the motor casing from becoming caked up with solids (sludge) when the submersible motor pump operates e.g. in a sump. Such a coating of sludge on the motor would impede the efficient dissipation of the motor heat losses. The presence of the cooling jacket, which also acts as a suction jacket, ensures that the solids are entrained by the pump.

Special importance in hard coal underground mining operations is attached to the flameproofing (firedamp-proofing) of all electrical equipment used underground, and this includes the submersible motor. Thanks to its water fill and to the fact that it operates totally sub-merged in water, the submersible motor is flameproofed (firedamp-proofed) in ideal fashion. The cable leading out of the motor is led into a pressure-tight, firedamp-proof and explosion-proof cable junction box. When the submersible motor pump is installed, the power supply cable from the distribution is also connected inside this junction box. The box is then sealed water-tight with a cover. In cases where a second cable is required, a second cable junction box must be provided, and similarly a third box must be provided for the control current cable of the thermomonitor. These cable junction boxes are attached to a special rising main pipe which is connected to the non-return valve on the pump, and which constitutes a component part of the submersible motor pump. The pump execution illustrated in Figure 8 has

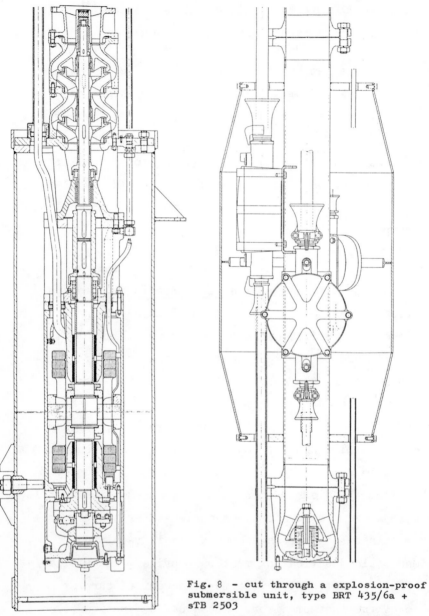

Fig. 8 - cut through a explosion-proof
submersible unit, type BRT 435/6a +
sTB 2503

left: lower part with motor and pump
right: upper part with cable connection
        box

been approved as firedamp-proof (flameproof) by the German Bureau of Mines.

A smaller size submersible motor pump of firedamp-proof execution for horizontal installation is illustrated in Figure 9 ; it was développed for the special purpose of roadway (drift) dewatering. Its motor is sealed by means of a metal carbide mechanical seal. It is filled with water and vented via two pipes. The motor is supported in relation to the cooling and suction jacket via a series of setscrews. The jacket is vented at the top through a hole fitted with a screwed plug; it is also fitted with two skids to facilitate transport in the mine, and with two sturdy carrying stirrups. The cable junction box is mounted on the jacket.

An orifice plate is fitted downstream of the non-return valve and upstream of the discharge line, which can be altered or removed completely according to requirements. The submersible motor pump is switched on and off automatically in function of the upper and lower water levels via two electrodes which are adjustable on a rail.

This particular submersible motor pump is a compact and sturdy pumping set, easy to handle in the mine. Its principal data (with the orifice plate removed) are as follows:

Capacity	3.8 cu.m/hr (17 USGPM)
Total head	51 m head of water (167 FT)
Pump efficiency	60%
Motor rating	1.5 kW
Motor efficiency	71%

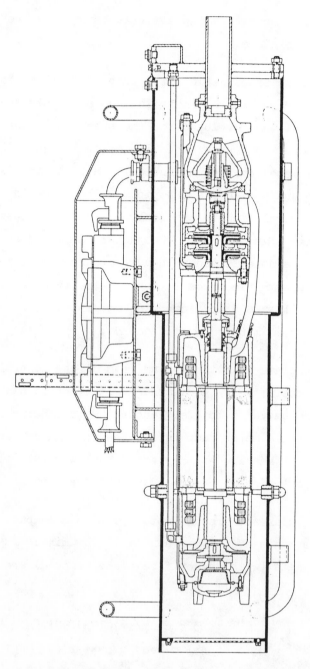

Fig. 9 – cut through a explosion-proof submersible
unit, type UPD 62/6 + sDF 0203

| Motor speed | 2870 r.p.m. |
| Operating voltage | 500 V |

Materials

Reference has been made to the problem of abrasive wear
on page 9 . This problem can be attacked by the use of
specially abrasion-resistant materials, apart from low
rotational speeds and various design measures. The
chemical quality of the water is another important aspect
in the selection of the most suitable materials, and this
is of particular importance in mining applications.
Because of the great variety of requirements, it is often
difficult to say in advance which materials will be the
most suitable ones.

Although the pump manufacturer is always anxious to
standardize his material executions as far as possible
and for every possible individual component, it is clear
that the requirements of the mining industry are so
diverse that new adaptations and adjustments have constantly to be made.

The "Noridur" and "Norihard" alloys have been specially
developed by KSB itself for use in contact with chemically aggressive and abrasive media pumped. Please refer
to our special leaflets for details on these alloys.

Summary

1.) Advantages of submersible motor pumps in comparison
    with conventional pump designs for mine drainage:

- No NPSH problems, because pump is completely submerged

- Direct connection without necessity for a booster pump, i.e. always ready for instant start-up, easy to automate
  Can be controlled from above ground if required

- Maintenance-free
- Can be installed in the sump, no pump room required
- Small diameter, low peripheral speed, reduced rate of wear if the water contains solids

2.) Advantages of the water-filled motor in comparison with the oil-filled motor and the canned motor
- No special seal required (only prevention of liquid exchange)
- All the required ratings and voltages are available and have been proven in service

Capacities up to	5000 cu.m./hr	(22 000 USGPM)
Total heads up to	1200 m	(4000 FT)
Motor ratings up to	3000 kW	(4000 HP)
Voltages up to	10000 V	

- Exceptionally good cooling, can therefore be used to pump warm media if required
- Exceptionally quiet running and plain bearings with a long service life
- Firedamp proofness (flame proofness) requirements are easy to meet

SECTION 3

Drainage Control for Underground Mines

30

Hydrogeological Problems and Their Resolutions at the Friedensville Mine

by Kenneth R. Cox, Manager, Friedensville Mine,
The New Jersey Zinc Company,
Center Valley, Pennsylvania, USA

The Friedensville orebody is situated in Upper Saucon Township, Lehigh County, Pennsylvania, approximately five miles southeast of the city of Allentown, and four miles south of the city of Bethlehem.

The Friedensville area, physiographically, is located in a small reentrant, known as the Saucon Valley, of the Great Valley Province into the Reading Prong of the New England Upland. The Saucon Valley, itself, is a lowland somewhat oval shaped approximately eight miles long and four miles wide, surrounded by ridges except where it is connected with the Great Valley through a break in the rim, known as Saucon Gap.

The floor of the Valley is underlain by lower paleozoic dolomites and limestones. The area is one of low relief possessing numerous sinkholes with an average elevation in the Valley of approximately 375 feet above sea level. Exploration drilling revealed and mine excavation has confirmed fractured and weathered ground in excess of 1,000 feet below the Valley floor. These characteristics have resulted in considerable porosity and permeability which developed over the eons establishing a very complex underground drainage system.

Zinc ore at the Friedensville Mine occurs in the lower part of the Beekmantown formation of Ordovician age. The ore is associated with a westerly plunging, asymmetrical anticline, overturned to the north, with present mining and development along the south limb.

The mineralogy is simple, consisting of sphalerite and pyrite with dolomite and quartz as gangue minerals.

Mining of zinc ore in the Saucon Valley dates from 1855, following original discovery in 1845 at the site of what later became the Ueberroth Mine.

The ore outcropped on surface which enabled four open cut pits: the Ueberroth, Old Hartman, Triangle and Correll to begin mining operations during the succeeding years.

As the depth of the quarry increased, recourse was made at the Ueberroth to mine underground which finally reached an approximate depth of 300 feet.

Excessive volumes of water were encountered due to extensive seepage through the highly fractured and weathered country rock, and in an endeavor to overcome this difficulty, the largest Cornish pump then in existence was installed at the mine.

The following is an excerpt from an article entitled, "History of Lehigh County, Pennsylvania" published in 1884:

> "Various pumping engines were introduced from time-to-time, but none that was equal to the work assigned to it until 1872, when "The President", a mammoth engine, was erected and put in operation, and which realized in a full measure the expectations of the Company, as it easily and speedily rid the mines of water. As this is the largest engine in the world, a description of it may not be uninteresting.
>
> It is a vertical condensing engine, ten feet stroke, with a cylinder of cast iron one hundred and ten inches in diameter, and weighing forty tons. It has two flywheels thirty-five feet in diameter, weighing ninety-two tons apiece, four walking-beams weighing

twenty-four tons apiece, twenty-six other
pieces weighing over seven tons apiece,
while the nut, made of steel, which secures
the piston rod to the cross-head, weighs
eleven hundred pounds. The total weight of
the engine is six hundred and sixty-seven
tons. Sixteen boilers supply the steam
for it, it has three thousand three hundred
horse-power, and is capable of raising
seventeen thousand gallons of water per
minute from a depth of two hundred and
twenty feet."

By 1893, all mining ceased in the area, due to high cost
of production, adverse water conditions, expiration of
patents for zinc oxide manufacture and competition with the
high grade ores from the New Jersey area.

During the succeeding years, The New Jersey Zinc Company
acquired title to the properties and an extensive program
of prospect drilling and hydrologic investigation was continued intermittently to delimit ore occurrence and study
the problems resulting from underground water.

It was not until 1945, the decision was made to locate
the new Friedensville shaft and in 1947 preliminary
operations were initiated.

Early in 1948, ground was broken for the new shaft. The
finished cross section of the steel lined and concrete
reinforced shaft is 20 feet - 6 inches by 13 feet. It was
decided that sinking would be accomplished by pressure
grouting the ground surrounding the shaft and excavation
would descend through an impervious zone.

During excavation of the shaft, however, outbreaks
occurred at 75 feet, 146 feet and 247 feet below the
collar and flooding was allowed to fill the shaft to
ground water level for stabilization preparatory to
casting underwater plugs by the Prepakt method.

Shaft stations and pump stations were excavated as the
shaft was sunk to a depth of 1260 feet.

In 1971, after more was learned about the orebody, the
shaft was deepened to a final depth of 2070 feet. Bulkhead
doors were provided to protect the shaft and new pumping

facilities were installed to increase the capacity from 22,000 gallons per minute to 40,000 gallons per minute with room for a maximum of 50,000 gallons per miute.

418 Level Pump Station

It was not until January of 1958, that development work and drawdown of the water table permitted mining to commence. The method of mining is best described as modified open stope. Basically, mining is performed in the following manner:

A -20% decline is driven along the hangingwall following the approximate plunge of the orebody. At 30 foot vertical intervals, horizontal entries are driven from the decline along the hangingwall contact outlining the orebody.

Stopes 37½ feet wide are advanced from the hangingwall across the orebody to the footwall leaving pillars 35 feet wide by 60 feet long for support. This procedure is repeated advancing downward on the orebody.

Mining is accomplished through the use of mobile diesel powered equipment. All mine development work and stoping

follows established test hole patterns with followup
grouting procedures when required. In areas of suspected
water potential, long hole test drilling of 100 or more
feet is undertaken using a diamond drill or a mobile
mounted 5 inch rotary percussion drill.

20 Ton Truck Being Loaded
By a 8 Yard LHD

On Tuesday, February 17, 1976, a diamond drill crew
was test drilling at the 1170 hangingwall drift in an
area where production had been suspended for approximately
a month and a half due to ground water conditions. An
attempt was being made through this drilling to learn more
about the areas water source and its potential.

At approximately 9:00 P.M., the diamond drill crew heard
a loud report from the adjacent stope. The two man crew
made a quick investigation of the noise and discovered a
large flow of water emanating from the upper left corner
of the rib-back juncture near the stope's face. Immediately,
the crew notified supervision and at once predetermined
emergency plans were put into effect. During the night, the
entire staff was called in for emergency assignments. The

following morning corporate officials, federal and state
regulatory agencies were notified of the water outbreak.

The Outbreak

Measures were taken the following day to establish
maximum pumping plant efficiencies, methods to measure
water inflow, availability of water storage in the lower
mine levels, monitoring of the water table, measuring
the underground filling rate, and collecting samples of
the mine water inflow for analysis.

The Engineering Department established that the rate
of inflow from the outbreak was nearly 35,000 gallons per
minute. This flow, combined with the existing mine discharge of 26,500 gallons per minute, totaled approximately
60,000 gallons per minute or 86,400,000 gallons per day.

It is of interest to note that under the existing conditions it was quite difficult to measure an inflow of this size. However, personnel from the Engineering and Geology Departments utilized all measurements available and projected that the high water mark would be reached very early in the morning of February 25. Actual cresting occurred at 4:30 A.M. that morning after the water had risen well into the 1170 level. At 7:00 A.M., the water for the first time was going in a positive direction.

As the inflow dropped off and the mine water receded, the final bulkhead door on the 1850 level was opened on April 14, 1976.

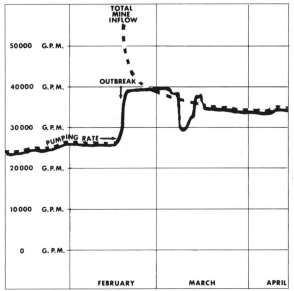

Inflow vs. Pumping Before and After the Outbreak

While the mine was being dewatered, the staff at Friedensville was busy studying ways to control the free flowing water. It was decided that concrete plugs, constructed with piping and valves would be used for water control.

A diversion drift measuring 50 feet long by 8 feet wide by 8 feet high was driven to intercept the water near the base of the outbreak. Upon completion of this drift, the primary water route was then prepared for installation of the first concrete plug. This plug which measures 25 feet long by 21 feet wide by 15 feet high was filled with coarse aggregate and then injected with sand and cement. Through the base of the plug, three - 20 inch pipes with valves were provided to carry the water.

After completion of the first plug, the water was allowed to flow through the 20 inch pipes and diverted away from the diversion drift. The small water drift was then prepared for construction of a 10 foot long solid plug.

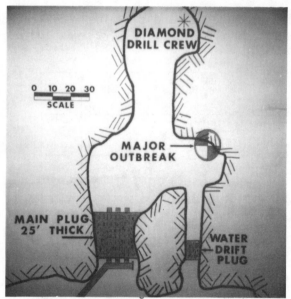

Plan View Of The Outbreak Area

Both plugs were pressure tested and grouted where necessary. The final phase of this project included installation of a 30 inch pipe line which carried the water to a system of water raises discharging into the sumps of the 1520 level pump station.

Although this appears to be an appropriate time to conclude this paper, there was one other significant incident that occurred in June of 1976. This event took place near the completion of the shaft deepening project which was mentioned earlier. Details, however, are quite complex and are discussed at this time in the simplest manner.

After the installation of the new ore handling facilities in the new shaft section, work began on removing the old

ore handling facilities (crusher, skip loading pocket).
This work was scheduled to be completed in approximately
one week. During this one week period, production hoisting
was stopped but mining continued and the new ore pass was
being filled. While these changes were being made, all
bulkhead doors on the lower levels were closed and secured.

Our problem began on a weekend with a call from the mine
that the 1520 level pump station had automatically shut down
due to a lack of water. After a quick inspection of the
mine, this was ruled out. Returning to the shaft to inspect
the 1520 level pump station, we learned from the pumpman
that the pumps were back on line and the situation appeared
normal.

Unfortunately, the situation was anything but normal.
As the evening progressed into early morning, the 1520
level pumps began to lose their prime, due to an unknown
blockage at the sump suction screens. Suddenly, we were
flooding the 1500 level. Extra help was called in and a
backflush line was installed from one of the main pump
discharge columns directly to the sump suction pipes.

The station was completely shut down as we opened the
valves on the backflush line allowing the water to pass
through the suction screens, in order to clear whatever
blockage was present. Our plan worked and the pumps began
to draw down the excess water.

Key personnel waited anxiously, realizing that the 1500
level bulkhead door had to be opened as soon as the level
was dewatered for inspection of the sumps and suction
screens.

At the proper time, the ditch valve on the bulkhead door
was opened, which produced a blast of water and air; valves
located near the top of the bulkhead produced a blast of
compressed air. The latches on the bulkhead door were
released but the door wouldn't budge.

For the first time, we realized what had taken place
behind the door to cause the emergency. Thirty thousand
plus gallons per minute of water was falling down a vertical
raise from the 1350 level to the 1500 level sumps. The
water raise was acting as an air pump, and the filling of
the ore pass with crude ore above the level blocked the
only exit for the increased volume of air.

Our system for measuring water depth in the sumps and
activating the pumps is accomplished automatically through
the use of a probe tank located in the pump station. This
tank is connected with the sumps and normally the water
elevation in the probe tank is the same as the sump, regulating the demand for pumps as needed. However, during the
time of this incident, the air pressure behind the bulkhead
door was much greater than atmospheric pressure. The water
elevation in the probe tank was much higher than the actual
sump level, causing the pumps to pull the sumps lower than
desired. In fact, it was later felt that the suction screens
were exposed. When this occurred, our suction screens became partially blocked by mud and plastic materials which
made their way into the sumps.

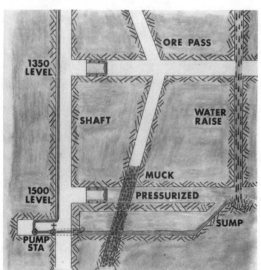

Idealized Section Of The Pressurized Area

The problem causing the condition was known, but opening
the door was still another matter since we couldn't budge
the door. After a harrowing several hours of jacking the
door open with one - 50 ton and two - 35 ton jacks, along
with fighting wind and a muddy water spray, the door was
finally opened wide enough for atmospheric equilibrium.
With this, another crisis ended.

It is needless to say that the challenges at times seemed
to be overwhelming for the small staff at the Friedensville
mine. Their devotion, personal drive, and professional
abilities will always be recognized as an outstanding
accomplishment.

31

The Role of Water in the Failure of Tailings Dams

by Edwin S. Smith,
Chief Engineer, Geotechnical Division,
and David H. Connell,
Project Engineer, Geotechnical Division,
International Engineering Company, Inc.,
San Francisco, California, USA

INTRODUCTION

At some of his earliest lectures, the young engineering student learns that hydrostatic pressure exerted by a body of water is proportional to the height of water. With this fundamental knowledge, the engineer is well aware of the significance of impounded water (and porewater) in his design of a tailings retention embankment. As the structures get larger, so the importance of hydro loading increases.

The improved efficiency of modern mining operations and metallurgical processes has resulted in the working of lower grade ores and, at the same time, in an intensification of one of the mill managers' major headaches--the disposal of tailings. As the quantity of tailings grows, the amount of water and fine tailings that must be handled is vastly increased, as is the potential for problems with water and saturated slimes.

In the past, the most common method of tailings dam construction has been to raise the dike with hydraulically placed coarse tailings obtained by gravity segregation or by cycloning. The crest of the dike was usually maintained just above the level of the slimes and pond. Often, this margin does not provide an adequate safety margin against extreme water loading conditions. Most of the newer tailings dams are designed and constructed by adopting techniques used for water retaining embankments; however, many dams that are constructed with hydraulically placed coarse tailings are still being used successfully.

If the ore tailings could be moved by other than hydraulic methods and if the deposit could be located away from stream channels, most of the potential water loading problems in tailings disposal operations would be eliminated; however, economic considerations dictate that these options are generally not available. A vast majority of milling operations require water for processing, and, thus, water serves as an inexpensive transportation medium for the tails in the form of a slurry. When this water is in the tailings disposal area and is supplemented by direct precipitation and surface runoff, many water control problems can develop. When the engineer does not provide for control of the water, the destructive forces are very evident, as shown in Figure 1.

This paper enumerates the more critical water loading conditions to which tailings dams and deposits are subjected. The potential failure modes resulting from these loading conditions are presented.

Figure 1

DEFINITIONS

General

In any discussion of the failure of structures, it is desirable (if not necessary) to provide a meaningful definition of failure. The International Commission on Large Dams (ICOLD) performed a study on "Failures and Accidents to Large Dams" in the period from 1965 to 1973(1). The reported incidents were divided into four general categories, namely:

> Failures
> Accidents
> Damage During Construction
> Major Repair

Because of the numerous varieties of incidents, these four categories were further subdivided into a total of eight;

> Dam Failure - Types 1 and 2,
> Dam Accident - Types 1, 2, and 3,
> Accident - Reservoir,
> Damage During Construction, and
> Major Repair.

As is readily apparent from these sub-categories, there is no single definition of failure that applies to accidents, incidents, damage, and repairs. For the purpose of this discussion, failure is defined as collapse of any part of a tailings deposit to a degree that would result in questionable safety, either during continued operation or if use is discontinued.

While tailings dams were not included in the study discussed above, most of the same general categories apply to incidents involving tailings structures. In fact, older tailings dams can be expected to have a much higher rate of incidents because of the lack of engineering and construction control and because of the type of construction (i.e., hydraulic fill).

Types of Water Loading

The types of water loading to which a tailings dam can be subjected include:

Flood Water
  Rain
  Snowmelt

In Situ Water
  Seepage
  Pore

Through practical experience and applied soil mechanics theories, techniques have been developed to control these water loadings. Properly designed water control systems will, at minimum cost, provide adequate stability of the tailings embankment and control the quantity and quality of water that leaves the disposal area. The decision on the type and extent of control systems will include consideration of environmental requirements, needs of the mill processing operation, and the risk and expense of failures.

Types of Failure

The most common failures, or incidents, to tailings dams that can be attributed to unfavorable water loads are in the form of:

1. Overtopping
2. Sliding
3. Liquefaction
4. Piping
5. Erosion

Some of these incidents will occur quickly with little or no warning (e.g., liquefaction), while in others, the structure will show signs of distress over a significant period of time (gullying, cracking, turbidity, etc.). If the disposal operation has not been banished from thought(2), time will generally be available to provide corrective maintenance. Combinations of these water loadings and incidents can and often do occur; erosion can lead to piping, and sliding can be followed by overtopping.

Overtopping - One of the most common causes of failure is overtopping by floodwaters. Because of the great susceptibility of cohesionless materials to erosion, retaining dikes constructed of coarse tailings must never be overtopped, or breaching and loss of the impounded semi-liquid slimes can be expected. Provisions should be made to pass major floods around a tailings dike. Generally, the problem is of major concern only for cross-valley deposits, where river diversion can be a critical factor in any economic feasibility study of a tailings disposal operation. However, the danger of flooding and overtopping the dikes of a side-hill deposit must also be considered.

Slide - Excess porewater pressures can reduce effective stresses within the tailings and can result in a decrease in shear strength. This reduction in shear strength could cause slope instability problems of many variations from local sloughing of particles at random areas along the face of an embankment to massive circular arc slides. A more detailed discussion of porewater pressures (neutral stresses) is presented in a subsequent section.

Liquefaction - Tailings dams placed by hydraulic methods using the upstream method of construction are particularly susceptible to liquefaction. This is a phenomenon where loose, saturated, fine grained material is subject to a large increase in porewater pressure due to lack of drainage, causing loss of effective stress. Because of their often catastrophic nature, most of the tailings deposit failures that have received publicity have been those resulting from liquefaction. Such failures occur instantaneously with no warning. They may be triggered by seismic or other vibrations, foundation spreading, or some form of dike collapse. Hazen (3) provides a clear description of the physical causes of liquefaction of sand.

Piping - Internal erosion (piping) of an embankment is caused by high seepage gradients within the soils. The potential for piping can be reduced by locating the decant pond as far as possible from the retaining structure and by providing an adequate drainage system.

Erosion - The loss of surface material due to direct rainfall or flowing surface water can result in an erosion failure or incident. In areas of heavy rainfall, some form of protection against erosion is usually required. Since a single storm rarely causes major damage, the problem is generally considered to be one of maintenance; however, if maintenance is neglected, the cumulative effects of intermittent erosion can produce a failure.

Risk

Because of the limits of knowledge in geotechnical engineering, there is uncertainty involved in the design and construction of earthwork structures. This uncertainty requires that the engineer or mill manager accept a certain amount of risk in the design and operation of the tailings disposal facilities. The degree of risk will depend on the consequences of failure and on the economic factors.

Mining folklore tells us that no tailings dam has ever been completed without at least one failure occurring during deposition. These failures, the term being undefined, could include everything from a slight nonconformity with the design to complete collapse. It is good economic practice in mill management to allow minor maintenance problems such as local sloughing to occur. If occasional problems do not occur, the mill manager is accused of being conservative in his tailings disposal design and lacking fiscal responsibility. However, the potential for major failures that could lead to loss of life or property must be considered in evaluating the risks.

In his paper entitled "Role of the 'Calculated Risk' in Earthwork and Foundation Engineering", Casagrande(4) describes the use of the observational approach in earthwork engineering. He explains that the continuous evaluation of observations and new information while construction is in progress presents the opportunity for reducing uncertainty and for redesigning effectively. His evaluation of the term 'Calculated Risk' suggests two steps:

a) The use of imperfect knowledge, guided by judgment and experience, to estimate the probable ranges for all pertinent quantities that enter into the solution of a problem.

b) The decision on an appropriate margin of safety, or degree of risk, taking into consideration economic factors and the magnitude of losses that would result from failure.

Casagrande presents a series of case histories involving calculated risks. Peck(5), in his discussion of the use of this method in applied soil mechanics, points out its advantages and limitations.

The observational approach is particularly applicable to tailings disposal and specifically in controlling the destructive forces of water. Smith, et al.(6), in their paper "Observational Approach to Tailings Dam Enlargement" provide an example of how the observational approach was used over a period of years for a tailings deposit. They summarize the procedure for application of the approach in the following manner:

1) Sufficient background data are obtained to define the nature and probable range of pertinent engineering variables.

2) Geotechnical analyses are performed, which include consideration of possible extreme conditions.

3) A systematic behavior monitoring program is established to provide a data base for continuing engineering analyses.

4) Alternative designs and standby operational procedures are studied, considering the possible extreme conditions.

5) Design changes are made based on actual conditions encountered.

Mining engineers and mill superintendents have been using the observational approach for many years in planning and constructing their tailings disposal operations. The continued existence of many of the old deposits confirms the success of the techniques used.

Monitoring programs can be very helpful during the construction and operation of tailings dams to evaluate the role of water in the safety of the tailings deposit. Piezometer, observation well, and weir readings are used to monitor pore water pressures within the embankment and quality and quantity of seepage releases. If these observations indicate potential problems that could lead to failure or pollution, the dike design or disposal method can be modified to resolve the problem. This is a simple example of how the observational approach can be used to reduce the calculated risk that mill managers are obligated to take for economical development of tailings disposal operations.

IN SITU WATER

General

In situ water consists of seepage and pore water. They represent water forms that affect the soil skeleton and its properties. For this discussion of in situ water, it is assumed that all the voids in the soil skeleton are continuous and filled with water.

To understand the role of water in the design of tailings dams and the prevention of possible failures, it is desirable to be familiar with: the effect of pore water on the shear strength of soils; the theory of seepage in soils; and the phenomenon of liquefaction.

Neutral Stresses

Neutral stresses or pore water pressures in a soil are the pressures produced by water load. They are determined from knowledge of static water level or from flow net construction. The total normal stress at any point in a saturated soil consists of two parts: the neutral (pore water pressure) and the effective stress. The effective stress is defined to be the total stress minus the pore water pressure. The effective stress in a soil controls physical properties of the soil skeleton such as compressibility, distortion, and shear strength(7,8). Therefore, every investigation of stability or settlement requires the knowledge of both total and neutral stresses.

The type of soil collapse that most concerns soils engineers and tailings dam designers is shear failure. The shear strength of a soil is determined in the laboratory by applying an axial load to a cylindrical sample in a manner similar to that used to determine the strength of concrete. The most common type of test used to determine shear strength properties is a triaxial compression test. The advantage of this type of test is that it permits the application of the three dimensional stress conditions found in the field to an undisturbed or compacted soil sample and thus makes it possible to study the stress-strain behavior and the ultimate strength under in situ conditions.

It is important that drainage conditions during the tests conform to conditions within the existing soil structure. If a series of tests is made at different confining pressures under drained conditions, the normal effective stress can be plotted against shear stress as shown on the Mohr diagram in Figure 2. The equation $S = C + \sigma \tan \phi$ describes the shear strength of soils. The parameters C and ϕ represent cohesion and angle of friction, respectively,

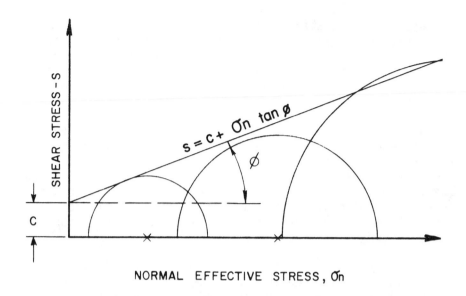

NORMAL EFFECTIVE STRESS, σ_n

TYPICAL MOHR STRENGTH ENVELOPE
FROM TRIAXIAL COMPRESSION TEST

Figure 2

and are usually almost constant for a given soil within a given range of normal stresses.

In evaluating the stability of a tailings dam slope, different potential failure surfaces are selected, and the total driving force is compared with the total resisting force along the surface. The driving force is generally obtained from the weight of material within the surface and the resisting force obtained from the shear strength along the surface. The Mohr's envelope is used to determine shear strength once the effective stress is determined by subtracting the neutral stress obtained from a flow net diagram from the total stress. Experience has shown that porewater pressures exert considerable influence on the safety factor agains a sliding failure.

Seepage Theory

Seepage theory is used in the design of tailings dams and water supply dams to determine the location and magnitude of potential problems resulting from water flowing through the dam or its foundation. These include excess porewater pressure, large hydraulic gradient and high flow quantities. When problem areas are identified, the design can include measures either to control the potential problem or to alleviate it. Uncontrolled seepage may result in piping, slope instability, or release of contaminants.

The flow of water through soils (or tailings) follows Darcy's empirical law, which states that the amount of flow is directly proportional to the hydraulic gradient. Darcy's equation is Q = kiA, where Q is seepage quantity, k is the coefficient of permeability, i is the hydraulic gradient, and A is total cross sectional area normal to direction of flow. Cedergren(9) provides a detailed discussion of Darcy's Law and seepage principle.

Flow nets are sketches to solve seepage problems in two dimensions. Casagrande(10) presents a method for the construction of flow nets and discusses its theoretical background and practical uses. Basically, the flow net is a graphical solution of the La Place differential equation for steady flow through isotropic soils, which assumes that Darcy's law is valid. Two sets of lines are drawn; these are flow lines and equipotential lines. Flow lines are drawn parallel to the general direction of water flow. Equipotential lines represent contours of equal pressure head, which intersect flow lines perpendicularly. The top flow line defines the phreatic surface. Piezometric pressures at any point can be estimated from the equipotential lines. The flow net (Figure 3) for a homogeneous dam, having no seepage control features and resting on an impervious foundation, shows the phreatic line intersecting the downstream slope. This condition would probably result

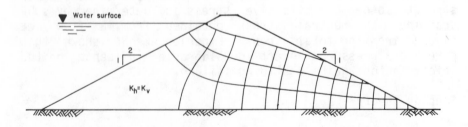

FLOW NET – HOMOGENEOUS EARTH DAM ON IMPERVIOUS FOUNDATION

Figure 3

in slope instability and piping problems. The addition of a toe drain or downstream blanket drain would lower the phreatic line and, in the process, would eliminate the potential for piping and slope instability problems, Figures 4 and 5.

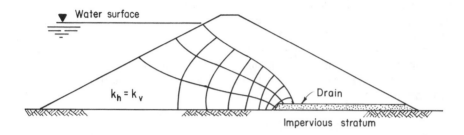

FLOW NET – HOMOGENEOUS EARTH DAM WITH BLANKET DRAIN

Figure 4

Figure 5

Liquefaction

Among the most spectacular, and often most disastrous, types of tailings dike failure is that resulting from liquefaction of the fine particles combined with a breach of the main retaining dike.

The often catastrophic nature of liquefaction failures results from the speed with which they occur and the absence of any warning. The material in an earth structure can be in a metastable state either continuously or periodically over a number of years until, eventually, a random event triggers spontaneous liquefaction. Among the numerous causes of liquefaction that have been found by investigation of previous failures are:

1. Earthquake vibrations.
2. Excess porewater pressures.
3. Large strains in loosely deposted materials.

All of these possibilities are applicable to tailings deposits and must be considered in the design and layout of a disposal area.

The liquefaction susceptibility of tailings deposits is most readily reduced by (i) increasing the in situ densities and (ii) eliminating excess porewater pressures. Mill superintendents are responsible for achieving the minimum requirements of either or both of these in situ material properties by the most economical method. Sound planning, combined with the adoption of relatively inexpensive modifications of disposal techniques during the early stages of an operation, can prevent problems from arising during later operations. Such problems, if allowed to develop, are invariably costly to eliminate.

SURFACE WATER

General

The effects of the surface water loading on a tailings deposit have considerable influence on the design and economics of the disposal. By analyzing the hydrology of the disposal location, the need for flood control and erosion control can be assessed. Many options are open to the designer to minimize the effects of potentially destructive surface waters. These options include: the location of tailings deposits in relation to the topography, whether it is a cross-valley, side hill, or flat ground deposit; the size of diversion works and spillway; and the type of erosion control. The tailings disposal operation must be designed to ensure that the retention dike will never be overtopped.

Hydrology

Local hydrologic conditions have a substantial influence on certain design aspects of surface water control. The relative amounts of average yearly precipitation and evaporation will determine the requirements for the most efficient handling of the estimated quantities of water. Where streamflow records are available, they are used to estimate the size of the spillway; where no records are available, flows into the tailings reservoir are based upon an estimate of precipitation runoff and snowmelt, taking into account the effect of local ground cover and soil conditions. These data and the volume of water in the tailings effluent and the water to be recycled are used to develop a water balance.

Rainfall and flood frequency curves can be developed from existing meteorological or streamflow data or by using methods contained in reference books on hydrology(11). A typical flood frequency curve is shown in Figure 6. The return period used in design will depend on the hazards downstream of the disposal area, the size and location of the deposit, and the type of tailings. Today, all large water supply dams are designed for the probable maximum flood.

Flood Control

Precipitation runoff from high rainfalls or snowmelts has to be controlled to assure safe operation of the tailings disposal area. Several methods are available for the control of floodwaters:

1. Diversion of water around the tailings deposit,
2. Impoundment of all runoff waters in the reservoir, or,
3. Provisions of an engineered spillway so the flow can be routed through the tailings reservoir with no damage.

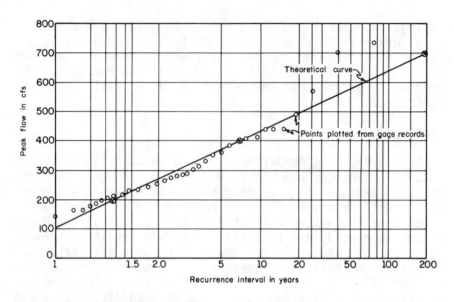

TYPICAL FREQUENCY CURVE OF ANNUAL FLOODS

Figure 6

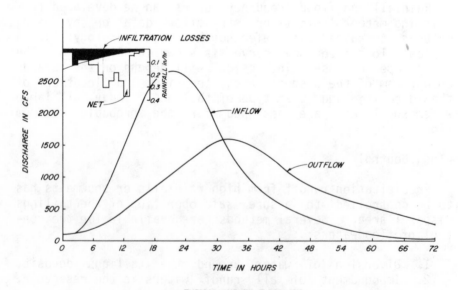

TYPICAL INFLOW FLOOD AND
ROUTED OUTFLOW HYDROGRAPHS

Figure 7

In a wet climate area where large surface runoffs occur, a diversion system can be in the form of a conduit under the tailings, a diversion ditch around the deposit, or a spillway around the tailings retaining dam. For a side hill tailings deposit, where the watershed is generally small, storage of runoff can often be economically feasible. Direct precipitation on any tailings deposit will require engineering for either storage or design for controlled spilling. If the type of tailings will allow emergency spills of excess floodwater without contamination, a spillway can be designed as part of the tailings disposal structure. When a design flood is assigned, the flood can be routed through the tailings reservoir and spillway. The width of spillway can be varied for the routing so that the economics of height of dam vs. spillway width can be optimized. Spillway routing techniques are discussed in Design of Small Dams(12), and a typical inflow flood hydrograph and routed spillway outflow hydrograph are shown in Figure 7. Davies(13) describes the Buffalo Creek failure that resulted from inadequate provisions for controlling floodwater.

Figure 8

Erosion

Because of the susceptibility of cohesionless materials to erosion, tailings deposits must be protected from flowing water. Heavy precipitation falling on embankment slopes will cause erosion if the slope is not protected. Also, water flow from discharge pipes, if not properly channelled, can cause surface erosion similar to that shown in Figure 8. Stream diversion channels must be protected against erosion and the potential for uncontrolled flow.

Slopes can be protected against erosion by placing a layer of well-graded gravel or by vegetating. Ludeke(14) and others (15) discuss the use of vegetative stabilization to minimize erosion. Aplin and Argall(16) list numerous references on stabilization of tailings dam slopes available in the technical literature.

CASE STUDY

Terzaghi(17) in his paper "Effect of Minor Geologic Details on the Safety of Dams", discusses the importance of not overlooking the most unfavorable possibilities expected under the existing geologic conditions. Equal importance must be given to engineering details and combinations of both geologic and engineering conditions.

Basic features are rarely overlooked by the engineer during the design of a tailings dam; a spillway is provided for control of floods, slopes are flattened to ensure acceptable stability, increased freeboard provides an adequate margin of safety against overtopping, and drainage features are specified to eliminate the possibility of piping. Periodically, changing loading conditions, which can critically affect the behavior of an ancillary feature of a tailings disposal operation, result in design modifications. These can temporarily solve the existing problem, but they can also provide the ingredients for a much more serious problem. An example of a combination of existing conditions and disposal modifications that resulted in a retention dam incident is given below.

Figure 9 is a plan of a typical cross-valley deposit with coarse tailings retaining dams at both upstream and downstream ends of the deposit. The river was diverted through a tunnel in the right abutment. Both retaining dams were constructed of hydraulically placed coarse tails. As the height of the tailings dam was increased, a rockfill anchor dike was constructed at the toe of the downstream retaining dam.

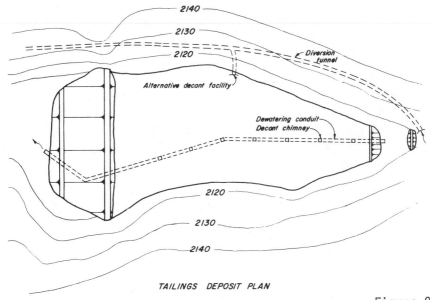

TAILINGS DEPOSIT PLAN

Figure 9

The original design included a reinforced concrete dewatering conduit placed in the valley bottom which was to be extended upstream as the tailings deposit was enlarged. Chimneys were used to control the location, size, and depth of the decant pond. New chimneys were added as the conduit was extended upstream. As the slimes inundated the lower chimneys and the decant pond moved upstream, the chimney openings were plugged at the top of the conduit. Figure 10 shows a developed profile through the deposit; a cross section of the reinforced concrete conduit is provided in Figure 11. Dewatering conduits are designed using the expected maximum loading from superimposed tailings. The estimated life of the mine and the size of the ore body provide the input data for determination of the final height of the tailings deposit.

Experience has shown that, for most tailings deposits around the world, the size of the ore body is usually under-estimated. As more ore is found, the size and height of the tailings deposit are often increased and the margin of safety of the concrete conduit diminishes. Over a period of years, the integrity of the structure decreases as a re-

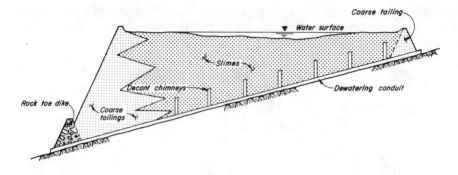

TAILINGS DEPOSIT PROFILE

Figure 10

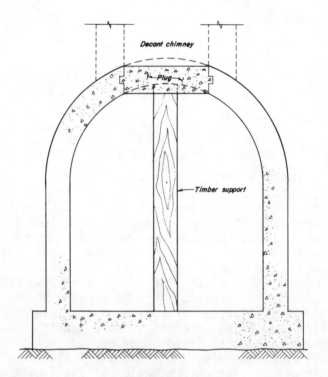

DEWATERING CONDUIT

Figure 11

sult of the increased surcharge and wear and tear during prolonged operation. The monitoring program of the various features of the disposal operation will often show where maintenance of a structure is required. In this particular case, when structural deterioration of the conduit was noted, timber struts were installed as a temporary support until a more permanent side-valley dewatering scheme was realized. The reinforcement of the damaged structure was an acceptable temporary solution for the standard operating loading conditions.

As is invariably the case, however, loads do change with time. Porewater pressures in the tailings increased every year during the spring thaw (snowmelt). Excess hydrostatic pressures on the deteriorated concrete in the conduit caused a collapse of the structure. Flow of the semi-liquid tailings into the conduit resulted in the formation of a crater on the surface of the tailings deposit, Figure 12.

The collapse of a section of the dewatering conduit in a tailings deposit is probably a much more common incident than records show. Generally, pollution occurs downstream; this is cleaned up immediately, where possible, and other routine maintenance operations are initiated. In this particular case, the consequences were not so routine--the tailings and debris from the collapsed conduit dislodged the downstream timber struts. The "dog-leg" in the conduit in the vicinity of the downstream toe of the dam was the final ingredient needed for the formation of an Accident, Type 1 (discussed above).

Figure 12

The tailings, timber struts, and concrete debris formed an impervious plug in the conduit in the vicinity of the downstream toe of the dam as shown in Figure 13. With the seepage into the conduit, the hydrostatic pressure increased excessively and opened cracks in the concrete structure. The hydraulic gradient of the seepage water from the conduit was more than enough to move the coarse tailings--piping started to occur through some areas in the rockfill toe.

Figure 13

Immediate steps were taken to reduce the pressures in the conduit by removing the debris plug. In addition, the rockfill toe was enlarged with a filter zone placed between the existing and new rockfill.

Within a few weeks the condition of the deposit was back to normal. The modifications that had been made to the retaining dam increased the margin of safety to allow for extreme loading conditions. Shortly thereafter, the conduit was grouted, allowing seepage water to pass through a 10-inch pipe in the conduit.

This is an example of how several successive dam incidents could have produced a failure if remedial measures had not been undertaken. The excess hydrostatic pressure produced the conduit collapse; the collapse caused the flow of tailings into the conduit; the flow of tailings caused the plugging of the conduit; the plugged conduit caused water to build up behind the plug; the increased water pressure opened cracks in the conduit causing the water to flow through the coarse tailings; and the seepage water under excess hydraulic gradient started the piping. This "domino effect" shows that water is constantly influencing the performance of dams and can be relied upon to find weak links in any disposal operation.

SUMMARY

Water plays a major role in the failure of tailings dams --it works either internally or externally. In situ water provides the ingredients for:

Increased neutral stresses, which reduce the shear strength. If, in the stability analyses, no allowance has been made for the higher neutral stresses (porewater pressures), the lower shear strength of the materials in the retaining dike will result in a decreased margin of safety and the possibility of slope failures.

Higher seepage forces, which set up the potential for piping. If the hydraulic gradient of the porewater in the tailings increases to the extent where particle movement occurs, a "pipe" (internal erosion) will form. Without remedial action (or a reduction in the loading conditions) the pipe will increase in size, causing collapse of the crest, overtopping, and washout failure as at Teton Dam [Chadwick, et al.,(18)].

Excess porewater pressures, which establish conditions that can result in liquefaction. Probably the least understood of the geotechnical phenomenon resulting in failure, liquefaction susceptibility can be reduced by increasing the density and keeping the porewater pressures to a minimum.

If the surface water in the watershed behind the tailings retaining dam is not controlled, damage or failure can occur:

Floods, resulting from heavy rainfall can overtop the crest of the dam and cause a washout; or where sidehill deposits encroach on floodplains, toe washout can occur followed by dike collapse.

Erosion, of fine cohesionless materials (tailings) occurs quickly; and, if remedial action is not taken, the crest can be breached, leading to total dam failure.

Each of the water loading conditions can result in failure without any contributing factors from other loading conditions. Combinations of extreme water loading conditions can have a cumulative effect that make it more difficult to determine the extent of calculated risk being taken. Increased safety factors, alternative control methods and emergency repair procedures must all be available to eliminate the role of water in the failure of tailings dams.

REFERENCES

1.   U.S. Committee on Large Dams (USCOLD), Lessons from Dam Incidents, USA, ASCE/USCOLD, New York, 1975.

2.   Davies, Edmund, et al., Report of Tribunal Appointed to Inquire into Diasaster at Aberfan, H.L. (316) H.C. 553/ 1966-67, Her Majesty's Stationery Office, London, 1966.

3.   Hazen, A., "Hydraulic Fill Dams", Transactions, American Society of Civil Engineers, Vol. 83, 1920, pp. 1713-1745.

4.   Casagrande, A., "Role of the 'Calculated Risk' in Earthwork and Foundation Engineering", Journal of the Soil Mechanics and Foundation Division, ASCE, Vol. 91, SM4, 1965, p. 1-40.

5.   Peck, R. B., "Advantages and Limitations of the Observation of Method in Applied Soil Mechanics", Geotechnique, Vol. 19, No. 2, 1969, p. 171-187.

6.   Smith, E. S., Poindexter, D. R. and Bleikamp, R. H., "Observation of Approach to Tailings Dam Enlargement", Proceedings of the Conference on Geotechnical Practice for Disposal of Solid Waste Materials, ASCE, 1977, pp. 461-474.

7.   Terzaghi, K., and Peck, R. B., Soil Mechanics in Engineering Practice, Second Edition, John Wiley and Sons, New York, 1967.

8.   Lambe, T. W. and Whitman, R. V., Soil Mechancis, John Wiley and Sons, New York, 1969.

9.   Cedergren, H. R., Seepage, Drainage and Flow Nets, John Wiley and Sons, Inc., New York, 1967.

10. Casagrande, A., "Seepage Through Dams", Journal of the New England Water Works Association, June, 1937.

11. Linsley, R. K., and Franzini, J. B., Water-resources Engineering, McGraw-Hill, New York, 1964.

12. U.S. Bureau of Reclamation, Design of Small Dams, 2nd Edition, Revised Preprint, United States Government Printing Office, Washington, D.C., 1974.

13. Davies, W. E., "Buffalo Creek Dam Disaster: Why It Happened", Civil Engineering, ASCE, July, 1973.

14. Ludeke, K. L., "Vegetative Stabilization of Copper Mine Tailings Disposal Berms of Pima Mining Company", Tailings Disposal Today, Proceeding of the First International Tailing Symposium, Miller Freeman Publications, San Francisco, 1973, pp. 377-410.

15. Argall, G. O., Editor, Tailing Disposal Today, Volume 2, Section 4, Papers on Reclamation, Vegetation and Abandonment, Miller Freeman Publications, San Francisco, 1979.

16. Aplin, C. L., and Argall, G. O., Editors, <u>Tailing Dispoal Today</u>, Proceedings of the First International Tailing Symposium, Miller Freeman Publications, San Francisco, 1973.

17. Terzaghi, K., "Effect of Minor Geologic Details on the Safety of Dams", <u>Technical Publication 215</u>, American Institute of Mining Engineers, 1929, p. 31-44.

18. Chadwick, W. L., <u>et al.</u>, Independent Panel to Review Cause of Teton Dam Failure, <u>Failure of Teton Dam</u>, Report to U.S. Department of the Interior and State of Idaho, United States Government Printing Office, Washington, D.C., 1976.

19. Smith, E. S., "Tailings Disposal and Liquefaction", Transactions, American Institute of Mining, Metallurgical, and Petroleum Engineers, Vol. 244, 1969, pp. 179-187.

32

Acid Mine Drainage Modeling of Surface Mining

by Vincent T. Ricca,
Professor of Civil Engineering,
The Ohio State University,
Columbus, Ohio, USA,
and Ronald R. Schultz, Project Engineer,
Burgess and Niple, Ltd.,
Parkersburg, West Virginia, USA

ABSTRACT

This computer model is capable of simulating the hydrology and acid mine drainage of watersheds which have
experienced surface mining or contain refuse piles. A
hydrologic model using climatological data, watershed
parameters, and mine operation information is used to calculate the amount of water runoff, percolation through the
site or pile, and subsurface drainage. As the water
traverses the system it picks up the acid generated by a
set of mathematical formulations describing the chemical
productions and removal mechanisms occurring in various
zones. The component contributions are summed, with time
preservation, and expressed as discharge rates loads. The
model is presented as a case study application to a surface
coal mine in W. Virginia, U.S.A.

INTRODUCTION

Coal is a major source of energy in the United States.
About half of the 3.2 trillion tons (1) of U.S. coal could
be surface mined. Surface mining in geologic areas containing pyritic materials can cause concern over the generation
of acid mine drainage.

Researchers at The Ohio State University have developed acid production simulation models for both deep mining and surface mining. When combined with a hydrologic simulation model, these total models will predict the minewater flow and its associated acid load. The detailed development of these models is presented in U.S. Environmental Protection Agency sponsored research reports (2,3). Attention in this paper will be directed towards the surface mine modeling portion of the research, in particular, the experiences the authors had in applying the model to a test watershed which had undergone extensive mining.

To accomplish this presentation, first a brief overview of the model will be discussed to acquaint the reader with its general structure; second, a description of the surface mine or refuse pile and the associated pyrite oxidation reaction will be reviewed; third, the data requirements for using the model will be listed; fourth, the model will be applied to a test site; and finally, the modeling results will be evaluated and discussed.

OVERVIEW OF THE MODEL

The total computer modeling for simulating surface mine and refuse pile drainage is accomplished by first generating hydrologic information by use of a hydrologic simulation model and then using that information as input for the acid mine drainage modeling. These models will be presented separately below with explanation on their linking.

Hydrologic Model

The Ohio State University version of the Stanford Watershed model (SWM) is a highspeed, digital computer model which provides a versatile, reliable tool capable of simulating the hydrologic behavior of a basin. This is accomplished through the integrated use of mathematical statements describing the hydrologic activities which occur within the hydrologic cycle. The model is programmed to work toward a complete balance between the volume of water entering the basin and the amount of water leaving the basin plus the water remaining as storage. This balance, which is computed during each water year and displayed at the end of that year, uses precipitation and initial soil moisture conditions as the input, and generates transpiration, evaporation, overland flow, interflow and groundwater flow as

the output. During the modeling process, a continuous
account is kept of the amount in all the activities of the
hydrologic cycle. Figure 1 shows a schematic diagram of
the moisture accounting process in the Stanford Watershed
Model (SWM).

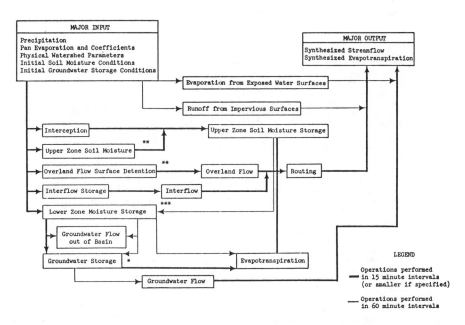

Figure No. 1: Moisture Accounting in the Stanford
Watershed Model

Data requirements for the SWM consist of a variety of
inputs involving: measurable and physical watershed parameters, trial and adjustment factors, selected or assigned
values; along with basic recorded data on precipitation,
pan evaporation, and daily streamflow. These parameters
are listed in Table I in their assigned Fortran computer
language names along with a brief description, units, and
sample value associated with the case study application
discussed later. There are also input-output control
options available which may be used to improve, extend or
analyze a simulation effort.

Of the two basic types of climatological data required
by the SWM, precipitation is the more important and is
usually more easily obtainable than evaporation because of
the larger number of stations which record either hourly or
storage gage daily values. Oftentimes precipitation data

Table No. I: Hydrologic Model (SWM) Input Parameters

MODEL PARAMETERS	PARAMETER DEFINITION AND UNITS*	CASE STUDY* VALUE
Measurable Parameters		
TCONC	Time of concentration of watershed, min.	540.
TNIC	Basin routing interval, min.	60.
A	Impervious fraction of watershed surface	0.0
AREA	Watershed drainage area, sq. mi.	29.2
CHCAP	Index capacity of existing channel, cfs	2000.0
ETL	Fraction of watershed in stream surface	0.002
IRC	Daily interflow recession constant	0.90
KK24	Daily baseflow recession constant	0.95
KSC	Streamflow routing parameter for low flows	0.85
KSF	Streamflow routing parameter for flood flows	0.934
L	Mean overland flow path length, ft.	1900.0
SS	Average ground slope within watersheds, ft/ft.	0.170
Trial and Adjustment Parameters		
CB	Index controlling the rate of infiltration	0.50
CS	Index for estimating soil surface moisture storage	0.40
CY	Index for time distribution of moisture entering interflow	5.00
EDF	Index for estimating soil surface moisutre storage capacity	1.00
EF	Seasonal factor adjusting infiltration and evaporation rates	1.00
EMIN	Minimum value of factor varying seasonal infiltration	0.50
GWS	Current value of groundwater slope index, in.	0.10
LZS	Current soils moisture storage, in.	2.00
LZSN	Soil moisture storage index, in.	3.00
SGW	Groundwater storage increment, in.	0.10
ATFLO	Parameter controlling adjustment of infiltration	10.0
ATCFS	Parameter controlling adjustment of infiltration	0.010
ATDR	Parameter controlling adjustment of infiltration	1.50
ATC2L	Parameter range adjustment of infiltration	0.250
ATC2U	Parameter range adjustment of infiltration	5.00
Assigned or Selected Parameters		
EPXM	Maximum interception rate for a dry watershed, in./hr.	0.18
K3	Soil evaporation parameter	0.20
K24E1	Groundwater evaporation parameter	0.80
K24L	Index for groundwater flow leaving the basin	0.20
KV24	Daily baseflow recession adjustment factor	1.00
NN	Manning's n for overland flow on soil surface	0.40
NNU	Manning's n for overland flow on impervious surface	0.012
RFC	Index for routing	6.00
UZS	Current soil surface moisture storage, in.	0.0
VOLUME	Swamp storage and dry ground recharge, ac-ft.	0.0
ETCORR	Adjustment factor for off-site evaporation data	1.0

*Values used for the Roaring Creek Study Watershed, West Virginia, U.S.A.

is not taken within the watershed, necessitating the use of records from stations outside the watershed. The decision on whether outside data may be used without modification depends on the proximity of the station to the watershed, how well the records reflect regional precipitation trends and how they compare with any incomplete records that may exist within the watershed. If unmodified records are inadequate or unrepresentative, the precipitation synthesizing techniques are employed.

The selection of evaporation data from an outside station is less critical than the choice of precipitation data due to the fact that daily evaporation varies to a lesser degree over a regional area. However, the fewer number of stations which record daily pan evaporation, combined with the suspension of daily recordings by many stations during the winter months, make adequate evaporation data difficult and sometimes impossible to obtain. This may be remedied in many instances by using records from outside stations and/or available local climatological data such as daily solar radiation, wind movement, dew point temperature, relative humidity and air vapor pressure to synthesize evaporation data.

Another type of climatological data is a grouping used as input to an optional subroutine that calculates snowmelt. The use of this subroutine improves the timing of runoff during winter and early spring; however, the amount of data needed to operate it is extensive and in most instances very difficult to locate or collect. Therefore, the subroutine is rarely used unless snowfall contributes a significant percentage to the total annual precipitation.

Physical data on the watershed concerning drainage areas, lakes, overland and stream flow characteristics, vegetative cover, etc. can be obtained from maps and aerial photographs. Soil moisture parameters are best evaluated with the aid of soil borings, well logs or a local geologic profile. Also a knowledge of the soil types and their moisture associated behavior is helpful.

Adequate streamflow data is essential to calibrate the hydrologic model. A minimum of three years of continuous average daily data is needed. Several isolated storm hydrographs are utilized to establish routing parameters and recession coefficients. Groundwater parameters describing percolation, water table fluctuations and slopes, and interbasin transfers, are determined through the aid of well records and boring logs.

Detailed instructions on how to acquire the requisite data, evaluate its suitability, and synthesize missing records are presented in the report and user manuals by Ricca, et al. (3).

The main role of the hydrologic model is to generate the surface and interflow components of the watershed which will

eventually be subjected to acid generation sources. The
daily amount of these waters are outputted which in turn
become input for the acid mine drainage model that follows.

SURFACE MINE-REFUSE PILE MODEL

Both surface mining and deep mining tend to produce waste
materials that are accumulated in refuse piles near the mine
sites. Due to the chemical nature of the wastes involved,
refuse piles generally tend to be acid producers. It was
with this phenomena in mind that Johnson (4) originally
developed the Refuse Pile Model. Johnson's model relies on
the Stanford Watershed Model for overland flow, interflow,
and groundwater flow data. Using these hydrologic inputs
and using the characteristics of the refuse pile itself, the
Refuse Pile Model simulates a continuous accounting of the
flow and of the acid produced, removed, and stored. However,
this model failed to simulate acid production in surface
mines or in refuse piles covered by a layer of inert
material. Maupin (5) adapted Johnson's model to include
strip mines and covered refuse piles. To do this, Maupin
developed three subroutines, two of which effectively eliminated the constant acid production used by Johnson. This
adaptation proved to be particularly effective since it did
not change the original linking to the Stanford Watershed
Model. It is Maupin's Combined Surface Mine-Refuse Pile
Model (SMRPM) that is the subject of this application.

A refuse pile is basically composed of materials that
have been mined with the coal. These materials usually
include clays, shales, and low grade coals, and often have
a high pyritic content. Since refuse piles are generally
close to the actual mining operation, their shape is affected
by the terrain of the mining area. In mountainous country,
steep-sided piles are often found due to the dumping of
material over existing steep slopes. Very broad, flat
topped piles are often found in flat or gently rolling
terrain. Ponds of water may sometimes be found on the
larger flat-topped piles.

Most refuse piles may be divided into three distinct
zones. The three zones of a typical refuse pile are illustrated in Figure 2. The first of these zones is the outer
mantle. In this zone, most of the fine material (clays,
powdered shales, and coal dust) have been removed by precipitation. The absence of fines produces a very porous soil

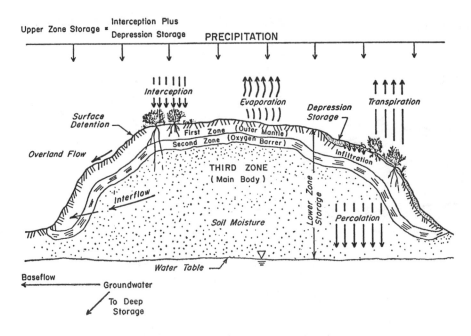

Figure No. 2:   Hydrologic Cycle on a Refuse Pile

in which the pyrite is readily exposed to both oxygen and
water. Therefore, pyrite oxidation will occur rapidly and
acid products will form. These acid products generally
inhibit the formation of any vegetative cover. The second
zone is composed of clays and other fine materials that
have become tightly packed due to rain action. This zone,
although very thin and containing some discontinuties,
exhibits a low permeability and forms an effective water
and gas barrier. This barrier tends to prevent significant
pyrite oxidation from occurring at lower levels of the pile.
Due to the barrier forming second zone, the main body of
the pile is subject to little weathering or pyrite oxidation.

Reclaimed refuse piles are often covered by a layer of
inert material as illustrated in Figure 3. Since this type
of reclamation will cause a refuse pile to behave in a
fashion similar to that of a reclaimed surface mine, both
reclaimed surface mines and refuse piles are modeled by the
surface mine option of the SMRPM. However, active surface
mines lack this layer of inert cover and are, therefore,
modeled by the refuse pile option of the SMRPM.

In a refuse pile, oxygen and water are readily available

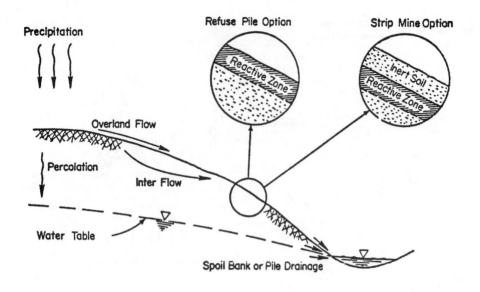

Precipitation

Refuse Pile Option

Reactive Zone

Strip Mine Option

Inert Soil

Reactive Zone

Overland Flow

Percolation

Inter Flow

Water Table

Spoil Bank or Pile Drainage

Figure No. 3: Illustration of the Refuse Pile and Surface
Mine Options

only in the outer mantle. Since both are required for
pyrite oxidation, it can be seen that the only significant
acid production will take place in the outer mantle. The
chemical reactions and equations governing acid production
from pyritic sources are discussed in detail in the research
reports (2,3). It will suffice here to identify the major
pollutants from these reactions as sulfates, ferrous iron,
and sulfuric acid. It is the acid production that is of
concern in this model.

The use of models to simulate the complexities of mine
drainage and pollution generation load necessitates rather
demanding data requirements or input information. This
information should reflect the physical, climatological,
geologic and hydrologic characteristics of the watershed and
should be representative of the coal mining operation and
its acid generation characteristics. Acid mine drainage
sources have three basic characteristics to be simulated:
the physical features of the pollutant source, the rate of
pyrite oxidation in the source system, and the transport of
acid products from the reactive sites by the mine drainage.
The SMRPM requires input information on: mining operation

physical parameters, pyrite oxidation parameters, acid removal parameters, and mine site discharge quantity and quality records. Table II lists the input parameters by their Fortran computer language names with a brief description, units, and sample value used in the case study application presented later. In addition to these listed variables, there are adjustment factors, and parameters to control the program and level of output generated.

Table No. II: Surface Mine Model (SMRPM) Input Parameters

MODEL PARAMETERS	PARAMETERS DEFINITION AND UNITS	CASE STUDY* VALUE
	Physical Parameters	
AREA	Total Watershed Drainage Area, sq. ft.	25938000.
Z1	Inert Layer Thickness, ft	0.0
Z2	Pyrite Layer Thickness, ft	3.0
A1	Acid Producing Area, sq.ft.	5706360.0
	Pyrite Oxidation Parameters	
A	Pyrite Reactivity (Frequency Factor of Arrhenius Form), hr^{-1}	4.00×10^{8}
DEOR	$\Delta E/R$ of Arrhenius Form, hr	1.27×10^{4}
DO	Depth Washed by Direct Runoff, ft	0.500
DOZ	Diffusivity of Inert Layer, ft^2/hr	0.0448
DOZA	Diffusivity of Pyrite Layer, ft^2/hr	0.0448
P	Total Atmospheric Pressure, atm	1.0
R	Gas Law Constant, $atm.ft^3/^{0}R.lb.mole$	0.7302
SOLACD	Solubility of Acid Products, mg/ℓ	20000.
T	Temperature, ^{0}R	508.43
XA1	Mole fraction of Oxygen in Atmosphere	0.208
	Acid Removal Parameters	
EXADIR	Initial Weight of Acid Dissolved in Direct Runoff Storage, lb.	0.0
EXAINT	Initial Weight of Acid Dissolved in Interflow Storage, lb.	0.0
EXALZ	Initial Weight of Acid Dissolved in Lower Zone Storage, lb.	0.0
EXAUZ	Initial Weight of Acid Dissolved in Upper Zone Storage, lb.	0.0
AMTACU	Initial Weight of Acid Adsorbed in Upper Soil, lb.	1000.0
AMTACL	Initial Weight of Acid Adsorbed in Lower Soil, lb.	1000.0
CO	Exponent Affecting Leaching of Acid by Direct Runoff	0.25
CEU	Exponent Affecting Leaching of Acid by Water Entering Upper Zone	0.05
OFF	Constant Affecting Leaching of Acid by Direct Runoff	1.00
UZF	Constant Affecting Leaching of Acid by Water Entering Upper Zone	0.10
IFF	Constant Affecting Leaching of Acid by Interflow	1.00
LZF	Constant Affecting Leaching of Acid by Water Entering Lower Zone	1.00
	Water Quality and Quantity Data	
FWR	Recorded Minewater Data, cfs	-----
ACR	Recorded Acid Load from Mine, tons/day	-----

*Values used for the North Branch of Flatbush Fork Study Watershed, West Virginia, U.S.A.

Mine and watershed description data include information on the total watershed area, the areal extent of the acid producing regions, the thickness of the pyrite layer, and the thickness of the layer of inert cover, if any. These data may usually be compiled from topographic maps, mine maps, and boring logs.

The pyrite oxidation data is of two types: those related to the conditions under which oxidation takes place and those related to the rate at which oxidation occurs. Values are needed for the pyrite reactivity, the diffusivity of oxygen through the stratum, the solubility of the acid products, and the temperature and pressure at the pyrite layer. Often, many of these data are difficult to evaluate due to the lack of prior analysis of the coal seam or pyritic material. However, two alternatives are available to acquire the necessary data; either samples of the acid producing materials may be collected for laboratory analysis to assign values, or initial parameter values may be assigned and adjusted by trial and error substitution until most suitable acid load simulation is obtained.

The acid removal parameters may also be divided into two categories: those dealing with the initialization of acid loads in various storage locations and those affecting the actual removal of oxidation products. These parameters are reported by Maupin (5) to be adjustment factors which must be re-evaluated until the best fit to recorded data is obtained.

Minewater quality and quantity data are required as input to the SMRPM for the purpose of providing a means of analyzing the success of a simulation effort. Accurate and frequent monitoring of minewater quantity and quality will provide the data necessary to achieve an accurate calibration of the model.

Detailed instructions on data acquisition for the SMRPM are available in the report and user manuals by Ricca, et al. (3).

CASE STUDY APPLICATION

The Hydrologic Model has been successfully applied to several watersheds in the Eastern coal fields of the United States. However, the Surface Mine-Refuse Pile Model had had only limited application due to the lack of sufficient hydrologic and mine drainage data for corresponding time periods. The test site selected by the authors, located near Elkins, West Virginia, had relatively complete data sets for the pair of models as a result of studies by the U.S. Environmental Protection Agency from 1964 to 1969. One aspect of their investigation was to monitor the site

climatology and drainage from the deep and surface mines
within the Roaring Creek and Grassy Run watersheds. Thus,
partial records of minewater quality and quantity were
available, as well as much of the other pertinent information on the physical and geological aspects of the area,
and the nature and extent of the coal mining activities.
Although not all of the input data necessary for modeling
were collected either completely or consistently, enough
information was compiled, by synthesis of missing data, to
apply the models. The Hydrologic Model was applied to the
entire Roaring Creek watershed while the Surface Mine-Refuse
Pile Model was applied to the North Branch of Flatbush Fork
watershed, a sub-watershed of the Roaring Creek watershed.
The following describes the experiences of this application.

Location

The North Branch of Flatbush Fork watershed is located in
east central West Virginia, within the Eastern coal fields
of the United States. This oblong watershed encompasses an
area of 0.95 square miles and is drained by the North Branch
of Flatbush Fork to Roaring Creek, a tributary of the Tygart
Valley River. Figure 4 shows the location of the study area
in West Virginia and the continental United States, and also
depicts the location of the North Branch of Flatbush Fork
watershed within the Roaring Creek watershed.

Climate

The climate of the study watershed is typical of continental mountain climates. The area is subject to cold winters
and mild summers and has an average normal temperature of
50.7°F. Average yearly precipitation is 45.92 inches with
the majority of this precipitation being the result of
intense thunderstorms during the summer months or large
scale, low intensity, cyclonic storms that occur in the
early spring. Snowfall in the area averages 47 inches and
usually occurs during the period from November to April.

Geology

The Roaring Creek watershed is composed of two distinct
physiographic areas which reflect the respective weathering
characteristics and structures of the underlying rock. The
western two-thirds of the watershed, which includes the

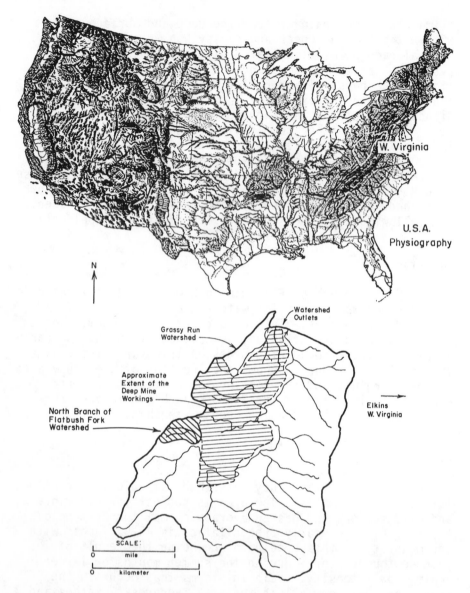

Figure No. 4:   Location of the Study Watershed

the North Branch of Flatbush Fork watershed, consists of
gently dipping beds of relatively non-resistant shales and
sandstones which form broad, flat uplands separated by
narrow, V-shaped valleys carved by tributaries of Roaring
Creek. The topography of the eastern one-third of the

watershed is dominated by mountainous cliffs and flatiron-like ridges carved from moderately dipping sandstone and conglomerate sandstone. A syncline separates the two physiographic regions and influences the establishment of the main direction of drainage for the watershed.

Coal and Mining Activities

The most economically significant coal seam in the North Branch of Flatbush Fork watershed is the Kittanning seam. Strip mining in the area has disturbed approximately 0.20 square miles or abour 21 percent of the watershed area. The strip mines lie on the high side of the Kittanning coal seam and drainage was generally into underground mines.

HYDROLOGIC MODEL APPLICATION

The Hydrologic Model (SWM) is applied to generate input for the Surface Mine-Refuse Pile Model. After the SWM is calibrated and is deemed to be successfully simulating the hydrologic behavior of the watershed, specific information on the direct runoff, interflow, and baseflow for the watershed is generated and stored on magnetic tapes.

Climatological Data

Precipitation data for the Roaring Creek watershed were obtained through the use of synthesis techniques which combined the hourly precipitation records for two existing weather stations located outside the watershed with existing hourly data taken in the watershed. Evaporation data was acquired through a combination of recorded and synthesized data.

Streamflow Data

Average daily streamflow data for Roaring Creek was taken from the United States Geological Survey (USGS) publication of Water Resources Data for West Virginia. The Environmental Protection Agency provided detailed hydrograph data needed to determine several streamflow routing and recession parameters required by the SWM.

SWM Inputs

The major SWM input parameters evaluated for the Roaring Creek watershed are listed in Table I. Determination and/or adjustment of values for most of the parameters followed guidelines and procedures recommended by Ricca (3). Special computational efforts were required in the case of K24L, the fraction of groundwater lost via inter-basin transfer. Due to the orientation of the mined coal seam and the extensive nature of the deep mine complex, some of the minewater originating in the Roaring Creek basin discharged into the adjacent Grassy Run watershed. Analysis of this moisture transfer involved the use of recorded minewater discharge data within the Grassy Run watershed and mine maps depicting the areal layout of the deep mine complex.

After the initial values of the input parameters were determined, the data was assembled for use. To enhance the utility of the model and reduce the cost of operation, the SWM source deck was compiled on disk, all evaporation, precipatation, and recorded streamflow data were transferred into 9-track magnetic tape. These measures reduced the amount of input data on cards to essentially those parameters shown in Table I, plus required program and input/output control data.

Hydrologic Modeling Experience

Analysis of the results of the initial run of the SWM for the Roaring Creek watershed indicated a general slight undersynthesis of streamflow for the water years modeled, a moderate undersynthesis of winter streamflow, and a moderate oversynthesis of streamflow for the summer months. In order to improve these situations, different values of several trial and adjustment parameters were tried following the sensitivity guidelines. Parameter changes progressed until satisfactory simulation results were obtained.

Hydrologic Modeling Results

The simulation results for water year 1967-68 represent the average success achieved during the hydrologic modeling effort. Results were generated in both tabular and graphical form and include the recorded daily streamflow annual and monthly summaries of recorded and simulated streamflow,

precipitation and evapotranspiration, end-of-the-month
values of certain key parameters, the water balance for the
year, the daily correlation coefficient, the daily soil
moisture status and recorded and simulated streamflow hydrographs. Plots of the recorded and simulated streamflow
hydrographs for Roaring Creek are presented in Figure 5.

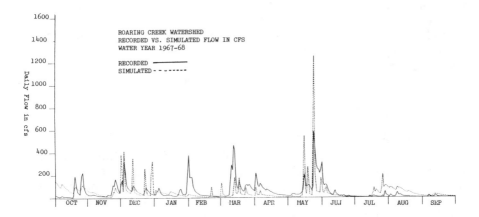

Figure No. 5: Plot of Recorded and Simulated Streamflow

As illustrated by Figure 5, the results of the hydrologic
modeling effort provide a reasonable simulation of the
overall patterns established by the recorded streamflow
hydrograph. However, a less successful simulation of
individual streamflow events was noted. Inspection of the
monthly results indicated a strong trend toward oversynthesis
in the summer months and undersynthesis in the winter months.
In addition, some simulated winter peaks appear to be out of
phase with the recorded data. The following possible explanations of the summer oversynthesis may be offered: the
synthesized precipitation record may not adequately represent
the intense local storms which occur in summer months, the
actual soil moisture may be less than the modeled volume, or
the synthesized evapotranspiration values used for this time
period may be too small. During the winter months, snowfall
and snowmelt, and their accompanying modeling problems, are
the most likely source of simulation difficulties. Although
the SWM is capable of handling this problem, the large
amounts of specialized data necessary to obtain a satisfactory simulation of snowmelt were not available for the study
watershed.

SURFACE MINE-REFUSE PILE MODEL APPLICATION

While the SWM was applied to the entire Roaring Creek watershed, the SMRPM was applied only to the North Branch of Flatbush Fork watershed, a small, sub watershed of the Roaring Creek watershed. This watershed was selected since surface mining was the predominant mining method and since surface mine drainage appeared to be relatively unaffected by deep mine drainage. In addition, minewater quantity and quality data were available for the watershed for the time period to be modeled. Water year 1965-66 was selected for the modeling effort since it exhibited the greatest frequency of minewater data collection.

Minewater Quantity and Quality Data

Minewater discharges were monitoring by a sampling station established by the EPA and located near the mouth of the North Branch of Flatbush Fork. Quality data were originally measured as milligrams/liter, but were converted to pounds of acid per day to be compatible with the SMRPM. Sampling frequency ranged from an average of once every five days for water year 1965-66 to a twice-monthly sampling for water year 1967-68.

Surface Mine-Refuse Pile Model Input Parameters

Table II presents the principal parameter values used for the initial run of the SMRPM in its application to the study area for water year 1965-66. Physical parameters were evaluated from topographic maps, mine maps furnished by the EPA and documented observations of the acid producing layers published in geologic survey reports of the area. Pyrite oxidation parameters were assigned values from a previous modeling effort due to the lack of the specialized data necessary for evaluation of the parameters. Finally, the acid removal parameters were assigned initial values which would be adjusted as the simulation effort progressed. Procedures and methods used to calculate and/or assign initial values to all of the SMRPM input parameters are described in further detail by Schultz (6).

Modeling Experience

Analysis of the results of the initial run of the SMRPM for the North Branch of Flatbush Fork watershed indicated that the total annual acid load had been greatly oversimulated due largely to the oversimulation of minewater flow. Adjustments to several key parameters were made to correct the oversimulation of minewater flow which in turn helped to alleviate the large oversimulation of acid load. In addition, several key pyrite oxidation parameters and acid removal parameters were adjusted until a satisfactory simulation of general trends observed in the recorded data was obtained.

Surface Mine Modeling Results

The total results of the modeling effort were generated in both tabular and graphical form. Output selected for presentation in this paper consists of the plots of recorded and simulated minewater flow and total acid load (Figures 6 and 7). Additional output includes tables of the simulated daily direct runoff, interflow, and baseflow, the total simulated daily flow, the simulated daily acid load in direct runoff, interflow, and baseflow, and the total simulated daily acid load.

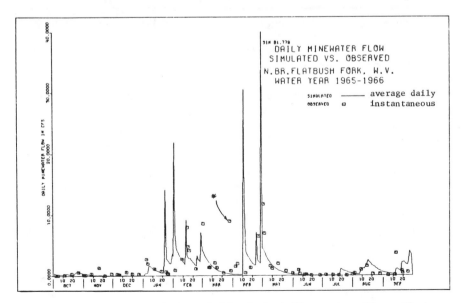

Figure No. 6: Recorded and Simulated Minewater Flow Plots

As illustrated by Figure 6, the results of this modeling effort provide a reasonable simulation of the general trends established by the recorded data. However, the lack of a complete record of minewater flows makes it virtually impossible to assess the accuracy of peak values. There is no reason to believe that spot field observations were timed to obtain peak discharges. Rather, it is likely that recorded flows merely correspond to random observations.

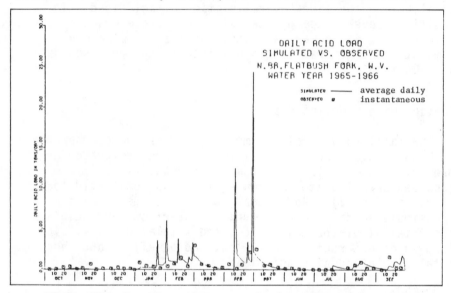

Figure No. 7:   Recorded and Simulated Acid Load Plots

As in the case of minewater discharge, the results of the modeling effort provide a reasonable simulation of the general trends established by the recorded acid load data as illustrated by Figure 7. Again, the infrequency of mine-water sampling makes evaluation of daily acid load values difficult. The total annual acid load, however, may be evaluated for accuracy. Recorded annual acid flow was reported by the EPA to be 224 tons, while an average of the minewater samples indicated a total load of 175 tons. The simulated acid load for water year 1965-66 of 198 tons agrees to within at least 12 percent of each of the recorded values. Although it is unlikely that the average of the minewater samples provides an accurate annual acid load due to lack of peak values, the trends established by the mine-water data remain as the major justification for model adjustment. A more complete minewater sampling would lead to greater agreement between the reported annual acid load and the annual acid load determined by sample averaging and would allow for a more accurate calibration of the SMRPM.

CONCLUSIONS AND RECOMMENDATION

The model application presented herein was only the first field situation attempt to verify its performance. The authors feel that the model is capable of performing well and that any shortcomings experienced can basically be associated with the completeness or consistency of the data employed. It takes several years of intensive effort to collect a complete data package on a surface mine drainage study. The one used herein was the best known to be available. As a consequence of this application, the deficiencies in data collection schemes surfaced. A paper was presented by Ricca (7) on data deficiencies in mine drainage modeling. Not only were the problems encountered discussed, but detailed recommendations were listed for future mine drainage data collection endeavors. Some of the salient recommendations are:

1) collect hydrologic and mine drainage quality and quantity data in the same time frame,
2) monitor climatologic events within the watershed; precipitation, hourly, and evaporation, daily. If snow is prevalent, collect snowmelt data,
3) gather information on the soil characteristics of the watershed and perform field tests on the overburden material,
4) analyze pyrite oxidation characteristics of the material comprising the mined coal seam and overburden,
5) acquire mine maps and operation techniques, and
6) locate and monitor major surface water diversions into the mines and/or transfers of water within the mine complex.

ACKNOWLEDGEMENTS

The authors are grateful for the assistance and support of their colleagues and sponsors throughout the development of the models. Pioneers in hydrologic modeling, Ray Linsley, Norman Crawford, and Douglas James; and in acid mine drainage, Edwin Smith, Kenesaw Shumate and Ronald Hill, have through their endeavors laid the foundation for our work. The interest, involvement, and support of the U. S. Environmental Protection Agency was most crucial to our continued research. Many thanks are extended to Eugene Harris and Ronald Hill for their technical and administrative assistance. Special thanks are given The Mining Institute at The Ohio State University and to Burgess & Niple, Ltd. Consulting Engineers for sponsoring the authors participation in this symposium. Finally, appreciation is expressed to our typist, Clarissa Alexander, for her help in preparing this paper.

REFERENCES

1. Mancke, R.B., The Failure of U.S. Energy Policy, Columbia University Press, New York, N.Y., 1974

2. Shumate, K.S., Smith, E.E., Ricca, V.T., and Clark, G.M., "Resources Allocation to Optimize Mining Pollution Control", U.S. Environmental Protection Agency, Contract No. 68-01-0724, EPA-600/2-76-112, 1976.

3. Ricca, V.T., Smith, E.E., and Clark, G.M., "Predictive and Pollution Abatement Model on Mine Drainage", Extraction Technology Branch, IERL, U.S. EPA, Contract No. 68-03-2008, Cincinnati, Ohio, Project Report submitted for review January 1979.

4. Johnson, S.E., "Computer Simulation of Acid Mine Drainage from a Refuse Pile", M.S. Thesis, Department of Civil Engineering, The Ohio State University, 1973.

5. Maupin, A.N., "Computer Simulation of Acid Mine Drainage from a Watershed Containing Refuse Piles and/or Surface Mines", M.S. Thesis, Department of Chemical Engineering, The Ohio State University, 1973.

6. Schultz, R.R., "Application of the Combined Refuse Pile Strip Mine Model for Acid Mine Drainage", M.S. Thesis, Department of Civil Engineering, The Ohio State University, 1977

7. Ricca, V.T., "Data Deficiencies in Acid Mine Drainage Modeling", Proceedings, U.S. EPA Conference on Environmental Modeling and Simulation, Cincinnati, Ohio 1976.

33

Seepage Control for Tailings Dams

by Earle J. Klohn, President,
Klohn Leonoff Consultants Ltd.,
Richmond, British Columbia, Canada

1. INTRODUCTION

Seepage control is a critically important aspect in the design, construction, and operation of tailings dams as it directly affects: the stability of the downstream slope; internal erosion due to piping; and pollution of ground and surface waters downstream of the dam. Methods for controlling seepage through embankments, abutments, and foundations have been extensively studied and developed over a period of many years in the field of conventional water storage dams. These procedures, which are considered standard practice in the conventional water storage dam field, are well documented in the published engineering literature. Moreover, these conventional seepage control procedures are directly applicable to the control of seepage flows in the embankments, abutments, and foundations of tailings dams. However, they must be suitably modified to account for the fact that a tailings slurry, rather than water is being stored behind the dam.

In the past, practically all tailings dams were constructed by some variation of the upstream method of construction. The original upstream method normally involved construction of a low earth "starter" dyke, 10 to 20 feet in height. This dyke was usually constructed from locally available borrow materials and was seldom subject to engineering design.

The tailings were discharged by spigotting off the top of the starter dyke. When the initial pond was nearly filled, the dyke was raised by borrowing material from the dried surface of the previously deposited tailings, and the cycle was repeated. As the height of such a dam increases, each successive dyke moves further upstream, and is underlain by the soft, previously deposited tailings. There is a limiting height to which such a dam can be raised before shear failure occurs, and the tailings flow out. In regions subject to seismic shocks, failure of this type of dam by liquefaction can occur at very low heights. In fact, the history of this method of dam construction is plagued with failures, some of them catastrophic. Figure 1 (9) presents a comparison between a conventional water storage dam and a tailings dam built using the upstream method of construction.

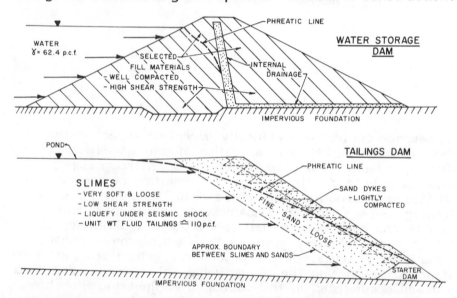

COMPARISON BETWEEN CONVENTIONAL WATER STORAGE DAM AND TAILINGS DAM BUILT USING AN UPSTREAM METHOD OF CONSTRUCTION

FIGURE I

Current, good engineering practice is to use downstream methods of tailings dam construction for all major tailings dams. In areas of high seismic risk where failure of the tailings dam poses a threat to life and property, downstream methods of tailings dam construction should be used for all structures regardless of their height. The downstream method of tailings dam construction evolved from a blending of the engineering knowledge and experience available in the field of water storage dams, with the knowledge of the mining operators responsible for construction and operation of tailings dams. The downstream method of tailings dam construction involves constructing the dam in a downstream direction from the initial starter dam. Consequently, as the dam is raised, it can be constructed over a carefully prepared foundation base rather than over previously deposited slimes, as is the case for the upstream method. Figure 2 (9) presents a comparison between a conventional water storage dam and a tailings dam built using the downstream method of construction. As might be expected, the downstream method of tailings dam construction permits far better control of seepage flows and pressures than does the upstream method.

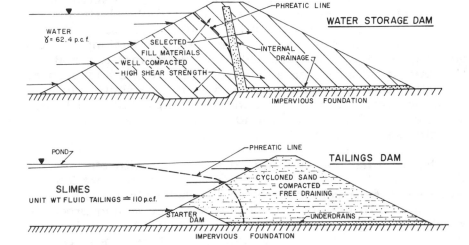

COMPARISON BETWEEN TYPICAL WATER STORAGE DAM AND TAILINGS DAM BUILT USING ONE OF THE DOWNSTREAM METHODS OF CONSTRUCTION

FIGURE 2

In some instances, dam safety and environmental pollution control regulations can have a major effect on the seepage control facilities required for either upstream or downstream tailings dams. In those instances where a closed circuit tailings pond is required (no discharge of effluent is permitted downstream of the dam), foundation cutoffs and foundation drainage wells may be necessary to prevent surface and embankment seepage from passing downstream of the dam.

The paper addresses the problem of seepage control for tailings dams. Conventional flow nets are presented to illustrate the effectiveness of various seepage control measures which are normally used in the design of water storage dams. The application of these measures to tailings dam design and construction is then discussed. Examples are presented illustrating some of the problems that can develop when uncontrolled seepage occurs. Also presented are several case histories illustrating seepage control measures incorporated into the design of several existing tailings dams.

II. PUBLIC CONCERN AND GOVERNMENT REGULATIONS

Tailings dams are important structures that involve two aspects of public concern. One is the structural stability of the dam and the possible release, if failure occurred, of very large volumes of water and/or semi-fluid tailings. Such an event would not only cause extensive downstream pollution but would also pose a serious threat to life and property. The other aspect of public concern is the possibility of pollution under normal operation, in which polluted effluent might escape through or around the tailings dam and enter the streams or groundwater of the area.

The potential pollution hazard associated with storage of the tailings slurry varies with different mining operations, and ranges from very severe for the radioactive wastes associated with uranium mining, to none for mining processes which merely grind up an inert ore without the addition of toxic chemicals during processing. In between these two extremes are a wide range of conditions that present either short or long-term, potential, pollution problems.

In response to public demands, Governments throughout North America and in many other parts of the world have enacted legislation relating to the safety and pollution aspects of the design, construction, and operation of tailings dams. Accidents such as the Teton Dam failure have served to focus the attention of both the public and the legislators on the issue of dam safety, and a trend towards stricter regulations affecting all aspects of the design, construction, and operation of tailings dams should be anticipated.

Pollution control regulations can have a very important impact on tailings dam design, and, in particular, on seepage control measures that are required to satisfy the regulations. In those instances where the effluent seepage is considered harmful, extensive cutoff and seepage collection facilities may be required to prevent seepage from reaching and contaminating the surface and groundwaters of the area. This would be the case where the effluent was considered to contain harmful chemical agents or was radioactive. In recent years, public concern about the storage of radioactive waste from uranium mining operations has greatly increased. (24) In some cases, complete lining of the uranium tailings pond has been required with suitable underdrainage and monitoring systems installed. In instances where the tailings dam is constructed on pervious foundations of great thickness, and pollution control requirements do not allow the loss of water from the pond, a hydraulic barrier may be required. This method of seepage control which is rather costly and complicated involves the installation of two lines of wells downstream of the dam. The upstream line of wells are pumping wells which lower the groundwater table, and the downstream row of wells are injection wells which maintain the positive hydraulic barrier. The method is illustrated schematically on Figure 3.

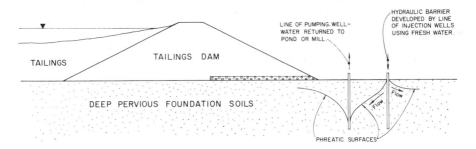

HYDRAULIC BARRIER— USED TO PREVENT SEEPAGE
DOWNSTREAM OF DAM

FIGURE 3

Obviously, regulations pertaining to dam safety and pollution are factors which must be carefully considered in designing and costing the tailings disposal facilities required for any new development. Satisfying these regulations unquestionably will add to the cost of tailings disposal and, in future, these extra costs must be considered a necessary part of the cost of production.

III. SEEPAGE THROUGH CONVENTIONAL DAMS

1. General

Tailings dams store water as well as tailings in their reservoirs. The volume of water stored and the location of the free water surface within the tailings pond varies from one mining operation to another. At one extreme, some tailings dams are designed to have water stored against their upstream face (8) and must perform the same function as a conventional water storage dam. (On a large number of projects the starter dam is designed in this manner with the remainder of the dam raised using sand tailings for dam construction and utilizing the slimes beach as the upstream impervious membrane). At the other extreme, some tailings dams have very wide slimes beaches against their upstream slope at all times and the free water surface in the tailings pond is located 1000 ft or more away from the dam. Most tailings dams fall somewhere between these two extremes such that they generally operate with a slimes beach several hundred feet wide against their upstream face. This slimes beach acts as the upstream impervious membrane for the tailings dam. In most instances the tailings dam itself is built of pervious, tailings sand. If, under unusual hydrological or operating conditions, pond levels should rise and flood the slimes beach we have the case of a sand dam with a free water surface against its upstream face. This, of course, is a most undesirable situation, the possible consequences of which are discussed in a following section.

In summary, it can be stated that tailings dams, like conventional water retention dams, store water. In some instances, and particularly for tailings starter dams, an appreciable depth of water may be stored against the upstream face of the tailings dam. In most instances a wide beach of slimes, acting as an upstream impervious membrane is located between the rising sand tailings dam and the free water in the pond. However, under unusual circumstances, this beach could be flooded bringing the free water surface up to the face of the sand dam. Obviously the seepage control measures that have been developed to protect conventional water storage dams have wide application to tailings dams. In the following sections of this paper these conventional seepage control measures will be reviewed and their application to various tailings dam designs considered.

2. Seepage Problems and Their Defences

The water stored behind a dam always seeks a means of escape. Control of this seepage presents a challenge to the designer because water will always find the path of least resistance for its escape route. This will take the seepage through pervious strata, joints, fissures, and cracks as they really exist, in and beneath the structure, rather than as assumed for purposes of the design analyses. For this reason, seepage control measures should always be conservatively designed and for important structures, instrumentation to measure piezometric pressures and seepage flows should be included as part of the design.

Seepage through dams may give rise to three basic problems that can create serious difficulties and in the extreme may lead to failure. These three problems are:

a) Piping – This occurs where exiting seepage flows pick up soil particles and move them out of the foundation or embankment. The continued removal of soil particles causes the unseen development of channels or pipes in the embankment or foundation. When these pipes connect back to the free water in the reservoir very large flows develop along the pipe and complete failure of the dam may occur. The Teton Dam failure (20) has been attributed to piping.

b) Slope Instability and Heaving – Seepage forces caused by the flow of water through the embankment or its foundations can cause instability of downstream slopes. If excess upward seepage forces develop in the foundation soils immediately downstream of the toe of the dam, heaving may occur.

c) Excess Water Losses – These occur when the embankment or its foundations are pervious. Apart from the obvious disadvantage of losing water, large seepage losses may or may not pose a problem for the dam. Generally, provided the seepage pressures associated with these large flows do not pose a stability or uplift problem and provided adequate protection against piping is given by properly designed filters, fairly large seepage flows can be accepted. However, it is normally considered good engineering practice to

minimize seepage flows by the introduction of relatively impervious elements in the upstream section of the dam and its foundation.

There are three basic defences used for the control of
seepage. These are:

a) Filters – to prevent piping and heaving. Basically, filters are designed to permit the free discharge of the seepage water but to prevent the
movement of soil particles. (The basic rules for
design of filters are presented in the following
section).

b) Seepage Reduction – to reduce water pressures
and seepage forces in the critical exit areas downstream of the dam. The methods used include:
impervious cutoffs, grout curtains, and upstream
impervious blankets.

c) Drainage – to reduce water pressures in the
embankment and foundation soils. The methods
used include: internal vertical interceptor
drains, horizontal blanket drains, strip drains,
toe drains, and relief wells.

Normally, the above three methods of seepage control are
used in combination. For example, the seepage reduction
methods used must almost be perfect, if they are to greatly
reduce downstream seepage flows and pressures. As this
is seldom possible to achieve, the seepage reduction methods
are usually combined with downstream drainage to ensure the
desired end-result. Similarly, all drains must be designed
to meet the filter requirements as their function is to get the
water out of the surrounding soil without loss of soil particles.

Filter Design – The filter design criteria specified by different designers and/or agencies (5, 17, 18, 19, 23) show
some variations but basically follow the criteria originally set
out by Terzaghi and confirmed by Bertram (1) about 40 years
ago. The author suggests the following criteria for filter
design:

Rule 1: $\dfrac{\text{The 15\% size of the filter}}{\text{The 85\% size of the protected soil}}$ should be less than 5.

Rule 2: $\dfrac{\text{The 50\% size of the filter}}{\text{The 50\% size of the protected soil}}$ should be less than 25.

Rule 3: The filter material should be smoothly graded and its grain size curve should approximately be parallel to that of the protected soil, in the finer range of sizes.
Gap-graded materials are not acceptable.

Rule 4: $\dfrac{\text{The } 15\% \text{ size of the filter}}{\text{The } 15\% \text{ size of the protected soil}}$ should be greater than 5.

Rule 5: The filter should not contain more than 5 per cent of particles, by weight, finer than the No. 200 sieve, and the fines should be cohesionless.

Rule 6: The maximum size of filter aggregate should not exceed 3 inches (protects against segregation).

Rule 7: For bases of plastic clay soils with low permeability, concrete sand may be used for the filter (ASTM C33)

Rule 8: For bases of non-plastic silt, rock flour, or varved silt, asphalt sand may be used for the filter (ASTM D1073)

Rule 9: For base material that ranges from more than 10% larger than a No. 4 sieve to more than 10% passing a No. 200 sieve, the filter design should be based on the material passing the No. 4 sieve.

Rule 10: To avoid movement of filter into drain pipe perforations or joints:

$\dfrac{\text{D85 filter}}{\text{Slot width}}$ 1.4 and $\dfrac{\text{D85 filter}}{\text{hole diameter}}$ 1.2

Rules 1, 2 and 3 are to ensure that the filter will not allow migration of particles of the protected soil. Rules 4 and 5 are to ensure that the filter has sufficient permeability. Rule 6 is intended to minimize the problem of particle segregation during placement. Rules 7 and 8 cover the case of placing filter against fine-grained, core materials. The sands are fine enough to prevent the migration of fine particles, are coarse enough to be free draining, and are sufficiently cohesionless to act as "crack stoppers" for the core. Rule 9 ensures that the filter design for broadly graded base material adequately protects the finer portion of the base. Rule 10 applies to the case of filter material placed around slotted or perforated drain pipe.

Figure 4 (18) illustrates the application of Rules 1, 2, 3 and 4. Rules 1 and 2 use the finest D85 and D50 gradation for the base against the coarsest D15 and D50 for the filter. Rule 4 uses the coarsest D15 for the base against the finest D15 for the filter.

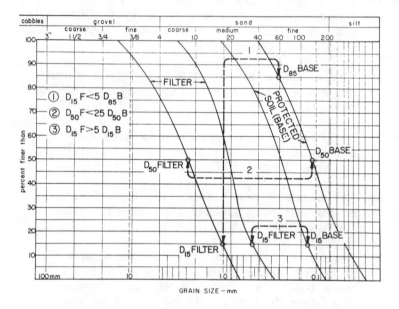

GRADATION REQUIREMENTS FOR FILTERS

(AFTER REFERENCE 23-TENTATIVE DESIGN GUIDE FOR MINE WASTE EMBANKMENTS IN CANADA)

FIGURE 4

Where graded filters are required, each successive filter must satisfy the filter criteria. Most drains are zoned and consist of an outer zone to prevent the movement of fines from the embankment or foundation soils and an inner zone of higher permeability to carry away the seepage flows. The coarser, inner zone must also satisfy the filter criteria relative to the outer zone to ensure that soil particles from the outer filter do not move into the coarse inner zone.

Relief Well Design - Relief wells are used as a means of relieving uplift pressures in pervious foundation soils that pass beneath the dam. They normally consist of an 18" to

24" diameter outer hole and a 6" to 10" diameter inner well screen. The annular space between the drill hole and the well screen is filled with suitable filter material. Relief wells are usually located at the downstream toe of the dam where they are accessible for both observation and maintenance. Quite often relief wells are used in conjunction with one of the seepage reduction measures (grouting, upstream impervious blanket, etc.) to control seepage gradients at the downstream toe of the dam. Relief wells flow by gravity and hence the amount of pressure relief that they can provide is controlled by the elevation of their discharge pipe. In some instances, the relief wells are allowed to discharge at, or slightly above ground surface, whereas in others they discharge into a buried collector pipe which leads either to a pumped sump or discharges at a lower topographic elevation.

Relief wells are commonly spaced at 50 to 100 ft centres. Flows should be measured and piezometers should be installed between relief wells to measure their effectiveness. In the event the original installation is inadequate, additional relief wells can be installed between the original wells. Relief wells must be able to maintain their initial capacity for long periods of time or be restored or replaced. A comprehensive 5 year investigation by the U.S. Army Corps of Engineers in 1972, (22) of relief wells on the Mississippi River showed that the specific yield of 24 test wells decreased 33% over a 15 year period. Incrustation on well screens and in gravel filters was believed to be the major cause (iron bacteria growth on screens and in filters from precipitation of iron oxides and hydroxides and calcium carbonates in gravel filters). This is an item which must be considered when a relief well system is included as part of the seepage control measures.

Relief wells must be designed to discharge water, without loss of solids. To ensure permanent performance without movement of soil particles, the well screens and their surrounding granular fill must satisfy the filter criteria outlined in a previous section of the paper. Detailed procedures for the design of relief well systems are presented in the list of references (5,13,21,23) appended to this paper.

3. Flow of Water Through Soils

The Flow Net - The flow of water through soils is directly proportional to the hydraulic gradient (Darcy's Law). The general differential equation for the steady flow of water through isotropic soils can be expressed mathematically by La Place differential equations. The graphical solution of the La Place equations is called the flow net. (2,5).

Flow nets may be sketched by hand, developed from model studies using dyes, or by using electrical analogs. More recently, digital computer solutions using either finite-element or finite-difference methods have been developed (7,12,16). The flow net is a grid formed by the inter-section of two sets of orthogonal lines. One set of lines, the flow lines, represent the direction of flow of the water, the other set of lines, the equipotential lines, are contours of pressure head. The top flow line defines the phreatic surface of the seepage flow. Piezometric pressures at any point are predicted from the equipotential lines. Seepage flows are predicted from the flow net using the following relationship:

$$q = k \cdot h \cdot \frac{n_f}{n_d} \quad \text{per unit of length}$$

Where:

q = rate of seepage flow

k = coefficient of permeability of the soil

h = the hydraulic head acting across the structure

n_f = number of flow paths in the flow net

n_d = number of equipotential drops in the flow net

Figure 5 presents a flow net for a homogeneous sand dam, having no seepage control features and resting on an impervious foundation. To simplify the presentation we have assumed that the vertical and horizontal permeabilities for the sand dam are equal. In practice this is seldom the case as the horizontal permeability is normally several times greater than the vertical permeability. This has a major effect on the shape of the flow net and the seepage control measures required. This aspect of the problem will be addressed in a following section.

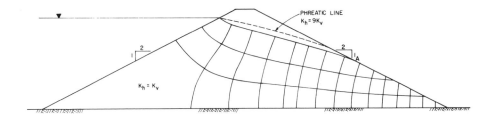

FLOW NET FOR HOMOGENEOUS DAM – NO UNDERDRAINS

FIGURE 5

On Figure 5 the phreatic line (top flow line) intersects the downstream slope of the dam at Point A. Below Point A the slope is saturated and water is flowing from the slope. These conditions create the following two problems:

1) High piezometric pressures in the downstream slope, which may cause slope instability.

2) High exit gradients for the seepage flows, which may cause piping due to internal erosion.

The potential instability and piping problems of Figure 5 can be cured by the introduction of suitable drainage measures. Figure 6 presents the flow net for the same sand dam ($k_h = k_v$) with a filtered toe drain added. The effects of the toe drain are readily apparent. The seepage flow no longer intersects the outer face of the dam and instead now intersects the filtered toe drain entirely within the dam section. However, the benefits derived from the toe drain may be somewhat misleading because, although the toe drain effectively treats the piping and surface sloughing problems it may not solve the slope instability problem, as the phreatic line remains high in the embankment and a large part of the embankment remains saturated.

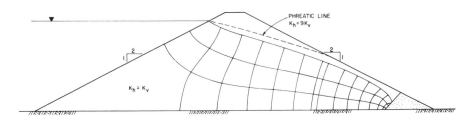

FLOW NET FOR HOMOGENEOUS DAM – WITH TOE DRAIN

FIGURE 6

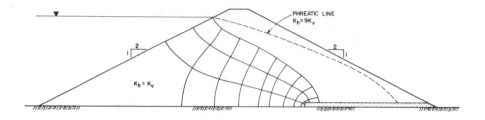

FLOW NET FOR HOMOGENEOUS DAM – WITH BLANKET DRAIN

FIGURE 7

Figure 7 presents the flow net for the same sand dam with a downstream blanket drain added. The blanket drain is much more effective than the toe drain in lowering the phreatic line and draining the downstream portion of the sand dam. Figure 8 presents a variation of the blanket drain whereby a strip drain, running parallel to the axis of the dam, is installed at about the centreline of the dam. Finger drains connect the strip drain to a toe drain at the downstream toe of the dam. For the assumed conditions ($k_h = k_v$) the strip drain is extremely effective and the downstream half of the dam is dry. Another type of extremely effective drain that is often used in homogeneous dam sections is the inclined or chimney drain. Figure 9 presents the flow net for this case. Finger drains connect the inclined drain to the toe of the dam. Drains should be very conservatively designed to ensure that their capacities are adequate to handle the maximum probable seepage flows and still maintain the line of seepage within the drain zone. For estimating the seepage flows that will be intercepted by the drain, the highest probable permeability should be used for the surrounding soil and the computations carried out based on flow nets.

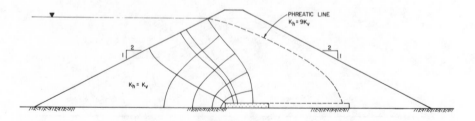

FLOW NET FOR HOMOGENEOUS DAM – WITH STRIP DRAIN

FIGURE 8

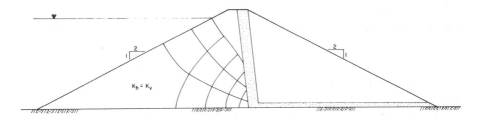

FLOW NET FOR HOMOGENEOUS DAM – WITH INCLINED DRAIN

FIGURE 9

Conversely, the lowest probable permeability values should be used for the drain, when determining the drain cross-section required. There are several factors which might add to the originally estimated seepage flows and therefore the required drain capacity may be unknown at the time the drains are designed. Such factors might include highly pervious zones in the foundations not found during design, development of cracks in the impervious core, windows in the grout curtain, drainage from consolidating slimes, etc. For these reasons, the author considers that drains should be designed initially to handle seepage flows several times greater than the maximum anticipated values.

Two types of drains are commonly used. One type utilizes a perforated pipe surrounded by filter material for the water bearing element, whereas the other type utilizes a coarse, drain rock zone surrounded by filter material. Pipe drains located beneath dams can become potential sources of internal erosion, should they collapse at some future date. Collapse can be caused by such events as corrosion of the pipe, excessive vertical load on the pipe, pulling apart at joints due to large strains and/or settlements, etc. Repair of a collapsed drainpipe which is discharging soil and water can be difficult without destroying thd drainage system. For these reasons if pipe drains are used they must be very conservatively designed and must have sufficiently generous surrounding filter zones that should the pipe collapse or pull apart, the surrounding filters will fill the void and prevent uncontrolled internal erosion from developing. The major advantage of using pipe drains as opposed to graded filters is , of course, the much greater hydraulic capacity that can be achieved. However, because of the inherent risks involved with the use of pipe drains, the writer considers that graded filters are preferable except perhaps in those instances where large hydraulic capacity is required, and suitable granular materials or quarried rock are not available.

Flow nets are used to estimate the volume of water that any particular drainage system must carry. As previously pointed out, these estimates should be generously high and the drain should be capable of handling flows several times those values indicated by the computations. Cedergren (5) outlines procedures for computing the size of a graded filter drain required for any given volume of seepage. Where pipe drains are used the required pipe drain sizes can be selected using standard hydraulic tables, once the gradients and pipe type have been chosen. All drain designs should be based on the premise that the hydraulic gradient will remain within the drain material.

Anistropic Soils - In the previous examples the soils were assumed to be isotropic, that is, possessing the same permeability in all directions. In actual fact, this is never the case for either naturally deposited soils or artificially deposited soils such as might be placed in an embankment. For well-stratified soil deposits, the horizontal permeability may be more than 10 times the vertical permeability. Even for compacted embankments where great care has been taken to minimize horizontal stratification, the horizontal permeability is likely to be in the order of 4 to 9 times the vertical permeability.

For embankments constructed of tailings sand placed in horizontal lifts, values of the ratio of k_h/k_v ranging between 4 and 10 have been found to reasonably represent field conditions. For embankments constructed by on-dam cycloning methods, a much more homogeneous sand deposit is obtained. Observations would suggest that for such deposits the k_h/k_v ratio is much less than that for hydraulically placed sands and may even approach unity. For spigotted tailings beaches, a ratio of $k_h/k_v = 9$ appears to provide a reasonable fit with observed piezometric pressures.

The flow net solutions presented for the isotropic case ($k_h = k_v$) can be applied to the anistropic case by means of a geometric transformation (2, 5). This involves either reducing all dimensions in the direction of k_{max} by the factor $\sqrt{k_{min}/k_{max}}$ or increasing all dimensions in the direction of k_{min} by the factor $\sqrt{k_{max}/k_{min}}$. The transformed section thus produced can then be used to draw up the conventional flow net. Once this is done, the flow net obtained is transposed back onto the true section. The resulting flow net will likely consist of rectangles rather than squares and the flow lines and equipotential lines are unlikely to intersect at right angles. Seepage quantities can be computed using the relationship:

$$q = \bar{k} \cdot h \cdot \frac{n_f}{n_d}$$

where $\bar{k} = \sqrt{k_{min} \times k_{max}}$ = effective coefficient of permeability

The higher the ratio of horizontal permeability to vertical permeability the higher the phreatic line and the larger the zone of saturation in the dam. The effects of increasing the ratio of $\frac{k_h}{k_v}$ from 1 to 9 is illustrated by the heavy dashed line on Figures 5 to 8 inclusive. It should be noted that the small toe drain shown on Figure 6 was inadequate for the case of $k_h/k_v = 9$ and consequently the phreatic line emerges on the downstream face of the dam.

The inclined drain (chimney drain) is one method of drainage that can be used to effectively intercept seepage, where the ratio of horizontal to vertical permeability is high and foundation drainage cannot effectively prevent saturation of a large part of the downstream section of the dam. Figure 9 illustrates such a drain.

Seepage Reduction Features – In those instances where the foundation and/or embankment soils are highly pervious, large seepage losses may develop unless some method for reducing seepage is incorporated into the design. For embankments, upstream impervious zones or central impervious cores are normally used for this purpose. Figure 10 (4) illustrates the effect of the relative permeabilities of the upstream impervious zone and downstream shell on the position of the phreatic line in the downstream shell, assuming no drains are installed at the foundation contact. The addition of a strip or blanket drain would draw the phreatic line down as shown on Figure 11 and would greatly improve the stability of the downstream shell.

For pervious foundations some type of foundation cutoff is normally used. If the pervious zone is not excessively thick, a cutoff trench, excavated without bracing and subsequently backfilled with compacted impervious soil, provides

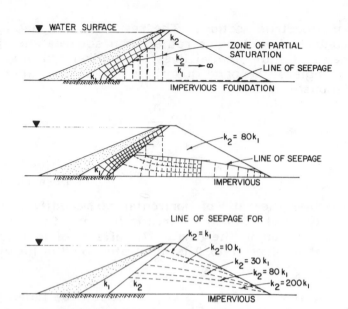

EFFECT OF RELATIVE PERMEABILITY OF UPSTREAM SLOPING CORE AND
DOWNSTREAM ZONE ON POSITION OF LINE OF SEEPAGE IN DOWNSTREAM ZONE

(AFTER CEDERGREN—REFERENCE 4)

FIGURE 10

a positive water barrier. Where the pervious zone is very
thick some other method of cutoff must be used. Such
methods include: slurry trench cutoffs, cement and bentonite cutoffs, and concrete cutoffs. To be effective, foundation cutoffs must thoroughly penetrate the pervious strata.
Partial penetration of the pervious strata by the foundation
cutoff may not significantly reduce the seepage. Figure 12
(5) shows the relative effectiveness of partial cutoffs. This
figure also illustrates the high seepage gradient that develops along the base of the cutoff and on its downstream face
in both the foundation and embankment zones. To prevent
the possibility of piping developing at these locations, suitable filters must be provided.

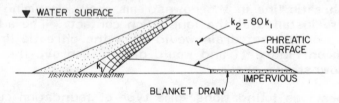

USE OF BLANKET DRAIN TO CONTROL PHREATIC LINE OF FIGURE 10

FIGURE 11

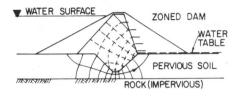

(a) PARTIAL CUTOFF

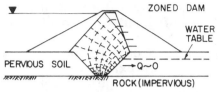

(b) COMPLETE CUTOFF

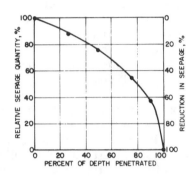

(c) RELATIONSHIP BETWEEN DEPTH
OF CUTOFF AND SEEPAGE FLOWS

(AFTER CEDERGREN— REFERENCE 5)

FIGURE 12

Where the pervious foundation is bedrock, grout curtains
are often used to seal the pervious rock. Grouting is not
a foolproof method of providing a cutoff in the bedrock because it is extremely difficult to ensure that all cracks and
fissures have been intersected and filled with grout. Past
experience has shown that even very thorough grouting of
bedrock foundations has not always produced the desired
results (3). Where the upper few feet of bedrock is fissured and cracked, surface treatment combined with shallow
blanket grouting is often used to seal the pervious rock.
The surface treatment usually consists of slush grouting or
shotcreting all the surface cracks. Blanket grouting is
usually accomplished by drilling shallow (20 ft) grout holes
on a 10 ft x 10 ft grid and grouting them up under low
pressure. The purpose of the surface treatment of the
bedrock is to adequately seal all cracks and fissures that
exist beneath the core and transition filters to protect
against the possible loss of soil into such fissures. Another
important detail is the provision of suitable filters and drains
between the earthfill dam and the bedrock downstream of the
grout curtain.

Figure 13 (5) shows the relative effect of different degrees of grout curtain effectiveness, on piezometric pressures under a dam. The figure also indicates how different degrees of grout curtain effectiveness influence the seepage flows. For example, even if the grout curtain is 90% effective, the seepage through the grout curtain is 55% of the quantity that would occur with no grout curtain. As the effectiveness of a grout curtain must always be somewhat suspect, a second line of defence should always be provided. Normally, this second line of defence is drainage. In the example shown in Figure 13, generous strip or blanket drains would be provided along the foundation contact immediately downstream of the core to collect and remove seepage flows that pass through the grout curtain.

In the previous example which is taken from Cedergren (5) the grouted zone was assumed to be 30 ft wide. A 90% effective grouted zone is assumed to have a permeability of one-tenth that of the ungrouted rock; if grouting is 95% effective, the permeability of the grouted zone is one-twentieth that of the ungrouted rock.

Upstream impervious blankets are often used, as an alternative to installing cutoffs, to reduce seepage through pervious foundations. Upstream impervious blankets serve to increase the length of the seepage path through the foundation, thereby reducing both the seepage flows and the hydrostatic pressures within the foundations beneath the dam. The greater the distance that the impervious blanket is extended upstream, the lower both the seepage flows and the hydrostatic pressures under the dam. Figure 14 presents flow nets for a homogeneous impervious dam, resting on a pervious foundation, with and without an upstream impervious blanket. The beneficial effects of the upstream impervious blanket in reducing seepage flows and uplift pressures is indicated on the figure. The critical area where seepage and heaving may occur is at the downstream toe of the dam. Drainage facilities such as a downstream blanket drain and/or downstream toe drain normally would be installed in this area to collect the seepage and protect against heaving and/or piping.

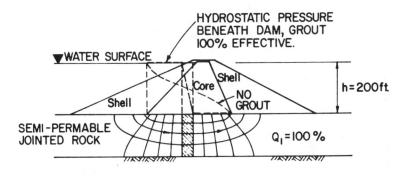

(a) TYPICAL FLOW NET (NO GROUT CURTAIN)

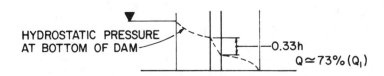

(b) GROUT 80% EFFECTIVE

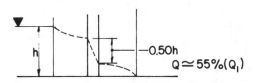

(c) GROUT 90% EFFECTIVE

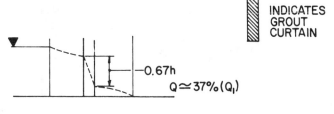

(d) GROUT 95% EFFECTIVE

EFFECTIVENESS OF GROUT CURTAIN ON
HYDROSTATIC PRESSURE AND SEEPAGE

(AFTER CEDERGREN—REFERENCE 5)

FIGURE 13

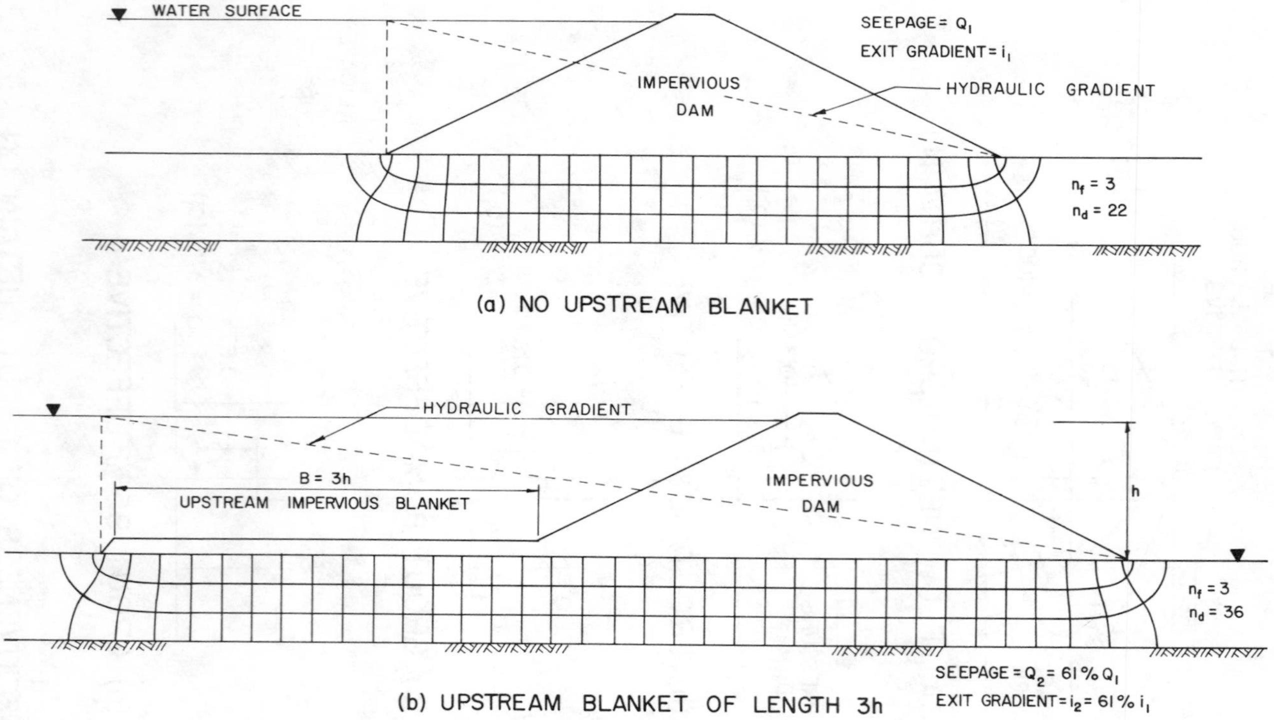

(a) NO UPSTREAM BLANKET

SEEPAGE = Q_1
EXIT GRADIENT = i_1

HYDRAULIC GRADIENT

IMPERVIOUS DAM

$n_f = 3$
$n_d = 22$

WATER SURFACE

(b) UPSTREAM BLANKET OF LENGTH 3h

$n_f = 3$
$n_d = 36$

SEEPAGE = $Q_2 = 61\% Q_1$
EXIT GRADIENT = $i_2 = 61\% i_1$

IMPERVIOUS DAM

HYDRAULIC GRADIENT

B = 3h

UPSTREAM IMPERVIOUS BLANKET

h

FLOW NET ILLUSTRATING THE EFFECT OF AN UPSTREAM IMPERVIOUS BLANKET ON HYDROSTATIC PRESSURES AND SEEPAGE FLOWS

FIGURE 14

IV. SEEPAGE THROUGH TAILINGS DAMS

1. General

The conventional tailings dam is constructed from the coarser fraction of the tailings and utilizes a broad spigotted beach of fine tailings as its water barrier. As previously pointed out, tailings dams fall into two broad categories, based on their method of construction. These are:

a) Upstream Method of Construction – the dam is raised by moving upstream over top of previously deposited tailings. Tailings excavated off the spigotted beach are often used for this purpose although cycloned sand or borrow materials may also be used. (Reference Figure 1).

b) Downstream Method of Construction – the dam is raised by moving downstream over a prepared foundation, usually including underdrains. Cycloned sand is often used as the construction material although borrow materials may also be used. (Reference Figure 2).

Both the upstream and downstream types of tailings dam normally rely on a spigotted beach of fine tailings to provide a water barrier. Although such beaches are relatively impervious, some seepage still occurs. The amount of seepage depends on the physical properties of the fine tailings, the height of the dam, and the width of the spigotted beach. For a given tailings dam, the wider the spigotted beach, the more effective the impervious barrier it provides, as the length of seepage path is increased and the phreatic line through the dam is lowered. Conversely, the narrower the spigotted beach, the greater the seepage losses through the dam and the higher the phreatic line.

Obviously, seepage control measures are required to control the seepage through the dam and prevent the phreatic line from emerging on the downstream face of the dam. For all downstream methods of dam construction this problem is easily handled using conventional drainage methods. Moreover, in those cases where the initial starter dam must be made impervious, to store mill start-up water, and a foundation cutoff is required, the cutoff for the starter dam also becomes the cutoff for the ultimate tailings dam.

For upstream methods of tailings dam construction, seepage control is a little more difficult. Ideally, the starter dam should be pervious so that it performs as a toe drain for the ultimate dam and keeps the phreatic line inside the dam. Upstream drains might be combined with the pervious starter dam to further improve underdrainage. Where the starter dam is required to be impervious for the storage of mill start-up water, other methods must be used to control seepage through the ultimate tailings dam. One procedure that can be used is to design the starter dam in such a manner that its upstream section provides the impervious membrane and the downstream section acts as a drain to provide a safe exit for the phreatic line. Another, more complex method of drainage would be to provide an underdrainage system upstream of the starter dam, collect the seepage in pipe drains, and carry outlet pipes through the dam to discharge the seepage water. The outlet pipes would have to be valved so that the mill start-up water would not flow out through the system prior to the deposition of fine tailings. Two potential disadvantages of such a system, are the risks involved in running pipes through the tailings dam over the entire life of the operation (i.e. corrosion, collapse of pipes, settlement damage, piping along pipelines, etc.) and the difficulties involved in ensuring that the upstream drainage system remained effective over the entire life of the operation and did not become clogged with fine tailings.

In the writer's opinion, the downstream methods of tailings dam construction are preferable to the upstream methods because the downstream methods lend themselves to sound engineering analyses and design. Consequently, tailings dams designed and constructed by these methods can be built to whatever standards are necessary to satisfy any particular site conditions and/or regulatory requirements. In recent times, use of downstream methods of tailings dam construction has become increasingly popular as tailings dam heights have increased and better engineered designs are required to ensure safe structures. Presently, great emphasis is being placed on the environmental aspects of tailings storage, with the requirement that seepage flows be carefully controlled and, in many instances, not allowed to leave the pond area and enter the surrounding surface or groundwaters. Under these conditions, the downstream methods of construction allow greater flexibility in selecting the most suitable seepage control procedures for any given set of conditions. The remainder of this paper deals with seepage control measures as applied to downstream methods of dam construction.

2. Seepage Control Measures

Quantity of Seepage - The first step in the design of seepage control measures for a given tailings dam is to estimate the quantities of seepage water that the system will be required to handle. Generally, there are five sources of seepage water during the construction of most tailings dams. These sources are:

i)   The free water in the tailings pond.

ii)   The construction water associated with dam
        building. (This may be cyclone underflow or
        the water used for transporting the sand for
        a hydraulic fill).

iii)   The water from the spigotting operation used
        to form the impervious beach.

iv)   The consolidation water squeezed out of the
        slimes as they consolidate in the pond.

v)   Precipitation falling on the tailings dam.

The quantity of seepage to be expected from the free water in the tailings pond can be estimated using approximate flow nets based on the anticipated width of beach and the permeabilities of the materials involved. Estimating the quantity of seepage due to spigotting is much more difficult, however, a reasonable approximation can be made by assuming that the spigotting completely saturates the beach so that in effect the free water in the pond extends to near the top of the spigotted beach. A flow net drawn for this condition should provide an estimate of the combined seepage, due to both the free water in the pond and the effects of spigotting.

Estimating the quantity of construction water that the drains must handle varies from a simple exercise for the case of on-dam cycloning, where all the construction water seeps into the downstream sand dam, to a complex exercise for the case where large volumes of hydraulic fill, transport water flow across the dam and then exit either upstream into the tailings pond or downstream behind the seepage recovery dam. For the on-dam cycloning, all the water contained in the cyclone underflow is assumed to reach the underlying drain. This value can be estimated with reasonable accuracy from the density of the underflow and the recorded tonnage of sand placed each day. For the case of hydraulic fill placement, where large volumes of water flow across the sand dam, the seepage loss into the dam may be estimated by assuming downward seepage under a hydraulic gradient of 1 and using the expression:

$$q = \bar{k} \, i \, A$$

where q = rate of vertical seepage

   A = total area over which the water is flowing

   i = hydraulic gradient (1 for this case)

   $\bar{k}$ = effective coefficient of permeability = $\sqrt{k_h \times k_v}$

The fourth potential source of seepage, consolidation water squeezed out of the slimes as they consolidate, is more difficult to quantify. In effect, this action adds an additional increment of pore pressure to the normal hydrostatic pore pressure that would exist in the slimes if they were completely consolidated under their own weight.

Mittal and Morgenstern (14) examine this problem and suggest a method for estimating the resulting combined seepage flows. However, when the writer attempted to apply this procedure to a particular tailings dam, the result obtained appeared to be appreciably higher than the actually measured values. Apart from the uncertainties in assessing the effective permeability of the slimes, another possible explanation for this difference is that the excess pore pressures due to consolidation exist only in the fine slimes, which are located out in the pond hundreds of feet from the dam. Consequently, most of the excess head is used up in flowing through the low-permeability, spigotted beach before reaching the free-draining, sand dam, drainage face.

In arid climates, seepage due to precipitation falling on the dam is generally a very minor item. However, in high rainfall climates precipitation can be a major contribution and may cause the sand dam to be almost fully saturated during long periods of heavy rainfall.

Of the above five outlined sources of seepage water, construction water from cyclone underflow or hydraulic fill placement operations is usually several times greater than all other sources combined. In designing the drains, the highest probable seepage flows that can enter the drains should be used and the drains should be assigned their lowest probable permeabilities and gradients. This is essential, as once constructed and buried, the drains must continue to perform satisfactorily throughout the life of the structure and, in many cases, for many years after the mining operation is completed. The author strongly recommends that all drains should be sized to handle flows several times the largest probable flows computed using the above outlined methods.

<u>Closed Circuit Tailings Ponds</u> – Closed circuit tailings ponds are required when pollution regulations forbid the discharge of tailings effluent from the tailings pond. This means that all water entering the tailings pond, which includes surface runoff as well as the tailings transportation water, must be stored in the pond and recycled through the mill. In those instances where the tailings effluent is considered toxic, seepage losses through the dam, its abutments and foundations, and the tailings basin itself, are required to be reduced to minimal values. These requirements can place severe limitations on the tailings dam design, construction, and operation and invariably add appreciably to the costs of the structure.

As previously discussed, conventional tailings dam design maintains a wide, spigotted beach in front of the dam. The wider this beach, the further the free water in the pond is kept from the sand dam. This tends to lower the phreatic line (at least in areas where the beach is not saturated by spigotting), and reduce seepage flows through the dam. However, for closed circuit operations where spring runoff and/or large rainstorms must be stored in the pond, large fluctuations in pond levels may occur. Such fluctuations may flood the beach and place the free water surface against the sand dam. As spigotted beaches commonly have gradients in the order of 1 percent, a 5 ft increase in pond levels would flood a 500 foot wide beach. Correspondingly, a 10 ft rise in pond levels would place 5 ft of free water against the sand dam. This would cause large seepage flows through the dam with the inherent risk of flow concentration and resulting piping due to internal erosion of the fine tailings sand. Such action can be extremely dangerous as it could lead to failure of the dam.

Obviously, the water balance in a closed circuit tailings pond must be carefully monitored and sufficient freeboard must be maintained to safely store floods from spring runoff or rainstorms. Where a spigotted beach is used as the upstream impervious membrane, it must be wide enough to absorb the expected maximum flood surcharge without having the free water surface rise up against the sand dam. If this cannot be achieved, then some type of impervious zone must be placed on the upstream face of the sand dam to prevent the development of excess seepage flows. This problem is usually most severe in the first few years of operation when the storage capacity of the pond is low and large fluctuations in pond levels are required to store flood flows. This situation may require the use of an impervious zone on the upstream face of the dam during the first few years of operation, reverting back to a spigotted beach as the pond capacity becomes large enough to absorb the floods with acceptable fluctuations in pond level.

The other aspect of closed circuit tailings pond design that requires special attention is the requirement that seepage losses out of the system must be minimized. This usually requires the inclusion of some seepage reduction features and a seepage recovery dam. In addition, a well-designed underdrainage system is required, which, of course, should be provided for all tailings dams.

Seepage Reduction Features – Minimizing seepage losses from the main tailings dam usually requires the inclusion in the tailings dam design of one or more of the seepage reduction features covered previously for conventional water storage dams. Where seepage losses must be minimized, some type of positive cutoff is required for the dam foundations and abutments. The simplest and most positive procedure is to excavate a cutoff trench through the pervious foundation and abutment soils and backfill the trench with compacted impervious soils. If a high water table and/or a great thickness of pervious soils make this method impracticable, then a slurry trench or some similar deep cutoff installation might be required. The cutoff is connected to the impervious zone of the starter dam and the ongoing construction of the tailings dam continues as normal.

Where the foundations and/or abutments are pervious bedrock, grouting may be required to seal off the rock beneath the impervious zone of the starter dam. The grouting program usually involves one or more of three basic types of treatment. These are:

Surface Treatment – used to seal up fissures and joints in the exposed rock surface. Slush grouting or shotcreting is normally used for this purpose.

Blanket Grouting – used to seal shallow fissures and joints that extend below surface of the rock. Grouting, using low pressures and holes drilled to shallow depth (20') and spaced on a grid at about 10' centres, is normally used for this purpose.

Curtain Grouting – used to seal pervious rock to great depths. One or more lines of deep drill holes are grouted under high pressure until no more grout is accepted by the rock. This is a complex and expensive foundation treatment and is not normally used with tailings dams.

Surface treatment of fissured and jointed bedrock foundations is very important where large hydraulic gradients are likely to develop across the impervious zone. Open cracks and fissures in the bedrock may permit the flow of water under high heads, which in turn can erode the core of the dam and cause piping to develop. One of the secondary protections against such piping is the provision of suitable filters and adequate drains downstream of the impervious core.

Downstream Seepage Recovery Dam – A seepage recovery dam is required immediately downstream of the main tailings dam to collect and store, for ultimate pumping back into the tailings pond, all seepages that emerge downstream of the tailings dam. The seepage recovery dam is designed as a conventional water storage dam and must have impervious foundations and abutments to ensure that none of the intercepted water escapes. Where the natural foundations and abutments are pervious, positive cutoffs must be provided. These may include such devices as: excavated cutoff trenches, slurry cutoff trenches, grout curtains in broken rock, etc. In the case where pervious foundations exist to great depth below the dam, such that it is not practicable to install a positive impervious cutoff, a hydraulic barrier, such as illustrated on Figure 3, might be installed downstream of the seepage recovery dam. However, this is not a desirable solution and every effort should be made in selecting a closed circuit tailings dam site, to find a location where a

positive cutoff can be constructed under the seepage recovery dam.

The major source of seepage flows into the seepage recovery dam is normally the construction water used to build
the main, sand tailings dam.   Lesser contributors are precipitation, and seepages through the dam and its foundations
and abutments.   Where relief wells are required to relieve
hydrostatic pressures under the main tailings dam, the flows
from these wells are also collected behind the seepage recovery dam.

The seepage recovery dam is the last line of defence
against seepage losses from the tailings pond facility.
Groundwater quality monitoring is normally carried out
immediately downstream of the seepage recovery dam to assess
the effectiveness of the seepage control features.   Such water
quality monitoring should be established well in advance of
the start of operations of the tailings dam to establish the
natural base levels for the groundwater.   As natural groundwaters often contain what might be considered unallowably
high concentrations of metals, fibres, or other undesirable
elements, it is essential that the content of the natural
groundwaters be clearly established before tailings storage
starts.   In the event that ongoing water quality observations
showed that contamination was occurring downstream of the
reclaim dam, further seepage control measures, such as
pumped drain wells and/or injection wells would have to be
considered.

Storage of tailings from uranium mining operations pose
special problems (24) that are beyond the scope of this paper.
The major item of concern is the movement of radionuclides
in seepage water, escaping from the tailings pond.   The
regulatory agencies tend to favour licensed repositories such
as used for powerplant and nuclear weapons waste.   The
mining companies tend to favour unlined tailings ponds.   In
between these two extremes are such methods as:

1) Disposal in mine workings

2) Disposal in lined and capped reservoirs

3) Double lined tailings ponds

4) Single lined ponds with monitoring systems and
   some form of backup.

As is the case for all tailings disposal problems, disposal of radium tailings is a site specific problem, the solution for which is likely to vary from site to site. However, there is little doubt that one of the most critical factors to be considered at all sites is the control of seepage flows containing radionuclides.

3. Seepage Problems

Water related problems probably cause the greatest concern, during the life of a tailings dam. The most serious problem of this type is the possibility of overtopping. This, of course, cannot be allowed to happen as it likely would result in failure of the tailings dam with subsequent loss of tailings and water. Consequently, if such a threat develops, it must be corrected by raising the dam and/or reducing the inflow of tailings and runoff into the pond. In the extreme case, where neither of these measures can be carried out in time to stop overtopping, an emergency spillway is required. Although emergency spillage must be considered a last resort, particularly where discharge from the tailings pond is considered to be a pollutant, it is a far better alternative than overtopping the dam and causing a large and sudden uncontrolled discharge of tailings and effluent.

Next to the threat of overtopping, seepage problems generally pose the most serious concern during the operating life of a tailings pond. As previously discussed, seepage through a tailings dam may give rise to three basic types of problem. These are:

a)   Piping, which occurs when seepage flows remove fine soil particles.

b)   Slope instability and heaving, which occur when excess hydrostatic forces, due to seepage flows, develop.

c)   Large Water Losses, which may contribute to a) and b) above, in addition to causing downstream pollution.

Piping is considered to be one of the most serious problems that can develop in a tailings dam, as, in the extreme, it could result in total failure of the dam. As previously discussed, properly designed drains and filters are the protections against piping. Drainage controls the phreatic line and prevents it from emerging on the downstream slope of the dam (Reference Figs 5 and 7). Drainage also reduces seepage pressures and exit hydraulic gradients. The lower the exit hydraulic gradient the less the likelihood of piping occurring. Filters permit the escape of seepage water, but prevent the movement of soil particles. All drains should be designed to act as filters.

One design feature, common to many of the older tailings dams, was the use of decant towers with discharge lines running through the base of the dam to a downstream pump-house. As previously discussed for drainage pipes, dam designers avoid, whenever possible, passing conduits through the dams. The reason is that they represent a risk, as a potential source of seepage and piping problems. This risk is even greater for tailings dams which are constructed of easily erodible tailings. Seepage collars around the pipe-lines do not guarantee their safe performance and may, in fact, give the designer a false sense of security. Poor back-filling procedures with or without seepage collars can lead to piping failures. Other factors which may have an adverse effect on pipelines passing through dams are: corrosion and ultimate collapse of the pipeline, collapse of the pipeline under high fill loads, and the pulling apart of pipe connections owing to large settlements and/or strains in the foundation soils.

Decant towers may also fail, although the risk of this occurring for a well-designed tower is probably less than that associated with the possible failure of a decant pipeline passing through the dam. Factors which may affect decant towers include: large negative skin friction forces caused by the settling tailings, shear movements in the tailings, and ice forces during spring breakup. For these reasons, some procedure other than the use of decant towers, with discharge lines running through the dam, should be employed for reclaiming water from the pond. A floating or movable pumphouse, located near the shore of the tailings pond, is a suitable method now in common use.

Figure 15 is a photograph illustrating piping that developed at the contact between a sand tailings dam and its abutment. The piping developed when a large spring runoff caused the tailings pond to rise, drown the beach, and come in contact with the upstream face of the sand dam. The rise in tailings pond levels had been predicted a year earlier and the dam had been provided with an upstream impervious zone of soil. Unfortunately, in the area where the piping occurred, careless spigotting had eroded away a small portion of the upstream impervious protection. Seepage occurred at this location, which happened to be near the contact between the sand dam and the abutment. The seepage flows concentrated along this contact, which was an impervious boundary, and the observed piping began to develop. Fortunately, the operators were aware of the seriousness of the problem and implemented repairs as soon as the seepage flows were noted. Repairs consisted of dumping impervious fill over the upstream face of the dam to block off the seepage entrance and filling of the downstream erosion area with sand and gravel filter material. The repairs were successful and no further piping occurred.

FIGURE 15 – PIPING AT DOWNSTREAM FACE OF SAND
          TAILINGS DYKE.

Figure 16 presents a section through a tailings dam constructed from mine waste rock. The dam was built in two stages. Stage 1 involved constructing a rockfill to close off a small bay on a large lake. The rockfill, which was deposited through a maximum of 80 ft of water, extended a few feet above lake level. Tailings were then discharged into the bay from the top of the rockfill and water was reclaimed from the pond by pumping. The operation proceeded smoothly until the top surface of the tailings emerged from the pond and a tailings beach developed. Concurrently, the water levels in the pond rose slightly above those in the adjacent lake. At this time, a sudden piping failure occurred and a significant volume of tailings and effluent flowed through the rockfill dam and discharged into the lake, much to the chagrin of the regulatory agency which was concerned about possible damage to fish life.

The cause of the failure was obvious, no filter had been provided on the upstream face of the rockfill dam. Consequently, as soon as water levels in the pond exceeded those in the lake, seepage flows developed towards the lake. These flows carried the fine tailings into the voids in the rockfill and the resulting piping failure occurred. A significant feature of this failure is that it occurred under a differential head of less than 1 ft.

Repair of the failure has involved pushing the free water surface in the pond as far back as possible from the rockfill dam. This was accomplished by placing a wide zone of cycloned sand over the existing spigotted beach. The intent of pushing back the pond and widening the beach was to lower the phreatic line and reduce the exit hydraulic gradients at the face of the "unfiltered" rockfill. It was also thought that the cycloned sand zone would help the situation by acting as a drain.

These remedial measures have been successful and the pond has now been raised to its ultimate height without further incident. Piezometric readings, taken when the dam and pond had reached the elevations shown on Figure 16, indicate that the phreatic line is below most of the cycloned sand zone. An approximate flow net is also shown on Figure 16. This flow net, which was drawn using the permeability parameters indicated on the figure, agrees reasonably well with the observed piezometric pressures, and confirms that pushing the pond away from the face of the dam has greatly reduced the exit hydraulic gradients at the face of the rockfill.

Figure 17 presents a section through a tailings dam constructed of mine waste rock, which suffered a piping failure in its early years. Also shown on the figure are the remedial measures undertaken by the owner and their effects on the piezometric line. An approximate flow net is also presented on this figure. Reasonable agreement is obtained between the observed piezometric pressures and those predicted by the flow net.

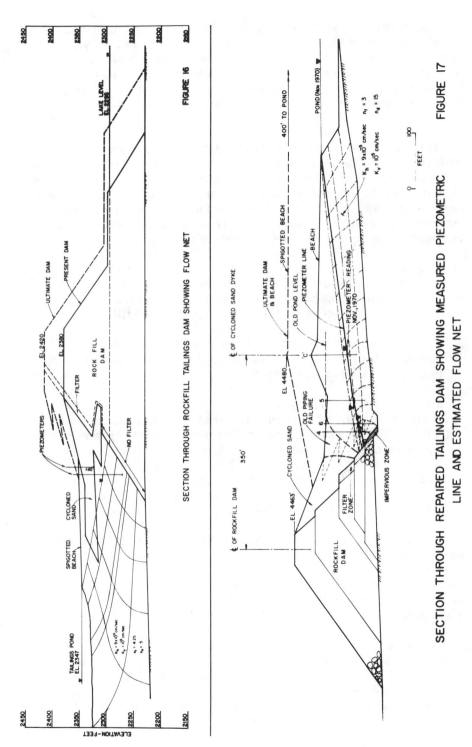

FIGURE 16

SECTION THROUGH ROCKFILL TAILINGS DAM SHOWING FLOW NET

FIGURE 17

SECTION THROUGH REPAIRED TAILINGS DAM SHOWING MEASURED PIEZOMETRIC
LINE AND ESTIMATED FLOW NET

The original design called for the placement of protective filters on the upstream face of the rockfill dam. Cycloned sand was to be placed over the filters and a spigotted beach was to be developed beyond the cycloned sand zone. The intent was to operate the pond in such a manner that a generous beach would be maintained at all times between the free water surface and the face of the dam.

Despite these good intentions the tailings dam suffered a sudden piping failure which caused the loss of large volumes of water and fine tailings. Approximately 10,000,000 gallons of water were discharged and a peak flow of 48,000 gallons per minute was reached. The sudden discharge caused considerable property damage downstream. A subsequent investigation into the failure indicated that:

1) The filter zones for the second and third lifts of rockfill were end-dumped from the top of the lift rather than placed in thin layers. No filters were placed on the fourth and fifth lifts of rockfill.

2) At the failure area the tailings beach was poorly developed with the free water in the pond close to the upstream face of the dam.

3) Sinkholes and fluctuations in seepage flows through the dam had occurred in this area at least twice during the summer prior to failure, indicating seepage was carrying the fine sand into the rockfill dam. The operators had filled these sinkholes with tailings and noted that seepage flows decreased and that no tailings were passing through the dam. This was interpreted to indicate that no problem existed.

The owners' and their consultants' solution to the problem was to reduce the possibility of further piping occurring by pushing the free water surface in the pond well back from the dam. This was done by building a second dyke across the tailings pond and then building a spigotted beach off the upstream face of the dyke as shown in Figure 17.

The remedial measures have worked well and no further piping problems have developed. The piezometric levels shown in Figure 17 were measured approximately one year after the failure had occurred. Since then the tailings dam has been raised to its full height without further difficulty and is currently being prepared for abandonment.

4. Case Histories Illustrating Modern Tailings Dam Designs

The seepage control features required for any given tailings dam must be based on a study of the particular requirements of the project. Obviously, these requirements will vary from project to project and will depend on such items as: foundation conditions at the site, materials to be used for construction of the dam, requirements for the starter dam (i.e. does it have to store start-up water for the mill), method of dam construction, and requirements to be satisfied for the pertinent regulatory agencies. To illustrate some of the seepage control methods currently in use several tailings dams have been selected for brief discussion.

Gibraltar Mines Ltd — Gibraltar Mines (10) is situated in central British Columbia, about 40 miles north of the town of Williams Lake. The mine is a low-grade copper, open-pit operation and has a capacity in the order of 40,000 tons per day. The present tailings facility will provide for storage of about 220,000,000 tons of tailings.

The Gibraltar tailings pond is located in a separate valley about 4 miles north of the mine and mill area. A plan view of the ultimate tailings dam, showing the layout of the extensive finger drain system, is presented on Figure 18. These finger drains, which constitute the underdrainage system, consist of a central, highly-pervious, quarried rock core, suitably protected by a surrounding filter zone. The drains are conservatively designed to handle flows several times larger than the maximum anticipated seepage. A typical section through a finger drain is also shown on Figure 18.

When completed, the dam will have a maximum height above stream bed of approximately 400 ft, and a crest length of 8,000 ft. Initially a small, 100-ft high, impervious, starter dam was constructed on the centreline of the ultimate sand tailings dam. The dam is being constructed from cycloned sand, using the centreline method of construction, which is a variation of the downstream construction method. The tailings are cycloned on the dam, using portable cyclones which are supported on skid-mounted, steel towers. The sand underflow from the cyclones is deposited directly onto the dam and assumes a natural slope that generally ranges between 3.5 and 4 to one. The transportation water in the "ropy" sand underflow, which equals approximately 500 gallons per minute, seeps downward into the underlying drainage system and is collected downstream behind a seepage recovery dam. The overflow from the cyclones is spiggoted to form a beach upstream of the sand dam. This beach, which is in the order of 1000 ft in width, provides the upstream impervious zone for the dam. The Gibraltar tailings dam is not operated as a fully, closed circuit, tailings facility, as some effluent discharge is permitted downstream of the seepage recovery dam.

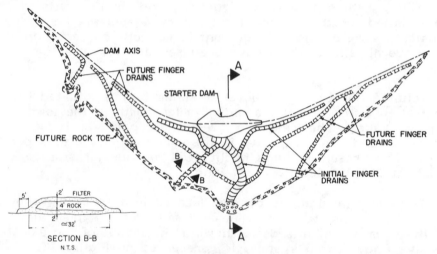

PLAN VIEW-GIBRALTAR TAILINGS DAM   FIGURE 18

A section through the Gibraltar tailings dam, at its point of maximum height, is presented on Figure 19. Also presented on this figure are the piezometric readings that exist at this section. From an examination of these readings it can be seen that piezometric levels are extremely low and in effect are located in the underdrains, downstream of the starter dam. The cycloned sand has a relatively high permeability and is sufficiently free-draining that the construction water from the cyclone underflow does not appear to appreciably affect the piezometric levels beyond the small area being filled. The wide spigotted beach at this site is very beneficial in reducing seepage from the tailings pond.

Also shown on Figure 19 is an approximate flow net, drawn up using the indicated permeability parameters. Using the approximate flow net, the seepage loss through the dam, for the present section is computed to be approximately 80 gallons per minute. As this dam has been shut down by strikes for almost a year it presents a unique opportunity to compare the computed seepage with the actual

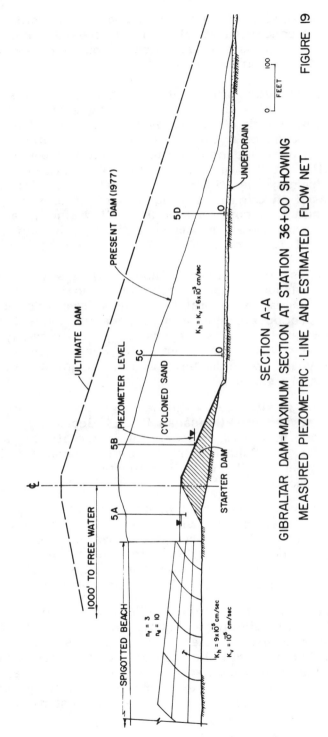

SECTION A-A

GIBRALTAR DAM-MAXIMUM SECTION AT STATION 36+00 SHOWING
MEASURED PIEZOMETRIC LINE AND ESTIMATED FLOW NET

FIGURE 19

measured seepage, with no contributions from construction water to be concerned about. In this case the average measured seepage is a value which compares reasonably well with the computed value.

One of the requirements of the Gibraltar tailings dam design is that it be able to withstand moderate earthquake shocks without risk of failing by liquefaction. The usual protective measures against liquefaction are either to compact the sand to a high density or to prevent it from becoming saturated. At this site, prevention of saturation by means of good drainage was the protection selected. Recent analyses, based on dynamic testing of samples of the cycloned tailings sand (11) confirm that the well-drained, sand dam will safely withstand a maximum earthquake having a Richter Magnitude of 7.0, and located 25 miles from the site.

Brenda Mines Ltd - Brenda Mines (10) is situated on a mountain plateau west of Okanagan Lake in South Central British Columbia approximately 40 miles from Kelowna, B.C. The mine produces copper and molybdenum concentrates from a low-grade, open-pit operation with a capacity of approximately 28,000 tons per day. For a planned mine life of 20 years approximately 200 million tons of tailings must be safely stored.

The mine is situated at the head waters of a stream flowing eastward into Okanagan Lake. Because the Okanagan Valley is one of the major tourist and recreational areas of Southern British Columbia, it was made a basic requirement for development of the mine that the tailings facilities be completely closed circuit.

The valley in which the tailings dam and tailings pond are situated has a steep gradient and is relatively narrow, requiring a high dam to provide the necessary storage volume. The dam was designed originally to rise 400 feet above the stream bed. Recent modifications in design have increased that height to approximately 500 feet above the stream bed.

A plan view of the ultimate tailings dam is presented on Figure 20. Also shown on this figure is the layout of the finger drain, underdrainage system and a typical section through one of the drains. As was the case at the Gibraltar tailings dam these drains, which consist of a quarried rock core, surrounded by a filter zone, are very conservatively designed and can handle several times the maximum estimated seepage flows.

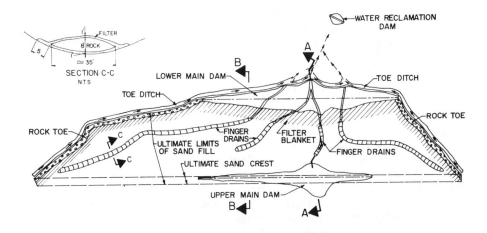

PLAN VIEW- BRENDA TAILINGS DAM   FIGURE 20

The dam will have an ultimate crest length of approximately 7,000 feet, a maximum base width of approximately 1,800 feet, and a maximum height above the downstream toe of about 500 feet. This dam is also being raised by the centreline method of construction (a type of downstream construction) which produces a vertical upstream face of inter-fingered cycloned sand and slimes. The final downstream sand slope will be approximately 3.5 horizontal to 1 vertical. Total sand requirements will be approximately 32,500,000 cubic yards.

An impervious starter dam, having a maximum height of 125 feet was constructed on the centreline of the ultimate sand tailings dam. The starter dam, which was constructed of rockfill with an upstream impervious zone and foundation cutoff trench, was used to store mill start-up water. At the downstream toe of the ultimate tailings dam a 175 ft high rock-fill toe dam was constructed. This large toe dam provides confinement to the lower portion of the sand tailings dam and serves to retain the embankment so that it could be sited next to the edge of a steeply dropping section of the valley. The tailings dam is being constructed from cycloned sand. The tailings are cycloned in a building located high on the left abutment and the sand underflow transported to the dam by sand line. The cycloned sand and water are deposited on the dam in large cells, following procedures similar to those used for placing hydraulic land fills. Large volumes of construction water are associated with the sand placement, this water seeps vertically downwards and into the underdrainage system. The volume of water involved is in the order of 2,000 gallons per minute. This water, which is collected by the underdrains is discharged behind the seepage recovery dam from where it is pumped back to the mill for re-use. The overflow from the cycloning operation is spigotted off the upstream face of the dam to provide a wide beach between the free water in the pond and upstream face of the sand dam. This beach provides the impervious upstream zone for the dam.

A typical section through the Brenda Dam, outside of the maximum central gully section, is presented on Figure 21. Also shown on this figure are the piezometric levels that exist at this section. An examination of this figure indicates that the underdrainage system is working effectively, with the phreatic surface being at the base of the sand fill and controlled by the finger drains. The large volumes of water used for placing the cycloned sand have some effect on piezometric levels, causing them to rise temporarily in the immediate vicinity of the filling operation.

Also shown on Figure 21 is an approximate flow net, drawn up using the indicated permeability parameters. Using this flow net, the estimated seepage loss through the dam is computed to be approximately 85 gallons per minute. This value is considered to be of the right order of magnitude and is very small compared to the volume of construction water that the drainage system must handle. Even if one assumes that the spigotting operation saturates the entire beach, the computed volume of seepage only increases by approximately 20%.

Figure 22 presents a section through Brenda Dam at its highest point, where it crosses the central gully section of the valley. It will be noted that water levels at this section are higher than those shown for the adjacent section. There are thought to be three reasons for this situation. First, during the early days of dam construction, it is believed that the filters surrounding the large finger drain became partically fouled by silty construction water, which concentrated in this low area. Second, as this was the lowest spot on the sand dam the finer sands and silt sizes were concentrated in this area. Third, this is an area that tends to collect foundation seepage water from the adjacent higher areas, in addition to those seepages attributable to the small lake of construction water which continuously ponded on the sand surface as the dam was raised. The combination of only partially effective underdrainage, an accumulation of finer silty sands, and an excess supply of construction

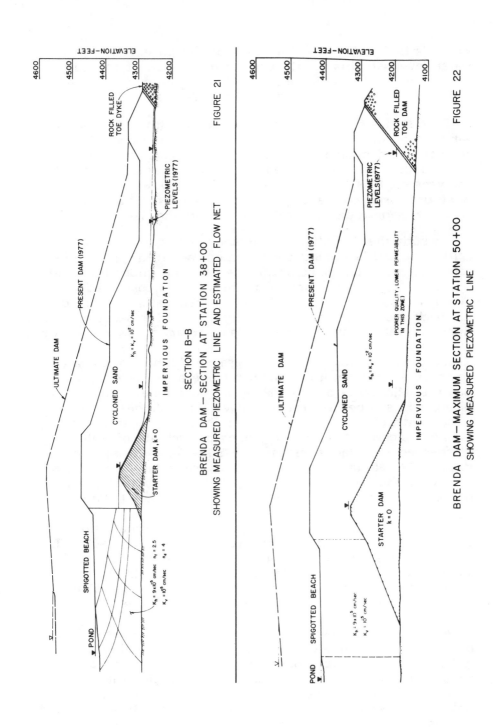

BRENDA DAM – SECTION AT STATION 38+00
SHOWING MEASURED PIEZOMETRIC LINE AND ESTIMATED FLOW NET

FIGURE 21

BRENDA DAM – MAXIMUM SECTION AT STATION 50+00
SHOWING MEASURED PIEZOMETRIC LINE

FIGURE 22

SEEPAGE CONTROL FOR TAILINGS DAMS **713**

water is believed to be the cause of the observed higher water levels in this area. Once construction of the dam is completed, it is anticipated that the observed water levels will drop down close to the level of the drains.

Brenda like Gibraltar, is designed to withstand moderate earthquake shocks. Also, like Gibraltar, the protection against liquefaction under modest earthquake shock has been to keep the downstream, sand shell well drained. Recent analyses confirm that the design will safely withstand the maximum probable earthquake anticipated for this area. (Richter Magnitude 6.5 at 15 miles from the dam).

At both the Gibraltar and Brenda tailings dams, the most critical period is during construction, when large volumes of construction water must be handled by the underdrainage systems. Once construction of the dams is completed and planned reclamation works push the free water in the ponds far back from the dams, the volumes of water seeping through the dams will be small and the downstream shells will be dry.

Reserve Mining Company - Reserve Mining Company (8) operates a large taconite, open-pit operation located at Babbitt, Minnesota on the Mesabi Iron Range. The crushed taconite is shipped by rail to Silver Bay, Minnesota where it is concentrated and pelletized into iron ore pellets. The tailings, along with 415,000 gallons per minute of water, are discharged from launders to Lake Superior. At full production 88,500 long tons per day of crude taconite are processed at the Silver Bay plant. Of this, about 29,500 tons become iron ore pellets and 59,000 tons become tailings.

Controversy over Reserve's practice of discharging tailings into Lake Superior had its beginnings in 1969. This controversy extended through numerous court actions. On June 1, 1977, Reserve began construction of its on-land tailings disposal facility at Mile Post 7. A general plan of the tailings disposal area is presented on Figure 23.

A very serious aspect of Reserve's tailing disposal problem is the existence of asbestos-like fibres in the tailings. A fibre is defined as a particle with a three to one aspect ratio. It is alleged by the regulatory agencies that these asbestos-like fibres are similar or identical to amosite asbestos. Asbestos fibres were claimed to be a health hazard because of their alleged link with cancer when inhaled. It was further alleged that these asbestos-like fibres were also a health hazard when ingested with water. As a consequence

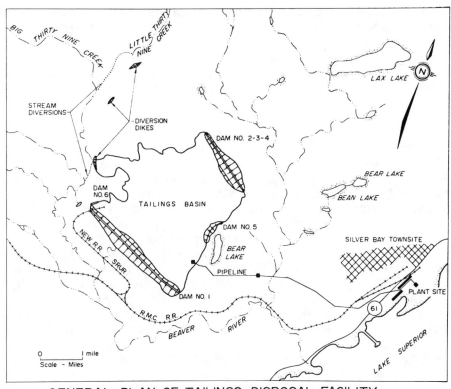

GENERAL PLAN OF TAILINGS DISPOSAL FACILITY
RESERVE MINING

FIGURE 23

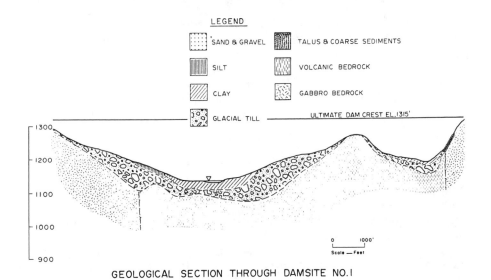

LEGEND

SAND & GRAVEL		TALUS & COARSE SEDIMENTS
SILT		VOLCANIC BEDROCK
CLAY		GABBRO BEDROCK
GLACIAL TILL		ULTIMATE DAM CREST EL. 1315'

GEOLOGICAL SECTION THROUGH DAMSITE NO. I
-RESERVE MINING

FIGURE 24

SEEPAGE CONTROL FOR TAILINGS DAMS **715**

of these allegations and the actions of the courts, Reserve Mining is legally required to provide a watertight tailings pond, operated as a closed circuit system, so that no asbestos-like fibres escape into the surface or groundwaters of the area. Reserve is also required to provide stringent dust control measures to prevent loss of fibres into the atmosphere.

From the outset, all dams were to be constructed by the downstream method, using the coarse tailings (minus 3/4" material) as a major construction material. Originally, Reserve proposed placing the excess coarse tailings, not required for dam building, west of the tailings pond. Also, the upstream faces of the tailings dams were to be sealed with a beach of fine tailings, a procedure conventionally followed for most tailings dam designs. However, the State objected to both the stockpiling of waste coarse tailings above the pond and the use of an exposed tailings beach to provide the upstream impervious facing for the dam. Their concern was the dust, allegedly containing potential cancer-causing, asbestos-like fibres, that might emanate from both these sources. Reserve's proposal to vegetate the waste piles and keep all tailings beaches wet by spraying when inactive was not acceptable to the MPCA. Consequently, in order to minimize any dust problem, Reserve agreed to:

- eliminate the tailings beaches by depositing all fine tailings underwater.

- eliminate the coarse tailings stockpile by also placing all coarse tailings underwater in the tailings pond.

- maintain essentially zero visible dust emissions from the dams and basin by minimizing the size of working areas and using dust suppressants on all inactive areas.

The stringent regulations imposed by the regulatory agencies concerning possible water losses from the tailings basin, coupled with the requirement that all tailings be disposed of underwater, made seepage control a major concern for this project. Fortunately, the tailings basin is relatively watertight as can be seen from Figure 24, which presents a section through the basin. The tailings dams are designed as water retention dams with a compacted upstream impervious zone and a compacted coarse tailings (minus 3/4" material) downstream zone. The starter dam is also an impervious water storage dam, which stores up to 30 ft of start-up water, under whose surface the first fine tailings will be stored. A typical section through the largest dam is presented on Figure 25.

Some of the seepage reduction features which have by necessity been built into the dam designs are:

1) Compacted, impervious, glacial till membrane on the upstream face of the dam.

2) Foundation cutoff trench carried into impervious glacial till or clay.

3) Slush grouting or shotcreting of rock surface under the impervious zone of the dam and the filters.

4) Blanket grouting on the rock abutments

5) At least 1 row of deep grout holes on the rock abutments.

The basic drainage features include:

1) Filter and drain zones downstream of upstream impervious zone.

2) Foundation blanket drain downstream of starter dam.

3) Relief wells across the downstream toe of the dam.

In addition, seepage recovery dams are provided downstream of each structure. As the anticipated seepages will be inconsequential, the main function of these dams is to collect surface runoff water which has flowed over the tailings dam. The state considers such water to be polluted as the dams are constructed of tailings.

Extensive stream diversions have been necessary to control the volumes of water that must be stored in the closed circuit tailings pond (Reference Figure 23). All diversions have had to be designed to handle the maximum probable storm. Similarly, the tailings pond has also been designed

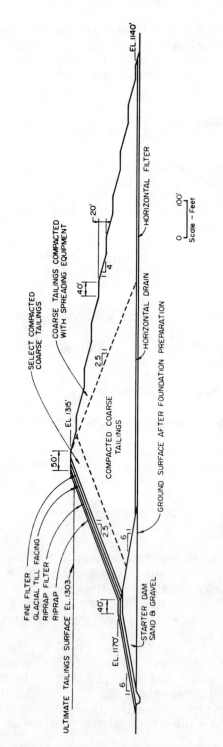

FINE FILTER
GLACIAL TILL FACING
RIPRAP FILTER
RIPRAP
ULTIMATE TAILINGS SURFACE EL. 1303

SELECT COMPACTED
COARSE TAILINGS

COARSE TAILINGS COMPACTED
WITH SPREADING EQUIPMENT

EL. 1315'

50'

40'

20'

4

2.5
1

COMPACTED COARSE
TAILINGS

HORIZONTAL DRAIN

HORIZONTAL FILTER

GROUND SURFACE AFTER FOUNDATION PREPARATION

EL. 1170'

40'

6
1

2.5
1

6
1

6
1

STARTER DAM
SAND & GRAVEL

EL. 1140'

0   100'
Scale – Feet

TYPICAL SECTION THROUGH DAM NO. I – RESERVE MINING

FIGURE 25

to handle a maximum probable storm and still maintain a safe freeboard.   Water reclaim is by floating, pump barge, having a maximum capacity of 10,000 gallons per minute.

Piezometers for measuring the seepage pressures that develop in the foundation soils downstream of the dams have been installed.   Also installed are wells for monitoring water quality.

GCOS Tar Island Tailings Dyke - Our last example, which is taken from previously published reports (6,15,16), illustrates a case where internal drains have been used to control the phreatic line.   The dam is being constructed of sand, using hydraulic placement procedures. The hydraulically placed sand is compacted to a high density, using vibratory compaction equipment. At this particular project the tailings pond contains a great depth of water, which is in contact with the upstream face of the sand dam. Under these conditions a fairly high phreatic line would be expected to develop through the dam under steady seepage conditions. A further factor, which adds to the seepage from the pond, is the transportation water used to place the sand on the dam. Locally, where hydraulic fill placement is underway, the phreatic line is raised by the added seepage due to this construction water.

Seepage analyses (16) using finite element procedures, were made for a large number of conditions.   According to these analyses the existing internal drains require a greater capacity to increase their ability to draw down the phreatic line.   The three phreatic lines shown on Figure 26 indicate where the analyses place the phreatic line for the three assumed conditions of:

a)   no internal drains

b)   perfect lower internal drain

c)   existing drain flows

The phreatic line obtained using the existing drain flow conditions provides a fairly good fit with the observed piezometric readings.   The higher piezometric pressures that are measured in the vicinity of the second internal drain were considered to reflect the hydraulic fill operations in this area. Using the same parameters as were used for this "best-fit" condition an attempt was then made to predict where the ultimate phreatic line might occur.   Extrapolated

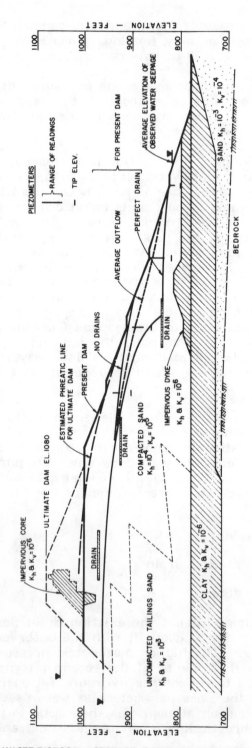

PIEZOMETERS

} RANGE OF READINGS

— TIP ELEV.

} FOR PRESENT DAM

AVERAGE ELEVATION OF
OBSERVED WATER SEEPAGE

SAND $K_h = 10^{-3}$, $K_v = 10^{-4}$

BEDROCK

PERFECT DRAIN

AVERAGE OUTFLOW

NO DRAINS

PRESENT DAM

ESTIMATED PHREATIC LINE
FOR ULTIMATE DAM

IMPERVIOUS DYKE
K_h & $K_v = 10^{-6}$

DRAIN

COMPACTED SAND
$K_h = 10^{-4}$, $K_v = 10^{-5}$

ULTIMATE DAM EL. 1080

DRAIN

IMPERVIOUS CORE
K_h & $K_v = 10^{-6}$

UNCOMPACTED TAILINGS SAND
K_h & $K_v = 10^{-5}$

CLAY K_h & $K_v = 10^{-6}$

DRAIN

ELEVATION — FEET

1100

1000

900

800

700

TYPICAL SECTION THROUGH
G.C.O.S. TAR ISLAND TAILINGS DAM

(AFTER MORGENSTERN AND KAISER — REFERENCE 20)

FIGURE 26

drain flows, based on past observations, were used in carrying out the computations. The predicted location of the final phreatic line is also shown on Figure 26. Although such predictions should be considered as approximate estimates only, because of the large number of variables which can affect such an extrapolation, they are nonetheless considered to be valid indicators of the trend which will develop as the dam is raised.

In this example, the dense sand embankment is considered stable, even though it has a relatively high phreatic line. The only point of concern is the probable development of local sloughing, slumping, and minor soil erosion at points where concentrated seepage might develop in the downstream slope of the dam during construction. Filters will be placed at such locations to control seepage and prevent piping from developing.

CONCLUSIONS

1. Seepage control is a critically important aspect in the design, construction, and operation of tailings dams. Uncontrolled seepage can lead to such problems as piping, slope instability and heaving, and excess water losses.

2. Seepage control methods developed for conventional water storage dams are directly applicable to controlling seepage flows through tailings dams. However, they must be suitably modified to satisfy the specific requirements of any given tailings dam design.

3. Pollution control regulations can have a major effect on the seepage control facilities required for any given tailings dam. In those instances where no discharge of effluent is allowed into the downstream ground or surface waters, extensive seepage reduction features may be required. These measures may materially add to the costs of the tailings storage facilities.

4. Downstream methods of tailings dam construction allow the greatest flexibility for selecting the most suitable seepage control measures required to satisfy any given set of site conditions and/or regulatory agency requirements.

5. Observational data from several operating tailings dams indicate that flow nets may be used to estimate seepage flows and to determine the location of the phreatic surface

through the beach and tailings dam with sufficient accuracy
for most design purposes. The greatest unknown is the
effective permeability of the tailings beach and the writer
recommends that the maximum probable values for both the
permeability and the permeability ratio (k_{max}/k_{min}) be used
for all computations. This procedure will produce conservatively high values for both the seepage quantity and the
location of the phreatic line.

6. Drains should be designed using the highest probable
seepage flows that can enter the drains and the lowest
probable permeability for the drains themselves. All drains
should be sized to handle flows several times the largest
value computed on the above basis. This philosophy is
considered essential to handle such unknowns as: highly pervious foundation zones not found during design, development
of cracks in an impervious zone, "windows" in a grout curtain, drainage from consolidation slimes, high pond levels
which flood the slime beaches, loss of drain's capacity with
time, due to plugging with fines or precipitation of salts,
etc. For tailings dams constructed using on-dam-cycloning
or hydraulic fill procedures, the largest volumes of seepage
that must be handled by the drains comes from the transportation water.

7. Drainage is particularly important for tailings dams located in areas of high seismic risk. Loose, saturated
tailings are subject to liquefaction under earthquake shocks.
The basic protective measures against liquefaction are compaction and drainage. For tailings dams located in areas
of low to medium seismic risk, drainage of the downstream
shell will in most instances provide adequate protection
against liquefaction. For tailings dams located in areas of
very high seismic risk, both drainage and compaction are
considered necessary.

8. Seepage control measures unquestionably add to the total
costs of the tailings storage facilities. However, they
greatly increase the overall safety of the tailings dams and
when properly designed and constructed satisfy both the
safety and pollution control requirements of the regulatory
agencies. The additional costs associated with constructing
adequate seepage control measures should be considered a
necessary part of the cost of building and operating a mine
in today's society.

ACKNOWLEDGEMENTS

The data presented in this paper has been drawn from many sources, a major source being our clients, to whom we extend our thanks for use of the data developed on their projects. The writer also wishes to acknowledge the assistance given him to several members of his staff who helped gather the data presented in this paper. In this regard, special acknowledgement is extended to Robert C.Y. Lo who carried out the analyses required for drawing up the several flow nets, and to Eric D. Pharey who prepared all the figures.

LIST OF REFERENCES

1.   Bertram, G.E., 1940 – "An Experimental Investigation of Protective Filters", Harvard University, Graduate School of Engineering, Soil Mechanics Series #7, Jan. 1940.

2.   Casagrande, Arthur (1937) – "Seepage Through Dams" (Originally published in Journal of the New England Water Works Association, June 1937). Republished by Boston Society of Civil Engineers, (1940) in "Contributions to Soil Mechanics", 1925–1940.

3.   Casagrande, Arthur (1961) – "Control of Seepage Through Foundations and Abutments of Dams", Geotechnique, Vol XI, No. 3, Sept. 1961.

4.   Cedergren, Harry R., (1973) – "Seepage Control in Earth Dams, Embankments" – Dam Engineering Casagrande Volume, 1973, John Wiley and Sons.

5.   Cedergren, Harry R., (1977) – "Seepage Drainage and Flow Nets", John Wiley & Sons.

6.   Great Canadian Oil Sands Tar Island Dyke – (1977). "Report by Design Review Panel" to Department of the Environment, Alberta Government, Edmonton, Alberta.

7.   Kealy. C. Daniel, and Richard A. Busch, (1971) – "Determining Seepage Characteristics of Mill Tailings Dams by the Finite Element Method". Report of Investigation 7477, Bureau of Mines, United States Department of the Interior, Jan, 1971.

8. Klohn, Earle J., and David Dingeman (1978) – "Tailings Disposal System for Reserve Mining Company" – Proceedings of the Second International Tailing Symposium, Denver, Colorado, May 1978, Miller Freeman Publications Inc.

9. Klohn, Earle J., (1972) – "Design and Construction of Tailings Dams", Canadian Institute of Mining Transactions, Vol. LXXV, pp 50-66, 1972.

10. Klohn, Earle J., and C.H. Maartman (1972) – "Construction of Sound Tailings Dams by Cycloning and Spigotting". Proceedings of the First International Tailing Symposium, Tucson, Arizona, 1972, Miller Freeman Publications Inc.

11. Klohn, Earle J., C.H. Maartman, R.C.Y. Lo, and W.D. Liam Finn (1978) – "Simplified Seismic Analysis for Tailings Dams". Proceedings of Specialty Conference on Earthquake Engineering and Soil Dynamics. ASCE, Pasadena, California, June 1978.

12. Lo, Robert C. (1969) – "Steady Seepage with Free Surface", Ph.D. Thesis, Harvard University, Cambridge, Mass.

13. Middlebrooke, T.A., and W.H. Jervis (1947) – "Relief Wells for Dams and Levees", Transactions of ASCE Vol. 112, pp 1321 – 1338.

14. Mittal, Hari K., and Norbert R. Morgenstern, (1976) – "Seepage Control in Tailings Dams", Canadian Geotechnical Journal, Vol. 13, No. 3, August 1976.

15. Mittal, Hari K., and Robert M. Hardy, (1977) – "Geotechnical Aspects of a Tar Sand Tailings Dyke". Proceedings of Conference on Geotechnical Practice for Disposal of Solid Waste Materials, Published by ASCE.

16. Morgenstern, N.R., and P. Kaiser, (1976) – "Seepage Analyses of the GCOS Tar Island Tailings Dyke" report prepared for the Tar Island Tailings Dyke Design Review Panel, Department of the Environment, Government of Alberta.

17. Sherard, J.L., R.J. Woodward, S.F. Gizienski, and W.A. Clevenger, (1963). "Earth and Earth-Rock Dams – Engineering Problems of Design and Construction", John Wiley and Sons.

18. Tentative Design Guide for Mine Waste Embankments in Canada, (1972) - Mines Branch, Mining Research Centre, Dept. of Energy, Mines and Resources.

19. Terzaghi, Karl and Ralph B. Peck, (1967) - "Soil Mechanics in Engineering Practice", John Wiley and Sons.

20. Teton Dam Failure, (1976) - Independent Panel to Review Cause of Teton Dam Failure - Report to U.S. Dept of Interior and State of Idaho on Failure of Teton Dam.

21. Turnbull, W.J., and C.I. Mansur, (1961) - "Investigation of Underseepage - Mississippi River Levees", Transactions ASCE, Vol. 126, Part I, pp 1429-1539.

22. U.S. Department of the Army, Corps of Engineers (1972) - "Investigation of Relief Wells, Mississippi River Levees, Alton to Gale, Illinois", Misc Paper 5-72-21 Waterways Experiment Station, Vicksburg, Miss., June 1972.

23. U.S. Department of the Navy, Naval Facilities Engineering Command (1974). "Design Manual - Soil Mechanics, Foundations, and Earth Structures" - DM-7.

24. Uranium Mill Tailings Management (1978) - Proceedings of Symposium Nov. 20, 21, 1978, Colorado State University, Fort Collins, Colorado.

34

Control of Seepage from Uranium Mill Tailings Ponds in the Elliot Lake Area

by J. B. Davis, Principal,
Golder Associates,
R. A. Knapp, Manager, Industrial Treatment,
James F. MacLaren Limited,
and K. W. Sinclair, Senior Civil Engineer,
Rio Algom Limited,
Toronto, Ontario, Canada

ABSTRACT

Since the beginning of mining operations in 1955, some 105 million tons of uranium mill tailings have been produced in the Elliot Lake area. Current contracts will result in the production of an additional 300 million tons of tailings and presently uncommitted reserves could result in the production of a further 250 million tons. This paper reviews the history of past mining activities and tailings management in the area, describes the seepage control measures at two tailings management areas (one developed in the late 1960's and the other presently under construction) and considers possible techniques to control seepage from future tailings areas.

INTRODUCTION

The Elliot Lake mining area is located in north-central Ontario at about longitude 82 degrees 36 minutes west, latitude 46 degrees 24 minutes north (see Figure 1). The topography is fairly characteristic of the Canadian Shield and may be described as rugged but of relatively low relief; elevation differences being generally in the order of 100 to 200 feet or less. Topographic highs consist typically of rock knolls or ridges and topographic lows generally contain swamps, lakes or streams.

Figure 1 - Site Location Plan

The area experiences an average total precipitation of about 38 inches of rainfall per year and the average annual evapo-transpiration is about 20 inches. Thus, as illustrated on Figure 2, the area is characterized by abundant lakes and streams; about 20 to 25 per cent of the total area being covered by water.

In an area of significant net precipitation, it is not practically possible to construct non-effluent producing tailings facilities. Consequently, current practice in the Elliot Lake area is to collect and treat all effluent from the tailings facility prior to discharge to the environment.

Figure 2 - Typical Elliot Lake Topography

Because of the topography, tailings are generally discharged into existing lake basins to take advantage of
natural containment by surrounding bedrock highs. As far
as is practically possible, all fresh water is diverted
away from the management area. Topographic lows around the
perimeter of the tailings area are closed by dams.

Current draft guidelines (1) suggest that the average
permeability of a tailings basin should not exceed 10^{-5}
centimeters per second and that the permeability of containment dams should not exceed 10^{-6} centimeters per
second. Because of the lack of impervious clay borrow in
the area, this latter requirement has recently led to the
incorporation of synthetic membranes or liners in the
containment dams.

REGIONAL GEOLOGY

The uranium deposits in the Elliot Lake area are associated with an approximately 10 mile wide sedimentary basin
of Pre-Cambrian Age which unconformably overlies meta-
volcanic and metasedimentary basement rocks. The ore occurs
in 2 to 15 foot thick pyritized quartz pebble conglomerate
beds located near the base of the sedimentary sequence and
is generally of low grade (1 to 3 pounds per ton).

Regional faults tend to occur at 3 to 4 mile spacing and, with the exception of Quirke Lake over-thrust fault, are steeply dipping and strike northwest-southeast (ref. Figure 3). Local faulting tends to be more intense (2 to 3 features per square mile) and, while generally steeply dipping, exhibit variable strike and persistence. Intruded diabase dykes are associated with the faults.

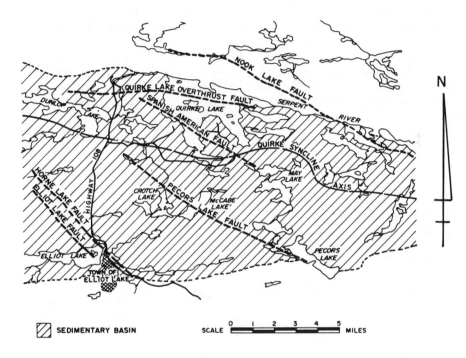

Figure 3 - Simplified Geologic Map

Overburden is restricted to topographic lows and, with the exception of recent bog or swamp deposits, consists predominantly of fluvial or outwash silty sands and gravels of glacial origin. Local deposits of essentially cohesion-less silty to sandy till also occur in topographic lows or plastered on the flanks of bedrock highs. The permeability of the till is typically in the order of 10^{-4} to 10^{-5} centimeters per second.

Groundwater appears to occur as a complex series of local "perched" regimes associated with the lake systems. The majority of groundwater transport between these local regimes occurs through overburden infilled bedrock lows or major discontinuities (e.g. faults) in the rock. However, the results of mining experience and recent geotechnical borings suggests that, with two or three possible exceptions, the permeability of the faults at depth is low; typically less than about 10^{-5} centimeters per second.

HISTORY OF MINING AND MILLING ACTIVITIES

The discovery of uranium in the Elliot Lake area in 1953 preceded, by a short interval, a critical stage in the "cold war". Governments demanded enormous quantities of uranium for atomic weaponry for western defence. The result was a frantic crash program whereby twelve mines (eleven with mills) were brought into production in the area over a span of four years (1955-1958) by seven different mining companies (2). The locations of these mines are shown on Figure 4.

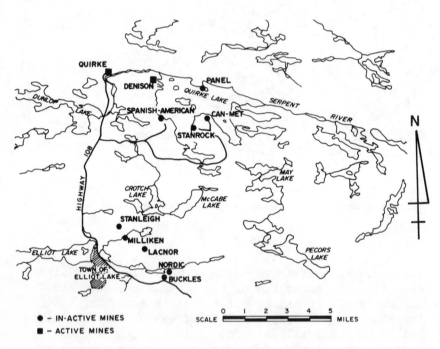

Figure 4 - Locations of Active and In-Active Mines

In 1959, the United States Atomic Energy Commission, to which most of the production was contracted, announced that it would not extend the contracts beyond 1962. As a result, most of the mines and mills closed, with only the Denison and Nordic operations remaining in production. The population of the Town of Elliot Lake subsequently dropped from in excess of 25,000 people in 1959 to about 7,000 in the early 1960's.

In 1968, the Nordic Mine closed and the Quirke mill was reactivated. Thus, at present only two mine/mills are in operation, Quirke and Denison, both of which have recently increased rated mill production to about 7,000 tons per day.

The history of past mining/milling operations in the Elliot Lake area and an indication of tailings production from the various mills are summarized in Table I. As indicated in this table, the total tailings production to date in the area has been of the order of 105 million tons.

TABLE I

SUMMARY OF URANIUM MILLING HISTORY

Mill	Operating Period	Nominal Mill Capacity (T.P.D.)	Total Quantity Milled (10^6 tons)
North Limb Mines			
Can-Met	May '58 - Mar. '60	3,000	6.1
Denison	May '57 - Present	4,500 - 7,000	33.0
Panel	Feb. '58 - June '61	3,100	3.6
Quirke	Sept. '56 - Feb. '61	3,000	4.1
	Aug. '68 - Present	4,500 - 7,000	23.0
Spanish-American	May '58 - Feb. '59	2,000	0.4
Stanrock	Mar. '58 - Nov. '60	3,000	6.1
South Limb Mines			
Lacnor	Sept. '57 - July '60	4,000	3.0
Milliken	Apr. '58 - June '64	3,000	6.3
Nordic	June '57 - July '68	3,700	13.2
Stanleigh	Mar. '58 - Jan. '60	3,000	2.0
Pronto	Sept. '55 - Apr. '60	1,500	2.3
	June '60 - 1970*	-	2.5
TOTAL MILLED TO DATE			105.6

*Copper tailings from adjacent property.

As indicated on Figure 5, tailings from the various milling operations are located in seven main areas; combined facilities having been used for some mines. During the 1950's and early 1960's, the most common form of tailings disposal was to end-discharge tailings into a nearby lake basin as shown on Figure 6. At that time, it was not recognized by either the companies or government regulatory bodies that radium would appear in the effluent (see

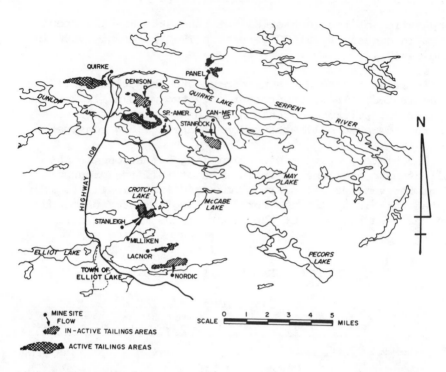

Figure 5 - Locations of Active and In-Active Tailings Areas

Figure 6 - Typical 1950's Tailings Area

following section) and no attempt was made to collect or treat the effluent from the tailings basins; the overflow went directly into the streams.

Where tailings encroached on topographic lows around the lake basin perimeter, pervious sand and gravel berms were constructed to contain the solids. However, no positive measures were taken to prevent or collect seepage through these structures.

At some properties, natural basins suitable to provide adequate containment were not available and conventional tailings "sand" dams were constructed by the upstream method (with or without cycloning) or waste rock perimeter dams were provided. Again, no positive seepage control or collection systems were incorporated into these structures, one of which is illustrated on Figure 7.

Figure 7 - 1950's Tailings Dam

By the late 1960's, stringent criteria had been established regarding the quality of effluent which could be discharged to the environment. Consequently, with the reactivation of the Quirke mill in 1968, measures were taken to either prevent or collect and treat seepage from the tailings management area as described subsequently in this paper, Concurrently, extensive works were undertaken at Denison's active tailings area to minimize and collect seepage. This system is described by Milligan et al., 1977 (3).

In 1976, a decision was made by Rio Algom Limited to reactivate their Panel Mine (described subsequently in this paper) and in 1978 long-term contracts between Ontario Hydro and both Denison Mines Limited and Preston Mines Limited (an affiliate of Rio Algom Limited and owners of the Stanleigh Mine) were announced. Preliminary design of tailings facilities to service both these contracts is currently underway.

A summary of the total past and possible future tailings production in the Elliot Lake area is given in Table II.

TABLE II

SUMMARY OF POSSIBLE TOTAL TAILINGS PRODUCTION

Total tailings produced to date (from Table I)	105×10^6 tons
Additional future production to fulfill existing contracts	300×10^6 tons
Additional uncommitted reserves	250×10^6 tons
Total potential tailings production	655×10^6 tons

As indicated by this table, based on existing contracts alone the total tailings production in the Elliot Lake area will be of the order of 400 million tons (dry weight basis) which equates to a total volume of storage required of about 350 million cubic yards.

TREATMENT OF TAILINGS EFFLUENT

Elliot Lake tailings are relatively coarse with 40 per cent passing a minus 200 mesh screen. For the low grade ores (typically about 2 pounds per ton and lower), the radium activity is about 250 pico-curries per gram or less.

During the 1950's and early 1960's while all properties were in operation, acid generation was not a significant problem and the elevated levels of radium 226 were an unknown quantity. Thus, as previously noted, impervious containment structures were not provided and attempts were not made to prevent or control seepage from the tailings areas.

Following the closure of all but two properties in the early 1960's, two major environmental problems emerged. The first problem was acid generation from pyrite oxidation in the inactive tailings areas which resulted in a serious pH depression in the regional river system. The second problem which came to light was the elevated levels of radium 226 in the discharges from the tailings areas.

During the mid 1960's both operating properties (Denison and Nordic) commenced the use of barium chloride for the control of dissolved radium 226. This was followed by the installation of seepage collection systems and lime and barium chloride treatment plants at all non-operating properties. This has resulted in the control of acidity and a great reduction in radium discharges to the receiving waters.

Current practice in the Elliot Lake area is to extract uranium in an acid leach circuit with ion exchange for uranium recovery and to neutralize the tailings with lime and limestone before discharge to the tailings basin. The resultant decant flows from the tailings areas, which include all process water discharged plus runoff, are characterized as a saturated calcium sulphate solution with neutral pH, very low levels of heavy metals and elevated levels of dissolved radium 226. Therefore, treatment consists of barium chloride addition for precipitation of radium barium sulphate followed by settling in large engineered clarification ponds. Typically, dissolved radium levels are reduced from between 300 and 1000 pico-curries per litre to 3 to 7 pico-curries per litre after treatment.

Although current contracts will extend mining and milling operations well into the twenty-first century, a primary area of concern to both the mining companies and regulatory bodies is the development of long-term abandonment strategies. A primary abandonment strategy developed for properties in the mid-western United States has been to "encapsulate" the tailings. This involves the application of as much as 10 to 20 feet of clean overburden and clay to reduce infiltration of water and exhilation of radon gas. This strategy is NOT applicable for Elliot Lake as virtually no clay exists in the area and overburden for fill is scarce.

Major research and development plans have been initiated to deal with long-term abandonment strategies. This work includes investigations into chemical fixation techniques, alternate encapsulation techniques, removal of radionuclides from the tailings and vegetative stabilization. The work carried out to date involving contouring and vegetation to promote runoff and increase rates of evapo-transpiration have proved to be very encouraging (see Figure 8 for example). Thus, vegetative stabilization is receiving the major research and development effort at this time.

Figure 8 - Example of Re-Vegetated Tailings

QUIRKE TAILINGS MANAGEMENT AREA

The Quirke mill was initially operated from September, 1956 until February, 1961 and tailings were discharged into the east end of a small lake basin known as Manfred Lake. The general location of the Quirke tailings management area is shown on Figure 5 and a more detailed view is shown on the 1964 aerial photograph, Figure 9. During this period, clarified effluent from the tailings area followed a local stream course around a high rock ridge to the north and thence to the Serpent River. Shortly before shut-down a rockfill starter dyke was constructed across the west end of the area (ref. Figure 9 for location); the intention having been to construct a "sand" dam by spigotting from west to east.

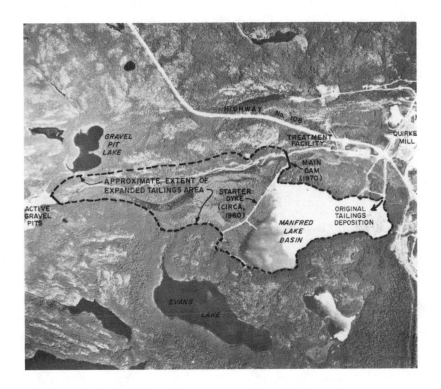

Figure 9 - 1964 Aerial Photograph of Quirke Tailings Area

In August of 1968, milling was resumed at Quirke and tailings were initially discharged into the west end of the Manfred Lake basin from the previously constructed starter dyke. Subsequently (1969) it was decided to incorporate the entire valley to the west of this initial area into a major tailings management scheme. To this end, a relatively short (550 foot long) "Main Dam" was constructed across the eastern outlet to the valley (ref. Figure 9). It was further decided to construct this Main Dam to an initial height of about 50 feet and to raise the water level in the basin to about elevation 1257 feet (an average depth of about 40 feet) prior to allowing discharge. Effluent was then "decanted" through an overflow spillway cut in the rock of the south abutment of the Main Dam and thence led by overland flow to a treatment facility located immediately downstream of the Main Dam.

In raising the water level to elevation 1257, it was recognized that, although there was adequate freeboard at the west end of the basin, a potential seepage problem existed through what were known to be extensive, pervious sand and gravel deposits which separated the tailings basin from an environmentally sensitive freshwater lake, Dunlop Lake, to the west. Further, diversion of the flow from Gravel Pit Lake through this area was required (see Figure 9 for location).

Main Dam and Treatment Area

The results of borings put down at the Main Dam site indicated that while the valley walls were composed of exposed rock, the valley floor was underlain by as much as about 50 feet of pervious sand and gravel (coefficient of permeability of 10^{-2} to 10^{-4} centimeters per second) and the groundwater level was essentially at ground surface. The underlying rock was found to be sound with a permeability (based on borehole packer tests) of between 10^{-5} and 10^{-6} centimeters per second.

At that time, it was considered impractical to construct an impervious cut-off to rock beneath the dam and, considering the fact that the treatment facility was located downstream of the dam, it was decided to permit foundation seepage; this seepage being collected and treated with the decanted effluent. Initially, it was proposed to install gravity relief wells along the downstream toe of the dam to collect the seepage. This proposal was abandoned in favour of a seepage collection pond between the toe of the dam and the treatment facility. This revised scheme is illustrated in plan and section on Figure 10.

Considering the lack of impervious (clayey) borrow material in the Elliot Lake area and the fact that controlled foundation seepage was to be permitted, it was decided to construct the Main Dam of pervious mine waste rock. A toe drain of select sand and gravel was provided to collect seepage and a tailings "beach" was spigotted along the upstream face during initial filling of the basin to minimize seepage (see Figure 10). With the provision of this tailings "beach" the total seepage through the dam and the foundations was estimated to be of the order of 700 to 800 gallons per minute.

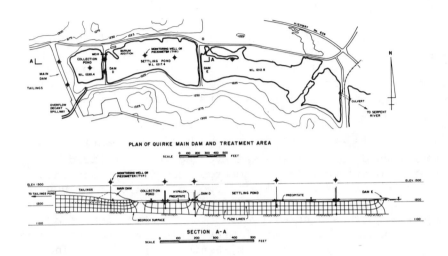

PLAN OF QUIRKE MAIN DAM AND TREATMENT AREA

SECTION A-A

Figure 10 - Quirke Main Dam and Treatment Area

In 1977, an extensive investigation consisting of geophysical surveys and borings together with the installation of monitoring piezometers and groundwater sampling wells was undertaken (see Figure 10). The results of these studies indicated that NO "untreated" seepage was escaping to the environment. The piezometric water levels in the Main Dam were very low and most of the foundation seepage was emerging in the collection pond (i.e. between the Main Dam and the treatment plant) with only a small amount, computed 2 to 3 gallons per minute, of "untreated" seepage passing Dam 'D' (ref. Figure 10). Further, the results of chemical analyses of groundwater samples obtained from sampling wells installed immediately downstream of the settling pond indicated that the filtered radium content approached "background" levels. It is interesting to note also that samples of groundwater obtained from wells installed in the foundations of the Main Dam contained only 2 to 4 pico-curries per litre of radium 226, suggesting that the radium was adsorbed by the local granular soils.

Gravel Pit Lake Diversion

As previously noted, a potential seepage problem was recognized at the west end of the basin where borings put down in 1969-70 indicated pervious sand and gravel deposits extended as low as elevation 1220 or some 40 feet below the proposed tailings pond level. Further, it was necessary to divert the outflow of Gravel Pit Lake (which originally flowed eastward) through this area towards the west.

Several alternative methods of constructing "conventional" impervious dams and cut-offs were investigated. Because of the lack of suitably impervious clay borrow, various types of synthetic core materials and synthetic liner materials were considered as well as various methods of extending the core/liner to rock.

Because of the high cost of providing "conventional" impervious dams, a scheme was evolved which utilized the diverted Gravel Pit Lake discharge (required in any case) to form "back-up" ponds behind two relatively small PERVIOUS sand and gravel dams (Dams 'A' and 'B') as illustrated on Figure 11. This scheme involved the construction of a control dam at the outlet of Gravel Pit Lake and the creation of two relatively small lakes, Ponds 'A' and 'B' behind the

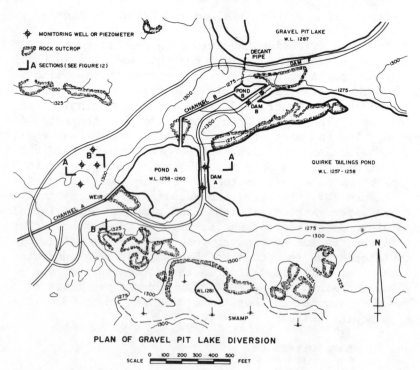

PLAN OF GRAVEL PIT LAKE DIVERSION

SCALE 0 100 200 300 400 500 FEET

Figure 11 - Gravel Pit Lake Diversion

two pervious dams. The water levels in Ponds 'A' and 'B'
were regulated to provide a positive head of "fresh water"
across the dams and thus prevent the seepage of contaminated
water out of the tailings area (see Figure 12 for illustra-
tive section).

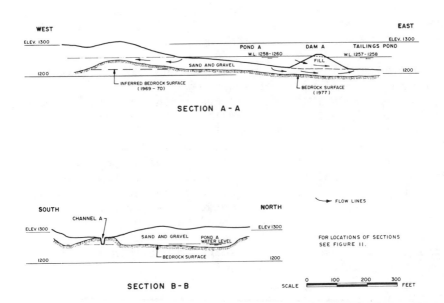

SECTION A-A

SECTION B-B

Figure 12 - Sections Through Gravel Pit Lake Diversion Area

Over the years, some problems have been encountered in
maintaining the design water levels in the freshwater back-
up lakes, particularly Pond 'A'. As a result, the water
level in Pond 'A' has, on occasion, fallen to within a few
inches of the tailings pond level but has never fallen below
the pond level.

Although on-going surface water monitoring has indicated
no leakage problem in this area, Rio Algom undertook a major
study in 1977 to confirm that untreated effluent was NOT

escaping into the groundwater from the tailings area and entering Dunlop Lake. The results of this investigation indicated that, while not as extensive as had been inferred from the 1969-70 borings, an overburden "window" existed between Pond 'A' and the freshwater lake to the west (ref. Figure 12). Further, while the overburden was highly pervious (coefficient of permeability of 10^{-1} to 10^{-3} centimeters per second) the bedrock was relatively impervious (coefficient of permeability generally less than 10^{-5} to 10^{-6} centimeters per second).

Piezometers installed in Dams 'A' and 'B' and their foundations confirmed that seepage was occurring from the freshwater ponds INTO the tailings basin. Further, samples of surface water from the Pond 'A' outlet and samples of groundwater obtained from sampling wells installed in Dams 'A' and 'B' and in the overburden "window" between Pond 'A' and Dunlop Lake all had the same chemical composition, including filtered radium, as did samples of the Gravel Pit Lake discharge. NO evidence of contaminated process water from the tailings basin was found. Thus, even with the relatively small differential head that occasionally exists between Pond 'A' and the tailings pond, the system is effective in preventing the escape of contaminants to the surrounding area.

Current and Future Activities

Following spigotting of the initial "beach" on the face of the Main Dam in 1971, a diagonal dyke was constructed across the "beach" from the south abutment to the north side of the valley (Dyke Number 1 on Figure 13) and open end discharging of tailings continued from the north valley wall. Subsequently, construction of a longitudinal waste rock and "sand" fill causeway across the beach from the south abutment of the Main Dam was begun. Dyke Number 2 (Figure 13) was constructed and "stacking" of tailings was commenced between the Main Causeway and the north valley wall.

At present, the capacity of the existing basin has almost been reached and studies are currently in progress to increase the capacity to about 80 to 100 million tons by major internal "stacking" and/or by raising the perimeter containment structures.

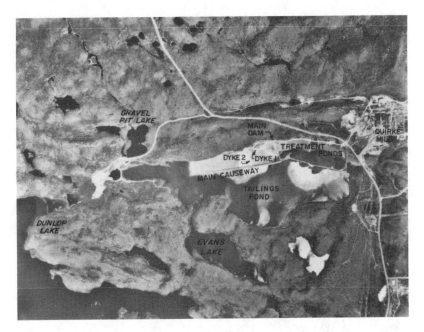

Figure 13 - Current Quirke Tailings Area

PANEL TAILINGS MANAGEMENT AREA

During previous milling operations at Panel Mine (February 1958 to June 1961) approximately 3.6 million tons of tailings were discharged into the west end of Strike Lake, a small lake basin located about one mile north of the mine and, to a lesser extent into a low-lying area immediately to the south (see Figure 5 for general location).

In 1976 a decision was made to reactivate the Panel Mine with a planned total production of 12 million tons of tailings. On the basis of site selection studies, it was decided to develop the Strike Lake basin as a controlled tailings management area, mainly because of the presence of the previously deposited tailings. Excluding geologic and topographic constraints, the development of this area was complicated by two factors.

(i)   It was originally anticipated that milling could commence as early as April, 1979. As the period available for design and construction precluded completion of the effluent treatment facility before the Autumn of 1979, the system was to be designed to store all process water and precipitation runoff for a period of at least 9 months.

(ii) The 1950's tailings beach in the area south of the Strike Lake had to be treated.

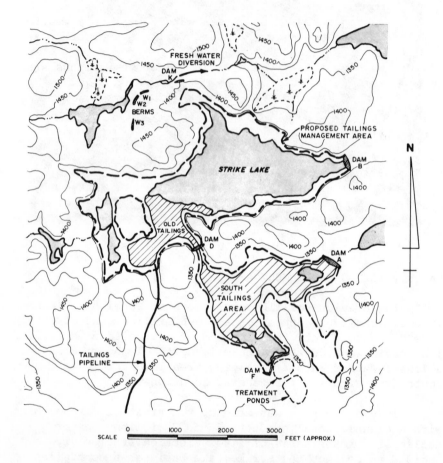

Figure 14 - Panel Tailings Management Area

To accommodate the various constraints, the scheme illustrated on Figure 14 was developed. This consisted basically of:

(a) Diverting the majority of freshwater inflow from the north away from the basin by the construction of Dam 'K', berms 'W1', 'W2' and 'W3' and diversion channel 'Y'.

(b) Raising the water level in the Strike Lake basin to elevation 1325 to maintain a water cover over the tailings by the construction of Dam 'B' across the existing eastern outlet of the lake and Dam 'D' across a narrow valley joining the Strike Lake basin to the South Tailings Area. Provision was made for subsequently raising this water level to elevation 1335 to accommodate future tailings production

(c) Raising the water level in the South Tailings Area to elevation 1315 by the construction of Dams 'A' and 'F' to flood the existing tailings and control runoff.

(d) Decanting water from the Strike Lake basin into the South Tailings Area by means of a side-hill decant at Dam 'D' and removing effluent from the South Tailings Area via a decant at Dam 'F'; the treatment facility being located immediately downstream of Dam 'F' and discharging via overland flow to Quirke Lake.

Containment Dams

In accordance with governmental guidelines, all of the perimeter containment dams, including Dam 'D', were to be made "impervious" and were to be capable of storing the 100 year design storm; excess precipitation being discharged untreated from the South Tailings Area via an emergency spillway east of Dam 'F' (because of operational considerations, the Strike Lake basin was capable of storing the maximum probable flood and no interim emergency spillway was provided).

Detailed geotechnical investigations carried out at the site in 1977 disclosed that, with the exception of Dam 'B', all of the dam sites were underlain by relatively thin overburden typically consisting of recent organic deposits and fluvial sands and gravels. At Dam 'B', located across the east end of Strike Lake, geophysical surveys indicated that within the valley floor area the depth of overburden ranged from about 40 feet (a local bedrock high) to in excess of 100 feet. Borings put down at the site indicated that the overburden varied from pervious sands and gravels to sandy till of moderate permeability.

Borrow investigations carried out in the area disclosed adequate localized deposits of granular borrow suitable for dam construction. In addition, two fairly extensive deposits of glacial till were located, one on the flank of the south valley wall immediately downstream of Dam 'B' and the second on the south side of the South Tailings Area. Although the permeability of the till, when compacted, was about 10^{-4} to 10^{-5} centimeters per second it did not meet governmental guidelines of 10^{-6} centimeters per second for "impervious" core material.

Based on the results of the pre-design investigations and considering the requirements of the draft governmental guidelines for the storage of uranium mill tailings, it was decided to construct the best (i.e. least pervious) dam consistent with good engineering practice and available borrow materials and to then incorporate into the design a synthetic impervious membrane. Several membrane materials were considered and eventually unreinforced hypalon was selected because of its ductility, ease of installation and resistance to chemical deterioration.

Where the overburden was thin (e.g. Dams 'A' and 'F') the overburden was stripped over the full base width of the dam, the surface of the exposed rock treated with "dental" or "slush" concrete beneath the core area and the dam founded directly on the rock. Where the overburden was thick (Dam 'B') or the site very restricted (Dam 'D' - a narrow "vee-notched" valley) a cut-off trench was excavated and the impervious membrane extended completely through the overburden and sealed onto the rock. In all cases, the membrane was secured to the rock by means of a concrete anchor beam and the rock was cement grouted to minimize seepage through joints and fissures.

Typical sections through Dam 'B' (sloping membrane with cut-off trench to rock) and Dam 'F' (founded on rock with a vertical membrane and concrete cut-off wall) are shown on Figure 15. Both sections incorporate a core of low permeability till, a chimney drain and a toe drain with collector (primarily for monitoring). In the case of Dam 'B', provision was made to raise the crest of the dam to accommodate the proposed future higher pond water level and the cut-off trench was located upstream of the toe of dam to permit work to proceed simultaneously on the dam and the cut-off. It is interesting to note that even with the omission of the impervious (hypalon) membrane, the total seepage through Dam 'B', the largest dam in the system, was computed to be less than 10 gallons per minute under the maximum design pond level (water level at elevation 1335).

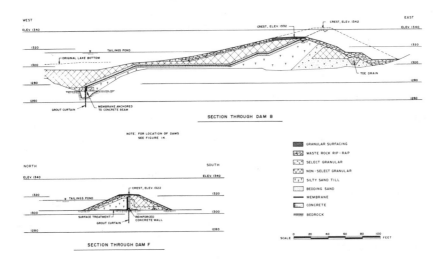

Figure 15 - Typical Sections - Dams 'B' and 'F'

Figure 16 - Installation of Hypalon Membrane - Dam 'B'

Work commenced on the freshwater diversion and on the Strike Lake containment dams (Dams 'B' and 'D') in early Spring, 1978 and the structures were completed and ready to receive tailings by the Autumn of 1978. A general view of Dam 'B' from the air showing the installation of the hypalon membrane is shown on Figure 16. The following quantities regarding this dam are interesting.

Total Volume of Earthfill	-	56,000 cubic yards
Total Area of Membrane	-	53,000 square feet
Total Length of Proof Grout Holes	-	2,250 feet
Total Volume of Grout Injected	-	114 bags

Foundation preparation for Dams 'A' and 'F' in the South Tailings Area commenced in 1978 and these dams together with the effluent treatment facility are to be completed during the Summer of 1979.

Containment Basin

As previously noted, current draft governmental guidelines suggest a maximum average basin permeability of 10^{-5} centimeters per second for a uranium mill tailings facility. This guideline is difficult to assess as it does not directly address the question of permissible seepage losses from the tailings area and, for rock rimmed basins where seepage is controlled by discrete joints and fractures in an otherwise impervious rock mass, average permeability is very difficult to measure by conventional methods.

In an attempt to establish the average basin permeability, an initial program of aerial photographic interpretation and detailed field mapping was undertaken to establish both major (e.g. faults) and minor (e.g. joints) structures around the basin. The results of this work indicated that the tailings area was located outside the sedimentary basin, the north shore of Strike Lake being composed of diorite and the remainder of the area being underlain by granite. The rock was more-or-less uniformly jointed with an average joint spacing of about 6 to 12 inches. Although the majority of the joints were steeply dipping, there was no evidence of a strong preferential seepage direction related to jointing; rather the various joint sets appeared to be uniformly distributed in strike. Although many of the joints evidenced moderate surface apertures due to stress release and surficial weathering, the results of borehole packer testing suggested that the permeability decreased rapidly with increasing depth.

As indicated on Figure 17, two major faults transect the area. The first, a regional fault known as the Nook Lake Fault strikes northwest-southeast and passes between the Strike Lake basin and the South Tailings Area. The second strikes northeast-southwest, passes under the western end of the Strike Lake basin and appears to terminate on the Nook Lake Fault.

Figure 17 - Panel Tailings Area Faults

To examine the average permeability of the rock (excluding major discontinuities) more definitively, a nearby "perched" lake which had a clearly defined catchment area and no discernible outlet was investigated (see Figure 17 for location). Careful examination indicated that while the lithology and general structure of the rock in the area of this lake were similar to that of the tailings area there were no faults. On the assumption that the rate of seepage through the rock was equal to the net precipitation falling on the basin (to maintain the "perched" lake level without overland outflow) an axisymmetric finite element flow analyses was carried out using known surrounding lake and stream levels as boundary conditions. Successive iterations indicated that the average mass permeability of the rock required to maintain the "perched" lake under average rainfall conditions was about 5×10^{-6} centimeters per second.

Using this average permeability value, the maximum proposed operating level in the Strike Lake basin, known boundary conditions and "best estimates" of the geometry (width) and permeability characteristics of the known faults, a similar analyses was carried out for the tailings management area. The results of this analyses indicated that, for normal infiltration rates, seepage would generally be INTO the basin from the surrounding rock; the only seepage out of the basin would be to the southeast and northeast along the faults and the total seepage rate would be only about 10 to 15 gallons per minute. As these computed seepage rates were considered acceptable and as there is at present serious doubt as to whether radionuclides actually migrate through a low permeability fractured rock, it was decided to monitor the faults by means of deep sampling wells rather than to institute perhaps inappropriate seepage control measures at this time.

Current Deposition Scheme

Commencement of milling operations at Panel is now scheduled for August, 1979 and, consequently, no tailings have yet been discharged into the Strike Lake basin. As a result of on-going studies a deposition scheme has been developed which involves the creation of exposed tailings beaches from elevated discharge points and the construction of internal dykes to divert tailings away from the decant at Dam 'D'. With this scheme, the maximum operating pond level in the Strike Lake basin can be maintained as low as about elevation 1316 or some 20 feet below the previously proposed maximum level. Thus, future raising of Dams 'B' and 'D' should not be necessary for current planned production.

FUTURE TAILINGS MANAGEMENT SCHEMES

To this point, typical tailings management schemes adopted in the Elliot Lake area during the mid to late 1950's have been reviewed and two specific types of seepage control measures conceived and approved in the late 1960's and in recent years have been described. As previously indicated, however, preliminary studies are currently being carried out for major expansions of both Rio Algom Limited's Quirke tailings management area and Denison Mines Limited's Long Lake tailings management area as well as for Preston Mines Limited's Stanleigh rehabilitation program.

Various schemes are being considered for these future operations; ranging from conventional impervious earthfill dams incorporating synthetic membranes (i.e. similar to the Panel scheme discussed above) to pervious "sand" dams constructed of the tailings themselves. Because of the scope of these future projects and the general lack of suitable borrow material in the area, schemes which minimize the size of perimeter containment structures (either through the use of internal "stacking" or "coning" by thickened slurry discharge methods - Robinsky, 1978 (4), or which include the use in whole or in part of mine waste rock or tailings "sands" are gaining increased favour. Further, although final solutions have yet to be defined, alternatives for abandonment are receiving increased consideration in the initial design stages.

Current thinking favours maintenance of as low a pond water level as possible and the development of long tailings beaches developed from elevated discharge points. This not only minimizes the size of the perimeter containment structures but also results in a sloped tailings surface which can be drained and stabilized upon abandonment. Although some dusting problems may result during operations, experience at Denison's Long Lake tailings area, where there is an approximately one mile long beach, indicates that the surface remains sufficiently moist to minimize dusting. If the discharge point has to be moved, however, the exposed beach could, if necessary, be temporarily stabilized by chemical or mechanical surface treatment.

The universal use of impervious containment dams is also being seriously questioned. During operations, impervious dams are not necessary if the seepage can be readily controlled, collected and treated (e.g. if the dam is located upstream of the treatment facility). Following abandonment, impervious dams may provide a false sense of security and may in fact be dangerous; the consequences of the failure of a dam retaining saturated tailings may be far more serious than the consequences of the failure of a dam retaining "drained" tailings. The fundamental question, however, is whether impervious dams are necessary or even effective at abandonment.

If the tailings are in fact perfectly isolated from surface water infiltration by a cover, as yet undefined, seepage through the pervious dams will gradually reduce over a period of a few years as the tailings drain. Thus, one would be left with essentially dry tailings producing no effluent as opposed to the "bowl of jelly" which could result with perfectly impervious dams.

If, on the other hand, the surface of the tailings is not covered by an impervious material (e.g. if the surface is vegetated) and if IMPERVIOUS dams are provided, in an area of net infiltration the water level in the tailings will rise until it overtops the dams. Thus, effluent will be produced, possibly in an uncontrolled fashion, despite the presence of the IMPERVIOUS dams. Consequently, as effluent production is inevitable, it is better to provide pervious dams so that the water can be removed in a controlled fashion and the water level in the tailings maintained at as low a level as possible.

The status of some current thinking regarding tailings management and seepage control can perhaps be best illus-trated by considering the hypothetical tailings basin illustrated on Figure 18. Assume that the site consists of a rock rimmed lake basin. Geological and hydrogeological studies indicate that, with the exception of the upper few feet, the rock is essentially impervious. Outlets from the lake flow east and west through relatively wide valleys and a stream enters the lake through a narrow valley from the southeast. The basin is separated from an environmentally sensitive river to the north by a low saddle. Treated effluent from the tailings is to be discharged through the valley to the west.

As illustrated on Figure 19, development of the basin as a tailings facility involves the construction of four dams across the topographic lows and the diversion of the inlet stream from the southeast. The basic principle of development involves discharging tailings along the north, east and south walls of the valley to form a long beach terminating in a tailings pond or pool at the west end of the site where it can be discharged to treatment. As the average slope of this beach will be about 0.5 to 1 per cent, on a major project the height of tailings at the east end of the basin (i.e. at Dam 'C') could be several tens of feet above the pond level (i.e. above the crest of Dam 'A').

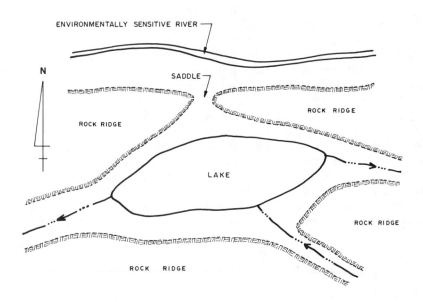

Figure 18 - Hypothetical Tailings Basin

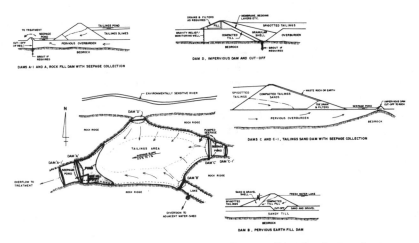

Figure 19 - Development of Hypothetical Basin

Each of the dams in this hypothetical basin serves a unique function and must be designed to meet specific criteria. Consequently, there are no engineering reasons, apart from government regulations, why they should have the same cross-section. The requirements and a possible design for each dam are discussed below.

Dam 'A'

This dam is located immediately upstream of the treatment facility and the tailings pond impinges directly against the face of the dam. In an emergency the dam could be subjected to overtopping. Thus, the dam must be stable both gravitationally and hydraulically but need not be impervious provided all of the seepage through and beneath the dam is collected and treated. Consequently, the dam may be constructed of mine waste rock provided appropriate drains and filters are incorporated into the design to control seepage and prevent migration of slimes. Seepage can be collected between the main dam and a downstream impervious but low head dam, Dam 'A-1'. To ensure that all seepage is collected, Dam 'A-1' may require a positive cut-off to rock; in this case a slurry trench diaphragm wall is illustrated. All seepage and decanted effluent collected between Dams 'A' and 'A-1' would be led to treatment.

Upon abandonment, a spillway could be constructed in Dam 'A' or it's abutment to drain the tailings pond and maintain a "dry" tailings surface.

Dam 'B'

Dam 'B' must fulfill two functions; firstly to divert fresh water into an adjacent watershed and secondly to retain tailings. If, by judicious design of the diversion, a positive head of fresh water can be maintained across the dam, the tendency will be for seepage to occur INTO rather than OUT OF the tailings area. Consequently, although seepage should be minimized, there is no need to provide an "impervious" dam. Thus, a conventional earthfill dam designed to minimize seepage as much as possible using locally available borrow material could be employed.

Dam 'C'

Dam 'C' is located at the far end of the basin from the tailings pond and will extend considerably above the pond level. Thus, overtopping of this dam is not possible.

Because of the long tailings beach, seepage at this dam will be minimal, particularly following abandonment, and, provided such seepage is collected and pumped back into the tailings area during operation, it can probably be tolerated. Construction of a tailings "sand" dam thus appears practical provided adequate filters and drains are incorporated into the design to control seepage gradients during operations. However, the use of a centreline or downstream method of construction is recommended rather than the more traditional upstream method.

Dam 'D'

At this site seepage must be completely prevented to avoid contamination of the environmentally sensitive river to the north. Consequently, an impervious dam and positive seepage barrier to rock must be provided. Although a dam incorporating a synthetic membrane and cut-off excavation to rock similar to the scheme adopted for Dam 'B; at the Panel tailings management area is illustrated on Figure 19, several alternative "impervious" dam sections are presently being studied for use at future tailings areas.

CONCLUSION

Control of seepage from the low activity tailings in the Elliot Lake area has ranged from minimal in the 1950's to, ideally, total control and long-term prevention in the 1970's. Neither extreme is necessarily correct; no control is unacceptable in the light of present technology - total long-term prevention is not practically possible in an area of high precipitation. The optimum practical solution lies somewhere between these extremes.

It must also be recognized that the control of seepage is very site specific. Not only do regional, geologic and climatic conditions affect the method of control but also the fundamental purpose and hence design of each dam within a given tailings area may be quite different.

REFERENCES

1. Atomic Energy Control Board, "Facilities for Retention of Uranium Mine-Mill Wastes", Licensing Document No. 23D, Draft No. 1, October, 1977.

2. James F. MacLaren Limited, "Environmental Assessment of the Proposed Elliot Lake Uranium Mines Expansion", prepared for Denison Mines Limited and Rio Algom Limited, March, 1977.

3. Milligan, V., Seychuk, J.L., and Turton, R.R., "Geotechnical Aspects of Disposal and Containment of Low-Level Radioactive Wastes", Proceedings of the 24th Ontario Industrial Waste Conference, Toronto, Canada, May, 1977.

4. Robinsky, E.I., "Tailings Disposal by the Thickened Discharge Method for Improved Economy and Environmental Control", Proceedings of the Second International Tailings Symposium, Denver, Colorado, May, 1978.

35

Groundwater Contamination Problems Resulting from Coal Refuse Disposal

by Jeffrey P. Schubert,
Land Reclamation Program,
Argonne National Laboratory,
Argonne, Illinois, USA

ABSTRACT

An inherent problem in the disposal of solid waste on land is the possibility of groundwater contamination by leachates from the waste. In the few studies conducted on the effects of coal refuse disposal on groundwater quality, significant impacts have been observed. Based on past and present rates of coal refuse disposal and current knowledge of water chemistry of runoff and seeps from refuse piles, significant groundwater contamination may be occurring in the eastern and midwestern United States.

Following a review of previous studies and a discussion of water quality problems related to coal refuse disposal, results from a three-year investigation of an orphan disposal site in southwestern Illinois are discussed. Although the coal refuse lay unreclaimed at the site for over 50 years, contamination of groundwater from acid leachate extended less than 200 m from the gob pile in the underlying calcareous, silty-clay till. Reclamation of the site in 1977 did not have immediate effects upon groundwater quality, but long-term changes are likely to occur. Slightly increased infiltration into the gob pile is causing greater flows of acid seeps from the base of the pile, which may be hindering plant growth and increasing erosion of soil cover around the base. Further hydrologic and geochemical research is needed to assess the full magnitude of groundwater contamination problems related to coal refuse disposal at other sites and to develop disposal and reclamation criteria that are practical and effective in preserving long-term water quality at disposal sites.

COAL REFUSE AND ITS DISPOSAL

Because coal often contains a considerable amount of rock and mineral matter, a significant proportion of coal mined in the United States is cleaned prior to use. Thinner seams, higher pyrite and shale content, and greater percentage of underground mining of eastern and midwestern U.S. coals require more of this coal to be cleaned than in the West. In 1974, about 574 million metric tons (574 Mt) of coal were produced in the U.S. Of that amount, approximately 60% (330 Mt) underwent mechanical cleaning, resulting in 89 Mt of coal refuse (1). In 1975, about 97.2 Mt of refuse were created (2).

Coarse refuse is separated from coal at preparation facilities by some form of density separation and consists primarily of carbonaceous shale, pyritic coal, pyrite lenses and nodules, claystone, and some sandstone and limestone. Until recent enactment of state and federal coal waste disposal regulations and guidelines, selections of disposal methods and sites were usually determined by convenience and economic considerations, with little or no thought given to long-term environmental consequences (3). Dumping usually occurred adjacent to preparation plants, which often was down the nearest hillside or into the nearest stream valley. Refuse piles can cover areas from less than 1 ha to more than 400 ha, range from 3 m to more than 100 m in height or depth, and occupy a volume up to 1,200,000 m^3 (4).

The fine coal and mineral matter suspended in the washwater slurry is pumped from coal cleaning facilities into impoundments where the sediment is allowed to settle; the clarified water is then decanted or pumped from the ponds. There are two common types of slurry impoundments: a) large shallow ponds enclosed by low levees and ground irregularities, and usually located in level to gently rolling terrain, and b) deep impoundments located behind relatively high dams constructed across stream valleys and ravines in hilly country. Slurry material can contain significant quantities of fine coal, with the remainder generally consisting of sand, shale fragments, silt, clay, and some pyrite. When abandoned, the dams or berms of the ponds gradually erode, are often breached, and erosion of the slurry materials can ensue.

The number of sizable active or abandoned waste piles and impoundments in the eastern U.S. alone is conservatively estimated to be 3000 to 5000, containing over 3000 Mt of refuse (5). The U.S. Bureau of Mines (6) has estimated that over 80,000 ha in the U.S. have been used for the disposal of coal-processing wastes during the period 1930-1971, with only 10,700 ha having been reclaimed. More than 1050 ha of gob and 660 ha of slurry material in Indiana (7) and approximately 2480 ha of gob and 1630 ha of slurry material in Illinois (8,9) presently lie unreclaimed. Past coal refuse disposal sites, in most cases, were neither properly designed nor reclaimed because state and federal requirements governing such activities were lacking.

The environmental problems associated with coal refuse disposal sites are many: sliding, dam failures, burning piles, acid water, siltation of streams and reservoirs, and land property devaluation. Because of pyrite oxidation and dissolution, acid water formation is ubiquitous and difficult to control at most refuse disposal sites in the eastern and midwestern U.S. Rainfall and snowmelt on the refuse areas result in continuous or intermittent effluents due to direct surface runoff and percolation of water through the refuse. Table I is a summary of water quality data collected by several investigators at coal refuse sites throughout the East and Midwest. The pH is generally low and values of most listed parameters are quite high. The differences between surface water quality (ponds, surface runoff, and seeps combined) and seep water quality are not significant. The acidic discharges from unreclaimed disposal sites usually are a serious detriment to water quality and aquatic biota in receiving streams, and numerous reports and papers document these impacts.

Table No. I

Water Quality of Runoff and Seeps from Coal Refuse Piles in the Eastern and Midwestern U.S.

Location	Refuse Type[a]	Water Type[b]	No. of Samples	pH[c]	Acidity	Specific Conductance	SO$_4^=$	Fe	Mn	Al	Zn	Source of Data
Illinois	G	Su	41	2.6	3500	4200	3900	430	17	200		(8)
Illinois	S	Su	21	2.4	2600	4400	3500	510	14	170		(8)
Macoupin Co., Ill.	G,S	Su	36	2.8	11475		9465	3310	41			(10)
		Su	7-11									(10)
New Kathleen Mine, Ill.	G	Su	>200	2.2	13520	12740	14340	3860			41.7	(11)
Pennsylvania	G,S	Su	7	2.9	13294	7516	15535	2304	103	515		(12)
West Virginia	G,S	Su	4	3.1		8550	6328	1367	43	73	0.2	(13)
Kentucky	G	Su	3	2.5		3947	4715	1344	34	231	3.8	(13)
Indiana	G	Su	3	2.5		6263	8720	2129	35	112	4.4	(13)
Macoupin Co., Ill.	G,S	Sp	5	3.1	6280		2891	3757				(10)
New Kathleen Mine, Ill.	G	Sp	>120	2.5	19062	16158	20641	5991				(11)
Pana, Ill.	G	Sp	3-6	3.7		3700	5787	1867	703	260	4.3	(14)
Pennsylvania	G	Sp	2	3.0,4.1			2300	15.3	70	68	2.6	(13)
West Virginia	G	Sp	1	4.9		5000	3800	260	9	3.6	0.2	(13)
Kentucky	G	Sp	2	3.8,6.9		1080	878	4.3	5.8	35.9	0.6	(13)
Indiana	G	Sp	1	2.3		1200	15000	4500	56			(13)

[a]G -- gob; S -- slurry material

[b]Su -- surface water (runoff, ponds, and seeps combined); Sp -- seeps and springs only

[c]Median pH in standard units; mean specific conductance in μmhos/cm at 25°C; other parameters are mean values in mg/L.

With ponded water commonly found at disposal sites (8) and moderate permeabilities in coal refuse, substantial amounts of acid water could be seeping into the subsurface. At the New Kathleen site in Illinois, it was determined that about 20% to 60% of rainfall infiltrated into the unreclaimed coal refuse (15,16). Thus, there exists a definite potential for groundwater contamination near coal refuse disposal sites, but no studies as yet have seriously addressed this possibility in the U.S.

Libicki (17) has reported on two disposal sites in Poland. Approximately 1500 m^3 of gob and fly ash were disposed of at the first site overlying a shallow sand aquifer, and 11 monitoring wells were installed within and around the disposal area. At the second disposal site, a total of 500,000 m^3 of gob were placed in a pit at a rate of 20,000 to 30,000 m^3/month, and fourteen monitoring wells were installed in sand and gravel around the pit. Total dissolved minerals in the shallow aquifer beneath the first site began to increase two months after disposal operations began. Initially, increases in pollutant concentration were related to intensity of precipitation, indicating episodic pulses of water percolating down through the disposal pit. Migration of dissolved constituents down-gradient of the pit was clearly evident after seven months. The following parameters were seen to increase in water down-gradient of the first site as compared to ambient water quality: specific conductance, total dissolved solids, chloride, sulfate, sodium, potassium, calcium, magnesium, ammonium, phosphate, cyanide, phenols, cadmium, strontium, copper, molybdenum, and boron. No noticeable increases in iron, manganese, aluminum, or chromium occurred, nor were there any apparent changes in pH. Observed impacts to groundwater quality at the second site, where only gob was dumped, were similar. Increases in molybdenum, strontium, and cyanide did not occur, but increased concentrations of aluminum, chromium, and iron were observed.

In the Yorkshire coalfield of England, Nicholls (18) reported the steady gradual decline of water quality in a public water supply well about 700 m from an active colliery gob pile and slurry pond. The very extensive gob pile was deposited across an outcrop of the Bunter Sandstone aquifer and onto sand and gravel deposits overlying the sandstone, thus enabling seepage water to easily percolate into the aquifer from which the well obtained its water. Table II shows water quality in the slurry pond, seeps from gob, and the well water over a period of nearly 50 years.

Table No. II
Effects of Coal Refuse Disposal on a
Well in Yorkshire Coalfield, England (18)

	Slurry Pond Water	Gob Seepage	Well Water			
			1919	1925	1933	1965
Total Hardness[a]	1090	--	126	163	414	2060
Sodium	1200	1750-3400	--	--	--	--
Chloride	2550	1300-3000	12.9	25.7	337	2925
Sulfate	480	2600-5500	--	--	--	--

[a]All values in mg/L.

Judging by the seepage water chemistry (e.g., near-neutral pH and relatively low concentrations of iron and manganese) of these European examples, the coal refuse at those disposal sites probably had very low pyrite content. In Canada and the western U.S., however, there are examples where seepage waters from sulfide-ore mineral wastes are extremely low in pH; in some of these cases, contamination of groundwater quality has been documented (19,20,21,22,23,24,25,26).

In 1975, the Illinois General Assembly created the Abandoned Mined Lands Reclamation Council to designate high-priority abandoned mined lands to be acquired and reclaimed by the state and to establish priorities to guide the selection process. Pennsylvania and other states have taken similar steps to reclaim abandoned lands where mining companies are not held responsible for environmental problems (e.g., Operation Scarlift Projects in Pennsylvania). With the enactment of the Surface Mining Control and Reclamation Act of 1977 (P.L. 95-87) by the federal government, funding and administration for the reclamation of abandoned lands has been delegated to the Abandoned Mine Land Reclamation Program and Rural Abandoned Mine Program of the Office of Surface Mining. Because acid drainage is a major problem at many disposal sites, reclamation techniques are needed to effectively control water movement and quality in pyritic mine spoils and coal refuse. To date, however, very little field research has been conducted to determine moisture movement, percolation, subsurface pyrite oxidation, leaching processes, or groundwater pollutant transport and attenuation mechanisms relative to this particular problem.

To assess the nature and magnitude of water quality problems resulting from an abandoned unreclaimed coal refuse disposal area, hydrologic and water quality monitoring began in November 1975 at a site near Staunton, Illinois, approximately 66 km northeast of St. Louis, Missouri. Six months after the investigation was initiated, reconstruction and reclamation of the site was begun in accordance with design and engineering plans developed by Argonne National Laboratory's Land Reclamation Program. This work included grading and liming of the coal refuse, covering with a calcareous, silty-clay till, and fertilizing and seeding the project area (27,28). Thus, it was possible to study not only the groundwater quality problems attributable to an unreclaimed "orphan" refuse disposal area, but also any modifications to the hydrologic system and changes in water quality (both surface water and groundwater) brought about by the reclamation activities. Only the groundwater aspects of the research program will be discussed in this paper.

DESCRIPTION OF DISPOSAL SITE

The Consolidated Coal Company Mine No. 14 opened in 1904 and operated until about 1924. Underground mining of the 1.8-m-thick Herrin (No. 6) coal, and crude cleaning operations near the mine mouth resulted in the accumulation of a large gob pile (about 25 m high and 1.8 ha in area) and 4.5 ha of slurry material north of the pile (Fig. 1). Extreme erosion occurred on the site in the 50 years following mine closure; the gob pile had deep gulleys cut into its steep sides and a large quantity of sediment had washed into adjoining lowland areas. The impoundment dam was breached by erosion, and runoff water from the entire site gradually wore down the low point in the dam, resulting in cliffs of exposed slurry material as much as 4.5 m in height. During rainstorms a portion of runoff water from the gob pile flowed into lowland areas surrounding the pile and underwent extended periods of evaporation and infiltration.

The disposal site before reclamation, showing locations of wells. Figure No. 1.

Between September 1976 and April 1977, the coal refuse was graded to gentle slopes. Ground agricultural limestone (175 t of $CaCO_3$ equivalent/ ha) was then disked into the gob material and a mixture of limestone and quicklime (175 t of $CaCO_3$ equivalent/ha) was disked into the slurry material. A 0.3-m layer of calcareous, silty-clay till was then placed over the regraded refuse material and the area was fertilized and seeded (Fig. 2). The earth dam of the slurry impoundment was reconstructed and a 0.5 ha pond was excavated at the north end of the disposal site, primarily to reduce peak runoff flow and sediment transport from the site. Additional details of the reclamation project are described by Zellmer (27) and Wilkey and Zellmer (28).

PRE-RECLAMATION GROUNDWATER QUALITY

Light rainfalls produced little or no runoff at the Staunton site prior to reclamation and intermittent seeps were observed at the base of the gob pile and slurry material. Thus, clear evidence was available that some

View of the reclaimed disposal site looking north.
Figure No. 2.

degree of saturated conditions existed at the base of the refuse materials. Heavy incrustations of metal sulfate and oxyhydroxide minerals formed where seep waters evaporated.

Twenty-two shallow (< 4.6 m) monitoring wells were installed in the glacial till surrounding the refuse pile and slurry area, and five wells were placed in the saturated slurry material (Fig. 1). Within 0.6 km of the refuse site, residents rely on shallow, hand dug wells and one drilled well for their water supplies. In addition to the 27 wells installed at the refuse site, 13 residential wells were monitored during the prereclamation study.

Pumping tests are planned for the future, but is is already apparent that the permeability of the till is low throughout most of the site area. All monitoring wells were bailed prior to sampling and recovery rates were low. In some cases, several weeks were required for a well to recover two to three meters. Most of the residential wells also had low specific capacities and poor recovery rates after heavy use. A few wells, however, exhibited greater permeability (e.g., M19) and the reasons for this are to be investigated further. A few thin, discontinuous sand lenses in the till were found in the north part of the site and may serve as zones of increased permeability. Jointing and fractures in the till may also provide avenues of increased groundwater flow (29). The water table in the till was generally less than 3 m below the land surface near the refuse pile and sloped gently away from the pile in all directions. For the entire area, however, the water table in the glacial material sloped toward the north and northwest (30).

Chemical analyses of water samples collected from monitoring and residential wells during 1976 before site reclamation are summarized in Table III. The wells are grouped in the table according to similarity of location and water chemistry. In an area less than 30 m from the north, west, and south sides of the gob pile (well group A), the median groundwater pH was 3.10 and ranged from 6.38 down to 2.27; the average acidity was 4000 mg/L. Concentrations of sulfate and most dissolved metals were extremely high and some parameters exceeded recommended drinking water standards by several orders of magnitude.

Well Group	A	B	C	D	E	F	G	H
No. of Samples	10	7	5	15	3	3	3	16
Spec. Cond[b]	19921	2489	2847	4249	2956	3954	8373	1696
Median pH	3.10	6.40	5.60	6.50	6.80	4.35	6.85	7.64
Min. pH	2.30	6.20	3.20	4.00	6.70	4.00	6.84	7.10
Acidity	4076	37.3	207	67.8	77.0	1784	76	22.3
Max. Acidity	31400	62	660	372	124	2604	105	59.8
Alkalinity	142	131	64	135	376	4.4	435	268
Bicarbonate	173	160	78.4	165	459	5.3	531	327
Sulfate	6330	329	1255	1064	856	3596	1719	433
Calcium[c]	490	88.5	438	249	304	435	500	137
Magnesium	246	41.9	80.4	108	69.5	149	279	70.1
Sodium	263	61	26.3	120	235	91	117	53.6
Potassium	15.9	0.3	4.0	1.3	14.1	17.2	0.8	3.88
Strontium	1.5	<.5	0.7	0.5	2.9	5.3	0.6	<.5
Aluminum	414	<.02	19.4	2.57	<.1	61.7	.06	<.5
Cadmium	1.00	<.01	.09	.01	<.01	.01	<.01	<.01
Chromium	.46	<.02	<.02	<.02	<.02	<.02	<.02	<.02
Copper	1.22	<.01	.05	<.02	<.02	<.02	<.02	<.02
Iron	1367	.24	119	2.61	6.89	933	.21	.039
Max. Iron	6010	.77	560	24.9	12.9	1840	.35	.20
Manganese	24.2	.45	9.28	7.26	.55	16.9	.16	.26
Max. Mn	62	.74	18.6	51	.80	41.0	.29	1.26
Nickel	1.52	<.02	.25	.094	.03	.81	.03	<.02
Zinc	59.0	.02	6.64	.734	.096	28.4	.097	.192
Max. Zinc	252	.05	23	10.4	.115	40.5	.104	1.95

[a]All chemical parameters are reported as mean concentrations, except pH
which is a median; minimum pH and maximum acidity, iron, manganese, and
zinc are also reported for most well groups.

[b]Specific conductance is reported as mhos/cm at 25°C, pH in standard
units, acidity and alkalinity as mg/L $CaCO_3$ equivalence, and other
parameters are reported in mg/L.

[c]Dissolved cations were analyzed from filtered, acidified samples.

Well Group Locations - Pre-Reclamation Monitoring

A. < 30 m from N, S, and W side of gob pile (M6,M7,M11,M12,M13).

B. < 30 m from E side of gob pile (M1,M2).

C. 30-60 m SW and W of gob pile (M10,M14,M15,M16,M17,M18).

D. 60-190 m S of gob pile (M3,M4,M5,M8,M9).

E. In saturated slurry material away from main drainage channel (M24,M26).

F. In saturated slurry material near main drainage channel (M22,M23).

G. Located in alluvium downstream of disposal site (M27).

H. All residential wells (R1 through R13).

Of particular concern were the concentrations of aluminum, cadmium, chromium, iron, manganese, and zinc. At distances of 30 to 60 m south and west of the gob pile (well group C), the groundwater had a median pH of 5.60, average acidity of 207 mg/L, and lower levels of most major and minor constituents relative to group A wells. Concentrations of aluminum, iron, cadmium, manganese, and zinc, however, were still much higher than the residential wells of the area (group H). Groundwater on the southeast, south, and west sides of the pile could have been contaminated by groundwater migration from the pile (subsurface transport) and surface water running off the pile and ponding in lowland areas (surface transport) with subsequent infiltration. Both processes were occurring, but the relative importance of each has not yet been quantified.

At distances greater than 60 m southeast, south, and west of the pile (well group D), concentrations of acidity and most dissolved metals were greatly reduced. However, moderately high specific conductance, acidity, sulfate, aluminum, iron, manganese, and zinc persisted in a few wells at distances up to 200 m from the pile. Water quality in the field east of the pile (well group B and well R2) was alkaline with low concentrations of sulfate and most metals (iron and manganese were slightly high). Based on data from the pre-reclamation monitoring wells, shallow groundwater quality was not significantly affected at distances greater than 200 m south and west of the gob pile and 30 m east of the pile. The till underlying the gob pile had a low permeability and the hydraulic gradient of the water table was also low; therefore, flow velocity of groundwater was low and transport distance of contaminants was not great. As the acid leachate flowed through the calcareous till, neutralization of the water took place and precipitation of metals probably occurred. An insufficient number of wells were located north of the pile to determine groundwater quality patterns in this direction.

Groundwater in the saturated slurry material exhibited diverse chemistries. Water in slurry material adjacent to the drainage channel leading away from the gob pile (well group F) had concentrations of acidity, metals, and sulfate similar to acid surface drainage from the pile. Monitoring wells in slurry material located farther away from the main drainage channel (group E) had water with much lower specific conductance, sulfate, and metal concentrations, and a net alkalinity. This suggests that surface water draining from the gob pile area was recharging the slurry material along the main channel. Well M27 (group G), located in the alluvium of the drainage channel leading away from the site (see Fig. 1), had water with a high specific conductance, high alkalinity, and high concentrations of calcium and magnesium relative to residential wells and relative to the surface drainage water. This indicates groundwater discharge, rather than recharge, along the streambed, thus causing dilution and neutralization of acid water in the stream (30).

Water in residential wells (group H) within 0.6 km of the disposal site contained primarily calcium, magnesium, sodium, sulfate, and bicarbonate ions (a normal assemblage for this area) and low concentrations of transition and heavy metals. The presence of zinc in some wells was probably due to the use of galvanized steel pipes in the wells.

POST-RECLAMATION GROUNDWATER QUALITY

All of the pre-reclamation monitoring wells except M19 and M27 were destroyed during the reclamation activities. In 1977, 45 new monitoring wells were drilled in the study area: 10 in the reclaimed gob pile, 16 in the till surrounding the gob pile, 12 in the slurry material, and 7 in the till surrounding the slurry area (Fig. 3). The wells range in depth from 2 m to 12 m. Monitoring of water levels and collection of samples from the 45 new monitoring wells, 2 pre-reclamation monitoring wells, and 15 residential wells was performed twice in 1978 (spring and fall) and once in 1979 (winter). More monitoring wells and a better distribution of wells allowed for a more complete study of the groundwater system following reclamation. Chemical analyses of 1978 well samples are summarized in Table IV.

Ten monitoring wells (group I) were drilled to the base of the reclaimed gob pile and showed a saturated zone of 0.4 to 4.7 m. Originally, it was assumed that grading the pile and reducing the steep slopes would greatly increase infiltration rates into the pile, but no significant changes in the basal saturated zone have yet been observed. The saturated basal zone has a large

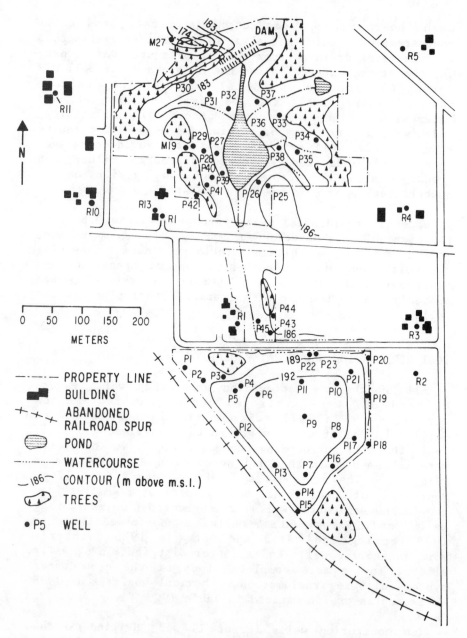

Locations of wells after reclamation.   Figure No. 3.

Average[a] Post-Reclamation Groundwater Quality

Well Group	I	J	K	L	M	N	O	P	Q
No. of Samples	20	12	15	6	19	17	2	1	29
Spec. Cond[b]	16559	9172	4825	3054	2793	2869	7526	2447	1362
Median pH	4.30	4.94	6.50	6.88	6.93	6.90	5.05	6.90	7.09
Min. pH	2.56	3.22	4.26	6.70	6.38	6.51	—	--	6.32
Acidity	15209	9290	1373	67.7	156	168	3820	74.4	44.2
Max. Acidity	89775	68040	12380	108	443	402	—	--	114
Alkalinity	42	203	186	212	498	539	88	484	212
Bicarbonate	51	248	227	259	607	658	108	590	259
Boron	3.86	2.37	.74	.24	1.04	.42	2.87	.80	.68
Chloride	39	24	53	22	59	37	40	69	26
Sulfate	21745	8012	3946	1414	853	1303	5800	475	600
Silica	226	64.4	27.3	21.6	18.3	18.7	36.1	10.2	17.9
Calcium[c]	421	477	411	376	233	339	468	202	202
Magnesium	919	646	575	205	129	263	469	123	104
Sodium	630	363	192	229	262	172	327	209	80
Potassium	51.3	18.7	3.2	2.79	5.71	5.30	8.03	<.5	3.27
Strontium	1.47	.66	.84	.72	1.37	.79	.50	<.3	.68
Aluminum	2104	873	14.6	<.05	.041	.77	62.5	.20	<.10
Arsenic	.631	.369	.0047	.0030	.0020	.0008	.018	.0008	<.002
Barium	.169	.0477	.0182	.0190	.0265	.0240	.0132	.0215	.0178
Cadmium	3.06	.904	.051	.006	<.005	.006	.021	.008	<.010
Cobalt	1.90	1.06	1.17	.027	.025	.038	.360	.040	.034
Chromium	.817	.336	.012	<.01	<.02	<.02	.01	.02	.04
Copper	.189	.119	.030	.010	.006	.013	.052	<.01	<.01
Iron	4172	1940	444	.613	6.39	1.74	937	.60	1.20
Max. Iron	14170	11100	4800	2.03	30.1	11.27	--	--	12.0
Manganese	82.7	60.1	90.6	2.11	4.59	3.14	30.0	.20	.20
Max. Mn	329	194	645	2.34	10.8	12.6	--	--	1.68
Nickel	6.56	3.39	1.26	.04	.02	.06	.97	.06	.01
Lead	.393	.254	.125	.070	.045	.093	.130	.030	.042
Zinc	322	136	22.5	.020	.019	.105	34.6	.230	.083
Max. Zinc	1465	825	245	.044	.073	.700	--	--	.590

[a]All chemical parameters are reported as mean concentrations, except pH which is a median; minimum pH and maximum acidity, iron, manganese, and zinc are also reported for most well groups.

[b]Specific conductance is reported as mhos/cm at 25°C, pH in standard units, acidity and alkalinity as mg/L $CaCO_3$ equivalence, and other parameters are reported in mg/L.

[c]Dissolved cations were analyzed from filtered, acidified samples.

Well Group Locations - Post-Reclamation Monitoring

I.   In base of gob material (P5-P11,P14,P21,P23).

J.   In till beneath or < 5 m from gob pile (P4,P13,P16,P17,P22,P24).

K.   5-30 m from gob pile (P3,P12,P15,P18,P19,P20,P43).

L.   > 30 m W and N of gob pile (P1,P2,P44).

M.   In saturated slurry material (P27,P28,P31,P32,P36-P41).

N.   In till around slurry material (P25,P26,P29,P30,P33-35,P42,M19).

O.   In saturated slurry material < 5 m from main drainage channel (P45).

P.   In alluvium downstream of disposal site (M27).

Q.   All residential wells (R1 through R15).

diversity of water quality characteristics, with pH varying between 2.56 and 6.46 and specific conductance between 2700 and 36,900 μmhos/cm. In general, the basal water has a low pH (< 4.30) and very high concentrations of acidity, boron, sulfate, silica, and dissolved cations. Particularly high are magnesium, sodium, aluminum, cadmium, cobalt, chromium, iron, manganese, nickel, and zinc. Also found in high concentrations are lead and arsenic, which were not analyzed during pre-reclamation studies. Groundwater in till beneath the pile or less than 5 m from the pile (well group J) has slightly higher pH, lower acidity, lower specific conductance, and concentrations of most ionic constituents of about one-half that found in the refuse leachate. At distances of 5 m to 30 m from the pile (well group K), a marked improvement in water quality is noticeable. At distances greater than 30 m west and north of the pile (well group L), groundwater in the till approaches the average residential well quality (well group Q) with the exception of sulfate, sodium, and manganese, which are moderately higher.

During grading of the pile at the beginning of the reclamation phase, the refuse was spread over a larger area, thereby covering most of the area southeast, south, and west of the former pile where groundwater was contaminated. Post-reclamation wells P15 and P18 (within 30 m south of the new pile edge) are in an area that formerly had relatively good water quality, but now show preliminary signs of acidification since the reclamation project. It is likely that the groundwater quality in this area will take several years to readjust to the new physical and hydrological conditions.

Since the reconstruction of the dam and the filling of the new pond with low-acidity water, groundwater levels in the slurry material (well group M) have risen and groundwater quality has greatly improved, with only boron, sodium, iron, and manganese slightly elevated above ambient levels (residential wells). The average water quality for these wells is very similar to that of the group E pre-reclamation slurry wells. The exception is well P45 (group O), located near the center of the site next to the drainage channel. As in some of the pre-reclamation slurry wells (group F), the water quality of this well reflects the acid water chemistry in the channel leading from the pile and indicates that the slurry material is being recharged to some extent from the channel.

Downstream of the dam in the channel alluvium, monitoring well M27 (group P) has lower concentrations of most constituents relative to pre-reclamation conditions (group G). This may be due either to seasonal effects and time of the single sample collection or to the large reduction of total dissolved solids in the site discharge which is mixing with groundwater in the alluvium downstream of the site.

Water quality of residential wells (group Q) has not changed significantly since reclamation of the disposal site. Although quite hard and high in sulfate in some cases, the residential wells do not appear to have been affected by either coal refuse disposal or site reclamation. Residential well R1 is closest to the disposal site (Fig. 3) and has only slightly higher concentrations of acidity, boron, sulfate, and calcium relative to other residential wells.

SUMMARY OF SITE INVESTIGATION

Groundwater quality within 60 m of the gob pile has not improved since reclamation and, in some cases, has declined because the pile was spread over a larger area. Although not yet quantified, it also appears that an increased amount of water infiltrating into the top and side terraces of the pile is causing greater flow of acid water seeping from the base of the pile and probably increased recharge of groundwater by the leachate. Concentrations of acidity and most metals in groundwater decrease with distance away from the pile and approach ambient levels at a distance of less than 200 m. Surface flow of acidic water to lowland areas around the pile may have been a significant transport mechanism in the spread of contaminants to the groundwater system.

Groundwater quality has greatly improved in the reclaimed slurry area (north part of site) because the acid drainage from the gob pile is now diluted and partially neutralized in the pond to create improved surface water quality. Interchange of water between the pond and the saturated slurry material, therefore, may be improving the groundwater quality. Also, with creation of the pond, water levels have risen in the slurry material and may be reducing the subsurface oxidation rate of pyrite by the exclusion of atmospheric oxygen.

It appears that neither coal refuse disposal at the site in the early 1900's nor the recent reclamation project have altered the relatively good water quality in residential wells within 0.6 km of the site. Well R1, located closest to the site, may have slightly higher concentrations of acidity, boron, sulfate, and calcium than the "average" residential well, but further investigation is necessary to determine if the well intercepts groundwater from the disposal site.

NEEDS FOR FURTHER RESEARCH

Water samples collected from the saturated base of a coal refuse (gob) pile can be extremely acidic and contain very high concentrations of boron, sulfate, and transition and heavy metals. Although the coal refuse lay unreclaimed at the Staunton site for over 50 years, the spread of contaminants in the shallow groundwater system occurred only in an area within 200 m from the pile and adjacent to the channel that carried surface water from the gob pile. However, at other sites in the country where coal refuse has been deposited on sand and gravel (e.g., glacial outwash material or alluvium) or in areas where bedrock aquifers are exposed at the surface, the greater permeabilities of these materials could permit impacts to groundwater systems much greater than those observed at the Staunton site. Such cases are of concern and should be investigated further.

The mechanisms of retardation or attenuation of contaminants as coal refuse leachate travels through the groundwater system are important processes that must be better understood. The mobility of the contaminants may be controlled by a variety of adsorption processes (e.g., cation exchange and adsorption by colloids, amorphous hydrous metal oxides, and organic matter), precipitation, and coprecipitation. These processes have been investigated for nuclear waste disposal sites (29,31) and municipal refuse disposal sites (32,33,34). A study of reactions between acid coal mine water and a variety of soils in Pennsylvania showed that higher values of base saturation, cation exchange capacity, pH, and $CaCO_3$

equivalent of the soils resulted in greater amounts of acidity, iron, zinc, aluminum, copper, and manganese being removed from the mine water (35). In addition, specific conductance of the water was reduced by reactions with the soil, indicating that precipitation of dissolved species, as well as cation exchange and adsorption phenomena, was occurring. With a better understanding of these processes, future disposal sites can be chosen with sufficient carbonate content and adsorption capacity to adequately retard contaminant migration.

Studies involving the movement of water within the piles are also recommended. Future plans for this research project include investigation of infiltration, moisture movement, and percolation of water through unreclaimed and reclaimed refuse material. It is apparent that water is perching on the gob-soil cover interface within the reclaimed gob pile at Staunton. Chemical bonding by the ground limestone or a textural discontinuity at that interface may be the cause. Subsurface movement of water along the interface on the sides of the gob pile may have contributed to sloughing, piping failure, and increased erosion of the soil cover on some areas of the hillsides.

One question that arises and may take many years to answer is whether the covering of coal refuse with a soil layer will control the subsurface oxidation and leaching of pyrite. At present, substantial amounts of soluble sulfate salts are present within the Staunton refuse pile and will produce an acid leachate for a considerable length of time. Theoretically, if pyrite oxidation is eliminated by reclamation, then the acidity of the leachate will gradually diminish as the salts are flushed from the pile. However, if the oxidation process is continuing, then the leaching of acid, metals, and sulfate from the refuse will persist. At some active coal refuse disposal sites, where concurrent reclamation is taking place, seeps from the refuse have been reported to be neutral to slightly alkaline. Whether this is common and whether reclamation techniques can effectively prevent acid leachate formation under long-term situations should receive further scrutiny.

The projected growth of coal production and cleaning will result in an estimated 155 Mt of coal refuse being produced annually by 1985 (36). Present and future disposal sites will be regulated through the Office of Surface Mining and state agencies. In addition, the possible classification of coal refuse as a hazardous or special waste under provisions of the Resource Conservation and Recovery Act of 1976 could lead to additional disposal regulations by the U.S. EPA. Also, the Office of Surface Mining, together with state organizations, will undertake numerous reclamation projects, costing millions of dollars, to correct hazards and environmental problems associated with abandoned disposal sites. With additional research into the hydrology and geochemistry of these disposal sites, valuable information may be used to develop reclamation techniques that will reduce infiltration, pyrite oxidation, and acid leachate formation, as well as identify siting criteria that will maximize retardation of contaminants as they travel through groundwater flow systems. From the research currently being conducted at the Staunton research site, it appears that future coal refuse disposal will not present significant groundwater problems if located on a calcareous, low to moderately permeable material, and if reclamation is carried out according to current regulations.

ACKNOWLEDGMENTS

P. F. Prodan, J. E. Edkins, and G. M. Kaszynski were of invaluable assistance during the installation of monitoring wells and collection of water samples. Analyses of samples were conducted by M. M. Master, M. W. Findlay, and several others of the Geosciences Laboratory, Argonne National Laboratory. S. D. Zellmer was instrumental in managing the multidisciplinary scientific and engineering activities at the site. A. Baltas typed the manuscript and is gratefully acknowledged. Funding for this research has been provided by the U.S. Department of Energy, Office of Health and Environmental Research (contract no. W-31-109-Eng-38), Illinois Institute of Natural Resources (Project No. 80.043), and the Abandoned Mined Lands Reclamation Council, Capital Development Board, State of Illinois (Project No. 555-090-004), and is gratefully appreciated.

REFERENCES

1. Westerstrom, L. W., and Harris, R. E., "Coal -- Bituminous and Lignite," preprint from Minerals Yearbook, 1974, U.S. Bureau of Mines, 1975, 57 pp.

2. U.S. Bureau of Mines, "Minerals Yearbook, 1975; Volume I, Metals, Minerals, and Fuels," U.S. Govt. Printing Office, Washington, D.C., 1977.

3. Wahler, W. A., "Coal Refuse Regulations, Standards, Criteria, and Guidelines," Proc. First Symp. on Mine Preparation Plant Refuse Disposal, Natl. Coal Assn./BCR, Inc., Louisville, Ky., Oct. 22-24, 1974, pp. 128-144.

4. McNay, L. M., "Coal Refuse Fires, An Environmental Hazard," U.S. Bureau of Mines, Information Circular 8515, 1971.

5. National Academy of Sciences, "Underground Disposal of Coal Mine Wastes," Report to the National Science Foundation, Washington, D.C., 1975, 172 pp.

6. Paone, J., Morning, J. L., and Giorgetti, L., "Land Utilization and Reclamation in the Mining Industry," U.S. Bureau of Mines, Inf. Circ. 8642, 1974, 61 pp.

7. Wobber, F. J., Wier, C. E., Leshendok, T., and Beeman, W., "Survey of Coal Refuse Banks and Slurry Ponds for the Indiana State Legislature Using Aerial and Orbital Inventory Techniques," Proc. First Symp. on Mine And Preparation Plant Refuse Disposal, Natl. Coal Assn./ BCR, Inc., Louisville, Ky., Oct. 22-24, 1974, pp. 64-77.

8. Nawrot, J. R., Haynes, R. J., Purcell, P. L., D'Antuono, J. R., Sullivan, R. L., and Klimstra, W. D., "Illinois Lands Affected by Underground Mining for Coal," Report to Illinois Inst. for Environ. Quality, IIEQ Doc. No. 77/11, March 1977, 195 pp.

9. Haynes, R. J., and Klimstra, W. D., "Some Properties of Coal Spoilbank and Refuse Materials Resulting From Surface-Mining Coal in Illinois," Rept. to Illinois Inst. for Environ. Quality, IIEQ Doc. No. 75-21, October 1975, 126 pp.

10. Illinois Environmental Protection Agency, unpublished reports and data, 1967-1974.

11. Barthauer, G. L., Kosowski, Z. V., and Ramsey, J. P., "Control of Mine Drainage From Coal Mine Mineral Wastes; Phase I -- Hydrology and Related Experiments," U.S. EPA, Water Pollution Control Research Series, Ret. 14010 DDH 08/71, August 1971, 148 pp.

12. Zavel, F. J., and Robins, J. D., "Water Infiltration Control to Achieve Mine Water Pollution Control," U.S. EPA, Office of Research and Monitoring, Rept. EPA-R2-73-142, January 1973, 185 pp.

13. Martin, J. F., "Quality of Effluents from Coal Refuse Piles," Proc. First Symp. on Mine and Preparation Plant Refuse Disposal, Natl. Coal Assn./BCR, Inc., Louisville, Ky., Oct. 22-24, 1974, p. 26-37.

14. Sukthumrong, A., "The Role of Earth Cover Depths and Upward Acid Diffusion on the Survival and Distribution of Vegetation on Coal Refuse Piles," unpublished Ph.D. dissertation, University of Illinois, Urbana, 1975, 126 pp.

15. Ramsey, J. P., "Control of Acid Drainage From Refuse Piles and Slurry Lagoons," Proc. Third Symp. on Coal Mine Drainage Research, Mellon Inst., Pittsburgh, Penn., May 19-20, 1970, pp. 138-144.

16. Good, D. M., Ricca, V. T., and Shumate, K. S., "The Relation of Refuse Pile Hydrology to Acid Production," Proc. Third Symp. on Coal Mine Drainage Research, Mellon Inst., Pittsburgh, Penn., May 19-20, 1970, pp. 145-151.

17. Libicki, J., "Impact of Gob and Power-Plant Ash Disposal on Ground Water Quality and its Control," Seventh Symp. on Coal Mine Drainage Research, Natl. Coal Assn./BCR,Inc., Louisville, Ky., Oct. 18-20, 1977, pp. 165-184.

18. Nicholls, G. D., "Pollution Affecting Wells in the Bunter Sandstone," in Groundwater Pollution in Europe, J. A. Cole (ed.), Water Information Center, Inc., Port Washington, N.Y., 1974, pp. 116-125.

19. Mink, L. L., Williams, R. E., and Wallace, A. T., "Effect of Early Day Mining Operations on Present Day Water Quality," Ground Water, Vol. 10, No. 1, 1972.

20. Galbraith, J. H., Williams, R. E., and Siems, P. L., "Migration and Leaching of Metals from Old Mine Tailings Deposits," Ground Water, Vol. 10, No. 3, 1972.

21. Williams, R. E., Kealy, C. D., and Mink, L. L., "Effects and Prevention of Leakage from Mine Tailings Ponds," Transactions, AIME, SME, Vol. 254, 1973, pp. 212-216.

22. Norbeck, P. N., Mink, L. L., and Williams, R. E., "Ground Water Leaching of Jig Tailing Deposits in the Coeur D'Alene District of Northern Idaho," Proc. Symp. on Water Resources Problems Related to Mining, Am. Water Resources Assn., Minneapolis, Minn., 1974, pp. 149-157.

23. Hawley, J. R., and Shikaze, K. H., "The Problem of Acid Mine Drainage in Ontario," Proc. Third Ann. Mtg. of Can. Min. Processors, Mines Branch, Dept. of Energy, Mines, and Resources, Ottawa, 1971.

24. Mead, W. E., and Condrat, G. W., "Groundwater Protection and Tailings Disposal," Preprint 2597, Am. Soc. Civil Eng. Ann. Mtg., Denver, November 3-7, 1975.

25. Johnston, R. S., Brown, R. W., and Cravens, J., "Acid Mine Rehabilitation Problems at High Elevations," Proc. Water Management Symp., ASCE, Irrigation and Drainage Division, Logan, Utah, August 11-13, 1975, pp. 66-79.

26. Farmer, E. E., Richardson, B. Z., and Brown, R. W., "Revegetation of Acid Mining Wastes in Central Idaho," USDA Forest Service Research Paper INT-178, Ogden, Utah, 1976, 17 pp.

27. Zellmer, S. D., "Staunton 1 Reclamation Demonstration Project Progress Report for 1977," Argonne National Laboratory, Report ANL/LRP-TM-14, December 1978, 58 pp.

28. Wilkey, M. L., and Zellmer, S. D., "A Reclamation Project at an Abandoned Deep Coal Mine," Jour. Environ. Eng. Div., ASCE, in press.

29. Grisak, G. E., Cherry, J. A., Vonhof, J. A., and Blumele, J. P., "Hydrogeologic and Hydrochemical Properties of Fractured Till in the Interior Plains Region," Proc. Conf. Glacial Till, R. F. Legget (ed.), Royal Soc. Canada, Spec. Publ. No. 12, 1976, pp. 304-335.

30. Schubert, J. P., Olsen, R. D., and Zellmer, S. D., "Monitoring the Effects of Coal Refuse Disposal and Reclamation on Water Quality in Southwestern Illinois," Proc. Fourth Joint Conference on Sensing of Environmental Pollutants, Am. Chem. Soc., New Orleans, Nov. 6-11, 1977, (1978), pp. 724-731.

31. Grisak, G. E., and Jackson, R. E., "An Appraisal of the Hydrogeological Processes Involved in Shallow Subsurface Waste Management in Canadian Terrain," Inland Waters Directorate, Fisheries and Environment Canada, Scientific Series No. 84, Ottawa, 1978, 193 pp.

32. Hughes, G. M., Landon, R. A., and Farvolden, R. N., "Hydrogeology of Solid Waste Disposal Sites in Northeastern Illinois," U.S. EPA, Solid Waste Management Series SW-12d, 1971, 154 pp.

33. Griffin, R. A., Cartwright, K., Shimp, N. F., Steele, J. D., Ruch, R. R., White, W. A., Hughes, G. M., and Gilkeson, R. H., "Attenuation of Pollutants in Municipal Landfill Leachate by Clay Minerals. Part 1 -- Column Leaching and Field Verification," Ill. State Geological Survey, Environ. Geol. Notes EGN 78, 1976, 34 pp.

34. Griffin, R. A., Frost, R. R., Au, A. K., Robinson, G. D., and Shimp, N. F., "Attenuation of Pollutants in Municipal Landfill Leachate by Clay Minerals. Part 2 -- Heavy-Metal Adsorption," Ill. State Geological Survey, Environ. Geol. Notes EGN 79, 1977, 47 pp.

35. Ciolkosz, E. J., Kardos, L. T., and Beers, W. F., Jr., "Soil as a Medium for the Renovation of Acid Mine Drainage Water," The Pennsylvania State University, Inst. for Research on Land and Water Resources, Tech. Completion Rept. for OWRR Proj. A-027-PA, 1973, 135 pp.

36. Pedco Environmental, Inc., "Study of Adverse Effects of Solid Wastes From All Mining Activities on the Environment," draft report to the U.S. EPA, Contract No. 68-01-4700, 1979, 304 pp.

36

Case Histories of Different Seepage Problems for Nine Tailings Dams

by K. E. Robinson, Partner,
Dames & Moore,
North Vancouver, British Columbia, Canada,
and G. C. Toland, Partner,
Dames & Moore,
Salt Lake City, Utah, USA

ABSTRACT

Seepage, oversteepened slopes, earthquakes, soft foundations, and pond operations are major design consider-ations for tailings ponds. However, of the numerous tail-ings investigations undertaken by our firm, control of seepage has been, by far, the most significant considera-tion. This paper discusses nine case histories of projects where seepage was, or could have been, a problem.

There is an obvious divergence of interests in the design of tailings dams. The requirements for control of pollutants in water courses and groundwater aquifers suggest designs with impervious dams and impoundment reservoirs. Conversely, drainage blankets, and/or pervious foundations and embankments improve stability and permit construction of the most economical structures.

This paper discusses projects that include a combin-ation of two construction methods - relatively impervious dams constructed using imported materials and relatively pervious "upstream construction" tailings dams, and two foundation types - relatively pervious and relatively impervious. Case histories include some that represent unusual conditions and others that represent the more general problems facing dam designers in the control of seepage.

INTRODUCTION

Tailings disposal problems have faced the mining engineer for many years. Historically the easiest and most economical solution was to discharge tailings slurry by gravity to the nearest body of water and let nature take care of the disposal problem. However, as communities and farming activities have encroached on mining areas, and fishing industries and interested individuals have applied pressure to government regulatory bodies, the need for properly engineered tailings disposal areas has become apparent. There are many factors that influence the final dam design utilized at a given site such as: topography, geology and foundation soils, tailings properties, method of deposition of slurry, hydrology, alternate use for the impoundment area for water storage or evaporation, availability of construction materials, time constraints, monitoring requirements, costs, stability, seepage limitations and reclamation. All these factors combine to place specific restrictions or boundary conditions on the designers ability to develop a cost effective structure.

Generally the item that affects the design of the impoundment facilities the most is the impact of seepage on stability and pollution control considerations. This paper discusses nine specific projects where seepage was a major factor in the design and/or remedial treatment was required.

It is unfortunately apparent in these case histories that what is good for stability is usually bad for contamination and vice versa. In some of the examples it is apparent that emphasizing one at the expense of the other has caused specific problems.

TYPES OF DAMS AND FOUNDATION CONDITIONS

The traditional way to construct tailings dams has been to use the "upstream construction" technique. This normally involves constructing a starter dam using existing natural soils within the ultimate pond area, mine waste rock or other borrow sources. Tailings are then spigotted from the face of the dam until the crest of these starter structures has been reached. Successive extensions of the dam are then constructed by excavating by hand, or machine, the tailings adjacent to the crest in a series of short steps as shown on Figure 1. Because most tailings materials are either relatively uniform fine sandy silts or silts with some sands, this procedure has often resulted in a stable structure

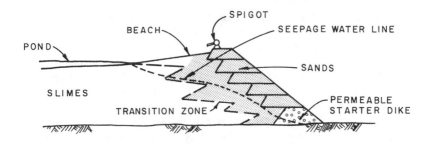

UPSTREAM CONSTRUCTION WITH TAILINGS

FIGURE I

because of the natural segregation of sandier materials near the face of the dam and progressively finer materials away from the dam until a "slimes" zone has been reached in the vicinity of the water pond. However, this type of structure can cause stability problems if: 1) the starter dam is constructed using relatively impervious material so that the phreatic surface rises to the outer face of the structure; 2) slimes pockets are permitted to form close to the crest of the dam so that seepage emerges in perched zones up the extending slope; 3) flood conditions combine with slurry deposition to result in a significantly high phreatic surface; or 4) significant earthquake loading results in liquefaction or high stresses in the tailings backfill. This paper discusses five projects where "upstream construction" has been used to raise tailings dams over both pervious and impervious foundations.

Pervious foundations are those that have a higher permeability than the tailings backfill - greater than 10^{-4} centimeters per second. These foundations are most conducive to dam stability as they provide a continuous drainage blanket under the tailings backfill. Impervious foundations, where the permeability is less than the tailings, are most suitable where seepage control is required. However, for this type of foundation more care is required in designing and constructing the dam to ensure overall safety.

Increasing pressure from society to reduce pollution of streams and groundwater aquifers, particularly from radioactive wastes has resulted in the need to prevent seepage

from some tailings impoundment facilities. Because requirements for milling activities may result in a need to store
water in the tailings pond for recirculation or evaporation
purposes, it may be more economical to discharge total tailings at high elevation against a hillside and have slimes
and water accumulate at the dam face. Under these conditions
it is necessary to construct relatively impervious dams with
imported materials using "downstream construction" techniques.
This type of construction is illustrated on Figure 2 which
shows a total dam completed in one construction phase, or a
staged structure with sloping upstream section of relatively
impervious material. Four projects where impervious dams
have been placed over impervious foundations are discussed

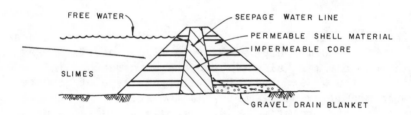

(a) TOTAL DAM

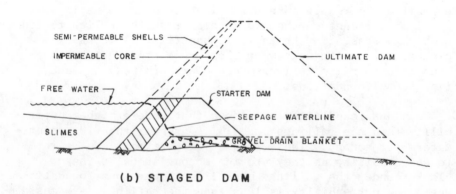

(b) STAGED DAM

DOWNSTREAM CONSTRUCTION
WITH IMPORTED MATERIALS

FIGURE 2

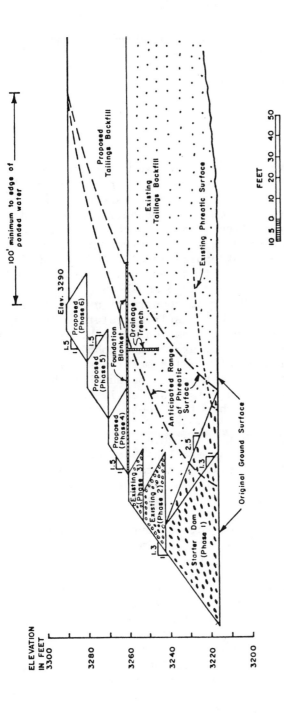

100' minimum to edge of ponded water

Elev. 3290

Proposed (Phase 6)

1.5

Proposed (Phase 5)

1.5

Proposed (Phase 4)

1.5

Existing (Phase 3)

Existing (Phase 2)

1.3

Starter Dam (Phase 1)

1.3

2.5

1

Foundation Blanket

Drainage Trench

Proposed Tailings Backfill

Existing Tailings Backfill

Existing Phreatic Surface

Anticipated Range of Phreatic Surface

Original Ground Surface

ELEVATION IN FEET
3300
3280
3260
3240
3220
3200

FEET

10 5 0   10   20   30   40   50

PROJECT I
TYPICAL
DYKE SECTION

FIGURE 3

including two cases where the foundations were not as impervious as had originally been anticipated.

RELATIVELY PERVIOUS FOUNDATIONS

Upstream Construction

Project 1.

This project involved the design of an extension to an abandoned silver tailings impoundment area in the Coeur d' Alene Valley of Idaho. The existing pond was constructed on limited land area where the southern boundary was defined by a railway and the Coeur d'Alene River and the north and west boundaries were defined by a relatively steep hillside. The impoundment covers an area of approximately 1400 by 300 feet. The maximum height of the dam of 45 feet had been developed in three raises between 1967 and 1975 as shown on a typical cross-section, Figure 3. Upstream construction techniques had already been utilized with a resulting relatively steep outer slope. Fortunately the foundation soils below the dam consisted of very pervious sand, gravel and cobbles and the starter dam was constructed of similar materials which were excavated within the impoundment area. Because of the topography, it was desired to raise the dam in three 10 foot lifts to a maximum final height of 75 feet.

Problems associated with the design of the raised embankment included: stability considerations because of the steep existing outer slope, slime pockets near the embankment face, control of the phreatic surface and development of a suitable decant system for the raised sections.

Piezometers installed prior to, and during, our investigations indicated that the phreatic surface was very low within the impoundment area and close to the foundation sand and gravel in the vicinity of the perimeter embankment. Standard flow net analyses indicated that the phreatic surface should be higher. Fortunately, it was possible to complete a full-scale, insitu, constant head permeability test for a period of about 6 weeks. A pond of water was maintained over about 50 percent of the tailings impoundment area by pumping water at the rate of 450 gallons per minute for about 16 hours per week. By monitoring piezometers it was possible to establish that the predominant seepage path is downward through the tailings backfill and into the permeable foundation gravels. This indicated that there are sandy areas vertically connected throughout the backfill near the embankment face which intersect slimes pockets that could otherwise cause perched water zones. This observation agrees with experience on other projects where granular foundations underlie tailings impoundment facilities.

Based on the field investigation and full scale permeability and laboratory tests, the raised embankment cross-section shown on Figure 3 was designed. This design included excavating a drainage trench through the upper area of the existing tailings to cut through some fairly continuous slimes zones to provide more positive interconnection between sand zones. The overall slope was flattened to 2 horizontal to 1 vertical from the original slope of 1.3 horizontal to 1 vertical. With the drainage provided, a range of phreatic surfaces as shown on Figure 3 is anticipated. Under these conditions the dam will be stable, even under design seismicity which was studied in detail as discussed in a paper by McKee, Robinson and Urlich (1978)*. To determine actual phreatic surfaces and provide for remedial action, if necessary, such as further slope flattening or keeping the pond more than the design requirement of 100 feet from the crest of the dike at any stage, a series of piezometers have been installed and additional piezometers will be placed during future extensions of the dam. Water level monitoring is vital to the design concepts discussed above, and requires specific mine action.

Project 2.

This project involved a tungsten disposal area near Bishop, California. Tailings have been discharged against a relatively steep talus-covered valley wall of Pine Creek Canyon. A series of four tailings ponds have been established over a 4000 by 900 foot area. The ponds are confined by Pine Creek on one side and the talus slopes on the other. The four ponds are constructed adjacent to one another in a stair-step configuration. The maximum embankment heights are in the order of 200 feet with side slopes developed by "upstream construction" methods of between 1.2 and 1.8 horizontal to 1.0 vertical, as indicated on the typical section shown on Figure 4. A unique feature of this project is the high perimeter embankment which was recently subjected to significant earthquake accelerations, with no apparent signs of distress.

*References are included at the end of the text.

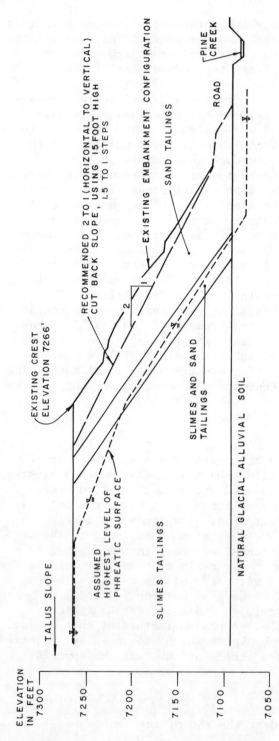

ELEVATION
IN FEET

TALUS SLOPE

EXISTING CREST
ELEVATION 7266'

ASSUMED
HIGHEST LEVEL OF
PHREATIC SURFACE

RECOMMENDED 2 TO 1 (HORIZONTAL TO VERTICAL)
CUT BACK SLOPE, USING 15 FOOT HIGH
1.5 TO 1 STEPS

EXISTING EMBANKMENT CONFIGURATION

SAND TAILINGS

SLIMES TAILINGS

SLIMES AND SAND
TAILINGS

ROAD

PINE CREEK

NATURAL GLACIAL-ALLUVIAL SOIL

PROJECT 2
TYPICAL
EMBANKMENT
SECTION

FIGURE 4

Foundation conditions below the tailings ponds consist of a combination of talus from the adjacent mountain slopes and finer grained, glacio-alluvial soils. The permeability of the foundation soils ranges from moderately low to high. However, the back boundary of all the ponds is formed by highly permeable talus which provides direct drainage into the more highly permeable foundation soils, as indicated schematically on the valley profile shown on Figure 5. Decanting of liquids from the pond surfaces has not been required because of the permeable nature of the talus backing. In Pond 3 where the talus tends to be somewhat less permeable, infiltration wells have been installed to provide decanting directly into more coarse talus at lower elevations.

With this highly permeable zone at the back of the impoundments, it was assumed that the phreatic surface was very low within the tailings near the embankment face and that this was the reason for the long term stable condition of the embankments. However, high water level readings in old piezometers resulted in our recent investigation. The purpose was to determine if the phreatic surface was high and, if it was, what remedial action to take, if any. Fortunately, our investigation, which included the installation of a number of isolated piezometers in each boring, detected only nominal perched water levels in some areas where slimes had been allowed to accumulate near the face of the dam. Overall stability was not adversely affected.

Of special interest during our investigation was an earthquake about 12 miles from the site of Magnitude 5.7 on the

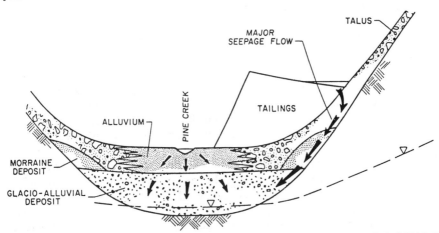

PROJECT 2   **SCHEMATIC OF VALLEY PROFILE**

FIGURE 5

Richter scale which caused estimated accelerations at the
base of the embankments of about 0.12g with peak accelerations approaching 0.2g. Drilling was in progress at the
time of the quake and our inspector observed numerous rock-
falls and minor slides on the adjacent hillsides. The drill
rig was shaking so violently that the drill rod bent in the
hole and a just recovered sample partially liquified. However, the embankment suffered no distress and the only signs
of disturbance were observed in areas adjacent to ponded
water back from the face, where settlement indicated minor
near surface liquefaction.

Back stability analyses of the slopes using the actual
earthquake loading conditions confirmed that the phreatic
surface had to be extremely low, as indicated on Figure 4,
and there was significant apparent cohesion in the sand zone
near the face of the dam. Tailings disposal by spigotting
from successive upstream construction lifts resulted in a
series of three zones of tailings including an outer sand
zone, an intermediate silty sand to sandy silt zone, and an
interior slime zone as indicated on Figure 4.

This project indicates that under extremely favorable
site conditions a very economical structure can be utilized
to store tailings to relatively high final elevations. However, our investigations did indicate that long term stability should be improved slightly by flattening the overall
slope as shown on Figure 4 to 2 horizontal to 1 vertical.
This flattening can be completed efficiently and economically
by utilizing the stripped material to raise successive lifts
of Pond 4 which is presently only 30 feet high.

Impervious Dams

Project 3.

This tailings disposal project located in Europe was
designed as an impervious dam founded on an impervious foundation. However, because of unusual conditions in the
immediate vicinity of the dam, problems developed which
required remedial treatment. It was intended that the dam
act as a water storage reservoir because of the need to
recycle as much water to the mill as possible. Because of
limited available borrow materials, it was necessary to
construct the 80 foot starter dam using rockfill with a thin
concrete liner on the upstream face to provide an impervious
boundary. Tailings would be discharged up the valley from
the dam to form a sloping beach front with slimes accumulat-

ing near the dam and a water pond adjacent to the structure. Foundations under the reservoir consisted of relatively impervious slates which have almost vertical bedding. The dam itself is founded on a vertically bedded Karstic limestone formation which forms the most resistant part of the valley. The strike of the formation is parallel to the axis of the dam and the limestone extends just past the upstream toe. The Karstic nature of the limestone was recognized and a grout blanket was placed over the exposed limestone in the reservoir area.

During initial filling of the reservoir sinkholes developed on a number of separate occasions which resulted in draining of the reservoir, subsequent repair by placing mine waste and debris in the exposed sinkhole and refilling of the reservoir. After the last sinkhole developed, an investigation was completed to establish the extent and degree of sinkholes that could exist in addition to those already observed, and to develop remedial measures to prevent further sinkholes from developing. This would be particularly critical during future extensions of the dam which would raise it to an ultimate height of 200 feet.

The area where the sinkholes were observed was immediately upstream of the toe of the concrete face in the center of the valley. At this location it had been extremely difficult to completely strip and clean the fine grained soils at the base of the valley during construction because of water and available space. During the subsequent investigation a number of interconnected sinkholes were uncovered when this area was carefully stripped. In addition, very extensive caverns were detected in the limestone formation in the left abutment near the crest of the ultimate dam.

Two solutions were proposed to solve the problem and permit tailings disposal as quickly as possible. One included deposition of tailings from the dam face to develop a sand zone adjacent to the dam. This would be combined with a granular drainage blanket over the Karstic limestone formation. This approch would keep the ponded water away from potential future sinkholes and provide a filter above the limestone. The second alternative, which was ultimately chosen, consisted of placing a ten-foot thick zone of mine waste over the limestone on the assumption that this material would bridge and plug potential sinkholes that could develop during future operations. Both solutions required extremely careful cleaning of all soil over the unprotected limestone and plugging of any openings in the limestone with a combination of mine waste and concrete.

Project 4.

This project is typical of a number of soda-ash plants in
the Green River area of Wyoming. These projects involve the
construction of relatively impervious dams to form a reservoir for the storage of insols and to act as evaporation
ponds for the disposal of liquids. A number of years ago
when these projects first evolved, environmental regulations
regarding seepage control were not as stringent as they are
at present. For this reason the original designs, while
cognizant of seepage potential, did not provide as positive
a cutoff to seepage losses as is now deemed necessary. One
specific project involved the construction of an earth
embankment with a maximum height of 80 feet. The dam was
constructed using a relatively impervious embankment section
as shown on Figure 6 with upstream and downstream slopes of
2.5 horizontal to 1 vertical. Because of the highly
fractured nature of the foundation rock near the surface, a
cutoff trench was included below the dam which tied into the
embankment. This design followed a comprehensive field
investigation including holes drilled through rock with
packer tests to estimate permeabilities. The design anticipated seepage losses in the order of 100 gallons per minute.

After filling, red stained water seeping beyond the toe of
the dam caused concern to regulatory agencies. Upon further
investigation, it was apparent that the approximate 150

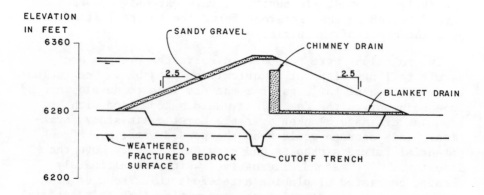

PROJECT 4
MAXIMUM
CROSS-SECTION   FIGURE 6

gallons per minute of observed seepage was indicative of
water losses from the reservoir which passes into fractures
that extended below the impervious cutoff toward the abutments of the dam. While the total volume of seepage was
not exceptional, and was within the limits of reasonable
estimates, the effect on environmentalists was significant
because of the color and its visual impact.

For this project remedial action was not required because
of the existence of an old pond at a lower elevation down
valley from the dam under consideration. This dam acts as a
secondary evaporation pond with excess water pumped back to
the upper pond. However, the significance of minor geologic
features such as interconnected fracture zones beneath
impoundment areas which could extend around abutments or
under the main fracture zone, that would be sealed by an
impervious cutoff, for these types of dams must be given
careful consideration in future projects. It is probable
that the best solution would include a small holding pond
downstream to collect and return seepage thereby reducing the
need for a comprehensive cutoff below the dam which may be
next to impossible to provide.

RELATIVELY IMPERVIOUS FOUNDATIONS

Upstream Construction

Project 5.

This project illustrates the potential problems that can
develop where upstream construction is utilized under uncontrolled conditions and unusual climatology. This project,
located on the western flank of the Rocky Mountain Trench
near Kimberley, British Columbia, involved the failure of an
iron tailings dike and the subsequent loss of 2 million tons
of stored tailings in 1948. Tailings had been deposited for
many years utilizing the old historical procedure of raising
the embankment by steps using hand mucking procedures and
tailings, with spigotting from trestles mounted on the crest
of the rising dam section. Details of the structure, height
and size are sketchy. However, based on discussions with
people involved and our observations, it appears that failure was the direct result of freezing conditions and a high
phreatic surface. That particular year snow melt and spring
runoff started a few weeks before the failure. However, a
later cold spell resulted in extremely low temperatures and
refreezing of the face of the dam which probably resulted in

a raised water surface as runoff and seepage water accumulated against the crest of the dam. A slope failure from static seepage conditions probably resulted and caused excessive shear stresses throughout the embankment and adjacent back-fill. This apparently resulted in liquefaction of a large mass of tailings which flowed down a valley towards the St. Mary River a few miles away. Fortunately the two work-men, who were attending the spigots and slurry disposal system at the time of the failure, were able to manoeuvre across frozen chunks of soil to the side of the valley as the sliding mass moved downslope.

Foundation conditions under the tailings area where the failure occurred are not known exactly. However, a recently constructed dam downstream from the failure area was placed over remnants of the old iron tailings spill which rested directly on relatively impervious glacial till. It is there-fore expected that the foundation materials in the vicinity of the failure are relatively impervious.

For the new embankment system it was possible to construct a 30 foot high starter dam using silica tailings as borrow material after placing an initial 4-foot thick lift of sand and gravel to develop a working pad. Because of the sensi-tive nature of the saturated tailings foundation materials at the site, it was necessary to construct the first 4-foot lift slowly while frequently monitoring piezometers installed in the foundation tailings. A series of upstream construction lifts will raise the ultimate structure to a total height of 80 feet. The first 2 lifts have already been completed. Because of the sensitivity of the structure to seepage, a number of piezometers have been installed and monitored on a regular basis. A carefully designed drainage blanket at the base of the starter dam combined with spigotting from the dam crest has kept the phreatic level well within the design requirements discussed in detail in a paper by Robinson (1978).

Project 6.

This project involves a uranium tailings disposal area where upstream construction techniques were used to build an embankment of over 150 feet maximum height. The impoundment area, including two separate ponds having a total area of about 50 acres each, is situated above the San Miguel River where riverbank side slopes are in the order of 30 degrees or less. Foundation conditions for the dam consist of

relatively impervious, sound sandstone. The 25 foot high
starter dam was constructed utilizing sand tailings from a
previous disposal area.

The outside face of the dam varies in slope from 1.5 to
3.0 horizontal to 1.0 vertical with the flattest sections at
the higher levels of the embankment as shown on Figure 7.
The steep lower dam section rests directly on relatively
impervious rock, resulting in seepage at the toe of the
section and some erosion and degradation. A slide in one
section of this lower slope occurred as a result of seepage
buildup combined with surface freezing which raised the water
level against the steep slope. We investigated the dam and
concluded that the factor of safety under steady state seepage conditions was 1.2.

To improve stability and eliminate potential erosion and
piping at the toe of the dam, we recommended that a rockfill
berm be placed on the downstream face, as shown on Figure 7,
and the pond be operated to keep decant water as far from the
face as possible. The rock buttress fill has not yet been

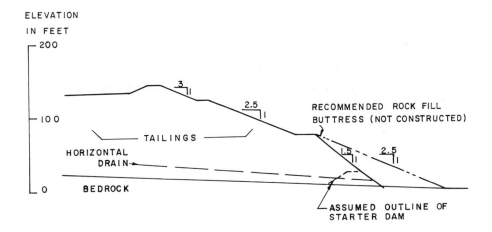

SCALE = 1"= 100'

PROJECT 6
TYPICAL
CROSS-SECTION   FIGURE 7

constructed. As an alternative to this remedial treatment, the owner requested a test section of horizontal drains be installed which, if successful, could provide a more economical solution to the seepage problem. Based on the test section, it was apparent that drain spacing would have to be less than 5 feet along the dam which was too expensive an undertaking. The close spacing would be required because of the permeability of the sands of about 10^{-4} centimeters per second, and the random pockets and layers of slimes that were within the zone requiring drainage. This can be a common problem for dams using "upstream construction" unless spigotting is completed under controlled conditions, with sufficient spigot points to minimize ponding near the crest where slimes would be deposited. The most significant factors affecting this project were the impervious rock foundation and the proximity of the pond to the dam crest.

Project 7.

A number of tailings ponds have been established at a large copper mine in Arizona. The first four ponds were located in small valleys on either side of a ridge so that they eventually combined as the tailings dams were extended to a maximum height of about 200 feet. Because of problems with one of the embankments, a new cross-section was designed for a high dam that is presently being used for tailings disposal.

Bedrock in the area is dacite which is sound where unweathered, but is generally covered by weathered rock and residual soil. This upper zone is a relatively impermeable 10^{-6} centimeters per second or less. The problem impoundment area was constructed using a 45 foot high starter dam of weathered dacite - well graded silty sand with gravel. A stationary cyclone was established which directed sands to the dam crest and slimes to the back pond area. Upstream construction was then provided by excavating beach sand and placing it in 6 to 8 foot lifts.

After the total height had exceeded 60 feet during early filling, the cyclone broke down and total tailings were discharged into the back of the pond. This forced the ponded water and slimes to rest against the dam face. This combined with the relatively impervious starter dam, raised the phreatic surface to critical levels and required remedial action. A series of "French" drains were installed along raised sections of the dam to collect near surface seepage and direct it to a collection system. This prevented seepage from emerging at the top of the starter dam. Provisions were then made to spigot total tailings from the dam crest and develop a beach at the face keeping the pond away.

The design of a new tailings disposal area required two starter dams. One dam initially stored sand tailings from a large cyclone while the second one was constructed 2500 feet upstream to store the slimes overflow. The 120 foot high main starter dam was constructed with a main downstream shell of broken rock in a 30 foot wide filter zone of minus 3 inch rock, and a 50 foot wide upstream zone of well graded broken conglomerate. A system of internal drains was incorporated into the final design.

Once the storage between the two starter dams was filled with sand, total tailings were discharged from the crest of the main starter dam so that standard upstream lifts could be used to complete the dam to its ultimate height of 630 feet.

With sand tailings stored behind the main starter dam and internal drains, a well designed system was established creating positive drainage and a low phreatic surface. For both the large dam system and the original pond, water level control was aided by establishing a minimum distance between dam crest and ponded water. For the large dam the pond set-back varies from 200 feet at the starter dam level to 750 feet at the ultimate crest.

Project 8.

This project is relatively typical of the impact of government regulations on the construction of uranium tailings impoundments. The project is located in Wyoming and required the design of tailings dam embankments 50 feet high over an area of 3000 by 3000 feet. This project went through many stages of design, review and redesign as the regulatory agencies required more stringent controls against seepage loss. It was a case where the designers suggested three alternative methods for controlling seepage and providing a safe structure, and the regulatory authorities eventually insisted on all three procedures being utilized.

The dam is presently being constructed with alluvial silty sands and sandy silts with an upstream slope of 3 horizontal to 1 vertical and downstream slopes of 2 horizontal to 1 vertical above and below an intermediate 15 foot wide bench. Soil conditions below the impoundment area consist of low permeability, poorly indurated siltstones and sandstones. This material has a measured permeability of 10^{-5} centimeters per second, and a water table 90 feet below the existing ground surface.

Because of an apparent overreaction to the control of radioactive waste, the owner was forced to include synthetic liners in the embankment and throughout the pond area. In addition the design was changed to require a 50-deep excavation below existing grade so that all tailings would be buried. The 50-foot high dam then forms a retention structure for stored liquids prior to effluent evaporation. Because of liner costs, the owner decided to construct the impoundment area in a grid of four stages so that capital costs could be deferred even though embankment costs would eventually be much higher.

The most serious concern to design consultants is the apparent need for redundant safety features. With the foundation material having such a low permeability and a significant capacity for radionuclide uptake by ion exchange, the need for placing a liner under the total impoundment facility was questioned. Even though the liner was utilized, the regulatory agency require an embankment stability analysis based on full saturation with 18 monitoring piezometers - requirements which are considered to be extremely conservative.

Project 9.

This tailings disposal project, located in the Shirley Basin, Wyoming, also involved uranium tailings. Foundation conditions consist of poorly indurated claystones and sandstones having relatively low permeability. The design included a maximum dam height of 60 feet, upstream and downstream slopes of 2 horizontal to 1 vertical and 2.5 to 1, respectively. The structure was raised in 3 stages with an impervious cut-off trench located at the toe of the first embankment stage. Succeeding stages were built in the downstream direction as shown on Figure 8. The main embankment section was constructed using a relatively low permeability clayey sand.

Of significance for this project was that the design required control of the phreatic surface with a chimney drain. Because it was not possible to find a suitable graded borrow material in the area that would satisfy filter criteria and provide the required drainage, it was necessary to satisfy

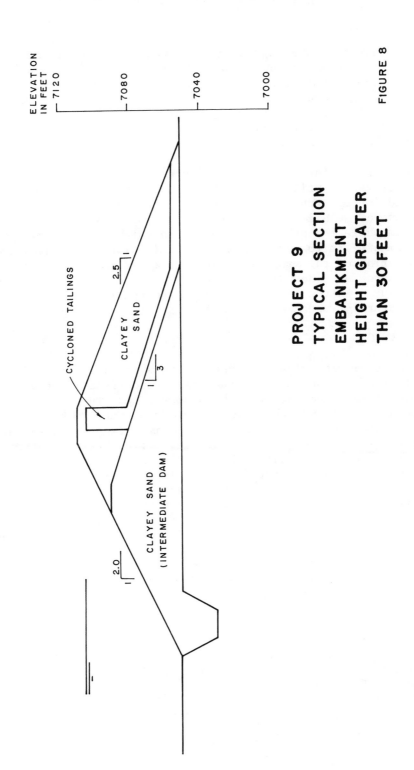

ELEVATION IN FEET

7120

7080

7040

7000

CYCLONED TAILINGS

CLAYEY SAND

2.5 | 1

| 3

1 |

CLAYEY SAND
(INTERMEDIATE DAM)

2.0

1 |

1 |

PROJECT 9
TYPICAL SECTION
EMBANKMENT
HEIGHT GREATER
THAN 30 FEET

FIGURE 8

the authorities that cycloned uranium tailings would be suitable. This was done and the chimney drain was connected to a blanket drain also constructed of cycloned sands. This material provided a stable dam section. Seepage passing through the structure is being collected by ditches just downstream of the toe where it is directed to a sump and pumped back to the reservoir.

Of further interest on this project was the fact that regulatory authorities did not agree on the most suitable method for construction of the dam. One agency requested the use of an all clay structure with no internal drainage system while the other insisted on an internal drainage system similar to that utilized. It is also of interest that monitoring of the pump back water from the collector ditch has shown low concentrations of radionuclides. This has been attributed to the effects of ion exchange in the dam fill and natural foundation materials.

CONCLUSIONS

The case histories discussed in this paper cover a wide variety of embankment and foundation conditions. These projects were chosen because, in some cases, they represent unusual conditions, while in others, they tend to be representative of more general problems facing tailings dam designers in the control of seepage. If pollution control requirements permit, it is most desireable to provide as free draining a structure as possible and use "upstream construction". However, if it is necessary to provide tight controls over seepage losses, and a permeable structure with a pump back system can not be utilized, then extreme care is required in assessing the near surface geological conditions. Seepage problems associated with foundation conditions in the reservoir can have a much more significant impact on the total facilities than a properly designed dam structure used to retain the perimeter of the tailings.

REFERENCES

McKee, B. E., Robinson, K. E., and Urlich, C. M. (May 1978) "Upstream Design for Extension of an Abandoned Tailings Dam" - Tailings Disposal Today, Vol. 2, Miller Freeman Publications.
Robinson, K. E. (1977) "Tailings Dam Constructed on Very Loose, Saturated Sandy Silt" - Canadian Geotechnical Journal; Vol. 14, No. 3.

37

Excursion Potentials at Uranium Tailings Disposal Sites

by Michael J. Taylor
and Phillip E. Antommaria, Project Managers,
D'Appolonia Consulting Engineers,
Denver, Colorado, USA

ABSTRACT

Current positions of the United States Nuclear Regulatory Commission (NRC) indicate that isolation of uranium tailings at disposal sites is the preferred method of groundwater protection, but that disposal of uranium tailings solutions in the groundwater is not a prohibited method of disposal. In either case, an understanding of the mechanisms of radiotoxic and chemically toxic element excursions away from the site is an important aspect of the system design or assessment. All economic isolation systems have the potential for leakage. Disposal of tailings solution in the groundwater assumes a system with a high percentage of tailings solutions lost by leakage. The degree of understanding of the site characteristics regarding excursion is proportional to the degree of leakage.

This paper discusses a site where nearly all tailings solution is lost by leakage, yet the site conditions are such that no adverse environmental effects are occurring. The radionuclides are being removed in the subsoils by co-precipitation and adsorption with the heavy metals in the tailing solution as the pH of the acid solution is raised by the alkaline soils. The understanding of the potential excursion or retention mechanisms at this site shows how the understanding of any site is important to reasonable and effective design of a uranium tailings disposal system.

INTRODUCTION

Seepage at uranium tailings disposal sites is of concern for (a) retention embankment integrity and (b) movement or excursion of the radiotoxic and chemically toxic materials from the facility to the surrounding environment. This paper concentrates on the concern of excurions and discusses the need for understanding the mechanisms of potential movements of toxic elements away from the disposal site. If the tailings solution is allowed to seep into the ground, an understanding of the mechanism is of utmost importance. Even if an isolation system is provided, the understanding of these mechanisms is important to minimize the need for extensive back-up and monitoring systems, and to understand the consequences of the isolation system failure.

Uranium mill tailings are the by-product of the ore processed for removal of U_3O_8. The process used at acid leach mills involves the removal of U_3O_8 by grinding the ore to a silt-sand consistency, leaching the ground ore with acid, removal of the U_3O_8 from the pregnant acid solution with an ion-exchange process, and disposal of the ground ore (tailings) and process waste water (tailings solution) at a tailings disposal site. The disposal site usually consists of a retention structure built from borrow or tailings and an impoundment to retain the solid tailings and tailings solution. The solid tailings contain radiotoxic elements (radium, thorium, uranium) and chemically toxic or detrimental elements (selenium, arsenic, iron, manganese, etc.). The tailings solution is acidic with a pH as low as 1.5 and contains elements similar to the solid tailings. The quantity of solid tailings is equal to the quantity of ore produced since the removal of U_3O_8 represents an infinitesimal volume reduction of the processed ore. The amount of tailings waste water is dependent on the mill process but can be as high as five (5) times (by weight) the solid tailings.

The radiotoxic and chemically toxic or detrimental elements in the tailings make the escape of this material to the environment a concern to regulatory agencies and the public. A significant portion of the recently issued "Draft Generic Environmental Impact Statement on Uranium Milling" (Nuclear Regulatory Commission, April, 1979) is devoted to this issue. As stated in that document;

> "Seepage of ...(tailings)... solution can
> potentially adversely affect groundwater
> aquifers and drinking water supplies."

The method of preventing this adverse affect has undergone much discussion over the past several years. As shown in Figure 1, at one end of the scale is the complete and total isolation of tailings and tailings solution. At the other end of the scale is the allowance for tailings solution to seep into the ground. The position of the NRC in this regard is set forth in the following statement from the "Draft Generic Impact Statement on Uranium Milling";

> "In general, the staff concludes that the
> most effective way to reduce potential
> groundwater contamination and associated
> health effects is to reduce the amount of
> moisture available to carry toxic contaminants
> away from the impoundments"... and ...

> "Although in general, the preferred approach
> towards groundwater protection is isolation of
> tailings and tailings solution, the staff does
> not consider complete prohibition of disposal
> in groundwater appropriate."

The NRC staff realizes that each site is a unique situation and the solution to tailings disposal is a site specific problem. Furthermore, although not clearly addressed in the "Draft Generic Environmental Impact Statement on Uranium Milling", complete isolation of tailings and tailings solution is an unachievable goal. All economic liner systems have the potential for leakage and that potential increases with time. A system which reduces this potential to an absolute minimum. It, therefore, is imperative that the site be understood as to the potential excursion paths from tailings disposal facilities, even though isolation is attempted.

This paper discusses the study of a site where tailings isolation was not attempted; yet protection of the groundwater is occurring. The lessons learned at this site can be applied to assessment of sites where isolation is or is not attempted; the lesson being that a thorough understanding of the potential mechanisms for excursions of radiotoxic and chemically toxic materials away from the tailings disposal facility is an important aspect of the tailings disposal system design. For systems that attempt isolation, this understanding can minimize

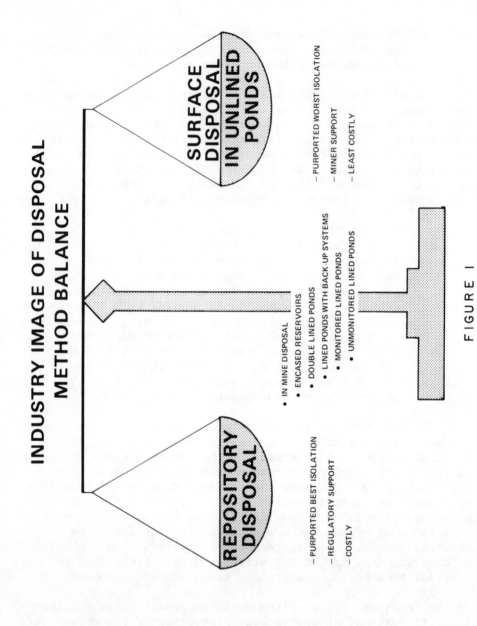

INDUSTRY IMAGE OF DISPOSAL METHOD BALANCE

REPOSITORY DISPOSAL

- PURPORTED BEST ISOLATION
- REGULATORY SUPPORT
- COSTLY

- IN MINE DISPOSAL
- ENCASED RESERVOIRS
- DOUBLE LINED PONDS
- LINED PONDS WITH BACK-UP SYSTEMS
- MONITORED LINED PONDS
- UNMONITORED LINED PONDS

SURFACE DISPOSAL IN UNLINED PONDS

- PURPORTED WORST ISOLATION
- MINER SUPPORT
- LEAST COSTLY

FIGURE I

the need for costly (and perhaps unneeded) secondary collection systems or back-up barriers; and can alleviate many of the fears associated with potential losses of tailings solution through the isolation system. At some sites, the conditions may be such that isolation systems are not required or can be significantly minimized.

The degree of site assessment depends on the intended disposal system. Not every site need be studied as extensively as the one discussed below, but understanding the excursion potential beyond the "isolation" barrier is an important aspect of a tailings facility design or evaluation.

DEFINITION OF THE EXAMPLE PROJECT

Site Location

Figure 2 shows an aerial view of the example site. The uranium mine and mill are located in central Wyoming. The area is characterized by relatively flat topography interrupted by sharply protruding granite peaks. Mountainous ridges exist at some distance to the south of the site.

Surface Orientation

Figure 3 shows the general site orientation including a milling operation and a tailings disposal area. The mill and the tailings disposal area are located in an enclosed valley surrounded by the sharp granite peaks typical of the area. Two relatively flat valley areas exist between the granite peaks to the southwest and northwest of the mill area and tailings disposal pond. Uranium ore is trucked into the mill area from the mountainous regions to the south of the site.

The site was constructed some 20 years ago in the late 1950's. Mining and milling have occurred since then with uranium tailings disposal occurring in the current location of the existing tailings pond. From available records, it appears the tailings pond was advanced by a modified upstream method of construction. In 1976, this method was changed to a centerline method of construction with compacted tailings used to construct the downstream portion of embankment. The tailings water has been and is retained against the tailings embankment and natural soils to the north of the site and up slope from the mill area.

The site operation is basically as follows:

FIGURE 2   SITE PHOTOGRAPH

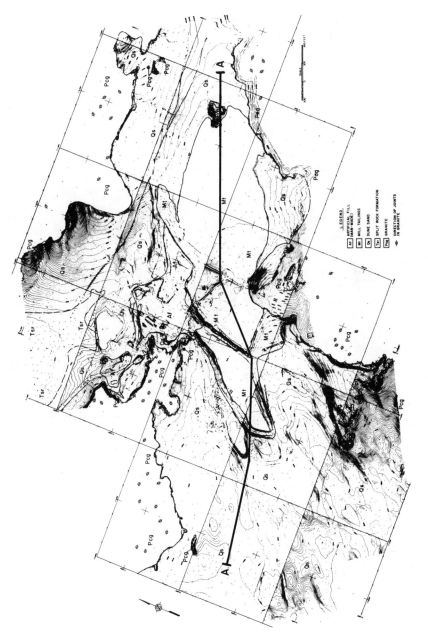

FIGURE 3 SITE GEOLOGIC MAP

LEGEND

Af ARTIFICIAL FILL (MAN-MADE)

Mt MILL TAILINGS

Qs DUNE SAND

Tsr SPLIT ROCK FORMATION

Pcg GRANITE

DIRECTION OF JOINTS IN GRANITE

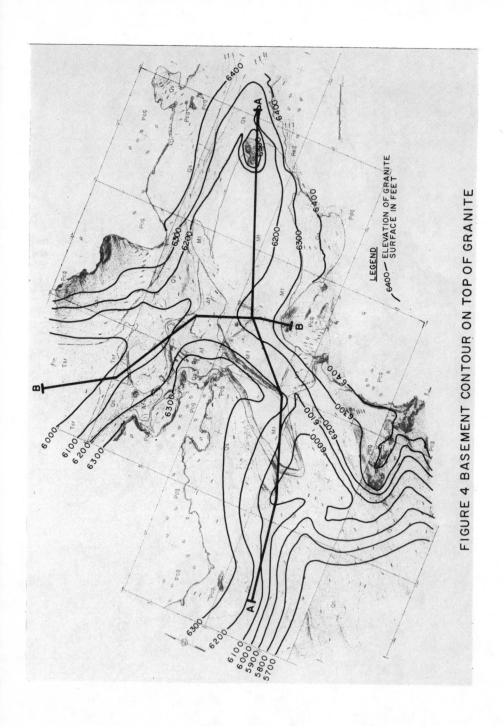

FIGURE 4 BASEMENT CONTOUR ON TOP OF GRANITE

LEGEND

6400 — ELEVATION OF GRANITE
SURFACE IN FEET

- Uranium ore is brought in from the mine via an access road through the northwest valley.

- The ore is crushed and processed by an acid leaching operation in the mill to remove the uranium.

- Water from the milling process is obtained by a series of wells located at the outer edge of the propertipdown slope (and down hydraulic gradient) from the mill area and the tailings pond.

- The process tailings are piped to the tailings disposal area by slurry line, utilizing the tailings water in the plant. The tailings are deposited on the tailings dike and segregated by beaching and sedimentation.

- The product of the plant is yellow cake which is shipped off site.

Further discussions of the plant operation are not applicable to this discussion.

Subsurface and Hydrologic Conditions

The subsurface condition at the site can basically be described as a "granite bowl" open at two ends and filled with sand and loosely cemented sandstone deposits. The granite peaks which protrude around the site and tailings pond have very steep slopes above ground. These steep slopes continue beneath the surface and eventually meet at depths as great as 300 feet below the ground surface. Figure 4 shows the top of granite contours and the slope of the bottom of the bowl to the open ends toward the southwest and northwest. Figures 5 and 6 show cross sections through the site at locations indicated on Figure 4.

Also as shown on Figures 5 and 6 the basement granite is overlain by a sandstone (loosely cemented) which in turn is overlain by an eolian sand and alluvial gravels. No lenses are apparent in the subsurface profile which would perch the groundwater table or cause isolated flows in this regime, although a few lenticular discontinuous lenses of clay silt material exist in the subsurface profile.

The groundwater movement on the site is governed both by the subsurface conditions as well as the presence of the

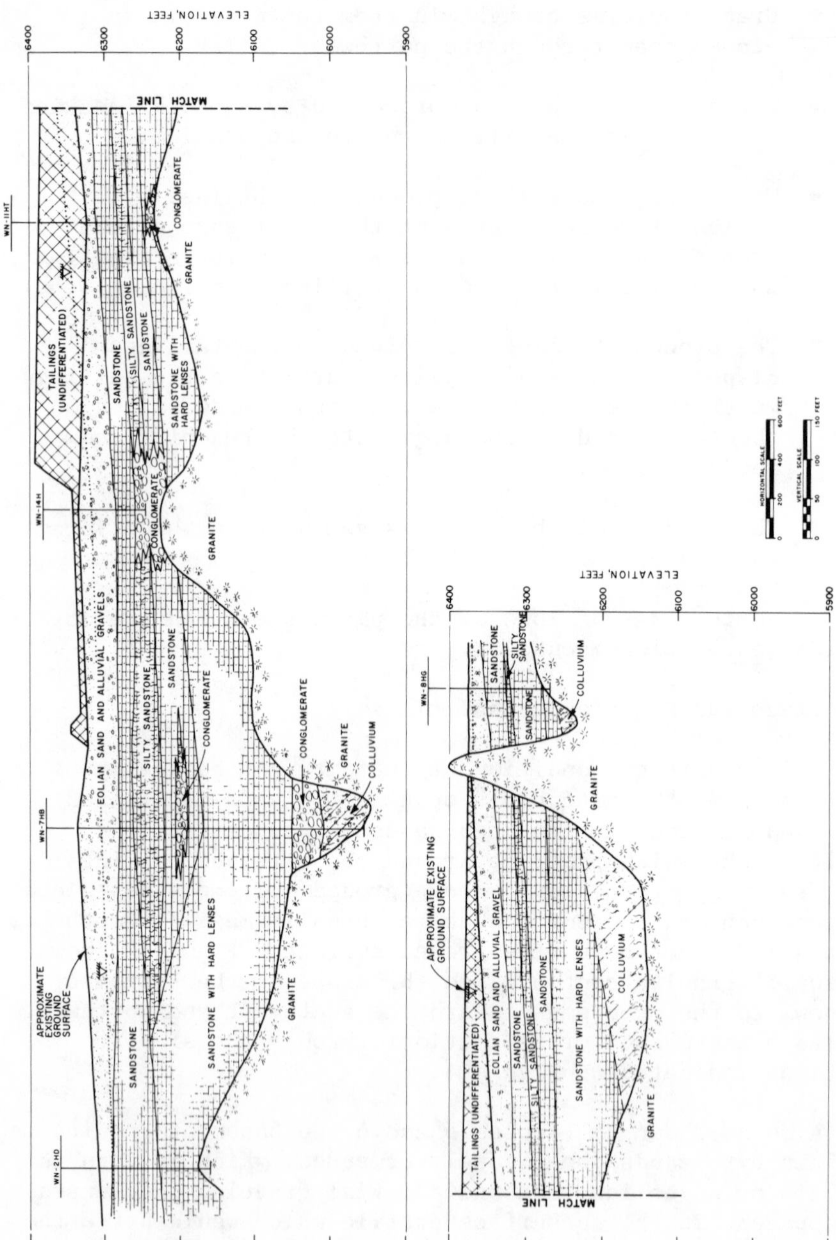

FIGURE 5 SUBSURFACE CROSS-SECTION A-A

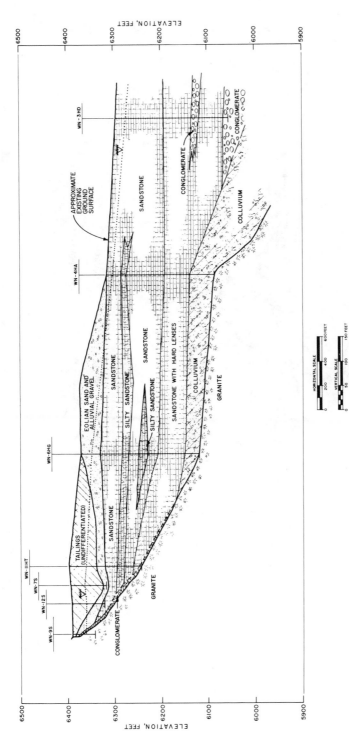

FIGURE 6 SUBSURFACE CROSS-SECTION B-B

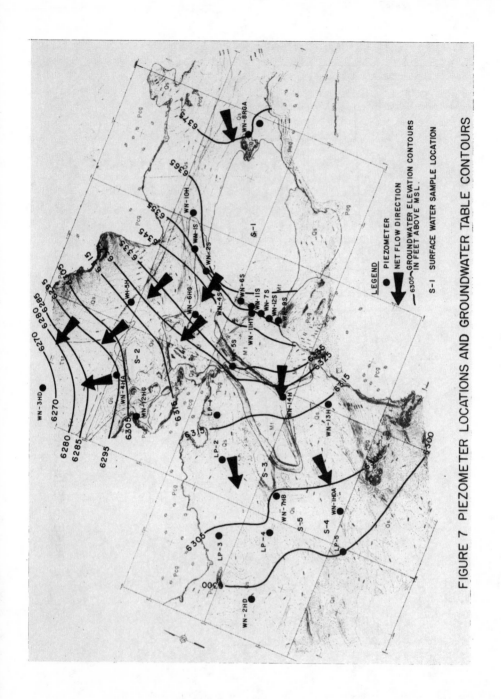

FIGURE 7 PIEZOMETER LOCATIONS AND GROUNDWATER TABLE CONTOURS

tailings pond on-site. Figure 7 shows the direction of groundwater flow as determined by on-site investigations. The groundwater is moving from the tailings pond through the valleys to the southwest and northwest. A few ponds which exist downstream of the tailings pond are indicative of a surfacing groundwater condition on the site.

The rate of movement of groundwater (or seeping tailings water) is governed by the permeability of the various strata. The average permeability of the sandstone within the saturated zone is near 1.5×10^{-2} centimeters per second (cm/sec). Although the eolian sand and tailings exhibited lower permeability in the range of 10^{-3} cm/sec to 10^{-5} cm/sec, the portion of cross-sectional area of flow in the valley is small for these materials. Most of the groundwater is moving through the sandstones.

The granite was considered to be a watertight hydrologic boundary. This conclusion was reached from two key observations on analysis including:

(1)   Borings were drilled into the granite and tested for permeability. In the majority of the cases the rock was found to be extremely tight and accepted little if any water. Where water take was achieved the permeabilities were 10^{-5} cm/sec to 10^{-7} cm/sec.

(2)   Cross sections were taken at both the southwest and northwest valleys. A field verified permeability was assigned to the cross sections and a theoretical flow determined using the hydraulic heads available for driving water through these cross sections. It was found that the calculated amount of water passing through these areas was very similar to the amount of water seeping from the tailings pond. This tended to verify that the water flowing from the tailings pond was passing downstream through the two valleys between the granite ridges and that the granite was essentially a hydrologic flow boundary.

The regional groundwater is relatively uneffected by the mounding caused by the tailings pond. As shown in Figure 8, the regional groundwater moves in a south/southwest direction. The mounding caused by the site is evidenced in the tailings pond area. A depression in the regional groundwater was also noted where the water is being pumped from the wells near the

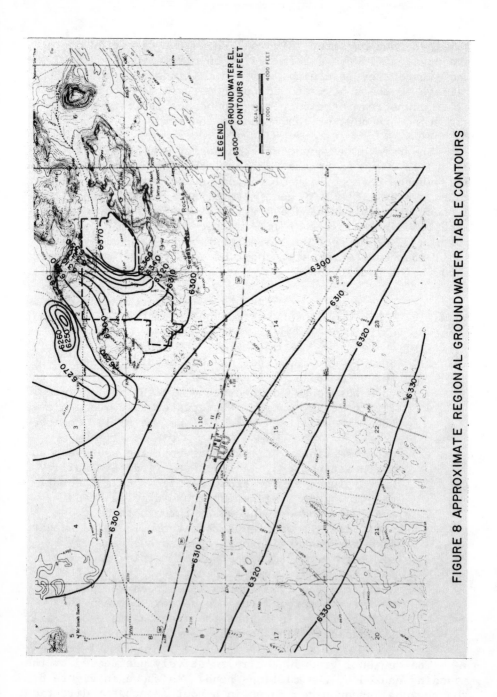

FIGURE 8 APPROXIMATE REGIONAL GROUNDWATER TABLE CONTOURS

northwestern part of the site downstream from the tailings pond.

Geochemical Aspects

As discussed later herein, the effect of the tailings disposal is related to the geochemical aspects of the tailings and tailings water as well as the subsurface and hydrologic conditions. The tailings and the subsoils at the site are characterized as follows:

- Tailings and Tailings Water--The tailings are a sandy material containing radionuclides including uranium, thorium, lead, radium-226 and various toxic chemical s including arsenic.and selenium. The tailings water has similar constituents with the radionuclides being generally in solution in the tailings water. The pH of the tailings pond water is approximately 1.95 due to the acid leach process used in the plant. Large concentrations of iron and manganese as well as substantial amounts of heavy metals exist in the tailings water.

- Subsurface Soil and Rock--The subsurface materials at the site basically consist of highly alkaline soils of a sandy nature with the aforementioned lenticular lenses of clay or silty type materials. The subsurface materials also are rich in sodium sulfates.

- Groundwater Quality--The groundwater at the site is neutral to slightly basic except directly adjacent to the tailings pond where the pH is affected by the tailings pond water.

Projected Operations

Tailings disposal for the next 20 years is proposed to be basically the same as has occurred over the past 20 years. Revisions in dike construction methodologies will improve embankment stability. As discussed above, upstream construction methods have been replaced by centerline methods. An increase in the height of the tailings dam (and the pond) by 50 feet is proposed.

OBSERVED RADIONUCLIDES AND TOXIC CHEMICAL DISPERSION

Method of Assessment

To assess the effect of the on-site operations over the past 20 years, the following program was undertaken:

- Wells were drilled about the site, water levels monitored and water samples of the groundwater taken for analysis for radionuclides and toxic chemicals. Figure 7 and many of the subsequent figures show well locations.

- During drilling, soil and rock samples were taken for radiological and toxic chemical analyses.

- Surface water samples were taken in all of the ponds existing downstream from the tailings impoundment and analyzed for radiological and toxic chemical characteristics.

- Near-surface soils and vegetation samples were taken at key locations to assess the effect of vegetations uptake of radionuclides, if any.

All samples of the water and soil were tested for radionuclide concentrations and toxic chemicals content. Vegetation samples were tested in a similar manner. The concentrations of these elements in the soils and waters at points between sample points were estimated based on prudent judgment and the hydrologic and geologic characteristics of the site.

Observations

The radionuclide dispersal in the soil, rock and water was found to be minimal about the site. The effects of radionuclide disposal were reviewed by plotting isoconcentration contours away from the tailings pond using observed measured points and interpolation between those points. The key elements evaluated were:

- Uranium

- Thorium

- Lead-210

- Radium-226

- Polonium-210

During the extensive environmental assessment of this

site, isoconcentration maps for each element were plotted. The maps were generated within the site bounds of the sub-surface saturated thickness. In this paper, only two iso-concentration maps, uranium and radium-226, are presented to represent the typical occurrences on the site.

As shown in Figure 9 the uranium concentration immediately downstream from the tailings pond is approximately 5.0 mg per liter. At the restricted boundary, the uranium concentration is significantly lower. These are considered well below acceptable limits.

Figure 10 shows a similar type isoconcentration map for radium-226. The radium concentrations a short distance from the pond are less than 1.0 picocuries per liter; well below maximum permissible levels.*

Toxic chemicals were assessed in a similar manner. Equal concentration contour maps were plotted to evaluate the dispersal of toxic chemicals away from the pond. Figure 11 shows a typical isoconcentration map for arsenic. Again it was noted that the toxic chemical concentrations a short distance away from the pond were relatively low, less than 0.002 milligrams per liter.*

Although these observations were of interest and in themselves showed that the tailings disposal operation was not creating a significant environmental effect, further evaluation was conducted to assess the reason for this phenomenon as discussed in the following section.

RADIONUCLIDE AND TOXIC CHEMICAL IMMOBILIZATION--A GEOCHEMICAL AND HYDROLOGIC PHENOMENON

It has often been hypothesized that radionuclides and toxic chemicals move at a rate similar to the hydrologic regime. At this site, radionuclides and toxic chemicals have been entering the groundwater for some 20 years, yet the movement away from the pond did not indicate a movement at a rate equivalent to the hydrologic regime (i.e., groundwater movement). A reasonable and logical explanation from a geochemical standpoint (coupled with the hydrologic aspects) is set forth.

---

* Maximum permissible concentration (MPC) for radium-226 is 5 picocuries per liter and for arsenic is 0.05 mg/l (1977 Drinking Water Standards).

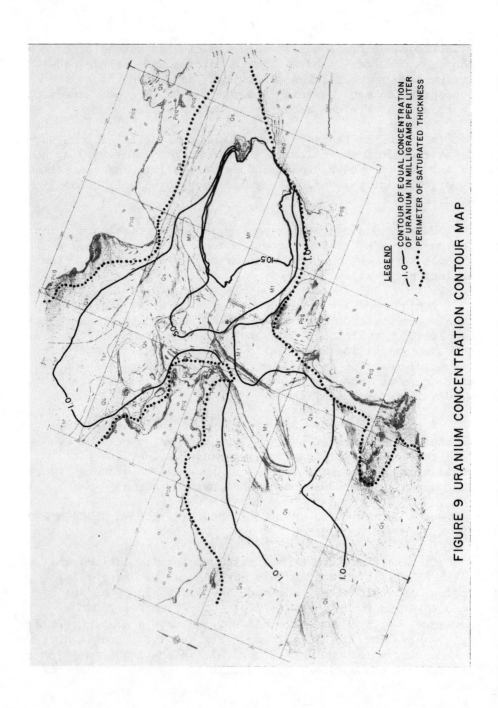

FIGURE 9 URANIUM CONCENTRATION CONTOUR MAP

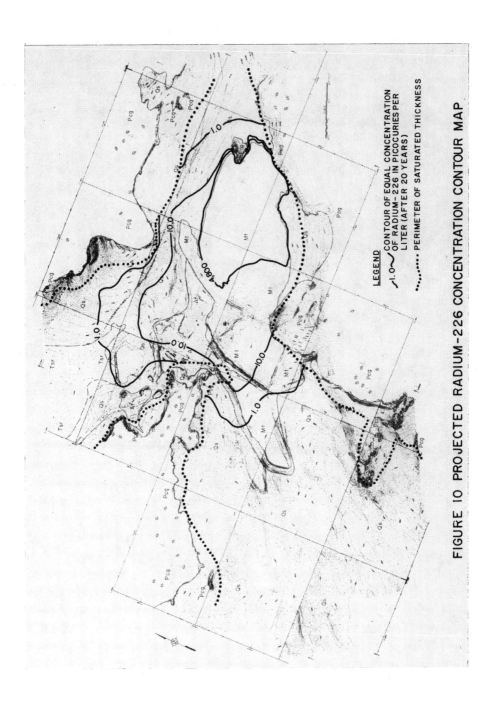

FIGURE IO PROJECTED RADIUM-226 CONCENTRATION CONTOUR MAP

LEGEND

—1.0—⌒ CONTOUR OF EQUAL CONCENTRATION
OF RADIUM-226 IN PICOCURIES PER
LITER (AFTER 20 YEARS)

········· PERIMETER OF SATURATED THICKNESS

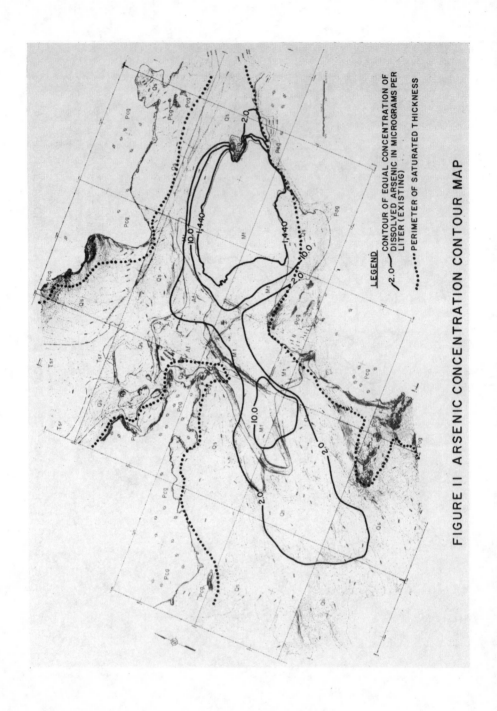

FIGURE II   ARSENIC CONCENTRATION CONTOUR MAP

LEGEND

—2.0— CONTOUR OF EQUAL CONCENTRATION OF
DISSOLVED ARSENIC IN MICROGRAMS PER
LITER (EXISTING)

········· PERIMETER OF SATURATED THICKNESS

The lack of radionuclide and toxic chemical movement at this site can be attributed to; (a) the co-precipitation of radionuclides and other ions with iron and manganese found in the tailings water, or (b) adsorption of the radionculides and ions on the surface of precipitated metal oxides in the groundwater regime. For the non-chemist, the simplified definition of co-precipitation and adsorption are as follows:

- Co-precipitation basically involves radionuclies becoming "entangled" in the lattices of oxides and hydroxides of metals such as iron and manganese. When the iron and manganese precipitate, these radionuclide elements are drawn out of solution and retained within the metal oxide and hydroxide precipitates.

- Adsorption occurs when iron and manganese pre cipitate and form solids with strongly charged surfaces. Radionuclides are attracted to these charged surfaces and are strongly held by sorption mechanisms on the surface. Further transport of the elements ceases through the immobilization of the precipitated solids by soil filtering action.

Figure 12 shows a schematic example of co-precipitation and adsorption. Further discussions of how these two phenomenon are occurring in the subject tailings pond site is discussed below.

pH Factor

A significant factor in any chemical reaction is the pH of the solution in which the elements occur. At the subject site, the pH of the tailings is approximately 1.95, i.e., extremely acidic. As was noted by on-site observations and shown on Figure 13, the pH of the tailings water seeping from the pond increases and becomes neutral or alkaline within a short distance of the pond.

The Role of Fe and Mn

Chemical analysis of the tailings water indicated a high concentration of iron and manganese in the tailings water (300 mg per liter Fe and 17 mg per liter Mn). At extremely low pH's these elements essentially remain in solution. However, as the pH increases the elements precipitate into a solid state, thus as the pH increases away from the tailings

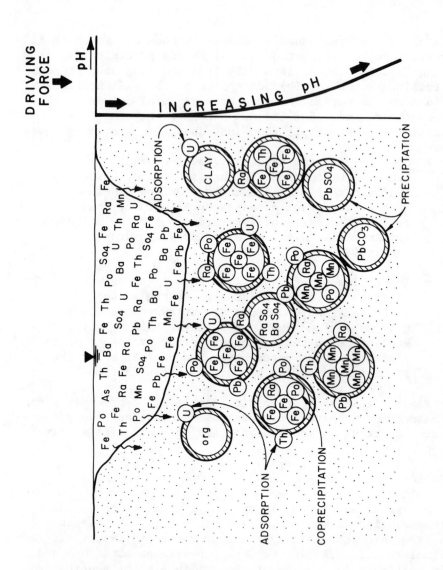

FIGURE 12 CO-PRECIPITATION AND ADSORPTION MODEL

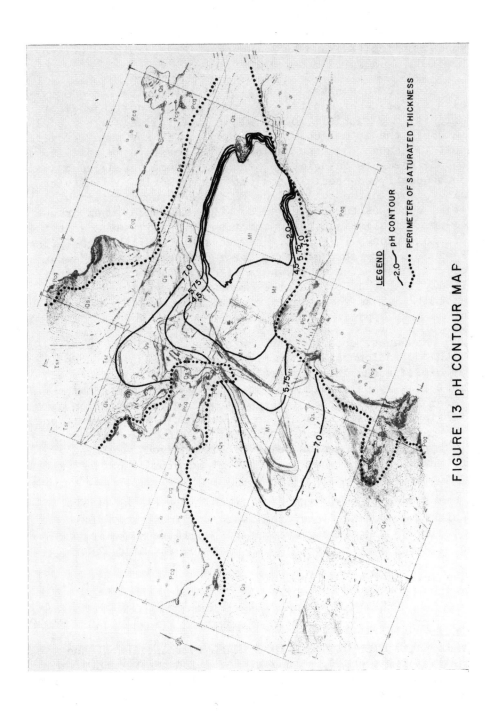

LEGEND

—2.0—— pH CONTOUR

•••••••• PERIMETER OF SATURATED THICKNESS

FIGURE 13 pH CONTOUR MAP

pond the iron (Fe) and the manganese (Mn) precipitate into the soil as a solid material.

The Fe ions have a generally high affinity for adsorption and/or co-precipitation with the radionuclide elements. Affinity may initially occur within the tailings water pond although the actual chemical occurrence in the pond is difficult to assess. If the radionuclide ions have an affinity to the Fe elements in solution, the two become entangled and are consequently co-precipitated out in the soil. Affinity can also occur in the soil at low pH and co-precipitation will still occur as the pH increases. Regardless of when or where co-precipitation occurs, adsorption is likely subsequent to precipitation. The highly charged surface of the precipitated Fe ion is very attractive to the radionuclides and adsorption occurs in the area of pH where precipitation occurs. It is likely that the Fe ions or elements will precipitate at a pH around 2.5. As shown in Figure 13, this would be relatively close to the pond.

Manganese does not show as strong a tendency to complex with the radionuclide elements at low pH's as iron does. To precipitate manganese oxides, Me^{+2} (as occurs in the pond) must usually be oxidized to +3 or +4 valence state which generally occurs at a higher pH than the precipitation of the ferric elements. However, co-precipitation is possible once the manganese begins to precipitate. Also the surface of the precipitated manganese is highly charged resulting in the potential for and the likelihood of adsorption on the precipitated solid.

Figure 12 shows the simplified schematic of the mechanisms which are probably occurring as the pH increases and the ferric and manganese elements are precipitated. The precipitating solids act as a sink for the radionuclides.

The Role of the Alkaline Soils

In order to obtain the precipitation as discussed, the pH must increase to a level to cause this chemical phenomenon. It is the alkaline soils which increase the pH rapidly at this particular site. Without that increase in pH, the radionuclides would, no doubt, move with the groundwater regime as long as the pH stayed at a level to keep the iron and manganese elements in solution.

The soils filter the precipitated iron and manganese thereby trapping the elements which provide the sink for the radionuclides.

The Role of Organic or Clayey Soils

Although the subsurface does not have significant clayey or organic soils, some lenses do exist which may help remove the radionuclides from down gradient aqueous transport. Clays have relatively large particle surface areas which have a high capacity for ion exchange-adsorption. When coated with Mn or Fe oxides this sorption potential increases significantly. Furthermore, the potential is increased with higher levels of ions in the transporting solution, as is occurring from the seeping tailings water. Finally, most sorption from solution occurs in the pH range of 4.5 to 9.0; the range existing in the soils as the pH of the tailings water is increased. The clay lenses beneath the site also act as a trap; especially in combination with the Fe and Mn concentrations in the seeping tailings water.

Hydrologic Roles

Two key hydrologic aspects of the site play an important role in this overall trapping mechanism. First, the ground-water mounding and flow is at such a rate that the alkaline soils can increase the pH within the restricted boundary, thereby providing the mechanism for the radionuclide trap. A significantly higher flow rate could cause the rise in pH to occur at a significant distance from the pond. Radionuclide transport outside the restricted zone could be a possibility for such a hypothetical situation.

The second element in the hydrologic regime is the withdrawal of the well water downstream of the tailings pond and its recycle to the plant. This sink provides a return mechanism should trace elements find their way to the site boundary.

Toxic Chemical Removal Phenomenon

Similar types of explanations are appropriate when viewing the lack of movement of toxic chemicals from the tailings pond area. Arsenic as discussed above, is trapped primarily because of the rapid increase in pH values away from the pond and the presence of heavy metals. If the conditions are right for co-precipitation of radionuclides and other heavy metals (as they are at this site), conditions will likely exist for removal of arsenic. The increasing pH is the prime controlling factor. As the pH rises, arsenic minerals generally become more stable. Therefore, as arsenic moves from the tailings pond (low to high pH's) the equilibrium increases and solubility for arsenic is limited. Again the adsorption of arsenic on precipitated ferric hydroxide or other active surfaces is a pertinent factor in limiting solubility and mobility. The precipitating ferric elements create a trap similar to that which occurs for the radionuclides. If the ferric ions are not present, the arsenic will likely precipitate out in heavy complexes.

PROJECTED EFFECT FOR FUTURE OPERATIONS

Since it is proposed to continue to operate this tailings disposal area for the next 20 years, the logical question is raised as to what distance radionuclides will move away from the pond due to the continued operations. To assess this problem, a model was created to predict radionuclide and toxic chemical element movements. The model incorporated the concepts of ion exchange, adsorption, coprecipitation and other mechanisms. Distribution coefficients for the various radionuclide and toxic chemical ions were determined by laboratory testing and theoretical assessment to rate these elements in a geochemical sense and to assess their potential for further movement. Distribution coefficients are a measure of the "sorption potential" for a given element species traveling through a given geologic medium. The hydrologic aspects were input as projected hydraulic gradients and consideration was given to the fact that the hydraulic gradient decreased in direct proportion to the distance from the tailings pond. The decrease in hydraulic gradient with distance increased the probability of the geochemical mechanisms since a lower flow rate allows a greater potential for further increase in pH.

Due to the large number of variables which required consideration in estimating the future migration and concentration of radionuclides in the area surrounding the tailings, a finite element computer model was used for the analysis. The model simulated migration of radionuclides and arsenic from the tailings pond during the remaining life of the facility. Based on this simulation it was possible to predict radionuclide concentrations at the boundary of the restricted zone for the ultimate period of operation. For further detailed discussions of the model used and the input parameters, the reader is referred to the report on open file with the United States Nuclear Regulatory Commission (NRC) concerning this project. A synopsis of the modeling results are discussed herein.

Although movement for all of the radionuclide elements reviewed during the baseline assessment were projected, only radium-226 and arsenic are provided in graphic form here for comparison with current isoconcentration contours. Figure 14 and 15 show the new contour maps for the projected movement of radium-226 and arsenic respectively. Comparison with Figures 9 and 10, show the relative movements from existing conditions. The other elements showed very small changes in projected movement. This is to be expected due to the rather high distribution coefficients for the elements which show small predicted increase. Radium-226, polonium-210 and arsenic have relatively lower distribution coefficients than do uranium, thorium and lead.

Even with the projected increase, the radionuclide concentrations are still relatively low at the restricted boundaries and well within the maximum permissible concentration levels.

A final assessment was made to review the potential for movement of radionuclides or toxic chemicals after abandonment. Essentially, no movement is anticipated after the tailings pond is drained and abandoned. The driving force for moving these elements (i.e., the low pH tailings water) will be eliminated. The elements will be bound in precipitates in soils a short distance from the ponds and will return to solution only if highly acidic water were to pass through the area. Without a tailings pond, this will not occur.

CONCLUSIONS

The example site has all of the necessary elements to allow operation of an unlined pond without detrimentally affecting the environment. The soils are sufficiently alkaline to raise the pH and are sufficiently fine grained to act as a filter for the precipitated and adsorbed ions. The hydrologic regime allows water movement at such a rate and in a uniform manner to permit the raise of pH and filtration to occur within the site boundary. Isolation barriers at the site would do little to decrease the detrimental effect of tailings disposal other than to reduce the distance of affects away from the pond.

If an isolation barrier were installed at this site or at a site with similar characteristics, the understanding of the transport mechanism would alleviate concerns over the

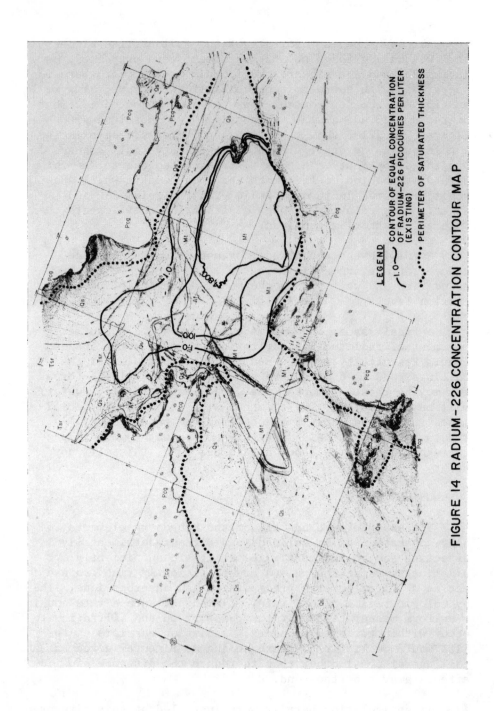

LEGEND

—1.0— CONTOUR OF EQUAL CONCENTRATION
OF RADIUM-226 PICOCURIES PER LITER
(EXISTING)

••••• PERIMETER OF SATURATED THICKNESS

FIGURE 14 RADIUM-226 CONCENTRATION CONTOUR MAP

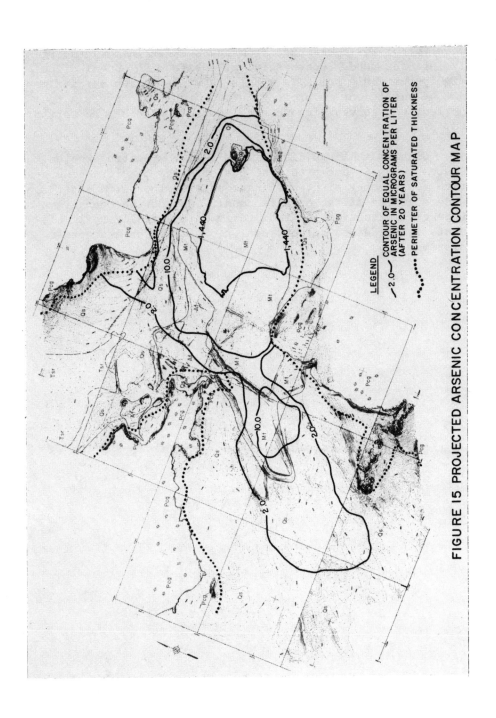

LEGEND

— 2.0 — CONTOUR OF EQUAL CONCENTRATION OF ARSENIC IN MICROGRAMS PER LITER (AFTER 20 YEARS)

••••••••• PERIMETER OF SATURATED THICKNESS

FIGURE 15 PROJECTED ARSENIC CONCENTRATION CONTOUR MAP

movement of toxic elements from any seepage which inadvertently left the pond. Conversely, at a site with non-alkaline, highly permeable soils, a single layer isolation barrier may not be sufficient to protect the environment. Systems to collect and convey seepage back to the pond could be warranted.

Uranium tailings disposal is a site specific problem. A system which is acceptable at one site may be ultra-conservative for another site, and inadequate at the third site. An understanding of the on-site conditions and the mechanisms of potential excursions of radiotoxic or chemically toxic elements is needed to select, design or assess an appropriate system.

LIST OF REFERENCES

1. Allen, S.E. (ed.), 1974, Chemical Analysis of Ecological Materials, John Wiley & Sons, New York, 565 pp.

2. American Public Health Association, 1975, Standard Methods of the Examination of Water and Wastewater, (14th Edition, APHA, Washington, D.C.

3. Anderson, W.P., 1977, Weed Science: Principles, West Publishing Co., New York, 598 pp.

4. Baker, D.E. and L. Chesnin, 1975, "Chemical Monitoring of Soils for Environmental Quality and Animal and Human Health," Adv. in Agronomy, Vol. 27, pp. 305-374.

5. Bear, J., 1961, "Some Experiments in Dispersion," Journal of Geophysical Research, Vol. 66, No. 8, pp. 2,455-2,467.

6. Bear J., 1972, Dynamics of Fluids in Porous Media, American Elsevier Publishing Company Inc., New York, 764 pp.

7. Black, C.A., (ed.) 1965, Methods of Soil Analysis, Part 2: Chemical and Microbiological Properties, Monograph 9, American Soc. Agronomy, Madison, Wisconsin, 1,572 pp.

8. Blair, W.F., A.P. Blair, P. Brookorb, F.R. Cagle, and G.A. Moore, 1968, Vertebrates of the United States (2nd Ed.), McGraw-Hill Book Company, New York, 616 pp.

9. Burt, W.H. and R.P. Grossenheider, 1964, A Field Guide to the Mammals, Houghton Mifflin Co., Boston, 284 pp.

10. Champan, H.D., (ed.) 1966, Diagnostic Criteria for Plants and Soils, University of California, Division of Agricultural Sciences, Riverside, 787 pp.

11. Cherry, J.A., R.W. Gillham, and J.F. Pickens, 1975, "Contaminant Hydrogeology: Part 1, Physical Processes," Geoscience Canada, Vol. 2, No. 2, pp 76-84.

12. Cotton, F.A. and G. Wilkinson, 1972, Advanced Inorganic Chemistry, Wiley-Interscience, New York, 1,145 pp.

13. de Josselin de Jong, G., 1961, "Dispersion In Flow Through Porous Media," Conf. on Groundwater Disposal of Radioactive Wastes, Berkeley, California.

14. Dean, John A., (ed.), 1973, Lange's Handbook of Chemistry, 11th Ed., McGraw-Hill Book Company, New York, 1,576 pp.

15. Denham, D.H., D.A. Baker, J.K. Soldat, and J.P. Carley, 1973, Radiological Evaluations for Advanced Waste Management Studies, U.S. Atomic Energy Commission, BNWL-1764.

16. Duguid, J.O. and M. Reeves, 1976, "Material Transport Through Porous Media: A Finite Element Galerkin Model," Environmental Sciences Division Publications 733, Oak Ridge National Laboratory, National Technical Information Service, Springfield, Virginia, 201 pp.

17. Eattah, Q.N., "Investigation and Verification of a Model for the Dispersion Coefficient Tensor in Flow Through Anisotropic Homogeneous, Porous Media with Application to Flow From a Recharge Well Through a Confined Aquifer," Ph.D. Thesis, University of Wisconsin, Madison, 1974.

18. Federal Water Pollution Control Administration, 1968, Report of the Committee on Water Quality Criteria, U.S. Government Printing Office, Washington, D.C., 234 pp.

19. Fenneman, Nevin, M., 1931, Physiography of the Western United States, McGraw-Hill, New York, 533 pp.

20. Figgins, P.E., 1961, The Radiochemistry of Polonium, NAS-NS 3037, National Academy of Sciences, Nuclear Science Series, National Technical Information Service, Springfield, Virginia, 68 pp.

21. Gera, F., 1975, Geochemical Behavior of Long-Lived Radioactive Wastes, Oak Ridge National Laboratory, ORNL-TM-4481, National Technical Information Service, Springfield, Virginia, 95 pp.

22. Gibson, W.M., 1961, The Radiochemistry of Lead, NAS-NS3040, National Academy of Sciences, Nuclear Science Series, National Technical Information Services, Springfield, Virginia, 158 pp.

23. Hamilton, J.W. and C.S. Gilbert, 1972, Composition of Wyoming Range Plants and Soils, Research Journal 55, Agric. Expt. Sta., University of Wyoming, Laramie, Wyoming, 20 pp.

24. Harleman, D.R.F., P.F. Mehlhorn, and R.R. Rumer, Jr., 1963, "Dispersion-Permeability Correlation in Porous Media," J. Hydraulics Division, Proc. ASCE, Vol. 89, No. HYZ (March 1963), pp. 67-85.

25. Harleman, D.F.R. and R.R. Rumer, Jr., 1963, "Longitudinal and Lateral Dispersion in an Isotropic Porous Medium," J. Fluid Mechanics, Vol. 16, No. 3, pp. 385-394.

26. Harmsen, K., 1977, Behaviour of Heavy Metals in Soils, Agricultural Research Report 866, Centre for Agricultural Publishing and Documentation, Wageningen, Netherlands, 171 pp.

27. Health and Safety Laboratory, 1972, HASL Procedures Manual, U.S. Energy Research and Development Administration, Publication No. HASL-300, New York.

28. Hem, J.D., 1970, Study and Interpretations of the Chemical Characteristics of Natural Water, U.S. Geological Survey Water-Supply Paper 1473, 363 pp.

29. Hyde, E.K., 1960, The Radiochemistry of Thorium, NAS-NS3004, National Academy of Sciences, Nuclear Science Series, National Technical Information Service, Springfield, Virginia, 70 pp.

30. Jenne, E.A., 1968 "Controls on Mn, Fe, Co, Ni, Cu, and Zn Concentrations in Soils and Water, the Significant Role of Hydrous Mn and Fe Oxides," In: R.F. Gould, (ed.), Trace Inorganics In Water, Adv. in Chem. Series 73, pp. 337-387.

31. Jenn, E.A., 1977 "Trace Element Sorption by Sediments and Soils--Sites and Processes," In: W. Chappel and K. Petersen, (eds), Symposium on Molybdenum in the Environment, Vol. 2, M. Dekker, Inc., New York, pp. 425-553.

32. Kendeigh, S.C., 1961, Animal Ecology, Prentice-Hall, Inc., Englewood Cliffs, New Jersey, 468 pp.

33. Killough, G.G. and L.R. McKay, 1976, A Methodology for Calculating Radiation Doses from Radioactivity Released to the Environment, Oak Ridge National Laboratory, ORNL-4992, National Technical Information Service, Springfield, Virginia.

34. Kirby, H.W. and M.L. Salutsky, 1964, The Radiochemistry of Radium, NAS-NS3057, National Academy of Sciences, Nuclear Science Series, National Technical Information Service, Springfield, Virginia, 205 pp.

35. Langmuir, D., 1977, "Uranium Solution-Mineral Equilibria at Low Temperatures with Applications to Sedimentary Ore Deposits," Geochimica et Cosmochimic Acta, Manuscript in review.

36. Langmuir, D., 1977, Personal Communication, The Pennsylvania State University, University Park, Pennsylvania.

37. Langmuir, D. and K. Applin, 1977, "Refinement of the Thermodynamic Properties of Uranium Minerals and Dissolved Species, with Application to the Chemistry of Groundwaters in Sandstone-Type Uranium Deposits," In: J.A. Campbell, (ed.), Short Papers of the U.S. Geological Survey Uranium-Thorium Symposium, Geological Survey Circular 753, pp. 57-60.

38. Latimer, J.N., W.E. Bush, L.J. Higgins, and R.S. Shay (eds.), 1970, Handbook of Analytical Procedures, U.S. Atomic Energy Commission, RMD-3008, 291 pp.

39. Lawson, Dennis W., 1971, A New Method for Determining and Interpreting Dispersion Coefficients in Porous Media, Ph.D. Thesis, University of Guelph, Guelph, Canada, 104 pp.

40. Lederer, C.M., J.M. Hollander, and I. Perlman, 1967, Table of Isotopes, (6th Ed.), John Wiley and Sons, New York, 594 pp.

41. Lisk, D.J., 1972, "Trace Metals in Soils, Plants, and Animals," Adv. in Agronomy, Vol. 24, pp 267-252.

42. List, E.J. and N.H. Brooks, 1967, "Lateral Dispersion in Saturated Porous Media," Journal of Geophysical Research, Vol. 72, No. 10, pp. 2531-2541.

43. Long, C.A., 1965, The Mammals of Wyoming, University of Kansas, Museum of Natural History, Vol. 14, pp. 493-758, Lawrence, Kansas.

44. Love, J.D., 1970, Cenezoic Geology of the Granite Mountains Area, Central Wyoming, USGS Professional Paper 495-C, 153 p.

45. Martin, A.C., H.S. Zim, and A.L. Nelson, 1951, American Wildlife and Plants: A Guide to Wildlife Food Habits, Dover Publications, New York, 500 pp.

46. Melsted, S.W., 1973, "Soil Plant Relationships," In: Recycling Municipal Sludges and Effluents on Land, National Association of State Universities and Land Grant Colleges, Washington, D.C., pp. 121-129.

47. Office of the Federal Register, 1977, Code of Federal Regulations: 10 Energy, Part 20 - Standards for Protection Against Radiation, pp. 144-172, U.S. Government Printing Office, Washington, D.C.

48. Oosting, H.J., 1956, Study of Plant Communities: An Introduction to Plant Ecology, W.H. Freeman, San Francisco, 440 pp.

49. Pickens, J.F., W.F. Merritt, and J.A. Cherry, 1976, "Field Determination of the Physical Contaminant Transport Parameters in a Sandy Aquifer," In: International Atomic Energy Agency Proceedings Volume, Advisory Group Meeting on the Use of Nuclear Techniques in Water Pollution Studies, (in Press), Cracow, Poland, December 6-9, 1976, 37 pp.

50. Pinder, G.F., and E.O. Frind, 1972, "Application of Galerkin's Procedure to Aquifer Analysis," Hydrol. Paper 41, Colo. State University, Fort Collins, 79 pp.

51. Robbins, C.S., B. Bruun, and H.S. Zim, 1966, A Guide to Field Identification: Birds of North America, Golden Press, New York, 340 pp.

52. Robertson, J.B., 1974, "Digital Modeling of Radioactive and Chemical Waste Transport in the Snake River Plain Aquifer at the National Reactor Testing Station, Idaho," U.S. Geological Survey Open File Report, IDO-22054, National Technical Information Service, Springfield, Virginia, 41 pp.

53. Rumer, R.R., Jr., 1962, "Longitudinal Dispersion in Steady and Unsteady Flow," J. Hydraulics Division, Proc. ASCE, Vol. 88, No. HY4 (July 1962), pp. 147-172.

54. Schroeder, M.C., and A.R. Jennings, 1963, Laboratory Studies of the Radioactive Contamination of Aquifers, University of California, Lawrence Radiation Laboratory, UCRL-13074, 54 pp.

55. Schwartz, F.W., 1977, "Macroscopic Dispersion in Porous Media: The Controlling Factors," Water Resources Research, Vol. 13, No. 4, pp 743-752.

56. Scott, R.C. and F.B. Barker, 1962 "Data on Uranium and Radium in Ground Water in the United States, 1954 to 1957," Geological Survey Professional Paper 426, U.S. Government Printing Office, Washington, D.C.

57. Sharma, R.P., and J.L. Shupe, 1977, "Lead, Cadmium, and Arsenic Residues in Animal Tissues in Relation to Those in Their Surrounding Habitat," The Science of the Total Environment (Journal), Vol. 7, pp. 53-62.

58. Sillen, L.G., and A.E. Martell, 1964, Stability Constants of Metal-Ion Complexes, Chemical Soc. (London) Spec. Pub 17, 754 pp.

59. Siegel, F.R., 1974, Applied Geochemistry, Wiley-Interscience, New York, 353 pp.

60. Soil Conservation Service, 1976, National Range Handbook-1, Dated July 13, 1976, U.S. Department of Agriculture, Washington, D.C.

61. Stebgins, R.C., 1966, A Field Guide to Western Reptiles and Amphibians, Houghton Mifflin Company, Boston, 279 pp.

62. Suarez, D.L. and D. Langmuir, 1976, "Heavy Metal Relationships in A Pennsylvania Soil," Geochimica et Cosmochimica Acta, Vol. 40, No. 6, pp. 589-598.

63. Taylor, F.B., 1971, "Trace Elements and Compounds in Waters," Journal of the American Water Works Association, Vol. 63, 728 pp.

64. TRW, Inc., Environmental Study on Uranium Mills, U.S. Environmental Protection Agency, Washington, D.C., February, 1979.

65. U.S. Environmental Protection Agency, 1973, Proposed Criteria for Water Quality, Volume 1, Publication PB-259 439, U.S. Department of Commerce, National Technical Information Service, Springfield, Virginia, 425 pp.

66. U.S. Environmental Protection Agency, 1976, Quality Criteria for Water, Publication PB-263-943, U.S. Department of Commerce, National Technical Information Service, Springfield, Virginia, 501 pp.

67. U.S. Geological Survey, 1970, The National Atlas of the United States of America, U.S. Department of the Interior, Washington, D.C., 417 pp.

68. U.S. National Oceanic and Atmospheric Administration, 1961-1976, Climatological Data, Wyoming Annual Summary, U.S. Department of Commerce, Environmental Data Service, Annual Summaries.

69. U.S. Nuclear Regulatory Commission, 1977, Final Environmental Statement Related to the Rocky Mountain Energy Company's Bear Creek Project (Converse County, Wyoming, Document No.

NUREG-0129, National Technical Information Service, Springfield, Virginia.

70. U.S. Nuclear Regulatory Commission, 1979, Generic Environmental Impact Statement on Uranium Milling, Document No. NUREG-0511, National Technical Information Service, Springfield, Virginia

71. Walsh, L.M. (ed.), 1971, Instrumental Methods for Analysis of Soils and Plant Tissue, Soil Science Society of America, Madison, Wisconsin, 222 pp.

72. Walsh, L.M., and J.D. Beaton (eds.), 1973, Soil Testing and Plant Analysis, Soil Science Soc. of America, Madison, Wisconsin, 491 pp.

73. Whitcomb, Harold A., and M.E. Lowry, 1968, "Groundwater Resources and Geology of the Wind River Basin Area, Central Wyoming," USGS Hydrologic Investigations Atlas HA-270.

INDEX

A

Aardvark drilling rig, 262, 269, 271, 432
Abandoned mines
  discharge of poor quality water, 187-188, 193-214
  effects on active mines, 495-496
  reclamation, 70, 762-763
  uranium, 735-736, 827
Acidification of water samples, 158
Acid mine drainage, 70
  chemistry of, 193-195, 199, 202
  corrective measures, 210-213
  inactive mines, 187-188, 193-214
  pH ranges, 552
  point source, 205, 208
  recharge sources, 195-198
  treatment, 159-160
Acid mine drainage modeling, 651-670
  application, 660-669
  data requirements, 653-655, 658-661, 669
  hydrologic model, 652-656, 660-661, 663-665
  moisture accounting process, 653
  results, 664-665, 667-669
Acid production, 193-195, 199, 202, 657, 658
  controlling factors, 552, 554, 558
  reduction, 210-213
  surface and underground, 202, 209
Adits, 517
  depressurization and pit slope angles, 41, 328-337
  effectiveness of, 45
  fan holes with, 334, 335
  monitoring, 329, 334
  permeability ranges, 332, 335
  pit bottom dewatering, 252
  runoff diverted by, 567
Adsorption, 80, 821, 822
Air injection drilling, 451-452
Air pressure, behind bulkhead doors, 625-626
Air rotary drilling equipment, 227
Alluvial-bedrock contact, 259, 261, 269
Alluvial valley
  aquifers and ground water, 353
  regulations, 77-78
Alluvium, 245, 346, 348, 350, 353, 554
  permeability reduction, 511
Aluminum, 187
Analysis of data
  piezometers and drainhole discharge, 247-250
  pumping tests, 284
Analysis of mine geohydrology, 529-534, 539-550
  accuracy, 46, 529, 546-547
Andesite, fractured, 326

Anticlines, 346, 352
Apparent transmissivity
  decrease, 393-395, 402
  leakage, 398-399, 402, 405
Aquifers, 38, 39, 105, 284, 350, 365-368, 372
  characteristics, 99, 119, 284, 285, 495
  coefficient of storage, 99, 110, 119, 367-368, 446, 575
  coefficients, 37, 99, 105, 106-107, 222, 398
  collapse from sand removal, 374
  computation of properties, 100, 222
  cone of influence, 222
  drawdown and subsidence, 378-380
  equilibrium pressure, 222, 368-369
  from confined to a water table aquifer, 38, 112-117
  from confined to unconfined states, 36, 102-103
  identification, 281
  leakage from lower, 39, 396-406
  local water budget, 37, 107
  number and piezometer requirements, 35, 132-138, 151
  pumping tests, 46-47, 222, 284, 285
  sands, 108-109, 367, 371, 374, 375
  standard grain size, 456
  steady state leaky equation, 46, 532-534
  transmissivity, 110, 118, 367, 393-395, 451
  upward flows, 398
Aquitards
  defined, 106
  number of piezometers required, 35, 132, 138, 151
Arsenic, 51, 802, 815
  isoconcentration map, 817, 820
  projected movement, 827, 829
  removal, 825-826
Artesian aquifer, 38, 112-117
Artesian dewatering, 362-382
  continuous pumping, 377-378, 380
  floor heave and stability, 362, 364, 368-370, 380
  free flow bores, 370, 371, 374
  monitoring, 377
  observation bores, 375, 376-377
  piezometric levels and flows, 369-370, 372-373, 375, 376-377
  pumping bores, 370, 371, 374-377
  pumping rate, 371, 372, 377, 380
  subsidence, 378-380
Asbestos
  cement castings, 374, 454-455
  fibers in tailings, 714, 716
  open pit mine, 423-436
Australian regulations, 82-83

Creek drainage into underground mines, 562-564, 568-569
Culverts, lined, 294
Cusums analysis of data, 248, 249
Cutoff walls, 109, 570

D

Darcy's law, 46, 443, 529, 636, 681
Decant pond, 643
Decant towers, 702
Deep well dewatering, 41, 411, 416
  costs, 295, 296
  depth, 288
  design, 284-288
  diameter, 41, 288
  drainage ditches, 293-294
  drilling, 288-289, 419
  location, 285-288
  monitoring, 295, 297
  number required, 284-285
  performance, 297-301
  perimeter, 283-284
  power supply, 293
  pumps, 290-292, 412, 418, 604-605
  shaft sinking water control, 579, 584, 587
De Glee formula, 400, 401
Delayed yield from storage, 112
Depressurization, 38, 118, 587-588
Depressurization, open pit mines, 328-337
  drainage, 324-326
  perimeter and in-pit wells, 326, 328
  pit bottom heave, 364, 368, 370
  rate of expansion, 326
  slope optimization, 324-327 *passim*
  toe drains, 326, 328, 334
  underground galleries, 326, 328
Design of dewatering systems, 312, 314-316
  calculations, 316
  deep well dewatering, 284-288
  underground dewatering, 591-593
Detritic materials, 494
Dewatering conduit, concrete
  debris plug, 646-647
  deterioration and collapse, 643-645
Dewatering systems, 219-231
  benefits from efficiency, 219
  conceptual design, 223
  costs, 37, 228, 231
  maintenance, 231
Diamond drilling, 328, 554, 555, 570, 621
  variable and sheared rock, 432
  water quality, 199, 200, 202, 205
Dikes, 239, 411
  failure, 793
  flooding and overtopping, 630, 639
  leakage and recharge, 567
  tailings dam construction, 627, 671-672
Dip, 281, 329, 354, 357
Discharge, 159, 228-230
  abandoned mines, 186-187, 193-213
  permits, 68
Ditch, drainage
  bentonite slurry, 484

Ditch, drainage *continued*
  deep well dewatering, 293-294
  pit bottom, 485
  self-sealing, 294
  surface, 484, 485
  well location, 286, 287
Diversion, 411, 516
  ditches, 237-240, 241, 411
  drifts, 623, 624
  surface streams, 419
Documentation, 145-146, 155
Dolomites, 281, 282, 289, 308
Draglines, 278, 464, 467, 469
Drainage
  determining factors, 493-497
  published information on, 493
  quantity of water removed, 496
Drainage methods
  active protection, 499
  compared, 500-501
  instantaneous protection, 499-500
  passive protection, 498
  prevention, 498
Drainage, open pit mines
  adits, 41, 329-337
  depressurization, 324-326
  perimeter and in-pit wells, 326, 328
  toe drains, 326, 328, 334
  underground galleries, 326, 328
Drain holes, 45
  drilling, 261-262, 431, 432
Drain length, 262-263, 269
Drain performance, 264-267
Drawdown, 118
  calculation of impact, 544-546
  curves, 222, 263
  distance and time, 449-450
  graphs, 110, 111, 113, 114, 115, 117
  inclined drains, 248
  interference and well spacing, 286
  phases, 442-443
  steady state leaky aquifer equation, 532
  subsidence caused by, 378-380
  water table and recovery, 297-301
Drifts, 411, 562
Drift "wells," 36, 102
Drill
  bits, 262, 272, 288, 453
  stem tests, 577
  string configuration, 289
  water volume, 555, 556
Drill holes, 46, 211
  documentation, 145-146
  number of piezometers in, 142, 144, 146-152
  piezometers in, 131-132, 143-144
  quality of water discharged, 199, 200, 202
  scheduling, 143, 148-151
  surface protection, 143, 149, 150
Drilling, 226-228
  air rotary, 227
  cable tool, 470, 475
  costs, 143, 148-150
  deep wells, 288-289
  environmental and exploratory, 155

M

Maintenance, 593
Manganese, 187, 223, 821, 824
Maps, 582
  applications for permits, 73
  isoconcentration, 817-820
  surface water flow rates, 385
Marine mining, 501, 513
Matrix recovery, 44, 467, 472, 475, 477
Metal flume, 250
Metal ion concentrations, 202-205, 208, 209
Methane, 119
Mine design and planning, 38-39, 325, 591-592
  bottom-up mining, 509
  drainage control measures, 256
  ground water control methods, 219, 220, 223
  ground water instrumentation, 125, 127
  prediction of dewatering pumpage rates, 98-103
  prevention of acid mine drainage, 210
Mineral content of ground water, 127
Mineral exploration, 125, 126
Mines
  corrected for acid production, 210-211
  geometry reduced to effective radius, 36, 102
  near large bodies of surface water, 108-112
Mining from the bottom up, 507, 509-511, 518
Mining, modified open stope method, 620
Models
  acid mine drainage, 651-670
  computer, 38, 105, 119, 395
  depressurization, 38, 119
  drainage method comparison, 500
  geohydrology, 534-538
  hydrologic, 652-656, 660-661, 663-665
  radionuclide movements, 826-827
  selection, 356-358
  surface mine-refuse pile, 656-660, 663, 666-669
Models for dewatering, 442-450
  one-dimensional, 442-443
  open pit mines, 446-450
  two-dimensional, 443-446
Models of water resource systems, 355-361
  flow system prediction, 343, 356, 359
  identification of mine water resources, 343, 345, 359
  phosphate sequences, 355-356
  reliability, 343, 359
  selection, 356-358
Monitoring, 377
  rock slide stabilization, 433-434
  tailings dams, 633, 644-645
  wells, 766-772
Mud flows, 496
  slump failures, 243-244

N

National Pollutant Discharge Elimination System (NPDES), 68, 185, 208
Natural springs, 348, 350
  fault structures, 352
  water analyses, 282

New Mexico, regulations of, 154-155
Nuclear Regulatory Commission (NRC), 801, 802

O

Observation wells, 37, 110, 111, 118, 440, 582-583
Office of Surface Mining Reclamation and Enforcement, 69-70
Oil shale underground mines, 525-551
"Open hole" measurements, 132
Open pit drainage and dewatering, 39-45, 219-506 *passim*
  costs, 295, 296, 483-484
  deep wells, 275-302
  facilities required, 411-412
  gravity connector wells, 44, 463, 469-471, 473-474
  horizontal drains, 258-274
  methods, 481-482, 484-490
  method selection, 482-484
  models, 446-450
  performance, 264-267, 297-301
  problems, 416-420
  purpose of drainage control, 410-411, 483
  rock slide causes and control, 423-436
  strata ahead of bucket wheels, 457-460
  summary of stabilization by drainage, 41-44
  See also Stability, open pit mines
Ore, 411
  costs from wet and dry mines, 509
  dewatering, 412, 414
  oxidized, 159
  wet, 236-237, 269
Overburden, 363
Overtopping, and dam failures, 630-631, 639, 701
Oxidation
  stockpiling of wet ore, 41, 236-237
  water transport of oxidized products, 159, 202, 209, 210, 211, 212, 552, 554, 558

P

Packers, multiple casing, 35
Pads at well sites, 289
Peat, absorption capacity of, 52, 159
Perched water, 281, 283, 729, 749, 750
Perforated casings, 432
Perimeter wells, 283-284, 326, 328, 412
Permafrost, dewatering in, 418
Permeability, 36, 45
  adit tests, 332
  differences in water pressure, 127
  equation to determine in-situ, 178
  expansion of depressurized zones, 326
  foundations and tailings backfill, 783
  horizontal drains, 261, 263
  limestone and dolomites, 308
  measured at intervals during drilling, 35, 136
  measurement verification, 145
  probe tests to evaluate, 328
  rock slide slope, 425-427, 434, 436
  tests, 40, 786, 813

Permeability changes investigation, 161, 166-183
  instrumentation, 167, 168, 173-175, 180
  near the mining horizon, 166-168, 170-172
  near the surface and extraction area, 172-180
  test boreholes, 166-170, 172-175
  test procedures, 168-170, 175, 177
  test results, 170-172, 177-183
Permeability reduction, 47
  chemical and bacteriological precipitates, 47,
    507, 513-514, 517
  plugging methods, 517
Permits
  application requirements, 72-74
  approval and denial, 74, 77
  discharge, 68
  effluent guidelines, 185, 187
  English, 84
  German, 85
  NPDES for point source discharge, 208
pH
  bacteria, 194, 195
  constant value for water samples, 157
  precipitation, 821, 824, 825
Phosphate field
  flow systems, 342-361
  models, 355-361
Phosphate mines, drainage control, 463-480
Phreatic surface
  depressurization, 326
  flow nets, 682, 683
Piezometers, 40, 198, 220, 390, 786, 794
  calibration, 141
  closed, 140-141
  cumulative sums analysis of data, 248, 249
  defined, 131-132
  depth vs. pressure head, 132-134, 136-137
  diaphragm type, 139, 140, 141
  effect of adits on ground water, 329, 334
  formation fluid type, 139, 140-141
  horizontal drain performance, 264, 266
  installation, 334
  location of seals and ports, 145
  multiple installation, 35, 142, 144, 146, 147-
    152, 243
  number in a single borehole, 440, 441
  number required, 35, 132-138, 151
  open, 138-140
  ports, 132, 145, 146
  profilers for location of, 35, 137
  protection, 143
  response time, 140, 141
  sealing requirements, 35, 146, 148, 151
  siting in pumping tests, 221
  valved, 138, 139, 141-142, 146, 147-152
Piezometric head, clay filled faults and adits,
    329, 331, 332
Piezometric levels
  aquifer flows, 372-373
  continuous pumping, 377-378
  inclined drains, 247-250
  observation bores, 375, 376-377
  pit bottom heave, 369-372, 378
Piezometric pressure, flow net agreement, 704

Pillars, 191, 313, 501, 515
  support, 620
Pipe drains, seepage control, 685-686, 702
Pipelines, 250, 252
  floating, 418
  pit bottom dewatering, 254
  polyethylene, 250, 254
  snow cover over, 416
  steamers for frozen, 256
Pipes
  concrete plugs, 623, 624
  in dewatering designs, 592
  frozen, 253, 256
Piping, tailings dam failures, 630, 631, 636, 637,
    646, 647, 677, 699
  causes and remedies, 702-706
  drains and filters, 701-702
  toe drains, 683
Pit
  excavation and flow systems, 355
  flooding, 342, 345
  water problems, 236-237, 269
Pit bottom
  dewatering, 252-256
  drainage ditches, 485
  vertical wells, 489
Pit bottom heave, 45
  artesian dewatering, 362, 364, 368-370, 380
  depressurization, 45, 390
  factor of safety, 369-370
  pumping bores, 370
  risk assessment, 384
Pit slope stability. See Stability, open pit mines
Plan, required for reclamation, 74
Planning agency, 66, 67
Planning drainage, 497-503
  comparison of methods, 500-501
  preventive methods, 498
  protective methods, 498-500
  underground mines, 502
Planning open pit drainage, 383-387, 440-450
  calculation of ground water outflow, 384-385
  calculation of precipitation, 386
  calculation of surface water flow rates, 385-
    386
  environmental impact, 387
  hydrological investigations, 440
  modelling, 446-450
  protective measures, 385, 386
Plugging
  conduits, 512-513, 519, 522-526
  connector wells, 474
  permeability reduction, 517
  pores and fractures, 511, 517
  sinkholes, 791-792
  test holes, 516
Plugs, 49, 159
  injection wells, 229
Pneumatic hammer, 227
Polish mines, 304-323
  design of dewatering systems, 314-316
  dewatering methods, 317-323
  geological and hydrological data, 306-312